THE ANIMAL KINGDOM

THE

George G. Goodwin

ASSOCIATE CURATOR OF MAMMALS,
THE AMERICAN MUSEUM OF NATURAL HISTORY

Charles M. Bogert

CURATOR OF AMPHIBIANS AND REPTILES,
THE AMERICAN MUSEUM OF NATURAL HISTORY

Dean Amadon
E. Thomas Gilliard

ASSOCIATE CURATORS OF BIRDS,
THE AMERICAN MUSEUM OF NATURAL HISTORY

Christopher W. Coates CURATOR
James W. Atz ASSISTANT CURATOR,
AQUARIUM OF
THE NEW YORK ZOOLOGICAL SOCIETY

John C. Pallister

RESEARCH ASSOCIATE, INSECTS,
THE AMERICAN MUSEUM OF NATURAL HISTORY

ANIMAL KINGDOM

THE STRANGE AND WONDERFUL WAYS OF MAMMALS, BIRDS, REPTILES, FISHES AND INSECTS. A NEW AND AUTHENTIC NATURAL HISTORY OF THE WILDLIFE OF THE WORLD.

FREDERICK DRIMMER, M.A.

EDITOR-IN-CHIEF

VOLUME I

GREYSTONE PRESS, NEW YORK

About This Book

THE ANIMAL KINGDOM is an epochal work in the field of natural history. Written by seven eminent naturalists on the staffs of the American Museum of Natural History and the New York Zoological Society, it has been four years in preparation, and comprises over two thousand pages and six hundred thousand words of authentic and interesting information about the wildlife of the world. It is far and away the most complete, authoritative, and up-to-date natural history in the English language today.

The Animal Kingdom will supply you with the knowledge you need if you are to understand the animals that share the world in which you live. Based on the most recent research and investigation, this great work explains simply and colorfully the intimate lives of wild animals, both common and exotic, of all lands — not only the mammals, but the birds, amphibians, reptiles, fishes, insects and other invertebrates. The writers tell you how you can recognize each important animal, where it lives, its habits, courtship, family life, how it raises its young, how it combats enemies and gets its food, and a wealth of other fascinating information — in short, the animal's natural history.

ANIMALS ALIVE

This is a book of animals alive. The distinguished authors of *The Animal Kingdom,* although outstanding scientists, are no mere dry-as-dust museum specialists. They have a deep love of animals and have tracked and observed them in the remote fastnesses of the earth.

In these pages they share many a thrilling adventure with you, many a startling encounter they have had in the wild — with the giant brown bears and the wolves of the Arctic tundra, with the lions of the African veld, the poisonous reptiles of the American deserts and woodland, the exotic birds of the rain forests of New Guinea, the strange insects of the jungles of South America. You will read of hairbreadth escapes, and the curious ways of primitive peoples in the native lands of these animals.

A BOOK OF MARVELS

This is a book of marvels as well. Animals have a way of not living up to our preconceived notions, yet what they will do often exceeds our most fantastic expectations. Thus the authors tell you about fishes that build nests in the water or hop about on land, about desert rodents that never drink water and will refuse it when offered, about ants that keep herds of insect "cows," salamanders that have elaborate courtship rites, young elephants that make their own playthings, bats that go fishing, whales that commit suicide, birds that cannot fly but can run faster than most other animals.

Nature teems with such oddities, and since they are of considerable scientific and popular interest, the authors describe them at length.

WHAT ANIMALS MEAN TO MAN

This is also a book about what animals mean to man. The story of how wild creatures are hunted and trapped or tamed is spread through these pages.

You will read here how the Japanese rear silkworms, how the Indians tame the elephant, and how South American natives hunt the capybara, the biggest rodent on earth, along the Orinoco and the Amazon. You will learn how the whale is fished today by modern fleets in the icy waters of the Antarctic, and the uses to which ambergris, whale oil, whale meat, and whalebone are put. Few stories are more tragic than those told here about the large-scale slaughter of fur seals, ostriches, birds of paradise, bison, Colobus monkeys, and other animals, which once brought these creatures close to extinction.

Bears and seals as entertainers — the comparative reliability of lions and tigers as circus performers — the humble origins of some furs with glamorous names — the ancestry of our domestic cats, canaries, and other creatures — these are merely a few of the fascinating subjects touched on, in which man and the animals are linked.

The authors also take you on diverting excursions into the romantic realm of folklore, tell you of the odd beliefs people have about animals around the globe, and explain the origin of many legendary beasts such as the unicorn and the sea serpent.

A WORK OF SCIENTIFIC INFORMATION

Although those aspects of animal life that are of most interest to the general reader have been stressed in *The Animal Kingdom,* and technical jargon has been avoided, this book is thoroughly scientific in approach and content. You will find highly accurate and lucid explanations of how such mammals as the weasel change colors with the seasons, how the heat-detecting mechanism of reptiles works, how birds can fly, how fishes breathe, and countless other important facts.

The wonderful story of the development of the animals is related simply and clearly, and frequent glimpses are afforded of the rich animal life of the past — of odd or spectacular creatures like the dinosaur and the four-toed horse that became extinct ages ago, as well as those that, like the dodo and the passenger pigeon, vanished within historic time. The common and zoological names of the various animals are given — approximately eight thousand are listed in the Complete Ready Reference Index at the end of this work — and their position in the scheme of living things is explained.

SEVEN EMINENT AUTHORS

To give *The Animal Kingdom* unimpeachable authority, the task of producing this monumental work was entrusted to seven leading authorities on animal life:

Book I — "Mammals of the Land, Air, and Waters of the World" — was written by George G. Goodwin, Associate Curator of the Department of Mammals of the American Museum of Natural History. Dr. Goodwin has studied mammals in their native habitat all over the world: his explorations have taken him to Siberia, Turkestan, Persia, Syria, Egypt, Kenya, Tanganyika, the West Indies, the Arctic, and many other remote places. He has collected forty-five hundred specimens for the Museum, and named sixty mammals new to science. He is the author of numerous articles and seventy popular and scientific publications, including *Mammals of Honduras, Mammals of Costa Rica, Mammals of Connecticut,* etc.

Although the mammals are not the most numerous of the animals, more interest attaches to them than to other forms of wildlife and so Book I is the longest in *The Animal Kingdom;* in point of fact it is the most up-to-date and comprehensive popular work on mammals of the world in the English language.

Book II — " Birds of the World" — is the work of two outstanding bird experts, Dean Amadon and E. Thomas Gilliard, Associate Curators of the Department of Birds of the American Museum of Natural History. They have devoted many years to the study of birds in North and South America, Australia, New Guinea, the Hawaiian Islands and the Philippines. Dr. Amadon and Mr. Gilliard are the authors of articles that have appeared in many leading scientific and popular periodicals.

Book III — "Amphibians and Reptiles of the World" — was written by Charles M. Bogert, Chairman and Curator of the Department of Amphibians and Reptiles at the American Museum of Natural History. A distinguished explorer and scientist, Mr. Bogert has made many notable scientific contributions concerning the reptiles and amphibians of the United States, Mexico, Central America, New Guinea, and Africa. He has taught biology and zoology at the University of California.

Book IV — "Fishes of the World" — comes from the pens of Christopher W. Coates, Curator, and James W. Atz, Assistant Curator, of the New York Aquarium of the New York Zoological Society. Mr. Coates is the leading public aquarist in the United States, and one of the leaders in the world. For his use of aquatic animals in medical research he has won two awards for Advancement of Medical Science. Both Mr. Coates and Mr. Atz are the authors of numerous scientific and popular writings in their field.

Book V — "Insects and Other Invertebrates" — is by John C. Pallister, Research Associate, Department of Insects and Spiders, at the American Museum of Natural History; he was formerly in charge of the Entomological Department of the Cleveland Museum of Natural History. An explorer, scientist, and lecturer of many years' experience, Mr. Pallister has studied and collected insects and other invertebrates in the United States, Canada, Mexico, Guatemala, British Honduras, Panama, Brazil, Peru, and on islands in the Pacific.

AN IMPRESSIVE GALLERY OF WILDLIFE PICTURES

Besides numerous black and white photographs and color plates, an impressive gallery of more than five hundred accurate drawings of animals in their natural surroundings illustrates this book. These pictures were prepared by a corps of highly skilled wildlife illustrators working under the direct supervision of the authors.

The greater number of the drawings of mammals, reptiles, amphibians, and invertebrates are the work of Thomas Voter, formerly Art Director of the American Museum of Natural History. Gardell Dano Christensen, noted wildlife artist, also drew some of the mammals; Russell Francis Peterson, Marjorie Statham, and Evelyn Hastings, all affiliated with the Museum, prepared a number of the insect drawings. The birds were drawn by Robert F. Seibert, formerly staff artist with *Audubon Magazine*. Lloyd Sandford, staff artist of the New York Zoological Society, drew the portraits of the fishes. Matthew Kalmenoff did the animal tracks.

Many other persons have given freely of their time and thought to help make *The Animal Kingdom* the classic work in its field. In particular, the publishers wish to acknowledge a debt of gratitude to Dr. Roy Chapman Andrews, President Emeritus of the American Museum of Natural History, for his generous encouragement during the initial stages. Dr. George G. Goodwin gave invaluable advice and guidance as the book grew, and so, too, did the other authors.

In its domain, this great work has no equal. We may still profitably follow the counsel of the Bible: "Go to the ant, thou sluggard; consider her ways, and be wise." There is no substitute for going out and seeing the animals at first hand, and it is hoped that the present work will encourage the reader to do so. But for a general understanding of the animals, however, we no longer need to travel afield, nor, indeed, to look into a multitude of books on the different classes of animal life. *The Animal Kingdom* now tells us, clearly and expertly, within the scope of a single comprehensive natural history, the things we want to know about the strange and wonderful ways of them all — the mammals, birds, amphibians, reptiles, fishes, insects and other invertebrates of the entire world.

FREDERICK DRIMMER
Editor-in-Chief

Contents — Volume I

BOOK I: Mammals of the Air, Land, and Waters of the World

By George G. Goodwin

false vampires — flesh-eating bats — yellow-winged bats — horse-shoe bats and cyclops bats — how bats sleep through the winter — America's nose-leaf bats and leaf-lipped bats — a visit with the javelin bats — leaf-chinned bats — flat-faced fruit bats — vampires, bats that drink blood — true insect-eating or common bats — little brown bats — fish-eating bats — pipistrelles — the neat noctule — red bats — long-eared bats — great northern or hoary bats — free-tailed bats — great guano deposits — bats in war.

Tree shrews: they look like squirrels — tame tree shrews — lemurs, the fox-faced "monkeys" of Madagascar—lemurs that sleep through the summer — the woolly lemurs — the indri — its protective coloring — how it got its name — the indri of legend — aye-ayes, mystery creatures of Madagascar — slender lorises — slow or gray lorises — the "bashful cat" — the common potto — like a little old man — a powerful hand grasp — the bush baby, ojam, or galago — a ball of bush babies — when the bush babies cry — tarsiers.

The night monkey or douroucouli — the uakari — capturing the uakari — the saki, intelligent and friendly — the howler monkey and its remarkable howl — family life of the howlers — the wonderful "monkey chain" — capuchins, or ring-tailed monkeys —full of pranks — squirrel monkeys — spider monkeys — a leap of thirty feet — family life among the spider monkeys — marmosets and tamarins, South America's "near-monkeys" — a fifty-foot fall — marmoset pets.

Macaques — monkey marauders — bullies and underdogs — rhesus monkeys — Europe's only monkey — the wily black ape — mangabeys, named for a place they never lived in — baboons, biggest of the monkeys — clever food-getters — baboon pests — the helpful tame baboon — hamadryas baboons — their battles — mandrills and drills — guenons, Africa's commonest monkeys — monkey mother love — a "sick" monkey — red monkeys — langurs, common monkeys of the Orient — the sacred monkey — proboscis monkeys — the guereza.

Contents—Volume II

BOOK I: Mammals of the Air, Land, and Waters of the World — *continued*

By George G. Goodwin

BOOK II: Birds of the World

By Dean Amadon
and E. Thomas Gilliard

whites — short-tailed pheasants — Impeyan pheasants — typical pheasants — peacocks — Argus pheasants — Congo peacocks — many kinds of chickens — cockfights — turkeys, wild and domesticated — their interesting history — guinea fowl — grouse — ruffed grouse — plains grouse and their weird booming — prairie chickens — prairie sharp-tailed grouse — sage hens — ptarmigan.

CRANES, RAILS, AND THEIR RELATIVES 998

Mesites, flightless relics — whooping cranes — sand-hill cranes — common cranes — African crowned cranes — limpkins — trumpeters — bustards — sun bitterns and their extraordinary dance — kagus, flightless birds of New Caledonia — cariamas: ancient and dignified — the diatryma, fantastic fossil — finfeet: skillful swimmers, sluggish fliers — button quails — rails, coots, and gallinules — the clapper rail — the purple gallinule — the American coot — some other rails and their elusive ways.

SHORE BIRDS, GULLS, AND THEIR RELATIVES 1011

Sandpipers — the woodcock — the jacksnipe — spotted sandpipers — plovers, extraordinary migrators — avocets and stilts: long-legged waders — pratincoles and coursers — phalaropes: they weather the wintry gales — crab plovers — thick-knees — seed snipe — oyster catchers — sheathbills — common sea gulls — Franklin gulls — great black-backed gulls — terns: they include the champion migrator — skimmers: they cleave the water — jaçanas or lotus birds — auks — murres — puffins — dovekies.

PIGEONS, DOVES, DODOS, AND SAND GROUSE 1034

Pigeons and doves — the difference between doves and pigeons — ways of the pigeons — American pigeons and doves — the passenger pigeon — the mourning dove — exotic pigeons of the tropics — dodos and solitaires — sand grouse.

PARROTS—LONG-LIVED AND LOQUACIOUS 1041

The Papuan lory — the pygmy parrot — the sulphur-crested cockatoo — great black cockatoo — the red, blue, and green macaw — the African gray parrot — the Carolina parakeet — lovebirds and their relatives — other remarkable parrots.

BOOK III: Amphibians and Reptiles of the World

By Charles M. Bogert

exterminators —the neotropical toad — the true frogs — the American bullfrog — the size of bullfrogs — what the bullfrog feeds on — the bullfrog's enemies — other frogs — the leopard frog — how natural selection works — specialization among frogs — the water toads — the midwife toad — frogs with built-in nurseries — the tongueless toads — the Surinam toad — the remarkable qualities of the Surinam toad.

Contents—Volume III

BOOK IV: Fishes of the World

By Christopher W. Coates
and James W. Atz

BOOK V: Insects and Other Invertebrates

By John C. Pallister

THE TRUE FLIES — BITERS, SCAVENGERS, AND POISONERS   1953

BOOK I: Mammals of the Air, Land, and Waters of the World

GEORGE G. GOODWIN

Understanding the Mammals

Many and wonderful are the differences we find among the mammals that live in the world today. They vary in size from the tiny shrew that weighs only a fraction of an ounce to the gigantic whale that weighs a hundred tons. They vary in habit from the timid little squirrel that feeds on acorns to the amiable dolphin that plucks fishes from the deep, and the ferocious big cats that sometimes prey even on man. Their diversity seems almost infinite, and their ways, whether formed by instinct or learning, are nothing short of amazing.

From the largest to the smallest, there is exquisite beauty and grandeur of form in nearly every type of animal; we see grace and rhythm in practically every motion. Each animal comes close to perfection in its own manner. True, none has quite learned to think and talk the way we do, but they have developed enough mental power for their own needs. Not only can some animals give voice to their feelings of love, friendship, fear, hate, and rage, but many have a system of code signals which they use to communicate with one another.

Outside man's domain, the mammals have made themselves at home practically everywhere. Looking at some of the hard, unfriendly places where they have settled, we are often compelled to marvel that they could survive there at all. We discover mammals living under conditions ranging from intense cold to tropical heat, from the rarefied air of snow-capped peaks to the depths of the ocean. On fields of floating ice and in the heart of the arid, burning desert, mammals have made their dwelling places.

Some mammals, such as the bats, have taken to the air. Others, like the squirrels and monkeys, have entered the forests and climbed the trees. The whales and seals have left the land and gone to sea. Animals have covered the face of the earth; some, such as the gopher and mole, have burrowed underground. Wherever there was living space for them, the mammals have moved in.

In all these different kinds of places, we find the mammals superbly equipped to meet nature's challenge. To withstand the rigors of a cold climate, many are clad in thick, woolly fur. Others that spend much of their time swimming in streams and lakes have oily hair that sheds water. The covering of the mammals may range from the superfine fur of the chinchilla to the barbed quills of the porcupine or to the horny shell of the armadillo.

WHY WE CALL THEM MAMMALS

An outer covering of hair is the peculiar property of the mammals. Not every mammal possesses one—a few, like the whale, are practically hairless. On the other hand, we do find hair on the bodies of most mammals. This is in sharp contrast to other classes of animal life. The birds, fishes, and reptiles are not protected by such a growth.

Still, this covering is only one of the typical features of the mammals. Strictly speaking, we consider everything that lives and is not a plant to be an animal—just what things make us call this group of animals "mammals" and nothing else? The name "mammal" comes from the Latin word *mamma,* meaning "breast." The mammals have glands that produce milk which they use to feed their young. Except for a few primitive mammals, which lay eggs, all bear their babies alive, and even the egg-layers suckle their young. It is in these characteristics that we find the sharpest differences between the mammals and other animals.

Mammals, of course, possess backbones and breathe air. Even a whale will drown if it cannot surface regularly to draw life-giving oxygen into its lungs. Like the birds, but like no other animals, the mammals have a four-chambered heart and a complete double system of circulation—on one side impure blood is carried to the lungs, where the poisonous gases escape; on the other side, after being refreshed with oxygen, the blood is piped back to the rest of the body.

Unlike the fishes and the reptiles—but again like the birds— mammals are warm-blooded. To maintain their body temperature, they rely not only on their hairy covering, but on still another mechanism other animals do not have: the sweat glands.

BEAVERS — RODENT LOGGERS AND BUILDERS OF DAMS

The beavers, North America's biggest rodents, erect their dams across streams, from the Rio Grande north to Alaska. Frequently a family of beavers work on a single dam, cutting down small trees and towing large branches and sticks to the desired site. They weave these building materials together with their forepaws. These sociable creatures dwell in a burrow in the bank of a river or lake, or else they construct a lodge in the water; the entrance is always below the surface, so that the beavers may go and come without being observed by their enemies. The animals' purpose in building their dams is to maintain the water at an adequate level for their various activities. (Illustration by Fred Ludekens, courtesy of Weyerhaeuser Timber Company.)

We never find more than two pairs of limbs on a mammal. Some mammals, like the kangaroo, have hind legs that represent an extreme in development. At the opposite end of the picture is the whale, which has lost its hind limbs altogether and acquired flukes to help it move about in the water.

Every mammal has front limbs, even the bats, which have developed them into wings for flight. In the whale they have become flippers. Look at the skeleton of a whale the next time you visit a museum and you will see the bones—vaguely reminiscent of those in the human hand—that gave the flippers support when the huge creature was alive.

The driving power of most mammals is centered in their hind limbs. All fast runners have longer tips on their toes to increase their speed, and they possess cushioned pads for support. Some, like the sheep, deer, and horses, have their toes encased in hoofs, and the middle toe or toes take over the function of the foot, at the expense of the other toes.

KEEN SENSES

As a rule, the senses of sight, taste, smell, hearing, and touch are well developed in the mammals. What an animal lacks in one sense, it frequently makes up in another. The mole, for example, is almost completely blind, but it has a highly sensitive nose and tail to guide it around in the darkness.

Some animals also tend to specialize in the development of one sense organ though not at the expense of another. The monkeys and their relatives, spending their lives in the trees, where vision is at a premium, often have unusually large eyes. In the deserts, where the sun is dazzling and where there is little opportunity to find cover, we often observe that the animals possess big ears, helping them to detect danger while it is still far off.

Most mammals live in a dull, gray world. Only a few—the apes, for example—have color vision. Others—usually animals that are active at night, like the cats—are famous because their eyes glow in the dark. The eyes, however, do not generate any light themselves; they merely catch up and reflect whatever light is present in the gloom. Behind this remarkable power lies an interesting fact. The inner wall of the eye is coated with a substance called "guanin." This has a metallic luster of silver or gold and brightens dimly lit images on the retina of the animal's eye so it can see them better.

The sense of touch is far more vital to an animal than you might suppose. Almost every motion is closely connected with the sense of touch. Nerve fibers end in tiny raised points on the skin which are known as touch spots. Except on the soles of the feet, a touch spot usually has a hair on it. The hairs themselves are not sensitive, but they act as levers to press the touch spots. Animals are guided in running or walking by this sense of touch. The long hairs or whiskers on the nose of the cat are connected with touch spots and supplement sight in dim light.

CAMOUFLAGED BY NATURE

The sharpest sense of animals is sight. It is the swiftest too: Seeing takes place with the speed of light. Falcons, hawks, and the fastest beasts of prey hunt by sight. A tiger may track a goat by scent but the final leap is guided by sight.

Still, many animals possess a means of defeating this exceedingly sharp sense. Protective coloration can create an optical illusion that will deceive the keenest observer. How inconspicuous an animal may be depends on how well it blends in with its surroundings. Natural camouflage not only enables an animal to escape detection by its enemies; it causes the flesh-eater to be less avoided by the animals it preys on.

GAY COATS ARE CAMOUFLAGE TOO

Some animals are gaudily colored, yet they are camouflaged nonetheless. The checkered sunfleck and leaf shadow pattern of the leopard, ocelot, jaguar, and giraffe, though contrasting and conspicuous when you view it in a zoological garden, fades to obscurity in the bush. In Kenya the author saw a leopard take its stand in a bright sunlit opening against a background of bush; but a white hunter, a sportsman, and his gunbearer could not see the animal at seventy-five feet although they gazed at the exact spot where it stood for fully fifteen minutes.

It might seem that the extraordinary, brilliant, clear-cut black-and-white-striped coat of a zebra would make it a marked animal that could not escape detection. Nor does it—on the open veldt. But the zebra must go regularly to some pool to drink, and here, where lions are poised to pounce, the stripes become an asset. At the water's edge, silhouetted against tall, light-colored reeds and a shadowy background, the showy zebra pattern fades to a beneficial obscurity. In the same way the vertical stripes of a tiger's coat bear a graceful resemblance to the bushy and grassy thickets of its hunting ground.

CAMOUFLAGE LIGHT AND DARK

Beasts of the open plains—such as lions, kangaroos, hares and the like —are noted for their lack of markings but they still illustrate the fundamental principle of animal camouflage. The under parts of these animals are usually white, or lighter than the color of the back. The brightest light comes from above and lightens the back but throws the under parts in shadow so that both upper and lower parts look alike; the outline of the animal is thus flattened and blotted out in certain lights if the animal is motionless.

Light and dark shades in the covering of an animal are often graded so that it is less conspicuous when viewed either from above or from below, depending on which aspect it is most often seen from. Many animals that live close to the soil are ground colored. A gray squirrel has an over-all covering of white-tipped hairs that make it hard to see in the trees, against the sky.

CHANGING WITH THE SEASONS

The camouflage pattern of an animal's coat is not always fixed. In regions where seasons bring drastic changes in temperature and in the color of the surroundings, some animals not only vary the thickness of their coat but change its color as a concealing factor. The ermine and varying hare, for example, have brown fur in summer, which makes it difficult to see them on the forest floor; in winter they are equally inconspicuous against a snow-covered background, for now their coats have been changed to white.

These temporary white winter coats of northern animals should not be confused with albinism. Albinism is a sign of weakness, often accompanied by pink eyes and poor eyesight, whereas the change in the ermine and the varying hare is a normal, regular happening.

MILLS THAT GRIND AND CUT

Almost anything that can be eaten serves as food for some kind of animal, and each creature is specialized more or less to one type of diet. The cattle are grass-eaters, the deer are leaf-eaters, the beavers eat the bark of trees. The wild cats live mainly on flesh; there are bats that actually drain the nectar of flowers; some animals depend on a diet of insects or shellfish, or fruits, nuts, and seeds.

To feed on these diets, hard or soft, mammals often have special kinds of teeth. In general, a mammal's teeth are not all the same, the way they are in the lower animals with backbones. In one mammal, like the tiger, we find large canine teeth that seize and rend the flesh of their prey, and cheek teeth adapted for biting; some have heavy molars that help in grinding, and other types of teeth.

The lower animals, like the shark, will grow a new tooth to take the place of an old one, and can go on doing this indefinitely. Not so the mammals—they have only two sets of teeth: the "milk teeth" and the "permanent teeth." They seldom have more than forty-four teeth, generally fewer. The monkeys of the Old World, for example, have thirty-two, the same number as man.

So far as teeth go, most of us have reason to envy the mammals; theirs will last them through life. Some mammals, like the beaver and other rodents—animals that gnaw their food—have long front teeth whose growth never ceases. The teeth of the horse and many other animals that grind their food continue to grow until late in life.

Animals that feed on tough, rough vegetation have sturdier teeth than those that eat soft, pulpy food. Insect-eaters like the anteater and the pangolin have no teeth whatever—instead, they have a long, extendible tongue to lick up their victims, which they swallow whole. Many whales are toothless, too; their mouths are provided with baleen, an efficient strainer that permits them to separate from the water the minute sea life with which they maintain their huge bodies.

Teeth provide valuable clues to the naturalist who is trying to identify an animal. They are often the one feature by which we can definitely recognize a species. It does not matter that the animal's bones may have been scattered or turned to dust a hundred, a thousand, or even a million years ago. If we find the teeth, they reveal the nature of the animal to us, for each species has its own typical set.

HOW ANIMALS MOVE ABOUT

All members of the animal kingdom live and move. We associate life with motion, and the panorama of life interests us only because it changes and moves. Indeed, it almost would appear that man's emotional stability is governed by motion. Inactivity brings loneliness and despair, while motion means life and brings hope. To no small degree, living things are pleasing to have around because they move. The stillness of death appears unnatural to us and causes us distress.

Motion is not confined to the animal kingdom—modern science has shown us that all matter is in motion. The sea and the air are at their grandest during a storm. The lightning flash followed by the growl of thunder reminds us that all is in action. Nature gives us no example of absolute rest. In time even the rocks grow old and crumble into dust.

Man, by observing nature, has been able to learn many valuable lessons. Seeing that birds and insects could fly, he eventually learned to fly himself. If he had never witnessed these models in the air, he might very likely have assumed that flight was impossible—had he thought about it at all.

The forces employed in walking, swimming, and flying are basically the same. It is largely because the elements in which the animals travel are different that their way of getting about varies. Land is more solid and firmer than water, and water has a greater density than air.

ANIMALS OF LAND, WATER, AND AIR

Whatever the element may be—land, water, or air—each has its advantages and disadvantages. On dry land a horse must not only support its own weight but also generate the power necessary to drive itself along. On the other hand, the body of a whale is supported by the buoyancy of the sea; all its exertions can be centered on moving itself, but it must make a greater effort to force its way through water than would be the case in air. Some birds like the albatross can soar for an hour without flapping a wing; but such a bird must have huge wing muscles to hold it suspended in the air.

An animal's power to move is centered in its limbs or other extremities. The wings of a bird support and carry it through the air. The tail of the fishes and the flukes of a whale are propellers that push these animals through the water—but its chief driving force here consists of the undulations of the body itself. Land mammals, of course, travel by means of their legs.

WONDERFUL FEET AND LEGS

Every living thing impresses us as a miracle of adaptation, once we look at it closely. Take the lowly housefly, for example. It has, on the ends of its feet, sucking disks that enable it to stay on a ceiling and walk upside down. The feet of the mammals are no less interesting. Animals that climb rocky mountain slopes have rubber-like pads on their feet as a safety device. The chamois, one of nature's ablest mountaineers, is shod with a pliable, horny hoof encasing a rubbery sole— a combination that will not only hold on slippery rocks but acts as a shock-absorber as well. A camel that travels over the shifting sands would quickly tire were its feet not equipped with a broad pad that spreads when it is pressed on the ground, giving added support.

With the exception of leaping animals, most land-bound mammals move diagonally forward—the right front leg and the left hind leg move forward together, alternating with the left front leg and hind right leg. This is also true of ourselves. As we put our right leg forward, our left arm moves with it; a similar action of our left foot and right arm follows. With this diagonal movement of the limbs the body twists and weaves forward with an even continuity of movement.

ANIMALS THAT PACE

There is no doubt that this pendulum motion of the limbs and body is the most efficient method for travel on land, yet not all four-footed animals progress in this manner. A very few amble or pace. In these the fore and hind limbs on one side move forward at the same time, first on one side then on the other. Pacing is hereditary and has been handed down among these creatures for ages.

Animals that pace have their body slung high on their legs but they are not restricted to any particular kind of dwelling place. The camel is the most popular example of a pacer but the llama, alpaca, and their wild camel-like relatives of the Andes are also pacers. The giraffe of the African veldt is a pacer, as is the okapi of the Congo forests. The hyena paces; some horses inherit a like tendency to pace. This is not artificial, although it is developed by trainers.

THEIR TAILS HELP THEM TRAVEL

The tail plays an important part in helping many animals to move about. Squirrels have need of a bushy tail to maintain their balance in the treetops and to guide their descent in their flying leaps. Many jumping animals have a long tail and use it as a rudder when sailing through the air. The great kangaroo makes long leaps sometimes covering about forty feet and is given an extra boost by its powerful tail. Passing from the great to the small, we find that all the jumping mice have exceptionally long tails to steer them through the air. Most monkeys have a long tail as a balancing organ; the South American monkey often can use it as a fifth hand.

Of course many mammals with only the scantiest trace of a tail do very nicely all the same. The African antelope, the impala, covers up to thirty-five feet in a jump without any assistance from its short tail. A jackrabbit has been known to clear a fence seven feet high; as many of us know, the little powder puff on the rear end of a rabbit is used as a signal and for nothing else.

SPEED RECORDS IN THE ANIMAL KINGDOM

Fishes are built for easy travel through the water. While a fish's principal power comes from the manipulation or weaving motion of the body, it possesses auxiliary motors for jet propulsion. In a sudden burst of speed a fish ejects a fast stream of water through its gills. It is generally accepted that the fastest living creature in the water is the sailfish, with a possible or estimated maximum speed of 68 miles per hour. The swordfish and the marlin are also fast travelers—they are reported as good for speeds up to 60 miles per hour. Dolphins are the fastest marine mammals with a motor power that can drive them up to 37 miles an hour.

BIRDS ARE FASTEST

The record speed for any animal is held by a bird—the frigate bird has a flying speed of over 100 miles an hour and has been credited with a hard-to-believe record of over twice this speed. The swifts are among the fastest of all birds, but it is doubtful if the spine-tailed swift ever attained 219 miles per hour, as recorded. The peregrine falcon can speed up its flight to around 100 miles an hour, not taking into account power dives or aid from favorable winds.

Geese, timed by airplane speedometer, can travel at 60 miles per hour, and they hold the altitude record of 29,000 feet, which is nearly 5½ miles. However, except during migration, birds usually fly at an altitude below 2,000 feet.

MAMMALS BUILT FOR SPEED

When we come to the mammals, the record, although good, cannot rival that of the birds. The fastest four-footed animal on land is the cheetah, with a stop-watch record of 70 miles per hour. It probably has an even greater maximum speed.

The Mongolian antelope and the American pronghorn can keep ahead of an automobile with the speedometer registering 60. The fastest speed ever recorded for a race horse is 48 miles per hour. Some hares come close to this—they can travel at a speed of 45 miles, which is about the same as the top speed for a big kangaroo.

In general, four legs are better than two; the top speed at which a man can run is only 22.8 miles per hour for 100 yards, while a greyhound can streak along at 40 miles and still be left behind by a hare. The slowest mammal is the sloth, which on the ground cannot hit a pace higher than five-tenths of a mile per hour.

In speed, the mammals have gone far beyond their reptile forebears. A man can easily escape from most snakes found in the United States and Europe. The African mamba, which grows to a length of 12 feet, is one of the fastest snakes on earth, with an estimated speed of 10 miles an hour. It is also one of the most dangerous, as it attacks without provocation and takes the offensive when man or beast enters its home territory.

SMALL BUT SWIFT

The smallest members of the animal kingdom are by no means the slowest. In the insect world there are dragonflies that can travel at 55 miles per hour; a worker honeybee 15, a queen 20, and a drone 25 miles per hour. The latter two have 330 wingbeats to the second!

ANIMALS OF THE NIGHT AND DAY

For most mammals, the bright sunlight hours around midday and the darkest hours of the night are a time for resting and sleeping. Some, like the tree squirrels and their kind, may be abroad during the warm part of the day, but most prefer to stay in their nests and dens, or hide in the underbrush.

It is when the shadows begin to lengthen that all nature really comes to life, and the woods and countryside hum with activity. In the twilight, most mammals eat their big meal of the day. Grazing and browsing animals, like the hippopotamus and the antelope, come out of their places of concealment and feed steadily in the cool of the evening and well on into the night. On the wing at sunset, the bats have eaten their fill of fruit and insects and returned to their roosts before midnight; they may go out hunting again in the wee hours of the morning.

There are a few strictly night prowlers, like the wolves, tigers, and other flesh-eaters, that will continue their search for prey all night if their hunger has not been appeased. Many rodents are not only active by night, but all through the day, too. They must eat constantly for they are energetic little creatures and their bodies quickly burn up all the food they can provide themselves with. By and large, though, most animals are active at dusk.

LIVING BY INSTINCT

An animal is born with an inherited sense that it obeys without question. It comes into the world with the ability to act and protect itself according to its immediate needs—without instruction or learning gained from experience. This is what we mean by animal instinct.

Instinct is generous and motherly; it gathers all life under its protecting shelter. It covers a wide field of animal behavior, from the simple reaction which directs a creature to move away from excessive cold or heat, to the more rapid reflex actions brought about by contact. It includes higher complex subconscious impulses such as love and hate, those that govern parental care, as well as the urge to migrate at certain seasons of the year.

Instinct works in many strange and mysterious ways. It tells a bird when and where to build its nest—but the bird is quite unaware why it builds the nest. Very young songbirds in a nest show no fear of a stranger and make no attempt to escape—not that they could if they tried. These same babies, fully feathered and ready to leave the nest, have somehow acquired the ability to fear and the impulse to flee from danger. Instinct leads the newborn mammal baby to its mother's breast to nurse and the newly hatched duckling to water. Contrariwise, it keeps the baby chick on dry land.

Instinct keeps an animal in constant readiness to act instantly and to meet any emergency without hesitation. Confronted by the sudden appearance of a mortal enemy, an animal does not make a haphazard dash for safety, but follows a definite method of escape, making all possible use of every advantage. The animal itself may be totally ignorant of why it follows such a course and is unable to foresee the result of its actions.

When a fox comes bounding along a woodland trail, a squirrel goes up the nearest tree, even though it never saw a fox before in its life. Instinct warns the squirrel of danger and forms its course of action. If it were a rabbit it would make its escape by dashing off on its long legs and not make the mistake of trying to climb a tree. It knows what to do, though it does not always know why.

ANIMALS CAN LEARN

Animals can and do acquire knowledge through learning during a lifetime. A successful life for a mammal is largely dependent on its ability to learn.

Tuition begins in infancy, when a mammal is to no small extent at the mercy of surrounding conditions. It acquires a working intelligence through watching the activities outside itself—their cause and effect.

The comparatively long period of childhood in a mammal, when the brain is pliable, permits a greater development along educational lines than we find in other animals. Under parental tuition the growing young are able to gain considerable useful knowledge that will benefit them in later life. They also learn important details when at play, and practice in fun the particular trades that later will serve them well in making a living. The mother takes her young on excursions into the outside world, where they get first-hand realistic knowledge in the field. Skill comes through practice and by following the example set by the experienced parent.

Curiosity, developed early in life, increases as a mammal learns. It brings a spirit of exploration and a desire for new experiences, enabling an animal to extend its activities into a broader field.

THE CLEVER ONES

Education and intelligence vary in quantity and quality with different kinds of mammals as well as with the individual. Some animals are more adaptable and learn quicker than others; animals that enjoy a long life have a better chance of perfecting their education than those that are short-lived.

Elephants, for example, often show considerable forethought and ability to figure things out for themselves. Those that haul the huge, heavy teak logs down the mountain slopes to the rivers in Burma are known to size up a difficult situation and maneuver logs into position without any prompting from the mahout. Some animals even learn to use tools and weapons, although only crudely. Baboons in their native land often pick up stones and throw them with a degree of accuracy at offending strangers. One Barbary ape in a zoo would hurl the contents of its drinking pan into the face of anyone who annoyed it. When the pan was replaced with a stone basin too heavy for the ape to lift, it cupped its hand and with a sudden swing of its arm continued to send a scoop of water at anyone it did not like.

Instinct is a necessity for the existence of all animal life. By their ability to learn, animals can go further and improve their living conditions, as well as their chances of survival.

ANIMAL FATHERS AND MOTHERS

In the care they give their young, the mammals surpass all other forms of life. It is true that some insects, fishes, reptiles, and amphibians show instinctive concern for the welfare of their eggs and babies, but with enormous numbers it is a matter of chance whether or not the young survive at all. The birds, on the other hand, are famous for the attention they bestow on their offspring; many nestlings are fortunate enough to have the companionship and protection of both mother and father. Still, the mammals as a group show more solicitude than most for the well-being of their babies.

Why should the mammal be a better parent? Earlier we dwelt on the fact that these animals bear their young alive. Many mammal babies are born without sight and are almost naked. For weeks or months they are dependent upon their mother's milk for nourishment. As a rule, they could hardly survive without the devoted care of their parents. The babies of the lower animals, in contrast, fend for themselves quite early.

AFFECTION AMONG THE ANIMALS

Man himself is more than just a beast of the field, but he is a mammal. The intimate life of wild animals is much like that of man in many ways.

The feelings of man and beast are perhaps closest during courtship. Both have the same natural instinct to have young and perpetuate their race; both experience passionate feelings of affection for their mate and of hatred for anyone who frustrates their desires.

Female wild animals, like humans, display a share of modesty during courtship and play hard-to-get, but will turn to decoy the male should his interest be lured toward some other female. Most pairs of wild animals, like man, prefer to do their lovemaking in privacy and, at the time, have little interest in anything but each other. Indeed, some species go off by themselves on a prolonged honeymoon.

Most wild animals live a very *orderly life*. There is a time for courtship and a time to be born, just as there is a time to eat, sleep, and engage in other activities. As a rule, life is so timed that the young are born in the spring of the year, when food is plentiful and there is a whole summer to grow and prepare for the winter.

Wild animals are exceedingly restless during the season of courtship; in fact at this time their behavior is unpredictable. Some males do not eat for weeks on end but, once the mating season is over, they all settle down to a regular, orderly life. All strife and enmity is forgotten. Warriors that battled in deadly earnest over some comely female, once more become inseparable companions.

HOW THE MOTHER BEARS HER YOUNG

Birth among the wild mammals is much the same as with people. When the wild mother's time draws near, she too begins to feel the natural pangs of labor. As the pain increases, she wanders off alone and seeks some secluded spot to be by herself. Least of all does she need male companionship. She does not shun her mate's company be cause she fears he will devour the babies—she is simply uncomfortable and in a surly mood. (A dying animal will also go off to meet its end alone.)

When the time comes, the prospective mother lies down on her bed of pain, but she is probably unaware of what is taking place. Once the baby is born, she is on her feet again, with all the maternal care and love of a mother for her newborn child showing in every nervous action. At its first cry she fondly proffers all the solicitude she can.

Being born is comparatively easy and natural with the wild creatures; there is little or no mortality at childbirth. There is no need for a doctor here as is so often the case with domestic animals, where crossbreeding has produced a baby too large for normal birth.

MOST FATHERS GO THEIR OWN WAY

Unlike the birds, few mammals enjoy the care of both parents. Usually only the mother lives in close association with the young during the early stages. This is understandable since she alone can supply milk. Male sea cows, however, show a marked interest in the young from the very first and will carry the newborn calf around while the mother feeds herself. Males among the herd animals are more typical —they show not the slightest concern for the young.

It is among the carnivores—the flesh-eaters—that we find the father taking a truly dutiful place in family affairs. He is the provider and brings food to the female while she is nursing her cubs or puppies. Later he provides food for the young as well, but he is not permitted in the nursery while they are very little.

THE MOTHER TAKES CHARGE

The young recognize their mother by scent or odor and that is just how their mother recognizes them. Her first duty in many cases is to lick the baby from head to foot. This is a way of establishing ownership. If this ritual were omitted, many a mother would not accept her young under any circumstances.

While the mother's care is largely instinctive, she labors hard in her babies' behalf, and takes earnest precautions to assure their safety.

Frequently she will fight for them to the death. Where a nest or den is disturbed by man, a new nursery is hurriedly put together and the young transported to it without delay. She weans them, accustoming them to the diet of their kind, teaches them how to hunt or get their food in other ways, and in general initiates them into their role in life.

So strong is the maternal instinct in the mammals that females that have lost their young will adopt homeless waifs that have accidentally lost their parents. There is an instance where a cat that had had her kittens destroyed went out into the woods and brought home a family of baby rabbits which she nursed as her own.

It is not uncommon to find young mammals staying with their mother a year or longer. Among some of the more sociable animals, the family may stay together until the youngsters are ready to go off in search of mates of their own. Many a mother, however, drives off her well-grown brood when she is ready to give birth to a new one. Such an action is a matter of instinct, of course, but it does serve to protect the helpless new babies from their older brothers and sisters in whom hunger may be stronger than family ties.

This does not necessarily imply that the family bond is irrevocably broken every time a female produces a new family. The breach is frequently bridged over into a lasting friendship that may continue for life. A great-great-grandmother mountain sheep will keep her children and her children's children in her fold, watching over them with motherly care for many years. A pack of wolves is usually all one family, but here the dog wolf takes his place as head of the family. Family relationships among the mammals are closely akin to those that exist among men.

The pioneer spirit of youth, the urge to conquer new fields, to have a home and children of their own is the underlying factor that causes the breakup of most families. Usually the males, in search of a mate, travel farthest afield and entice the young females to elope with them.

WHY ANIMALS LOVE COMPANY

The necessity of being born and cared for in infancy is often at the root of social behavior in the animal kingdom. Large families carry the social spirit forward toward community life.

There are, of course, many insects and fishes that never know their parents and yet live together in well-established groups. On the other hand, hyenas and some other animals are rank individualists and cannot tolerate the company of their fellows. Still, we may say that animals that live together in herds, schools, or flocks are in a general sense born to it, and feel ill at ease if separated. When forcibly broken up, a school of fishes, a flock of birds, or a herd of animals will probably join company again as soon as possible.

Many creatures have a genuine desire for intimate companionship with others of their kind and some develop a personal attachment for a particular individual, sometimes of another species; the friendship of man and his pets is a common example. We can often discern, too, an advantage gained by animals that live together. A musk ox is safe from attack by wolves only so long as it stays with the herd. When danger threatens, a herd of musk oxen form a circle; their horns present a bristling armor, sufficient protection against a whole pack of starving wolves. In the animal kingdom a sick, old, or very young creature cannot survive on its own for any length of time as a rule.

Animals will also perform a common labor to their general advantage. Beavers, working together, can build a great dam, a feat that a single animal would not be capable of.

All this is true not just of mammals, but of other animals. Robins and blue jays, normally enemies, will join forces with sparrows and songbirds to drive away an owl. Tickbirds are friends of the rhinoceroses. Not only do they rid the animals of parasites—they also give the alarm of approaching danger.

PUZZLING HABITS

There are, to be sure, numerous riddles in the social behavior of animals. The mountain sheep, for instance, present an interesting puzzle. Except during the short breeding season, the sexes never mingle. In British Columbia, the author came upon a herd of twenty-five rams; half a mile away he could see sixteen ewes with their lambs, keeping their distance. This strange segregation of the sexes also takes place among the bats and some other mammals. It is difficult to suggest a reason why it is practiced by these groups and not by the rest.

SOCIAL RANK AMONG THE ANIMALS

Social rank is recognized in many groups of animals. Among herd animals there is always a group leader. Usually this is an experienced cow, probably the grandmother of most of the herd. Then there is the master—a herd bull, pompous and self-assured, yet having little authority except at the mating season. Each member of a herd has its place and must wait its turn on the trail. In a pack of wolves, too, one is the leader, a position held by right of might. Others follow in a graduated scale of seniority and valor.

HOW LONG THEY LIVE

All living things, either animal or vegetable, grow old and die. They have their origin in a tiny seed or egg and pass through a regular development to the ordained end. The potential life span varies with the species. It may be long or short according to our standards, but to the individual itself it is a complete, full life cycle.

In a general sense the life span of a species varies with size. The larger it is, the longer it may be expected to live. This is not meant to imply that the biggest animal always lives the longest. The great blue whale is the largest animal that ever appeared on the earth, but there are smaller animals that outlive it. Still, by and large, the rule holds true.

The Oldest Living Thing. No living thing exceeds the giant California redwood in size and age. Sometimes towering four hundred feet skyward, many of these great trees living today were seedlings fifteen hundred years ago. We know that some redwoods actually lived four thousand years. There are many trees, especially among the cone-bearers and oaks, that pass the century mark. On the other hand, we find trees that are old at twenty-five years; some plants pass through a complete life cycle in less than twelve months.

Reptiles and Amphibians Are Long-lived. In the animal kingdom, the giant tortoises hold the record for longevity. A Marion's tortoise at Port Louis on Mauritius Island in the Indian Ocean was accidentally killed when it was 152 years old and there is reason to believe that it might have lived another hundred years. Alligators reach a grand old age; no doubt many of them pass the half-century mark.

Some of the Asiatic giant salamanders have lived more than fifty years in captivity. But the tales of toads and newts that have been found in walls or stones where they supposedly survived for indefinite periods of time are discounted nowadays.

Birds. Most birds live considerably more than one year and a few—like some parrots—may survive over fifty years. A swan in the Kensington Gardens, London, lived to the ripe old age of eighty-one years.

Fishes. The popular belief that fishes never grow old is discredited by science. As with other animals, the life span of fishes varies roughly with size. A carp will die of old age at fifteen years. The oldest fish of which we have a reliable record is a sixty-year-old European freshwater catfish, but some of the giant fishes undoubtedly live longer than that, according to James W. Atz of the New York Aquarium. At the other end of the scale there are a number of small fishes with a life span of less than one year.

Insects. Most insects have a life cycle of about one year or less. So far as we know, the seventeen-year cicada is the longest-lived of all the insects but it spends sixteen years and ten months of this time in the ground, developing toward adulthood. Its life as an adult lasts only a few weeks, during which its main business is breeding.

MAMMAL RECORD-HOLDERS

With actual records of over fifty years and possible estimates of up to seventy years, the Asiatic elephant seems to hold the record as the longest-lived of the wild mammals. Among the few other species that may reach or exceed a life of thirty years are the baboon, lion, bear, horse, donkey, rhinoceros, tapir, hippopotamus, and the giraffe, as well as the larger whales.

For their size, the apes, monkeys, and lemurs are the longest-lived of the mammals. The great apes are not fully grown until they are between fifteen and eighteen years of age, and it is not unreasonable to assume that they might live almost as long as man. All we know from individuals in captivity is that the chimpanzee and orangutan may live to be about twenty-five years of age.

Most cats are in the ten-to-twenty-five-year class. The wild dogs rarely live beyond twenty years, and most cattle, sheep, deer, and antelope—animals that chew the cud—have an average maximum life expectancy of about twenty-five years. Squirrels cannot be expected to live more than fifteen years, and rats and mice not more than six or seven. Shrews and field mice may live about a year or eighteen months, but few ever die of old age.

The untold thousands of years that animals like the cat, dog, horse, and cow have been under human control has neither increased nor decreased their life span. The lives of domestic animals are just as long as would be expected of them had they remained under natural conditions in the wild.

TEETH TELL THE STORY

The length of life in a large majority of mammals has a controlling factor in their teeth. Teeth take a definite time to grow and a less definite, but still limited, time to wear away. When the teeth of a mammal become useless for procuring food, the animal must die.

The loss of its teeth, however, is not quite so drastic an end to the animal as it might seem. Teeth are constructed to last the average life span of a species. Normally the animal would die of old age about the time, or even before, the teeth became useless. The long-lived animals that feed on tough, fibrous grass—the horses, for example—have high-crowned teeth that will take over thirty years to wear down completely.

There is no way known by which we can determine the exact age of a wild mammal. But we can gather a general idea from the wear of its teeth—provided we know the average life span of the species.

WHY EVERY ANIMAL HAS A SCIENTIFIC NAME

There are many living things that look alike but really are different; some that appear to be quite different are close kin. Many animals bear the same popular name; for example, "elk" is a term which for centuries in Europe has been applied to the moose, and in America to what a European would consider a red deer. Clearly, we cannot possibly discuss animals intelligently without first arranging them in a systematic scheme.

The modern method of classification, or taxonomy, is a natural one based on the grouping together of related forms of living things; we judge the closeness of their relationship by the degree of similarity we observe in their form and structure. Thus all living things may be sorted into two groups—plants and animals—called kingdoms.

The kingdom is composed of a number of major divisions, each known as a phylum. Every phylum in turn is split up into classes. Each class may be divided into orders; each order into families; each family into genera (plural of genus); and each genus into species. Sometimes it becomes necessary to form special intermediate groups such as the subphylum, the superclass and the subclass, the superorder and suborder, etc. The scientific name of a creature consists of the names of the genus and species to which it belongs; these are printed in *italic* type.

TRACING THE WOLF

Let us, for example, trace the wolf through the successive groups. It will be a long journey, but we shall get a good idea of the meaning of the terms we have just been talking about. We place the wolf in kingdom Animalia (the animal kingdom), which includes all living things except the plants; phylum Chordata (all animals with a backbone, or vertebral column, and never more than two pairs of limbs), including the mammals, reptiles, amphibians, and fishes; class Mammalia, the mammals (in which all members possess some hair and suckle their young).

At this point we have only reached the mammals. We still have quite a way to go to classify the wolf completely. So, faring onward, we place it in subclass Theria (all living mammals that bring forth their young alive, excluding the egg-laying mammals); order Carnivora (mammals that have sharp teeth for a flesh diet, and toes armed with claws or nails); family Canidae (doglike runners with a long head, unsheathed claws, and long, strong canine teeth); genus *Canis* (typical doglike animals, but excluding the foxes and their relatives); species *lupus* (true wolves).

Now, leaving aside the explanations, let's take the same trip again, this time on an express that will permit us to get a quick picture of the position of a particular kind of wolf in the scientific scheme of things. It is placed in kingdom Animalia, phylum Chordata, class Mammalia, subclass Theria, order Carnivora, family Canidae, genus *Canis*, species *lupus*, subspecies *nubilus*.

Canis lupus nubilus Say, one of the several forms of true wolves, is known to the layman as the buffalo wolf. In scientific literature the name of the person who first described the animal is given following the scientific name—in this instance it was the American zoologist Thomas Say.

In the world today we have eighteen orders of living mammals, 118 families, a minimum of 932 genera, and roughly 3,500 species. The number of species and subspecies listed in 1936 was placed at a total of 14,464, and in round figures 15,000 will serve for the present day. Strange and fascinating creatures they are, almost every one of them. Not the least intriguing are the ones we shall first have a look at, the primitive mammals that lay eggs.

The Spiny Anteater and the Duckbill Platypus—Mammals That Lay Eggs

NATURE has a way of surprising us with her creations. We generally think of mammals as animals that bear their young alive, yet in Australia, Tasmania, and New Guinea there are some that actually lay eggs.

These egg-layers are odd creatures with odd names—the spiny anteater or echidna, and the duckbill platypus. Their mouths are long and beaklike, like a bird's, but there the resemblance ends; the spiny anteater is covered with spines and coarse hair, the duckbill with fur. The one is a burrower, the other a swimmer. Really, they are not so close to the birds as they are to the reptiles, from which they are descended. We consider them the most primitive of living mammals.

The snakelike traits of these animals are striking. We have seen that, like the snakes, they lay eggs. These have thin shells and large yolks, the same as reptile eggs. What is more, the platypus and the spiny anteater have the bony shoulder girdle of their reptile ancestors —other mammals discarded it when they rose from the ranks of the lower animals far back in the dim ages of geological time. Other features, too, emphasize the closeness of the relationship.

Still, the spiny anteater and the duckbill platypus are mammals, even though we must place them in a special order—the Monotremata, or monotremes. Like their more advanced relatives, they suckle their young with a mammary gland. They have not quite developed a nipple or a teat; the milk comes out of a group of small pores in the skin of the abdomen. All in all, they are strangely fashioned creatures, living symbols of the old and the new in the animal kingdom.

SPINY ANTEATERS—AUSTRALIA'S "PORCUPINES"

The Five-toed Spiny Anteater, or Echidna, *Tachyglossus,* is a shy, small animal native to Australia, Tasmania, and New Guinea. The Australians often call it a "porcupine," for short, sharp spines are mingled with the brownish gray hair that covers its chubby body. When this creature is on the defensive, the spines present a disturbing prospect to any attacker.

The spiny anteater is not in the habit of standing and fighting, however. It has a better way out—it can burrow in the earth with amazing rapidity. The powerful spadelike claws on all four feet can excavate a shaft so fast that it is useless to try to dig the animal out. Oddly enough, it does not dig down head first, as do most burrowing animals, but goes straight down in a horizontal position.

GETTING ITS FOOD

This curious creature is permanently on a soft diet: it has no teeth. Its muzzle looks like nothing so much as a slender beak, and on the end of it is the tubelike opening of the mouth. Ants and termites are the spiny anteater's usual fare. It will slash open an anthill with its strong claws, then thrust its narrow snout in after the tiny inhabitants. The animal's long, snakelike tongue darts out, snatches them up, and then crushes them against the roof of the mouth. Feeding time is strictly at night; this little mammal stays in hiding by day.

BABY ECHIDNAS

Echidnas are slow breeders. Usually the female lays only a single egg a year. She does not hatch it the way a bird does, for she has her own built-in incubator. This is simply a pocket of skin on her abdomen, rather like a kangaroo's pouch. Inside are the mammary glands, to provide nourishment.

A QUEER-LOOKING "PORCUPINE"
The spiny anteater or echidna, native to Australia, is called a porcupine there because of its prickly spines, but it is really uniquely different from that animal. One of the last remaining mammals that lay eggs, it hatches and carries them in a pouch on its abdomen until the babies' spines become uncomfortable. True to its name, it feeds almost solely on ants and termites, catching them with its long tongue and crushing them against its palate.

The egg, soft-shelled, with a parchment-like covering, hatches within a few days, and the baby is carried about in the mother's pouch until its growing spines become a nuisance to her.

Except for size, young and old look alike, and there is no difference in appearance between the sexes.

ANTEATERS TAME AND WILD

You might suppose the spiny anteater would be a strange animal to choose as a pet. Yet it has often been tamed, and shows a friendly nature once it has overcome its shyness.

Between fifteen and twenty inches is the average length of an echidna. It has only a snip of a tail. The Tasmanian Spiny Anteater is larger than its Australian cousin, and its few short spines are almost concealed in its thick woolly fur.

Still larger is the Curve-beaked or Three-toed Spiny Anteater, *Zaglossus,* which makes its home in the mountains of New Guinea and Salawati. It reaches a length of about thirty inches, and the beak is exceptionally long.

All the echidnas belong to the family Tachyglossidae ("swift tongue"). They are land animals, with no exceptions.

DUCKBILL PLATYPUSES—A STRANGE COMBINATION

The Duckbill Platypus, *Ornithorhynchus,* is an even stranger egg-laying mammal than the spiny anteater. Its scientific name comes from the words *ornis,* meaning "bird," and *rhynchos,* meaning "snout." As its name tells us, the platypus has a bird's beak, or a duck's bill, which it uses for nuzzling in the mud and slush when foraging for worms, aquatic grubs, and other favorite foods. But the bill, instead of being hard and horny, is soft and leathery and is charged with sensitive nerves.

In contrast to the spiny anteater, which has an aversion to water, the platypus is expert at swimming and diving. Its body is admirably adapted for these activities. Its grayish-brown fur is as thick and close as that of an otter, and the tail is flattened like that of a beaver, but well furred. The animal has broadly webbed feet, the front ones furnishing the driving power in the water.

MOTHER DUCKBILL AND HER BABIES

The duckbill breeds once a year. In preparation for her young, the female digs a den laboriously, in the bank of a stream. It is a spacious chamber with a tunnel entrance under water, and also has an air shaft, or ventilator. When the chamber is finished, she lines it with leaves from the gum tree, and shredded grass. She allows no males into her den as she waits for the eggs to arrive.

Finally they come, about fifteen days after mating time. There are generally two of them—one more or less is possible—in a clutch (the name used for the normal number of eggs in a bird's nest). They are soft-shelled and about the size of a pigeon's egg, but rounder. Perhaps to avoid any chance of their being lost in the spacious leafy nest, the two eggs are firmly sealed together side by side. If there are three, they are sealed in a triangle.

Like a bird, the new mother is broody during incubation. For this period of lethargy she locks herself in her underground den by plug-

A MOST UNUSUAL ANIMAL

The duckbill platypus, found in Australia and Tasmania, is another rare mammal whose young are hatched from eggs. Its body, well suited for swimming, has a bewildering set of features—strong webbed feet, a duck's bill which is soft and sensitive instead of horny, and a flat tail that reminds us of a beaver's.

ging up the entrance with six or eight inches of earth. She does not sit on the eggs like a bird or carry them in a pouch like the echidna, but clutches them to her breast and rolls up into a ball. It takes nine or ten days to complete the incubation.

At first the young platypuses are naked, blind, and helpless, with queer little beaks. The mother platypus, like the mother spiny ant-eater, feeds them on milk secreted in her teatless mammary glands. During these early weeks, the development of the babies is remark-ably slow. When two months old, they are covered with short fine fur but must still depend on their mother for body heat, and their eyes have not yet opened. It is all of four months before the youngsters see the light of day. They are amiable little creatures, and play like puppies.

Even at mating time, the male and the female show little or no affection for each other. But they do like company. After the breeding season is over, the platypuses dwell together in a burrow with general living quarters for both sexes.

THE DANGEROUS MALE

Among the platypuses, the male is the deadlier of the species. On his hind foot he bears a horny, hollow spur. Not only is it sharp—at its base there is a gland containing a poisonous secretion, so that the whole arrangement is rather like the fang of a venomous snake. The spurs are the only means of defense the male platypus possesses, but he wields them with great skill, driving them home with a slashing or stabbing stroke. The wound it produces may be quite serious.

One could hardly call these amusing-looking duck-faced creatures large: full-grown males have a length of about two feet, including the tail, and the females are smaller still. The platypuses form a distinct family (Ornithorhynchidae), dwelling in Australia and Tasmania.

Animals with Pouches—Kangaroos, Opossums, and Their Relatives

EVEN a small child knows what animal mother carries her babies about with her in a pouch. Without question, the kangaroo is the best known of the pouched mammals.

Still, we shall find many other fascinating creatures to claim our attention in this group. Not only do the colorful little koala, the strange Tasmanian devil, the opossums, the wombats, and the bandicoots belong to it, but it also includes such little-known curiosities as pouched mice and moles, and even an animal that can launch itself in the air, the flying phalanger.

These creatures have gone one step higher than the duckbill platypus and the spiny anteater on the evolutionary ladder. They bring forth their young alive instead of in eggs, but still in a very incomplete stage of development.

At birth, the hands and feet of these tiny bits of life are well formed, and somehow they manage to scramble through the mother's fur to the pouch on her abdomen. They find it a warm, comfortable haven, equipped with milk taps, and they become inseparably attached to her teats for the rest of their early life. However, they are too young to suck, and so their mother feeds them forcibly by contracting the muscles in her mammary glands. Literally, she injects nourishment down their throats.

We call these animals "marsupials" (order Marsupialia), after a Latin word meaning "pouch." Not all female marsupials have a pouch in which to carry their young, but most of them have some sort of receptacle for this purpose.

WHY THE MARSUPIALS LIVE WHERE THEY DO

One of the strangest facts about the marsupials is connected with where they live. All, with the exception of the opossums of America and a few others, make their home only in Australia and nearby regions. How did they get there? Why don't we find them anywhere else? Their ancestors, already flourishing when the dinosaurs still walked the earth, were spread far and wide over this planet in remote times. They were among the commonest of the early mammals.

At the time the marsupials came into being, Australia was joined to other large land masses. The pouched animals—an opossum seems to have been the first of them—were easily able to enter it. But, later, great geological changes took place. Australia became separated from neighboring areas, an island continent.

In all other places, new and more advanced kinds of mammals developed and grew to be dominant. These were the forebears of the animals that cover the earth today—the placentals, which bear their young alive without need for the protection of pouches. The new-comers wiped out the ancient marsupials almost everywhere. In the Americas, a few managed to hold out: the opossums. In Australia, however, the marsupials were protected by a wall of water, and life remained easy for them till the coming of man.

PRIMITIVE ANIMALS

Among the marsupials, we find eaters of flesh as well as eaters of plants and insects. Teeth are numerous—often there are more than forty-four. Milk teeth are a rarity, however. The marsupials possess a double womb, and generally lack a placenta, the organ by which our "modern" mammals nourish the young in the mother's body. It is for this reason that marsupial babies are so undeveloped at birth.

These animals are not outstanding for their intelligence; on the whole, their brains are small.

OPOSSUMS—AMERICA'S ONLY MARSUPIALS

The Common or Virginia Opossum, *Didelphis,* the only marsupial found in the United States, is at home from South America to New England. It looks rather like an oversized rat and is credited with being the stupidest creature in the American woods. Its highest show of animation is a silly snarl. It is bad-tempered, unresponsive and in-different to company.

Prowling about in the cold damp woods and swamps in the gloom of the night, sometimes the opossum is caught in a flash of light. For a moment its eyes shine like two red balls of fire. It is so shocked at being confronted with danger that its limited mental capacity is over-whelmed. The opossum suffers a temporary paralysis, falling into a state of coma. To all outward appearances the creature is dead. It is this curious behavior on its part which has given rise to the popular phrase "playing 'possum."

So far as we may judge, the ambitions of the opossum are simple ones: to find a snug warm nest safe from beasts of prey, to multiply its kind, and to fill its belly. Everything edible is food for the opossum—roots, fruits, insects, and small mammals. It is one of man's helpers, for it is a great destroyer of rodents. But some of its nightly wanderings take it into barnyards, where it cannot resist the temptations offered by young birds and eggs. And so, to its misfortune, it runs afoul of farmers.

Hunting the opossum is a popular sport, and the roasted flesh is considered a delicacy by Southerners. A long coat of grizzled hair mixed with fur covers the animal, an added lure for the hunter; this fur has considerable commercial value.

——BIRTH AND DEATH AMONG THE OPOSSUMS. With their numerous enemies, both human and animal, opossums seldom die of old age. Seven years is about as long as they live.

UGLY, STUPID, AND ADDICTED TO FAINTING SPELLS
The common or Virginia opossum is considered unattractive, unlovable, and stupid. The familiar expression "playing 'possum" comes from this animal's peculiar habit of falling into a coma when it is suddenly exposed to danger. It is one of the very few marsupials living outside the Australian region. Other opossums dwell in South America.

In northern latitudes the opossum breeds once a year, and tragedy is often present from the very first. The female may bear as many as twenty offspring, tiny mites hardly larger than a bee. About half are doomed at birth, for a strange reason.

The mother rarely has more than thirteen teats, or "feeding stations," frequently only eleven. The first comers make haste to reach her pouch and establish themselves at these sources of food. Each fixes itself to a teat, to remain fastened there for weeks. Late arrivals find all accommodations taken. They starve to death. Still, the breed owes its very existence to the fact that it is so prolific.

The surviving babies grow rapidly. In about a week they are some ten times their size at birth. When they grow too large to fit into the mother's pouch, they climb onto her back. Here, their feet and tail entwined securely in her long hair, they stay fixed much of the time, till they are ready to make their own way in the world at the age of two months.

When full grown, the Virginia opossum is hardly an attractive creature. It is about the size of a house cat (two feet or more from its nose to the tip of its tail) but its legs are much shorter, and it has a longish snout. Large dark eyes shine in its white face. It has more teeth than the average land mammal. Its furry, grayish-white body weighs about eight pounds, and ends in a naked ten-inch tail.

——A REMARKABLE TAIL. The Virginia opossum is an able tree climber, and often sleeps in the branches. Its hind feet as well as its forefeet have an opposable digit—that is, the great toe is formed like the thumb on the human hand. Its long, scaly tail has a prehensile (grasping) tip; the opossum can curl it into a tight hook and use it as a "fifth hand" to carry a bunch of leaves or hang from the branch of a tree.

The opossum's tail developed as a grasping instrument in South America, where the group originally came from. Tails of this type are well developed in many widely separated tree-living mammals of that continent, among them certain monkeys, anteaters, rodents and carnivores. We do not find this extra anchorage so completely perfected by mammals elsewhere, except to some extent in the marsupials of the Australian region.

——"THE INCREDIBLE MOTHER." Strange as it may seem, the American opossum was the first of the marsupials encountered by western civilization. It was discovered by the Spanish explorer Pinzón in 1500. In fact, it was presented at the court of Ferdinand and Isabella, where it created quite a sensation.

Knowing the opossum for the humble creature it is, we find it hard to understand the amazement it produced among the early Spaniards. They described this new kind of animal as a frightful beast with a face like a fox, the tail of a monkey, ears like a bat and human hands.

Below, on the belly, they said, it has a second belly hanging down like a great sack or pouch in which the animal carries its young. To them it was "the incredible mother."

"Opossum" is an American Indian name. In the language of the Algonquians it means "white animal." Earlier we saw that the Virginia opossum is the only pouched mammal dwelling in the United States. All other American marsupials make their home in Central and South America. The opossums belong in the family Didelphidae ("double womb").

SOME INTERESTING OPOSSUMS OF CENTRAL AND SOUTH AMERICA

The Yapok, *Chironectes,* is unique among the opossums or, for that matter, among the marsupials—it is the only member of its order really at home in the water. Because of this peculiarity, we often call it the Water Opossum. It even derives its name from a river, the Oyapok, in Guiana.

The yapok is smaller than the Virginia opossum—its head and body are twelve inches long, its tail about fourteen. It is a handsomer animal by far, and is noted in particular for the striking color pattern of its fur. Almost black in hue, its coat is broken by transverse bands of silvery white, producing a unique marbled effect. The fur is soft, but dense enough to shed water.

——THE YAPOK GOES FISHING. The yapok's hind feet are broadly webbed for swimming. It can swim and dive with the facility of an otter. Its skill in the water is proved by the fact that it has been taken in eel and fish traps set deep down in swift streams.

The jungles of South America are the home of the yapok. It may be found as far south as Paraguay, as far north as Mexico. A night prowler, it hunts its prey in the impenetrable darkness of the tropical forests. Here, amid the constant chorus of frogs and chirping insects, it swims along fresh-water streams and lakes, searching for the shellfish, crayfish, and other forms of water life on which it feeds.

——THE YAPOK'S DEN. It is not hard to recognize a yapok's den in the jungle. Webbed feet and finger tracks on well-trodden runways lead to a hole in the ground. It is usually in a bank, just above water level. Around it, sticking in the mud, you will find the remains of crayfish, bits of fins, and fish heads. As a temporary resting place, the animal may also make a surface nest of leaves or grass on the ground.

The female yapok produces about five or six babies in a litter. Provided with a perfect pouch, she carries them about with her on her daily excursions in the water for food. When too big to fit in the mother's pouch, the little yapoks must stay home, but the family ties are not broken until they are well grown.

A WATER-LOVING OPOSSUM

The only opossum that has a special liking for water is the yapok or water opossum, found in the South American jungle. This animal is an excellent swimmer and diver, very much like the otter. The yapok is smaller and more attractive than its relative, the Virginia opossum; its deep black coat is banded with stripes of silvery white.

The Four-eyed Opossum, *Philander,* owes its common name to an oddity in its appearance. On its head are four yellowish-white spots that resemble eyes. Except for this and its smaller size (head and body are about ten inches, tail eleven) and short close fur, it rather resembles its cousin the Virginia opossum.

——A Courageous Opossum. *Philander* is common in tropical America, from Vera Cruz, in Mexico, south to Brazil. It favors forested country from sea level up to four thousand feet. The natives call it the "zorro," which means "fox" in Spanish. They esteem it because it is a plucky little fellow, always ready to defend itself against great odds. Such a show of spunk is a rarity in the Virginia opossum.

——The Mother Is Ever Watchful. The female four-eye is a builder. She weaves a neat globular nest of dried leaves and grasses in thick foliage, where it will be hidden from her enemies. She makes it about a foot in diameter, with the chamber roughly the size of her body. Here she bears her family of five or six young.

Like other opossums, this one carries her babies with her wherever she goes. Mother four-eye is forever on the alert, and will slip silently away from her snug retreat at the least sign of danger, bearing her babies to safety.

It is not uncommon for small opossums to be carried away in bunches of bananas, and on occasion a much-perplexed zorro has found itself far from home in a New York fruit market, surrounded by a wondering crowd of spectators.

The Woolly Opossum, *Caluromys,* is a beautiful, ornate creature, distinguished by its golden tawny back and light-colored withers mark. The extraordinary tail, heavily furred for one-third of its length with the rest naked, measures about twenty inches—just about twice as long as the animal's head and body.

The woolly opossum makes its home in the woodland, from Mexico to Paraguay. The most tree-loving of the opossums, it spends the greater part of its life in the top branches of forest giants. Fond of privacy, it builds its leafy nest in thick foliage at a considerable distance from the ground. Because it has rather small and weak teeth, it stays pretty much on a diet of pulpy fruits and small insects.

The Murine or Mouse Opossum, *Marmosa,* is called "murine" because of its color—the word means "mouse gray." Actually its coat may vary from pale gray to tawny. The creature is ratlike in size, measuring up to half a foot in head and body length; its naked tail may be twice as long. Across its eyes it usually has a distinctive black facial mask.

The murine opossum is a forest-lover. It spends much of its time in the trees, hunting for beetles, moths, and sleeping butterflies. It is also fond of ripe fruits, especially the soft pulpy kind such as bananas. Like most of the American opossums, it is strictly a night prowler.

This 'possum often uses a bird nest for a dwelling, but it may build its own nest of green leaves far from the ground. In their leafy home, the opossum family finds a measure of safety from the usual host of flesh-eaters ready to devour it—cats, wild dogs, and large snakes—but it is still exposed to its most dreaded foes, the owls.

——MARSUPIAL WITHOUT A POUCH. Although the mother murine opossum has no pouch, her babies do not suffer any special disadvan-

AN OPOSSUM OF CENTRAL AND SOUTH AMERICA
The murine or mouse opossum, shown here on the ground, spends many of its hours in the trees. We find it in forests all the way from Central Mexico to Patagonia; there are no fewer than forty-nine species and one hundred subspecies of this common creature. Named for its mouse-gray color, it is rat sized and often has a black mask on its face.

tage. They cling to her with their tiny feet and mouths as though for dear life. So strong is their hold that if you tried to pick up one of these tiny mites you would have to lift the mother, too.

——A MOTHER'S TRICKS. Sometimes a baby may be separated from its mother. She does not go over and pick it up with her teeth the way a rat would, but noses the infant under her so it can grasp her fur. A mother has been seen to toss her baby in the air with her snout and catch it on her back.

——Useful Pets. These small animals have their uses. When taken young, the murine opossum makes a nice pet. It is very valuable about the house in tropical countries, for it devours the cockroaches that lurk in every dark corner. It catches mice with the skill of a house cat.

——A Great Race. The range of these little opossums extends from central Mexico to Patagonia, and from sea level to eight thousand feet. They are a great race: there are forty-nine species and one hundred subspecies of murine opossums.

Of these, one of the largest is Alston's Marmosa, of Central America and Colombia—it measures seventeen inches over-all. The smallest is the Least Murine Opossum of the province of Formosa, Argentina; this dwarf is only two and one-half inches in head and body length, with a tail equally long.

Some species breed three times a year and have up to ten or eleven young in a litter. Others apparently have up to nineteen—at least that is the largest number of teats they possess.

Australia's Pouched Mammals

Except for the American opossums we have just been looking at, all the marsupials live in Australia and the islands of the South Pacific. In fact, we find few mammals but marsupials in this region. The herd animals of the plains and prairies are marsupials; the equivalents of our rabbits, moles, cats, and wolves are marsupials. There is even a marsupial tiger.

Protected by the vast expanse of the Pacific and neighboring seas for millions of years, the pouched animals led a secure existence in the isolation of their island homes. This marsupial paradise began to draw to an end with the coming of man. Besides killing large numbers of animals for their fur, he brought in the cat and the dog; these two have taken their toll. To make matters worse, imported rabbits and sheep graze bare the plains where the pouched mammals used to feed.

Today the native animals are definitely on the way out. Some species of the marsupial flesh- and insect-eaters (family Dasyuridae, or "bushy tails") have been exterminated almost completely.

MARSUPIAL FLESH- AND INSECT-EATERS

The Thylacine, Marsupial Wolf, or Marsupial Tiger, *Thylacinus,* is the largest of the flesh-eating marsupials. It is easily recognized: it is about the size of a collie and has sixteen to eighteen distinctive chocolate-brown stripes running across the rear of its back. Wiped out in Australia, this savage creature is making a last-ditch stand in Tasmania.

The marsupial wolf lies up during the daylight hours in a rocky lair. It waits till dusk before it ventures out to hunt in the valleys and plains. Here, under normal conditions, it tracks down wallabies and other Tasmanian marsupials. When it cannot find them, as is the common case today, it preys upon flocks of domestic sheep and poultry. For these depredations it has a black mark against its name.

WOLF, DOG, OR TIGER?
Thylacine, marsupial wolf, or marsupial tiger are three of the names by which this largest of the flesh-eating pouched animals is known. It preys upon wallabies, other Tasmanian marsupials, or sheep and poultry. Its head can easily be taken for a dog's, while its brown stripes remind one of the zebra.

The marsupial wolf is a formidable foe. Although not so swift as a true North Country wolf or even a domestic dog, it is a tireless runner and follows its prey until the victim is exhausted.

Man is the marsupial wolf's chief enemy. When hard pressed by danger, according to reports, the animal seems to abandon its normal running gait; it speeds away in a series of kangaroo-like leaps. Normally it will not attack a human being unless it has been cornered. It is more than a match for the average dog. With its back to a wall, the "wolf" can fight off a whole pack.

——A FEROCIOUS FEMALE. The female marsupial wolf has a pouch large enough to carry four babies. In guarding them, she shows the same maternal fortitude we see in other animals.

On one occasion, a traveler who was about to cross a creek by means of a fallen tree, found his way barred by a thylacine, undoubtedly a female. She barked at him fiercely, uttering the guttural coughlike sound this animal makes when alarmed or excited. Finally, with some difficulty the traveler made his way to the opposite bank. There, under a tree fern, he found two marsupial wolf babies in a nest of dried fronds.

The marsupial wolf's scientific name, *Thylacinus cynocephalus*, is very appropriate; it means "pouched animal with a dog's head." On this "dog's head" the muzzle is fairly long and pointed; the ears are broad and rounded. In color the thylacine is brown. Its chocolate stripes begin just behind the shoulders; they increase in length until they reach the thighs, then decrease and disappear a short distance down the tail. Because of them the animal is also known as the Zebra Opossum or Zebra Wolf. It has a total length of some sixty-five inches, including a tail twenty inches long.

The Tasmanian Devil, *Sarcophilus,* despite its forbidding name, is no more fearful than any of the other flesh-eating mammals. It is a chubby, short-legged creature not more than about three feet long. Superficially it resembles a small bear. Its ferocious expression and jet black color earned it the popular name of "native devil."

Like the marsupial wolf, the Tasmanian devil once roamed over much of Australia. Nowadays, however, it survives only in Tasmania. It is a land animal but haunts the borders of rivers or beaches. There it finds a variety of food such as rats, mice, frogs, crabs, and the like. Most of its natural prey has been greatly reduced in numbers; and it has little alternative but to raid the sheep ranges and chicken farms. Its powerful jaws and muscular neck enable it to maintain a stranglehold on a victim considerably larger than itself.

The call of the "devil" at night can hardly be said to cheer the lonely traveler. It is an eerie sound: a low, yelling growl followed by a snarling cough. It has not helped the animal's sinister reputation.

The Tasmanian devil mates in March and April; the young generally come in May. About a month after the babies are born, the she-devil builds a nest in the rocks for them; they are now too big to be carried around in her pouch and would be a hindrance when hunting. The little "devils" are good tree-climbers, more so than the adults, which can only go up a slanting trunk.

——NOT SO BLACK AS IT LOOKS. People often credit the marsupial devil with an untamable disposition. Still, its character is not so black as its appearance. Taken young and reared in captivity, it makes an excellent pet. It is as frolicsome as a kitten but more affectionate. It washes its face with its paws like a house cat but uses both hands at the same time, fitting them together. After licking them thoroughly, it rubs them over its head.

NOT SO SINISTER AS ITS NAME
The Tasmanian devil was given its name because of its deep black color and forbidding look. Yet it is simply another one of the flesh-eating marsupials, with nothing especially sinister to its habits except an appetite for domestic animals. See how appropriately powerful are its head and neck. The animal is seldom seen, for it is almost extinct.

This bearlike animal is not like a bear in every way. Most bears have only a stump of a tail; the Tasmanian devil's may be a foot long. Although very powerful, the creature has its strength centered forward; its hindquarters are noticeably weak. Its coat of coarse black hair is splashed with irregular blotches of white on the rump, throat, and shoulders.

The Marsupial Cat, *Dasyurus,* looks more like a weasel or a skunk than a cat. Despite its small size—it is less than a foot long, with a bushy tail almost the same length—it is a bold, fearless hunter, endowed with considerable intelligence. It makes its home in Australia and New Guinea.

Like the skunk, the marsupial cat hunts its prey at night. It feeds to a large extent on lizards, rats, mice, and insects. It will raid poultry pens and for that reason is disliked by the settlers.

——Stalking Its Prey. The marsupial cat is an accomplished bird-stalker. It will creep up on a heron with all the skill and stealth of a tiger. When the bird's head goes down and its attention is elsewhere,

A HUNTER OF CONSIDERABLE REPUTE

The marsupial cat hunts down lizards, rats, mice, insects, and especially birds, with great cunning and skill. By a strange chance of nature, many of these cats do not last long after birth. The female may bear twenty-four at one time, yet can feed only the half-dozen her six teats will accommodate. A life of persecution awaits the babies that survive.

the cat moves quickly forward. When the heron raises its head to look about, the cat stops dead in its tracks. Thus, with a sharp eye on the bird's movements, it advances and halts by turns, until it has drawn close enough for the final spring.

The marsupial cat is as much at home in the trees as on the ground; it will make its den in a hollow tree or in a crevice in the rocks. It sleeps during the day.

——DOOMED AT BIRTH. Nature, as we shall see again and again, often produces more animal babies than can possibly survive. Seldom do we find a more startling example of this than among the marsupial cats: the female, although equipped with a well-developed pouch, possesses only six teats, yet she may bear as many as twenty-four young at a time. Eighteen of these are doomed at birth.

There are several different species of marsupial cats. The typical animal has reddish or olive-brown fur, profusely dotted with large and small white spots on the head and over the body.

MARSUPIAL MICE

Among the animal oddities that dwell in Australia, Tasmania, and New Guinea, not the least remarkable are the marsupial mice. Miniatures of their kind, they vary in size from about nine to sixteen inches, and usually have a tail shorter than their head and body. Most will feed on anything they can find: insects, small animal life, eggs, and vegetable matter. Some, like the Vampire Marsupial, live in trees; others—the "Jerboa," the Marsupial Rat, and the Mulgara—dwell on the ground in desert wastes.

The Jerboa Marsupial Mouse, *Antechinomys,* is particularly noteworthy. It has greatly enlarged legs and feet on which it hops around like a mouse-sized kangaroo. Its face is pointed, with long whiskers on the snout; it also has three or four long whisker-like hairs that extend backward from its wrist to well behind its elbow. Its ears are enormous and it has a long tail tufted at the tip. All in all, it presents a curious spectacle.

This strange little creature lives in holes in the ground in Australia. Its diet consists of insects in the main, but now and then it attracts and kills mice.

The Crest-tailed Marsupial Rat, *Dasyuroides,* of the sandy desert regions of central Australia, is nearly as big as a house rat. Its fur is reddish brown, and its tail has a crest both below and above. The animal lives in burrows on the sandy and stony tablelands. Although said to be a night prowler, the crest-tail has a fondness for basking in the warm sunshine.

The Brush-tailed Phascogale, *Phascogale,* a beautiful blue-gray bushy-tailed marsupial rat, is active in the trees; for this reason and its general appearance it was known as a squirrel to the early colonists.

The brush-tailed phascogale has some of the American pack rat's habits of collecting. This has been responsible for some curious incidents. For example, once a member of a group of foresters found that a banknote was missing from his possessions. He could not help but suspect his friends; for a while a strained feeling prevailed in the foresters' camp. Finally the men felled a tree nearby. They were amazed to find the banknote neatly stowed away in a phascogale's nest in the tree.

The Vampire Marsupial, as this phascogale is often called, feeds mostly on insects. Occasionally it kills and eats larger animals as well. It serves a useful purpose in keeping under control the hordes of rats and mice that have established themselves in Australia. Reports have it that the little marsupial follows plagues of rodents, putting in full time in an effort to reduce their numbers.

In a poultry pen the brush-tail will kill more fowl than it can eat. Because of this habit, many Australians mistakenly believe that it sucks only the blood from the throat of its victims.

The Crest-tailed Pouched Mouse, *Dasycercus,* a redoubtable creature of the desert region of Central Australia, is only the size of a large mouse. It is reddish brown in color, and has a crest of stiff hairs at the tip of its tail; its nose is long and pointed.

The mulgara, as it is frequently called, is fearless and ferocious for its size. It will attack and kill a large mouse and devour most of it, starting at the head.

Indeed, common mice are important to the prosperity of the mulgara. On several occasions it has multiplied in an astonishing manner during mouse plagues; at other times its numbers may dwindle. In the 1905 mouse plague, human intervention could not check the increase of the rodent spoilers. Then this ravenous little flesh-eater went into action. In a short time it had cleared entire districts of the plague.

Actually, the mulgara is not so fierce as this account may suggest. Many consider it an affectionate little creature. Certainly it behaves like one toward its own kind. Mulgaras love warmth. They bask in the sunshine, stretched out in lizard-like fashion with their heads resting on each other's backs.

The female usually has about seven babies in a litter, but she has no pouch. Nature offers many strange sights, but few excel this humble one: mother mulgara staggering along in search of food with seven youngsters hanging from her nipples.

The Banded Anteater, White-banded Bandicoot, or Numbat, *Myrmecobius,* is about the size of a large house rat but looks more like a squirrel, bushy tail and all. (Although it spends much of its time in the forest, it apparently does not, like the squirrel, climb trees.) It has been encouraged in Australia because it serves as a control against termites, but under natural conditions it is fast disappearing; it is now found only in the southwestern part of the continent.

Most other anteaters do not have any teeth; the banded anteater, however, has even more than the average mammal. Yet it prefers to let this fine equipment remain idle—it does not chew its food but swallows it whole. From the sharp-pointed face an extendible tongue darts out, and quickly licks up ants and termites. With its long claws it can dig into cracks and crevices and hook them out, too.

The banded anteater travels about in broad daylight as well as at night. Rather slow in action, it moves along in a succession of short leaps; at intervals it rests on its haunches to have a look around. Many birds and animals find it an easy prey.

Shy and inoffensive in its ways, the banded anteater will not attempt to bite even when caught. In captivity, it will lap up sweetened milk by the rapid motion of its long tongue. The extreme extent of its vocal powers is a snuffling grunt.

The female banded anteater does not have a pouch. She produces four young, and these have only the protection of her coarse hair. The aborigines claim that she makes her den in a hollow tree, where she leaves her young when they are too large to carry around.

The banded anteater is about seventeen inches long (including seven inches of bushy tail). It wears a coat of rather coarse, harsh, brightly colored fur. Six or seven white stripes run across its rich reddish-brown back.

MOLES WITH POUCHES

The Marsupial Mole, *Notoryctes,* of Australia, is in no way related to our common mole. Still, there is a striking likeness in size and form.

Its forefeet, or hands, are greatly enlarged and end in strong claws, wonderful tools for excavating tunnels in the earth. Its eyes and ears are small and poorly developed. The tip of the marsupial mole's nose and its tail are naked and covered with coarse skin; its coat of close soft fur is like the common mole's, but the color is yellowish white instead of almost black.

——THE MAD SCRAMBLE OF LIVING. Moles in general expend a tremendous amount of energy, and the marsupial mole is no exception. It must feed every hour, day and night; its life is little more than a continuous search for food.

The marsupial mole eats with fevered haste, and will devour a handful of worms in a remarkably short time. Having satisfied its hunger for the moment, it will abruptly fall fast asleep. It wakens with a start and continues on its mad scramble for more food. It is an animal that lives in alternate spasms of great activity and complete rest.

——AN ANIMAL THAT "FLOWS ALONG." This little creature makes its burrows about three inches below the surface. It leaves no permanent tunnel. At regular intervals it will break the surface soil and stick its nose out to breathe more freely. Above ground, it moves with a rapid shuffling motion—it seems almost to flow along.

We know little or nothing about the breeding habits of the marsupial mole. Like most marsupials the female has a pouch in which to carry her young. The moles of this type make up the family Notoryctidae ("southern diggers").

BANDICOOTS—"BADGERS WITH POUCHES"

"Badger with a pouch"—that is the meaning of the family name of the bandicoots (Peramelidae). They are curious little animals, some as small as a chipmunk, others as big as a rabbit. All have long, narrow feet with long claws, and usually a long, pointed face; most possess a rather short tail. Their hind legs are enlarged so that they can hop around like kangaroos; their forefeet and claws are suited for digging in the ground in search of larvae and insects.

——A STRANGE WAY OF FIGHTING. The bandicoot is a fighter with techniques of combat all its own. Two bandicoots will not battle face to face; they prefer to chase one another around. The assault is made by jumping and simultaneously striking with the powerful hind feet.

A well-placed blow cuts out a batch of hair and skin from the victim's back.

In killing its prey the bandicoot uses a like technique. Having hunted down a worm or a mouse, the bandicoot kneads it to a pulp on the ground with rapid strokes of its forefeet and then eats it. Its food, for the most part, consists of insects, but it will also eat roots, fruits, and vegetables.

ITS EARS GIVE IT A RABBITY LOOK
The rabbit bandicoot's or bilby's mark of distinction is its rabbit ears, which, together with its long, pointed face, give it an unusual appearance. Nevertheless, it is a true bandicoot or "badger with a pouch." Bandicoots are pugnacious animals, but they never fight face to face. Instead, they pursue one another in circles, jumping and hitting out with their long hind feet. Thanks to their sturdy claws, they can dig with amazing speed.

The bandicoots are well known and widely spread over Australia, Tasmania, Papua, and New Guinea. The Rabbit Bandicoot, or Bilby, is the oddest looking, with its large, leathery, rabbit-like ears and long, pointed snout. The Spiny Bandicoot has sharp spines mixed with its fur. And the Pig-footed Bandicoot, now a rare species, gets its name from its hooflike claws. Some species have ornate stripes on the lower back.

The Common Bandicoot, *Perameles,* is a slender, gray-brown animal with fairly large pointed ears and a sharp, pointed face. It is about twenty inches long, tail and all. The Australians call it a "thill" or "moncat" and consider its flesh delicate and excellent food.

By day this little marsupial seeks shelter in hollow logs or crevices in the rocks; sometimes it will construct a rough nest. At night it becomes extremely active, hunting for insects and digging worms out of the ground with its long, sharp claws. When alarmed, it will spring high in the air.

May and June are breeding time for the common bandicoot. The female produces two young, which she carries about in her well-formed pouch. She is a little smaller than the male, but is colored like him.

There are a number of species of common bandicoots native to Australia and Tasmania. We can easily distinguish them from one another by the characteristics mentioned in their common names: the Long-nosed Bandicoot, the Orange-backed or Desert Bandicoot, the Tasmanian Barred Bandicoot, and Western Barred Bandicoot.

AUSTRALIAN POSSUMS, GLIDERS, AND KOALAS

The Cuscus, *Phalanger,* is a rather large, lazy, furry animal with a long whip of a tail which it uses to hold on to things. Like all of the phalangers, gliders and possums that make up its family (Phalangeridae—these are all "opossums" of a sort, but are here called "possums," to differentiate them from the American family), the cuscus spends most of its time in the trees. It has a light-colored patch on its rump from sitting and sleeping for long hours in forked branches.

Between sunrise and sunset the cuscus remains hidden in hollow trees or conceals itself in masses of vegetation. During the hours of darkness it comes to life. But even now activity is by no means its strong point. It presents a perfect picture of slow motion as it inches through the trees, feeding steadily on leaves. According to report it catches and eats birds and small mammals.

The cuscus gives off a foul odor, which makes it an easy animal to detect. Any disturbance will bring a ceaseless chatter of protest from it. It is said to be simple to capture for the reason that, stared at incessantly for some time, it will suspend itself by its powerful tail and hang this way until it drops to the ground from fatigue.

Northern Queensland, New Guinea, the Celebes, the Solomons. and a few other islands of the South Pacific are the home of the cuscuses. They dwell further east than most other marsupials, but are not too common anywhere.

The cuscus is known as the "kapoune" to the natives of New Ireland, and as "coes-coes" to the Amboyna natives. Full grown, its body measures from fifteen inches to twice that length; the grasping tail adds another fifteen inches to it. The animal is much sought after for its flesh by the natives everywhere. They roast it whole over peat coals.

The Spotted Cuscus, *Spilocuscus,* is not only a strikingly colored creature—it is one of the relatively few mammals in which the sexes differ distinctively in color pattern. Basically, they vary from brownish

ONLY THE MALE IS SPOTTED
The male and female spotted cuscus, unlike most other mammals, each have a different color pattern: the male's back is spotted with white or gray marks but the female's is completely unspeckled. The cuscus passes its days sitting quietly and snugly in trees, becoming energetic only at night. Its long tail is a fine grasping tool.

to grayish white. On the back the dark-colored males are spotted with white; the light ones are spotted with gray. But the color of the female's back is uniform and unbroken by any markings.

The female cuscus has a well-developed pouch in which she carries her two to four young. Rarely do we discover her without at least one baby in her pouch, and so we assume that she breeds the year round.

The spotted cuscus is at home in New Guinea, New Britain, the Admiralty Islands, and Cape York. In its ways it reminds us of its cousin *Phalanger*. It spends the day curled up in the fork of a tree among thick foliage, and its motions are slow in daylight. The rounded face, thick woolly coat, and grasping tail (this last item makes up about half of the spotted cuscus's length of three feet, six inches) give the animal a monkey-like appearance but its slow movements are anything but simian. It does wake up and become more active at night.

The Australian or Vulpine Possum, *Trichosurus,* is in Australia the commonest and most familiar of all the marsupials. You can quickly tell this handsome furry little fellow from the others by its thick brush of a tail, its pointed face, and long ears. As a matter of fact, it was these features that suggested the name "vulpine" (foxlike) opossum to the early naturalists.

——A Versatile Marsupial. The Australian possum is the most adaptable of the marsupials. Although built for a life in the trees, it thrives in almost treeless plains; it may make its den in rabbit holes as readily as in the upper branches of the giant gum trees. It is at home even in the suburbs of large cities, just like the gray squirrel in America. We do not see it about during the daylight—indeed, strong light is harmful to its eyes.

——Paralyzed with Fear. Insects are the staple diet of the Australian possum. It will also eat a variety of leaves and vegetable matter and, on occasion, meat, but it is not a habitual killer. Its arch-enemy is said to be the great monitor lizard or goanna, which climbs the trees to attack it in its retreat. The possum is so paralyzed with fear that it makes no attempt to escape. Indeed, on close acquaintance, this creature proves to be rather stupid. Even newly caught adults show little resentment to captivity so long as they get enough to eat.

The brush-tail possum, as the Australians often call it, breeds in May or June—usually only once a year. While the female has two teats, rarely will more than one young be found in her pouch at a time. The baby is ready to leave this warm shelter in September, and family ties are usually broken in November.

Brush-tails are attractive creatures. The various species range in color from pale gray to blackish or reddish brown. On an average, they are about thirty inches long (one-third of this is the flat, bushy tail). The underside of the tail is naked for grasping; the ears are erect and pointed.

——A VALUABLE FUR-BEARER. The beautiful, thick close fur of this animal has made it of great economic importance as a fur-bearer. About a million possum skins are taken in one season for export. Despite this persistent persecution, the Australian possum survives in remarkable numbers.

The Sugar Glider or Flying Phalanger, *Petaurus,* is a small, attractive, downy-furred creature with large, soft eyes and a long, bushy tail. Its home is in Australia, New Guinea, and the neighboring islands, where it is known as the flying squirrel. Actually, it is not a true flying squirrel, though the resemblance is fairly close.

IT GLIDES THROUGH THE AIR

The sugar glider is a pretty little animal that lives in trees and is remarkably adept at gliding from one to another. Stretching taut the membranes attached to the sides of its body and its limbs, it catapults itself from the top of the tree. When landing, it twists its body upward in order to break its speed and it reaches the ground upright.

Home to the sugar glider must always be on high. This little animal makes its nest or den of leaves either in the crotch of a tree or inside a hollow gum tree, about twenty-five feet or more above the ground. It is a rather friendly creature, and half a dozen adults may take up companionable quarters in the same den in a hollow tree.

The sugar glider is active only by night. Insects, fruits, and leaves are its favorite foods. It has a curious habit of wrapping its tail around a bundle of leaves or twigs and carrying them to its nest. It is partial to blossoms of the manna gum tree, and also licks the leaking sweet sap of this tree, a habit which has earned it its name.

——How the Glider Travels. The sugar glider, we have said, also goes by the name of "flying squirrel." While it cannot actually fly, it is a first-class glider. In place of wings it has folds of loose membrane attached to the sides of its body between the fore and hind limbs. When it spreads its limbs, these folds are stretched out tight, making a wonderful gliding surface.

Usually the sugar glider likes to travel from the top of one tree to the base of another. In its glide it may cover a remarkable distance. Launching themselves from the height of a tall tree, some of the larger species may sail almost a hundred yards before they reach the earth.

While gliding, the animal uses its tail as well as the membranes. Its body plays an important role, too, in these airy maneuvers. The glider twists it at a sharp upward angle just before landing. This way it checks its speed so it can come to rest in an erect position, ready to scramble upward into the branches without loss of time.

Strangely enough, not only do these gliders bear a strong resemblance in structure to the true flying squirrels, but their gliding habits are much the same. However, the animals of each group are not related. Each has developed its method of travel on its own.

——Baby Gliders. Baby gliders number one or two in a litter at most. Usually they are born about July. The period of pregnancy, as with all marsupials, is short; about three weeks. The babies grow fast. When they are two months old they are fully clothed in fur and ready to leave the mother's pouch.

At birth, a sugar glider can look forward to a life of from seven to ten years. Few will die of old age, however, for the gliders live surrounded by natural enemies. Chief among them are the owls—in particular those known as the Barking or Winking Owl and the Powerful Owl.

We could hardly call even the largest of the sugar gliders big animals. The several different kinds range in size from seven inches in head and body length, with a tail eight inches long, to an over-all length of thirty inches. They vary in delicate shades of color from brownish gray to blackish brown.

The Pygmy Glider, or Feather-tail Glider, *Acrobates,* owes its name to its minute size. It is no more than six inches in length, half of which is tail. It is common in the eucalyptus forests of eastern Australia.

The pygmy glider's habits are rather like those of its big relative, the sugar glider. It is a creature of the darkness. Its soft downy fur muffles all sound so that it travels in silence like a shadow in the night. During the day it hides in hollow branches.

This tiny creature makes a globe-shaped nest of dried leaves and shredded bark. Usually it bears four young, and the mother carries them around in her pouch till they are big enough to take care of themselves.

The Honey Possum or Noolbenger, *Tarsipes,* of southwestern Australia is a beautiful wisp of an animal. It is only seven inches long, four-inch tail and all. Three black stripes run down its gray back; its face, limbs, and feet are a dull reddish brown.

The body of the honey possum is superbly adapted to the kind of life it leads. Indeed, of all the marsupials, this animal is one of the most specialized. Like many of the birds and insects, it is built to get its food from flowers—a long, pointed muzzle and a long tongue enable it to reach into trumpet flowers for nectar and pollen. It will also devour large quantities of honey. Its teeth, small and weak, do not permit it to eat anything more solid than soft-bodied insects.

——IT FOLLOWS THE FLOWERS. Like most other small opossums, this one sleeps all day and comes to life at night. Its whereabouts at any particular time is governed by the flowering plants and trees, some of which are in bloom at all seasons of the year. When the tea tree is in flower it is there—then, later, when the bottle-brushes and gum trees are in bloom, we see it among them.

——QUAINT AND SPRIGHTLY. In its behavior the honey possum is

quaint and sprightly. Its agility is truly remarkable: it is quite at ease hanging upside down by its tail from a slender twig while it noses into a flower on a branch below. Unfortunately, in captivity this amusing little fellow does not survive long.

The female honey possum (she is slightly larger than her mate) bears one to four babies at a time, and has a roomy pouch in which to carry them. The nest is built in the tall grass or tea trees; sometimes a deserted bird's nest does duty as a lodging.

The Koala, *Phascolarctos,* has sometimes been described as the model of our toy teddy bears. Although it looks like the typical bears, it is in no way related to them.

Large bushy ears, a protruding black nose, and no tail are peculi-

A LIVING TEDDY BEAR

The koala is not a bear, nor is it even related to the bear in any way; it merely happens to look like one. Only three feet in length and weighing up to thirty pounds, this little animal has a charming disposition. Some have said that it provided the original pattern for our common toy bear but the so-called "teddy bear" was modeled after a grizzly bear cub shown in a cartoon with Theodore Roosevelt in 1902, and was named for that famous conservationist with his consent, we are told.

arities of the koala. Its eyes, small but bright, always exhibit a perplexed expression. This charming little animal seems to be just a living toy—it measures less than three feet in length and weighs up to thirty pounds—designed by nature for a child's delight.

The koala has indeed been copied as a toy, but it was by no means the original model of our toy bears. Various toy bears were on the market in the nineteenth century. The first one known as a "teddy bear" seems to have been made in the first years of the present century. A newspaper cartoon in 1902 depicted Theodore Roosevelt in the role of the protector of a grizzly bear cub, and a toy manufacturer obtained his permission to design a toy bear and call it "Teddy's bear." The name was soon shortened to the one we know so well.

——Koala Babies and Parents. A baby koala is a long time a-growing. At birth the koala is not more than an inch long and barely as fat as a lead pencil. Despite its small size, there is never more than one baby in a litter. This only offspring is deposited in the mother's pouch, where little by little it acquires the form we know so well.

At six months the baby is fully furred, has its eyes wide open, and is beginning to take an interest in the outside world—it is now ready to make a daring excursion on its mother's back. A year goes by, and the cub is still a comparatively helpless bundle of fur with sharp black eyes; it clings to its mother's back wherever she goes. In fact, a mother will carry her spoiled youngster until it is nearly as large as herself.

Sometimes, when several females happen to be nursing their children together, the youngsters may become mixed up. No one seems to mind which gets whose milk—a fact that is most unusual among wild as well as domestic animals. After the meal is over, the young return to their rightful mothers. Occasionally one mother will look after her neighbor's baby as well as her own. The father koala, however, shows no interest in family affairs; he is rather annoyed when the baby climbs on his back.

A koala is full-grown when four years old and may live to the ripe old age of twenty. It feeds on the foliage of the eucalyptus tree and the blue gum. In captivity it makes a choice pet but rarely survives very long. Even in the wild a change from one grove of eucalyptus trees to another may prove fatal.

This charming little native of Australia is now found only in limited numbers from Queensland to Victoria.

The Ring-tailed Possum, *Pseudocheirus,* may be as small as a small squirrel, as large as a cat. It has comparatively short fur and a long tail, tapered to the tip, which it can coil around a branch or use as an extra hand. Its thumb and forefinger close to meet the other three fingers— a useful arrangement for a tree-dweller whose life may depend upon the strength of its grip.

Most of all, the ring-tail prefers to make its home in the wet rain forests. Thanks to its wonderful hands and tail, it is extremely graceful in its movements in the trees. It builds a nest like a squirrel and feeds on vegetation.

Like the cuscus, the ring-tail is a night prowler. It has a fixed vacant stare that suggests stupidity, but such a judgment is hardly called for. The stare may be due to the animal's sensitive eyesight, which is adapted especially for the dark. Sight is its guiding sense in the forest at night.

The ring-tailed possum is very quarrelsome with its fellows. But the grievances are not deeply rooted and the fights are not severe. Usually, the female is the aggressor.

This animal breeds in the first part of the year. Usually two young are born at a time. At birth, they are a dark, leaden color. They are ready to leave the pouch by the end of April, when they look exactly like their parents.

We find several different species of ring-tails in Australia and New Guinea. They vary in color from light gray to dark reddish brown. The Green Possum, or Striped Ring-tail, has a peculiar greenish tinge to its fur, overlaid with a glistening golden wash, which immediately identifies it since green is a unique color among mammals. It is at home in scrub forests in the mountains of Queensland.

The Great Flying Phalanger, *Schoinobates,* is the largest of the flying possums, being about the size of a house cat. It has set some impressive flight records. In a flying leap it has covered a distance from the top of one 100-foot tree to another 120 yards away.

This big possum is a good climber, too. It utters a peculiar gurgling squeal as it mounts from branch to branch, searching for tender shoots and blossoms of the eucalyptus tree and leaves of the peppermint gum, its rather dainty fare. Its den is a hollow, high up in the trees, which it lines with shredded bark and dead leaves.

Although the pouch of the female great flying phalanger is provided with two nipples, rarely does it house more than one baby at a time. The youngster remains attached to the mother's nipple for six weeks. Soon after, its eyes open and its body gets a downy covering of fur. Four months after birth, the baby is out of the pouch and clinging to the mother's back as she goes about on her nightly excursions for food.

You will come upon these animals in the Australian forests, from Queensland to Victoria. The great flying phalanger is about fifteen inches long and it has a bushy, grasping tail that may reach twenty inches. The fur, ashy gray in color, is long and soft; the ears are large and naked. Its flying membranes are attached to the elbow—not to the wrist, as in the smaller gliders.

WOMBATS—SKILLFUL DIGGERS

The Common or Naked-nosed Wombat, *Phascolomis,* lacks the grace of the possums and phalangers; with its thick chubby body and short legs, it looks and moves about rather like a small bear.

The wombat is a burrower—that is why the Australians often refer to it as a "badger." Its sturdy limbs and stout claws are fine equipment

THE TUNNEL-DIGGING WOMBAT
The common or naked-nosed wombat is often called a "badger" in its home, Australia, because it is such a proficient digger. Its burrow has a nest at the end, and is commonly fifteen feet long; however, the wombat can dig one six or seven times as long. Notice the animal's sharp claws and sturdy legs, well suited for tearing open the earth.

for penetrating the ground. The animal sometimes digs a burrow that extends up to a hundred feet in length, with an underground nest chamber at the end. More usually, however, its burrow is about fifteen feet long.

——ITS TEETH GROW THROUGH LIFE. By day the wombat will hide in its den. When darkness has made the world safe for it, this large, coarse-haired creature emerges to search for food. Strictly a vegetarian, it feeds on grasses, roots, and the inner bark of trees. For such a diet it needs stout teeth. It has them, too—powerful gnawing instruments that continue to grow throughout life, like a rodent's.

The wombat is endowed with a reasonable share of intelligence. It makes a good pet, and readily responds to kindness. In captivity it shows an even disposition. It will eat all kinds of vegetables, and is especially fond of new hay, which it will eat stalk by stalk. A hoarse, growling cough is the loudest sound it produces.

——THE LONG-LIVED WOMBAT. Wombats may live a long time—some tame ones have been known to survive as long as thirty years. They are solitary in their habits, except at mating time. The wombat's breeding season is from the middle of April to the end of June. Usually, the mother raises only one young at a time and carries it around in her pouch in typical marsupial fashion.

——WHERE WE FIND THEM. It is in the coastal regions and the hills of southeastern Australia—from New South Wales to Queensland, Tasmania, and Flinders Island—that we find the common wombats. The naked-nosed variety owes its name to a bare patch on its muzzle. In color, it varies from almost black to yellowish buff or grizzled. It is practically tailless, and about forty inches long on an average, but large wombats may come closer to four feet and weigh eighty pounds.

Still, all of these are pygmies compared to their ancestors. Ancient Australia, as we know from the fossil record, had a giant wombat the size of a hippopotamus!

The common wombat is only one of a number of different kinds which make up the family Phascolomidae. Another kind, in contrast, has soft fur and a hairy nose. The thick coarse covering of some has been used to make door mats. The flesh is said to taste like pork.

WALLABIES, PADEMELONS, AND KANGAROOS

Wallabies—Small Kangaroos. In a popular sense the wallabies and pademelons are nothing but rabbit-sized kangaroos. If they were larger they would be called kangaroos, since it is size, in general, that determines which is which. Some wallabies, however, grade up to the size of small 'roos.

Like their big cousins, the wallabies possess excessively large and long hind limbs and feet for hopping and leaping. (*Macropodidae,* the family name which we give to them and the kangaroos, means "great feet.") Their tails are usually long, stout, and powerful; the animals use them more as props and balancing organs than as a means of giving themselves an extra boost when they jump along.

A large number of different kinds of wallabies dwell in Australia, New Guinea, Tasmania, and the neighboring islands. They are dainty, attractive creatures, often gray or brown in color, and have harelike habits and great speed. Most of them live on the open plains and do not make a burrow but lie up in "forms"—small depressions in the ground worn down by constant use; others live in the rocks or brush.

Like the rabbits and hares, the wallabies feed on grasses, leaves, and other forms of vegetation. Some species are more or less sociable and live in colonies; others are solitary except during the breeding season. A number come out of hiding only at night, while others are about in broad daylight, although they are not around during the hottest part of the day. Usually, they raise only one offspring at a time.

The Banded Wallaby is the most strikingly marked of all. It has eleven or twelve short stripes running across its gray back from the saddle to the base of the tail. One species, the Nail-tailed Wallaby, is called that because it has a horny projection at the tip of the tail.

The Rock Wallaby is a notable type. Its hind feet are well padded to prevent slipping after a long leap on the well-worn rocks. Like the larger kangaroos, this wallaby loves to bask in the sun, often sitting bolt upright on some rocky point. But it is far from being asleep, and at the first sign of danger disappears in a flash. It performs some astonishingly daring leaps without bringing its forelimbs into use and, when pursued and separated from its rocky castle, will unhesitatingly bound into leaning trees at top speed.

KANGAROOS—SOME LIVE IN TREES

Where They Got Their Name. But for their greater size, the kangaroos are practically the same as the wallabies not only in appearance but in habits as well. They owe their name to Captain James Cook, the famous English explorer of the eighteenth century. In the dialect of the Endeavor River aborigines the word "kangaroo" means "I do not know," and when Captain Cook asked the natives what they called the kangaroo, that is what they are said to have replied; kangaroos the animals have been ever since.

Actually, kangaroos had been heard of by western civilization long before the time of Captain Cook. Captain François Pelsaert, wrecked on the treacherous coast of Australia while carrying Dutch immigrants to the Moluccas in 1629, was the first European to make a report on them. The opossums, America's marsupials, were known much earlier.

There are many different kinds of kangaroos. In general they live on the ground, but one has become a creature of the trees. To the world at large, the Great Kangaroo is the most familiar type. Not so well known is the Rat Kangaroo, which is roughly as large as a rabbit but more like a rat in appearance. Some rat kangaroos are hoppers, like the average kangaroo, while others move about rapidly on all fours.

Once, the natives hunted the kangaroo extensively for its meat. It is still hunted, but is much harder to find nowadays. Its hide makes an excellent leather for gloves and boots.

The Great Kangaroo, or Forester, *Macropus,* is the largest of all the kangaroos. A male, or "boomer," may stand five to seven feet high and weigh up to two hundred pounds when full grown. The female, or "flyer," is smaller. The great kangaroo dwells in the inland plains of New South Wales and the open forests and brush country of Queensland, southwestern Australia, and Tasmania.

The outstanding feature of the great kangaroo is its extremely lengthy, powerful hind limbs, on which the animal hops about. The long, mighty tail serves it as a prop and also gives added impetus to its leaps.

Traveling at a normal rate, the kangaroo jumps from five to ten feet at a time; when pressed for speed, it can cover fifteen or twenty feet in a single bound. According to the nature writer "Mopoke," the record jump was made when a Queensland kangaroo chased by dogs cleared a mass of dead timber ten and one-half feet high; the length of the leap was twenty-seven feet.

——Kangaroo "Mobs." Kangaroos are often encountered in herds or "mobs." In the early pioneer days a "mob" of a thousand head was not unusual, but today it is doubtful if a mob of a hundred could be found. They travel great distances and have no fixed home. Like cattle they lie down and sleep on the ground. As a rule, their diet consists of vegetable matter. Fifteen years is the average life span.

THE GIANT HOPPER
A large and powerful animal, the great kangaroo may weigh up to two hundred pounds and stand five to seven feet high. With the aid of its strong hind legs and thick, massive tail, it can hop along at a speed of twenty-five miles an hour. It is a grazer and must compete with sheep and cattle for its livelihood.

——Baby Kangaroos. The young kangaroo or "joey"—rarely, if ever, is more than one raised at a time—is carried in the mother's pouch for the first six months. As the joey develops, it takes more and more interest in the outside world, peering about from its safe retreat while its mother hops along, sometimes at a speed of twenty-five miles per hour when she is in a hurry.

If hard pressed in flight, the female will toss her young into a thicket and lead the pursuers away. Relieved of the extra weight, she may now make good her escape and return later to pick up her joey.

——GENTLE UNLESS PROVOKED. Kangaroos love to take their daily bath in a river, and on occasion they even indulge in sun bathing. In public parks they will join picnickers and expect to get some of the spoils when lunch is over. They are timid and harmless unless forced to defend themselves. A large male with its back to a tree or wall can protect himself from a whole pack of dogs, and any individual that approaches too close is ripped to shreds by his powerful clawed hind feet.

——OLD MALES ARE BOLD. Old males have a reputation for boldness. An interesting tale about one of them is related by Carl Lumholtz, in his book *Among Cannibals:*

"A stalwart Highland shepherd was on his way home one evening with his dog, when suddenly he discovered a large object in front of him. Having lately come to Australia, he had scarcely seen one of these animals before, and being very superstitious he thought it was the devil himself. Meanwhile the dog attacked the monster, but instead of taking flight, it assumed the form of a great kangaroo, came up to the shepherd, put its arms around him and hopped away with him. The dog pursued the bold robber until the latter let go of its victim."

——DIFFERENT KINDS OF GREAT KANGAROOS. There are three groups of great kangaroos. The first kind, the Great Gray Kangaroo, or Forester, is found in the open forests and brush country of Queensland and southwestern Australia. The second, the Tasmanian Forester, is the only large kangaroo in Tasmania. It is more reddish brown than the mainland gray kangaroo and has coarser and longer fur.

The third, the Red Kangaroo, has a wide range that extends throughout the plains and open forest country of Australia. It is richly colored, powerful, and one of the most graceful of the large kangaroos. The male is a brilliant wine-red shade. The female, or doe, is more slender than the male, more lightly built, and has great speed. A soft smoky-blue in color, she has been named the "blue flyer." The red kangaroo is probably the largest and the most gregarious of the kangaroos.

A related form is the Wallaroo or Rock Kangaroo, *Osphranter*. The wallaroo is a large, stocky, powerful kangaroo of the coastal ranges and inland mountains of Australia.

The Tree Kangaroo, *Dendrolagus,* like the other kangaroos, comes from a line of ground-hoppers but has taken to the trees. It still retains the long hind limbs for leaping, but they have become shorter and broader, and the foot pads are rough, to assist in climbing. The animal reaches a length of four feet, about half of which is the tail.

THE KANGAROO THAT TOOK TO THE TREES

The tree kangaroo is the only one of the kangaroos that has taken up permanent residence in the trees. Though it is still built for hopping, its hind limbs have become shorter, the better for climbing. Using its long tail to help balance and steer itself, this curious animal makes long, flying leaps in the trees.

The tail is slender, with a thick brush at the tip, and serves as a rudder in flying leaps in the trees, as well as a balancer.

The tree kangaroo sleeps during the day curled up in the crotch of a tall tree. Frequently several animals occupy the same grove. After sunset they descend to the ground, always backing down tail first, and visit a waterhole for a drink. Their food, in the main, consists of the leaves of the white cedar as well as ferns, creepers, and many kinds of fruits.

Natives hunt the tree kangaroos with the aid of trained dingos, the native dogs of Australia, and relish its flesh as food. Usually one of the natives goes up the tree to stir the animal up. When it leaps down, the natives grab it by the tail or else it is caught by the dogs. A tree kangaroo, when disturbed, will jump down out of a tree from a height of thirty to fifty feet.

Essentially a forest kangaroo, this animal is at home in the mountains and high tablelands of northern Queensland. There are two species in Australia: Lumholtz's Tree Kangaroo and the Dusky Tree Kangaroo. In New Guinea there are four; they vary in color from grizzled and white-tailed to grayish brown and golden chestnut with yellow rump and tail.

The Musk Kangaroo, *Hypsiprymnodon,* is the most primitive and the smallest of the kangaroos. It has an over-all length of eighteen inches (including a six- or seven-inch tail, which is quite hairless and covered with a scaly skin). Reddish brown in color, it is a more slender and prettier creature than the rat kangaroo. It has a peculiar musky odor from which it gets its name.

The habits of the musk kangaroo are much the same as those of the typical kangaroo. Exceedingly shy, it hops around with a rapid motion. It is about in broad daylight and hunts for grubs and insects by turning over débris in the brush. This diet it supplements with tuberous roots, fruit, and berries. Sitting up on its haunches, it will hold a piece of fruit in its forepaws and munch it in a very human fashion.

The musk kangaroo lives in Queensland, where it haunts the damp brush and scrub country bordering lakes and streams. It breeds during the rainy season, which lasts from February to May. The female usually bears two tiny young and carries them around in her pouch.

The Insect-Eaters—Shrews, Moles, Hedgehogs, and Their Relatives

MOST OF the shrews, moles, and their kin are little known to us, for they prefer to keep out of man's way. Some live in the trees, a few swim, but the greater number are burrowers; many, like the moles, stay underground practically all the time. They are small or tiny creatures, and, when we do catch a glimpse of them, we may take them for mice or rats.

Enormous appetite, great courage, and pugnacity are typical traits of these little animals. All are high-strung and extremely nervous; a sudden fright or shock may even prove fatal to some. They live at high speed, they sleep little, and have a short life.

We find some members of this group in practically every part of the Temperate and Tropical Zones except Australia. Because they feed mostly on insects, they are known as insectivores (order Insectivora). Not all live on such a restricted diet; some eat a wide variety of animal and vegetable food. They have many teeth, extremely sharp and small, and a long snout. They patter along on flat feet armed with claws. Fur or, as in the case of the hedgehog, spines cover their bodies; some wear a coat that is a combination of both.

The insectivores are extremely interesting to us because they are among the most primitive of the mammals. Their brains are decidedly simple, without convolutions, and their teeth are like those we find in the oldest fossil mammals. They even have a collar-bone rather like the shoulder girdle of their reptile ancestors.

NEIGHBORS OF THE DINOSAUR

These small, shy creatures are actually living relics of the original stock from which our modern, or placental, mammals arose. Over fifty million years ago, when the earth still trembled to the tread of the dinosaur, there were already insectivores that looked much like the common shrews of today. They must have escaped notice then as they do now; one of them, the long-extinct minishrew, became the great-grandparent of the whales, elephants, horses, and cattle, the apes, and man.

Like two other ancient creatures, the opossum and the oyster, the insectivores have joined the ranks of the immortal. How have they managed to survive through the ages while many animals that sprang from the same stock—the woolly mammoth and the saber-toothed tiger are good examples—have disappeared from this planet?

The reason seems to be that the insectivores have changed little from the primitive forms, and always remained obscure. But the specialized animals grew still more specialized and could not, like the lowly insectivores, adjust to changing conditions.

SOLENODONS—WEST INDIAN RARITIES

The Solenodon, or Alamiqui, *Solenodon,* looks like a long-snouted rat. A rare and peculiar creature, it is about the size of a red squirrel and has rather long, coarse, limp fur, rusty brown in color. Its head, exceedingly long, ends in a sharply pointed snout; the nine-inch tail is naked and scaly. The solenodon's home is the West Indies.

The solenodon is seldom seen outside the exhibition cases of a museum. This is not surprising, since the animal is extremely scarce and never comes above ground during daylight hours. It bores under rotten logs in the jungle floor and beneath loose rocks, searching for bugs, snakes, and burrowing animal life. When pursued, it is said to practice the so-called "ostrich stunt" of sticking its head in a hole, leaving its entire body exposed. But we have little accurate information about its habits.

Two facts are hard at work making this animal rarity still rarer. First, the solenodon's rate of reproduction is slow. So far as we know, it produces only one young in a litter. Second, although it has few natural enemies, it is preyed upon by domestic cats, dogs, and the recently introduced mongoose, which have all but exterminated it.

——MYSTERY OF THE SOLENODON'S ORIGIN. Where the solenodon came from—how it came to be part of the impoverished animal life of the West Indies—is a mystery. It has no relatives on the American

mainland and but few distant ones where it lives. Perhaps it is a survivor from ancient times, when Cuba and Haiti were the highlands of
an old continent, now long sunk beneath the waves.

NEAR THE END OF ITS TRAIL
The Haitian solenodon, like its cousin the Cuban solenodon, is rarely seen outside a museum.
One reason it is so rare is that it has only one baby in a litter; another is that cats and dogs
prey upon it. The little solenodon is close to extinction.

In any event, the solenodons make up a distinct family (Soleno-
dontidae). There are only two species in it: the Cuban Solenodon,
with a tawny yellow head; and the Haitian Solenodon, which is darker
brown in color. They are about two feet long from the tip of the
snout to the end of the tail.

TENRECS—MADAGASCAR'S SHREWS AND HEDGEHOGS

On the island of Madagascar we find a group of strange insect-eaters
known as the tenrecs. Restricted to just this one area, with no close
relatives elsewhere, they must inevitably remind us of the isolated
solenodons of the West Indies.

The tenrecs and the lemurs are Madagascar's most important native mammals. The island has been separated from the mainland of
Africa for long ages, and few other types of animals have had an op-

portunity to come in. Yet in many ways the little tenrecs make up for their absence. They have specialized, and there are two main kinds, making up the family Tenrecidae: those with soft fur and those with quills. We might consider them to be Madagascar's shrews and hedgehogs, its moles, its mice, and, to a large extent, its rats.

TENRECS WITH SOFT FUR

The Rice Tenrec does the work of a mole. Living underground, it uses its enlarged feet to dig in search of worms and grubs. Its tunnels serve to drain excessive moisture in the ground, and its excavations have improved the fertility of the land. However, it does considerable damage to the rice crops, since it injures the plants' roots as it digs beneath them. It is about the size of a small rat, and has a short tail.

Another kind, the Marsh Tenrec, has broadly webbed feet for swimming; it hunts water-living insects like our water shrews, and is roughly the size of a rat. The Pygmy Tenrec, smallest of the Madagascar tenrecs, resembles a tiny long-tailed shrew. It lives in holes in the ground and feeds on small insect life.

More remarkable is the Long-tailed Tenrec. Although the body of this little creature is only about two inches long, it has a five- to six-inch tail. It possesses forty-seven vertebrae (one more than the tree pangolin, formerly supposed to have the greatest number) strung together to form the tail, which is four-sided and angular. Among mammals, only jumpers have tails that are proportionately so long; and since its hind feet are large, the long-tailed tenrec can jump when there is need. In general, it looks like a long-snouted mouse, reddish brown in color.

SPINY TENRECS

The Common Tenrec, *Tenrec ecaudatus,* is not only the largest tenrec —it is the largest of all the insectivores. This giant of a pigmy order still does not seem very impressive to us: full grown, it measures a mere twelve to sixteen inches. Its head is actually one-third the entire animal. It lacks a tail—"tailless tenrec" is the meaning of its scientific name.

The common tenrec resembles the solenodon a little: it has an elongated face and a long, pointed snout for rooting in the soft earth. Its fur is soft and yellowish brown in color. When it is quite young the animal sports a coat of brownish spines mixed with coarse hair; as it grows, it loses most of the spines except in the collar around its neck and shoulders. When danger threatens, the spines are erected, presenting a bristling array of protective armor.

AN ODD INSECT-EATER

Madagascar has a number of curious animals all its own; not the least interesting of them are the tenrecs. Relatives of the shrews, they take the place of the moles, rats, and mice on the island. Shown above is one of the most attractive of the group: the streaked tenrec, a spiny creature with decorative white lines on its yellowish-brown back. It is hardly half a foot in length. Tenrecs are among the most primitive of the mammals.

The common tenrec is a mountain-dweller. It lives in holes in the ground and ventures abroad in search of bugs and insects only after nightfall. Although not a sociable creature, it is not exactly solitary either; it has some of the largest families in the mammal world, fifteen to twenty-one young not being unusual. Any mother furnishing milk to so many hungry mouths is kept constantly busy.

From June to December the common tenrec goes to sleep underground for a long, hard-earned rest. At this time the natives dig it out for food.

Other tenrecs look more like the European hedgehog; they are armored like it, though their spines are not so stout. One of the handsomest is the Streaked Tenrec; it is covered with long, slender spines and has three decorative white lines running along its yellowish brown back. The animal is only about five inches long and has practically no tail.

POTAMOGALES—STURDY SWIMMERS OF AFRICA

The Potamogale, or Otter Shrew, *Potamogale velox,* of western equatorial Africa, is the champion swimmer of the insectivores. This streamlined animal looks like an otter: its limbs are short, its head is broad and flattened. Close fur covers its cylindrical body, which joins evenly with the thick neck.

One of the potamogale's most striking features is its powerful, flat-sided tail. It makes up almost half of the animal's two-foot length. This rear emphasis is not wasted by the potamogale. Having no webbed feet to aid it in swimming, it uses the tail instead; swinging it back and forth in the water, the potamogale propels itself along much like a fish. It can achieve a fair rate of speed, too, and that is why scientists call it *Potamogale velox*—"the swift water-weasel."

Fresh-water crustaceans and small fish are the potamogale's fare. It finds them in the forested watercourses it haunts in its central and west African homeland, which extends from the Cameroons to Angola and the Belgian Congo. The potamogales form a distinct family (Potamogalidae) among the insectivores.

GOLDEN MOLES—AFRICA'S UNDERGROUND TORPEDOES

The vast continent of Africa has no true moles like the ones we find in the Northern Hemisphere. But it does have their counterparts in its golden moles. These little underground torpedoes look somewhat like the true moles and behave like them.

The golden moles are burrowers, and the claws on their forefeet are greatly enlarged for digging. They have cylindrical bodies and pointed muzzles, but only a trace of a tail. The fur is full and soft, usually with a brilliant metallic luster varying from golden bronze to violet.

The Cape Golden Mole, or Goudmoul, is the best known of the family. It has brilliant shades of gold in its fur—no question how it came by its name. One of the smallest of its kind, it is only about four and one-half inches long. Another, the Red Golden Mole, burrows deep in the ground and like the common garden mole pushes up mounds of earth. Still another, the Little Golden Mole, is usually less than four inches long; it travels just below the surface of the ground. Largest of all is the Giant or Forest Golden Mole; it has a length of nine inches and is dark golden brown in color. It spends most of its time above ground.

The golden moles dwell only in southern Africa. There they range from the Cape of Good Hope north to the Congo, but are absent in the region about Angola and Rhodesia. They make up the family Chrysochloridae—a group that beautifully illustrates nature's habit of developing animals that look like those we encounter elsewhere and even lead the same kind of life, but are nevertheless different.

HEDGEHOGS—THEY ROLL UP INTO SPINY BALLS

The hedgehog is a night prowler. A quill-covered creature less than a foot long, it trots about with a jaunty gait, but its best speed is slow compared with that of its enemies. Fat and tender, it is a choice morsel for any beast of prey.

But acquiring that morsel is the problem. When surprised on its nightly wanderings, the hedgehog makes no attempt to run away unless a shelter is close by. Instead, it rolls itself up in a ball and draws its head and feet together at the inside. Now it is a sphere of bristling spines that defies attack.

BATTLE BETWEEN A HEDGEHOG AND A VIPER

The hedgehog does not use its spines as a weapon. They are strictly a means of defense, though the hedgehog knows how to employ them effectively in getting its food. Just how effectively you will see in this extraordinary report of how a hedgehog tricked an adder into biting itself to death:

"Everyone knows that a hedgehog is a sworn enemy of reptiles in general and of the viper in particular, but few perhaps are aware in what way he contrives to overcome so recalcitrant and dangerous an enemy and make a meal of it.

"My keeper was going his round this summer in a woods which is unfortunately infested with vipers, when he espied an enormous one asleep in the sun. He was on the point of killing it with a charge of shot when he perceived a hedgehog coming cautiously over the moss and noiselessly approaching the reptile. . . .

"As soon as the hedgehog was within reach of his prey, he seized it by the tail with his teeth and quickly rolled himself into a ball. . . . The viper, awakened by the pain, at once turned and made a terrific dart at him . . . infuriated, it extended itself, hissed and twisted

IT ROLLS INTO A BALL
The hedgehog really does roll up into a prickly ball when danger threatens. The animal makes good eating, but the bristling spines baffle attack. Some beasts of prey have found a way to solve the problem—the fox will roll Mr. Hedgehog into a pool of water where he must uncurl or drown. Although the hedgehog's quills resemble those of the porcupine, this is merely a matter of coincidence; the porcupine belongs in another group, the rodents.

with fearful contortions. . . . In five minutes it was covered with blood . . . and lay exhausted on the ground . . . when the hedgehog quietly unrolled himself." (Ferdinand Coste, in the magazine *Zoologist*, 1887.)

The wily fox is perhaps a more formidable enemy for the hedgehog. Foxes are credited with enough forethought to roll the hedgehog into a nearby pool of water, where it will open up and swim rather than drown. Then the fox grabs its prey by the head and the struggle is ended.

FACT AND FICTION ABOUT HEDGEHOGS

Hedgehogs are widespread throughout most of the Old World except Australia and Madagascar. We do not find them anywhere in the New World. Because they are such remarkable little creatures, a curious lore has grown up about them in different countries through the ages. The natives in Hopei province, China, for example, will tell you to treat the hedgehog with respect, for it is a sacred animal. In Europe, you will often hear that the hedgehog milks cows.

Hedgehogs, of course, do not drink milk, except their mother's. They feed on all manner of creeping things—bugs, cockroaches, beetles, slugs, snails, worms, frogs, rats, mice, and bird eggs, as well as snakes. In fact, they will eat any kind of animal life that they can catch and kill.

They seem equally unexacting about their abode. A cavity in the rocks, a hole in the bank, or a hollow stump will suffice just so long as it is warm and dry. In countries where the winters are cold, the hedgehog hibernates.

THE EUROPEAN HEDGEHOG

In Europe, the best known of the hedgehog family is the Common Hedgehog, *Erinaceus europaeus*. Its homeland extends from England and Ireland all the way east to maritime Siberia, Manchuria, and Korea.

This little animal generally breeds twice a year. About a month after mating time five to seven young are born. The baby hedgehogs spend their early days in a nest of dry leaves and grass that their mother has provided for them in a chamber just below the surface of the ground. They are blind at birth and covered with soft white spines. But in a week the tiny "hogs" can see; the spines are hard at the end of three weeks and colored like an adult's. In a month the babies are old enough to follow the mother into the outside world.

In spite of their name, hedgehogs are not hogs, but insectivores. Most hedgehogs are chocolate brown in color, with the tip of the spines yellowish white. The spines are closely packed, and cover the back up to the ears. Coarse hair takes the place of the spines on the face, legs, and under parts.

Although a hedgehog's spines are sharp enough, they are not barbed like a porcupine's. You can pick the animal up by hand without hurting yourself. It is seven or eight inches long on an average (ten for a large male), with a tail of hardly an inch. From above the hedgehog's body appears egg-shaped; its head is sharp and like a wedge. Males and females look much alike.

Hedgehogs of Other Lands. We find many different kinds of hedgehogs in various parts of the world. Some are only four or five inches long. Closely related are the Gymnures, small ratlike animals, and

AN ANIMAL THAT SMELLS LIKE AN ONION
The common moonrat, a cousin of the hedgehog, lives in Asia. It has an odor like an onion, that makes its enemies keep their distance. We do not find any members of the hedgehog family outside the Old World.

the Moonrats, of Asia. These hedgehogs are covered with hair instead of spines; one, the Common Moonrat, has a peculiar onion-like smell that is offensive at close range. All are placed in the family Erinaceidae, with the common hedgehog.

ELEPHANT SHREWS—SWIFT LITTLE HOPPERS OF AFRICA

The elephant shrew of Africa is one of the oddest animals in a group full of oddities. No bigger than a rat, it has a flexible, sensitive snout that projects stiffly before it. Its chubby, soft-furred body ends in long hind legs; the creature hops around on them like a kangaroo. It has large eyes, unlike most insectivores.

HIGH-STRUNG RUNNERS AND FIGHTERS

Elephant shrews are sun-worshipers and love to bask, stretched out, in the warm sunshine. Though most active during daylight hours, they are known to be about on moonlight nights. Walking at leisure,

IT ALMOST SEEMS TO HAVE A TRUNK
The elephant shrew of Africa is a long-snouted creature often not much bigger than a mouse. It may walk on all fours or hop around on its long hind legs like a kangaroo. The elephant shrew is a high-strung little being, and often gets involved in furious fights with its kin. The animal shown above is known as the checkered elephant shrew because of the markings on its back. The life of a shrew is a short one—fifteen months, at most.

the elephant shrew may go on all fours. But on the least provocation it leaps away like a little ball of fur, bouncing along, and heads for a retreat on the rocks or the nearest hole in the ground.

While not a typical burrowing animal as judged by its claws, the elephant shrew can quickly dig its way out of sight in reasonably soft soil or sand. Its den may be a crevice in the rocks or a burrow it has dug in the ground. Besides the usual front door entrance, the elephant shrew's burrow has an emergency exit; it is inconspicuously situated on the surface a few feet from the main entrance, and drops perpendicularly down. If an uninvited guest with a big appetite comes down the main hallway, the shrew scoots away via this escape hatch.

The elephant shrew, like most insect-eating animals, is not a particularly sociable creature: it lives either singly or in pairs. When several are confined in a cage, they box furiously with their hind feet, ripping bunches of hair from the coats of their opponents. As they fight, their ears and whiskers vibrate constantly.

Baby elephant shrews come one or two in a litter. At birth they are fairly big compared with their mother, and well clothed with fur. Their eyes are already open or will be very soon. Mother elephant shrew is attentive to her babies' welfare. For example, a female was taken carrying her twin young around attached to her teats. Upon release she made sure that the babies had a firm hold before she bounded away.

There are many kinds of elephant shrews in Africa, from the Cape to Algeria. They occupy almost all types of country; these animals are at home in the deserts of the Sahara as well as the forested regions of the Congo. Most species in the group (family Macroscelididae) are small, with a body about four or five inches long and a tail of the same length. The largest is the Checkered Elephant Shrew, a forest-loving species of the Congo and Kenya. Its body is about eleven inches long, and it has a nine-inch tail. Its back is marked like a checkerboard, with four or five rows of evenly spaced light and dark square spots.

TRUE SHREWS—SMALLEST MAMMALS IN THE WORLD

The smallest mammals in the world belong to the shrew family. Most shrews are tiny—the largest is scarcely as big as a house rat. Relatives of the moles, they are mouselike animals with a long, pointed head, minute eyes, and short, rounded ears that are almost concealed in the soft fur.

Shrews live just below the surface of the ground. Their favorite food is insects, and they play an important part in the control of the injurious species, especially before the larvae develop and leave the ground. Shrews also hunt their food under fallen leaves and rotting vegetation. They feed almost continuously, and can consume their own weight in food every three hours. Constantly on the move, these high-strung creatures are active in all seasons, by day and by night.

Two or three times a year, the shrew breeds. Young born in the early spring will scarcely last the year out, but those born in the later summer, barring accidents, live through to the following year. The rate of reproduction varies in different places. In one place, shrews may outnumber all other species of animals and fairly swarm over the land; just a few miles away there may be scarcely any shrews.

THE WELL-ARMED SHREW

Shrews have lots of enemies. Hawks, owls, snakes, weasels, cats, foxes, and fish will kill a shrew on sight. But few will eat it, and for a very good reason: the shrew has a pair of glands, one on each flank, that secrete an objectionable, strong musky odor. An animal with a sense of smell finds it hard to tolerate.

Many people that have never before seen a shrew, experience an eerie feeling when one comes along for the first time. There is a widespread belief that the bite of the shrew is poisonous. The more intelligent pooh-pooh the idea; they even let shrews bite them and suffer no ill effects. The fact is that most shrews have poisonous saliva glands in the lower jaw, but the poison is capable only of a slightly crippling effect on a small mouse. There is one exception—the bite of the American short-tailed shrew may actually kill a mouse.

The feature that distinguishes the shrews from all other animals is their front teeth. Those of the upper jaw are hooked and have a supplementary prong. The lower front teeth are long and project straight forward. These creatures are often classified by the color of their teeth or the length of their tails. Thus there are red-toothed shrews and white-toothed shrews, long-tailed shrews and short-tailed shrews. Some, known as water shrews, are capable swimmers. They form a great family, the Soricidae; here we can look at only a few of its most interesting members.

SOME INTERESTING RED-TOOTHED SHREWS

The Long-tailed or Red-toothed Shrew, *Sorex,* is found in incredible numbers and varieties in many parts of the Northern Hemisphere—

in the Old World as well as in the New. Besides the lengthy tail for which it is named, the animal has a long head with almost sightless eyes and a sharply pointed muzzle. The body is small and covered with thick, soft, blackish-brown fur. Its limbs are short. The name "red-toothed," sometimes applied to it, refers to the tips of its teeth, which are heavily coated with deep brownish-red pigment.

The long-tailed shrew is one of the most active mammals alive today. It is almost always astir—in neither light nor dark, summer nor winter, does it slow down. It feeds almost constantly; if deprived of food even for two or three hours it will die of starvation.

Although some species weigh no more than a few grams, they can withstand temperatures of from 75 to 85 degrees below zero Fahrenheit. The Pygmy Long-tailed Shrew, *Microsorex*, weighing about two and one-half grams—actually less than a dime—is the smallest animal in America. Another little shrew, the Least Long-tailed Shrew, *Sorex minutus*, is one and one-half inches long, with a tail slightly shorter. It is the smallest shrew found in Great Britain, with a range extending across into Asia.

Long-tailed shrews, like other shrews, are very aggressive and, when not feeding, they are fighting each other. There are few without some battle scars. A shrew can live peaceably only with its mate; it even shows devotion during the breeding season. Occasionally five or six shrews are found together in one nest but they are all of one family, not yet broken up.

The American Water Shrew, *Sorex palustris,* an excellent swimmer, is one of the most interesting animals in North America. At first glance it looks like a miniature muskrat without eyes and ears (they are so minute), but the face is more pointed.

This little creature is large in comparison with other shrews: its head and body length will reach three inches, and the tail is almost as long again. The tail is compressed at the sides. Swinging it back and forth, the shrew is able to achieve considerable power and shoot rapidly forward in the water. Its hind feet are especially long and conspicuously fringed with stiff hairs for swimming. Its thick black, velvety fur is so dense that it keeps the animal's body dry in the water.

——It Walks on Water! We have said that the water shrew is an excellent swimmer. For its size, it compares favorably with our fastest fresh-water swimmers, such as the otters. It can dive, float, or run along the bottom of shallow pools; and, believe it or not, this dainty little animal can actually walk and run on the water without breaking through the surface film! The feet hold globules of air as it skims across a quiet pool.

Water-walking unfortunately has its drawbacks. Skimming along the surface, the water shrew is an easy prey for the swift-swimming trout or pickerel.

This animal seems less quarrelsome than most shrews and may ever be sociable. Several often live together in a hollow tree stump overhanging a stream. Once a year, the water shrew raises a family of six.

The water shrew frequents watercourses, usually at a moderate elevation, in the northern United States and Canada. It is more active by night than most shrews, and feeds on water spiders, fresh-water crustaceans, and tiny fish.

The Cinereous Shrew, or Masked Shrew, *Sorex cinereus,* is the commonest of the shrews in the northern United States and Canada. It is a tiny creature, yet so ferocious that if two are placed together in a small container, one will slay and devour the other in the space of a few hours.

———A Wisp of an Animal. Even in adulthood the cinereous shrew is just a wisp of an animal. It weighs no more than three and one-half grams (the weight of approximately one teaspoonful of water); newborn, it is one-tenth of a gram. The animal is brown above, grayish below. Its life is spent in the dark shadows, under leaves, and in subsoil runways. And so, despite its abundance, it is rarely seen.

A leaf or grass nest in a hollow log, under a stump, or in a hole just below the surface of the ground, is the house where the young shrews are born. Often the nursery consists of a ball-shaped bundle of grass, about eight inches through, with a three-inch chamber in the center; the entrance is a small hole in the side.

———Babies as Little as Honeybees. Mother shrew bears six babies as a rule, but she may have as many as ten. At birth, they are naked, with wrinkled pink skin, and about the size of a honeybee. The mother must be endlessly active in order to satisfy her own hunger as well as to maintain the milk supply needed by her growing family. At one week the tiny tots are beginning to get some fur. A week later, they are fully clothed; during the third week they cut their first teeth and their eyes are open.

When a month old, the tots are weaned; they are now adults and must go out into the world to make a home for themselves. In place of mother's milk the adolescent shrew gulps down crickets, grasshoppers, slugs, and larvae of flies, moths, and earthworms; shrews destroy hordes of injurious insects. A shrew has its playful moments and will toy around with a beetle just as a cat will play with a mouse.

——1,200 HEARTBEATS A MINUTE. The cinereous shrew is perhaps the most sensitive, high-strung, and nervous of all mammals. When it is excited, its heart speeds up to twelve hundred beats a minute, a fabulous rate. (Compare that to the normal human heartbeats of sixty-five to ninety per minute!) The animal nearly always dies within a few minutes of capture—even when caught in a trap with a door padded to deaden the sound and shock.

——THE ESKIMO AND THE SHREW. Nervous though the shrew is, we have seen that many people around the globe view it with dread. The Eskimos, in particular, treat it with great caution. They believe that if the animal is disturbed, it will dart at the intruder, burrow through his flesh, enter his heart, and kill him. Meeting a shrew, an Eskimo will stand still as a stone until it has passed by, and thank his lucky stars that he has escaped unharmed.

Life expectancy for the cinereous shrew is about fourteen months —a rather good span considering the host of enemies a tiny creature like this must face.

The Common Red-toothed or European Shrew, or Shrew Mouse, *Sorex araneus,* is a little animal that dwells in great numbers in England, western Europe, and east across Asia. Its body is dark brown in color, and may measure up to two and one-half inches; the tail, an inch shorter. For its size, this creature has played an enormous role in European folklore.

Like other shrews, the common red-toothed shrew is very pugnacious. Five or six at a time have been observed squeaking and quarreling among themselves for no apparent reason; in an instant two or three will be at one another's throats, biting and rolling over in confusion. Then one darts off with the others in fast pursuit, and when they catch up with it the rough-housing starts again.

——BABIES IN A BALL OF GRASS. This shrew begins to breed in April. When the mating season opens there is a constant battle among the males, and they utter shrill cries as they fight their fast and furious duels. The breeding season lasts until November.

Mother shrew bears three or four broods a year, with from five to eight young in each. They are tiny, naked, pink little atoms at first but grow very rapidly. The nursery is a neatly woven ball of grass or leaves placed in a wood pile or a tuft of grass. It has interlocking blades of growing grass woven into the dome, and is well-roofed to shed moisture; there is an entrance at the side. The young stay at home until nearly fully grown.

——A High Death Rate. European shrews are often found dead without a mark on them. The rate of mortality is very high for various reasons. Shrews often die of starvation or are drowned out by heavy rain; many die of shock during thunderstorms. All flesh-eaters prey on the shrew—hawks, owls, jays, crows, weasels, foxes, cats.

——The "Dangerous" Shrew. European folklore had it—and perhaps still has it, in some places—that a shrew would die if it crossed the path of a human being. It was considered dangerous to livestock. The superstitious believed that whenever a shrew scurried over a horse, cow, or sheep, it would cause the animal extreme anguish and even the loss of any limb the shrew touched.

As protection against this accident, Europeans of the past kept a shrew-ash. They made it by boring a hole in the trunk of an ash tree; an unfortunate live shrew was thrust in the hole, which was then securely plugged up. They believed that touching the shrew's victim with a twig from this tree immediately relieved the pain. The ceremony was accompanied by incantations long since forgotten.

Perhaps because the shrew was considered so obnoxious—or possibly because it is such a fighter—the English-speaking peoples have borrowed its name to describe a turbulent or brawling woman.

Shrews were held sacred by the ancient Egyptians; they supposed the animals were blind and regarded them as an emblem of primal night and darkness. The city of Buto, said Herodotus, was a place of sacred sepulture for these little animals, and mummified shrews have been found in Thebes.

The Old World Water Shrew, *Neomys,* is a handsome little native of England, the mainland of Europe, and northern Asia. Although mostly blackish brown in color, it has silvery-white under parts. Its head and body length is about two and one-half to three inches or more, its tail about as long again.

The Old World water shrew has habits much the same as the American water shrew's. A frequenter of small streams and marshes, it is a first-class swimmer. Often, however, it is found at considerable distances from water; in England it is as common along the hedgerows as in the streams. It makes its nest in a hole in the bank, lining it with leaves and dried grass. Here the female raises the four to eight young she produces in one litter.

This shrew feeds on water insects and crustaceans. It can be easily and safely caught by hand under the banks of shallow brooks; in captivity it will kill and eat prey as large as frogs.

——THE WATER SHREW IN ACTION. Dovaston, at the beginning of the last century, was one of the first English naturalists to take particular notice of this beautiful little creature. Here are some of the water shrew's habits as he observed them:

"It dived and swam with great agility and freedom, repeatedly gliding from the bank under water, and disappearing under the mass of leaves at the bottom, doubtless in search of insect-food. It very shortly returned and entered the bank, occasionally putting its long, sharp nose out of the water and paddling close to the edge. . . . Sometimes it would run a little on the surface, and sometimes timidly and hastily come ashore, but with the greatest caution, and instantly plunge in again."

SOME NOTABLE SHORT-TAILED SHREWS

The American Short-tailed Shrew, *Blarina brevicauda,* is an animal of special value to the farmer, since it kills insect and rodent pests. It has a short, thickset body, covered with soft, bluish-black fur, and weighs up to thirty grams (approximately one ounce). With its bobtail, it has a length of about four inches. Its teeth are pigmented with a deep red stain.

This short-tailed shrew is common in the eastern United States; it ranges from southeastern Canada south to Florida, and west to Manitoba and Oklahoma. It lives in fields or under dead leaves on the forest floor. Not only does it feed on the larvae and worms it finds here, but it also follows subterranean passages in search of insects

and mice. Driven by an insatiable appetite, it will kill and devour a
mouse its own size.

——A "POISONOUS" ANIMAL. The poison of the short-tailed shrew
is very similar to that of a cobra. A large dose of saliva, drawn from
the glands in its lower jaw and injected into a mouse, will bring about
convulsions and death from failure to breathe. Still, human beings
do not have to fear these little killers. The writer has caught many of
them by hand and suffered no ill effects from their bites.

This animal makes its home underground in a small hole, which
it lines with grass. It breeds three or four times a year. The mother
may bear as many as nine babies in a litter, but six is the average
number.

A SHREW WITH A COBRA'S POISON
The American short-tailed shrew is the farmer's friend. It is death to insects and rodents,
for its saliva glands contain a poison similar to a cobra's. This can quickly subdue a
mouse but does little hurt to human beings. Tail and all, this venomous little creature is
only some four inches long. It is active by day, but generally stays out of sight.

——LITTLE SHREWS WITH GIGANTIC APPETITES. We find a related
shrew in Asia, the Oriental Short-tailed Shrew. The smallest of its
kind in the Western Hemisphere is the Pygmy Short-tailed Shrew,
with an over-all length of about three inches. It dwells from Connecticut south through Mexico and Central America into South America; indeed, it is the only type of shrew we find in South America.

The following anecdote from the author's own experience with a captive Connecticut specimen (not over four grams in weight) well serves to illustrate the voraciousness of the group:

On one occasion a large can of night crawlers had been left in the animal's cage. The shrew climbed into the can, dragged out a worm, and slaughtered it after a skillful exhibition of avoiding the writhing coils. Then the bloody assault continued until every worm was completely mangled. Whereupon, after having carefully examined the can to see if any prey was still alive, the shrew proceeded to gorge itself on the torn remains.

WHITE-TOOTHED SHREWS—INCLUDING A "HERO"

The White-toothed Shrew, or Musk Shrew, *Crocidura,* is the common shrew of the Old World and the Tropics; we do not find it in America. Most of its kind are a uniform light gray or brown, but some are dark brown. They emit a powerful odor, as their common name tells us.

The African Musk Shrew is perhaps the most unpleasant, evil-smelling, and vicious of the insectivores. It will dare to attack animals much larger than itself, including snakes and small mammals. Its awful stench protects it from the attack of flesh-eating mammals and birds alike.

——A Cruel Custom. The natives place these shrews in tiny cages and sell them for a penny apiece. The purchaser who puts two in one cage with some scraps of meat will witness a mortal combat. Screaming over the scraps, the shrews proceed to tear each other to bits. The victor not only devours the booty but the vanquished foe as well.

Such frightful carnage may seem unwarranted, but not to the natives of tropical countries, where vermin multiply so rapidly that even the most vigorous measures hardly serve to hold them in check.

——Stench into Perfume. By some simple but secret method, the natives of West Africa convert the evil stench of this shrew into a delicate, fragrant perfume; it has a sweet smell something like that of sandalwood. In the process the shrew is boiled whole along with certain leaves and palm oil.

The musk shrew is spread over Asia and most of Africa, with several types in Europe. In the British Isles it is found in the Scilly Islands. It measures about two or three inches, with a tail almost as long, but some African species are the size of a rat. The fur is never quite so dense as in the northern shrews, and there is usually a sprinkling of extra-long hairs on the tail.

The Indian House Shrew or Musk Shrew, *Suncus coeruleus,* in its native India and Ceylon, is almost as closely associated with human dwellings as our house rats and mice. It is none other than Kipling's Chuchundra, referred to in his famous story "Rikki-tikki-tavi" as the creature that always creeps by the walls and never comes out in the middle of the floor.

——"MONEY MOUSE." This shrew is a big fellow: it is some six inches long, plus a tail half that length. In semi-darkness the animal's light bluish-gray color produces a peculiar, almost luminous, effect. When running, it has a queer habit of making a noise like the jingle of silver coins; the natives call it the "money mouse."

Although the house shrew has typically poor eyesight, this weakness has not prevented it from acquiring an outstanding record as a destroyer of cockroaches and other house vermin. It can be taught to come when called, and with a little coaxing will soon take roaches and other insects offered by hand. It will immediately kill a large rat placed in the same cage with it.

You might suppose that the house shrew would be especially welcome in tropical areas, where there are periodic outbreaks of rodent-borne plagues. Unfortunately it is killed on sight by the natives. Yet it is inoffensive to man, except for its rather musky odor. Tradition has it that this shrew will contaminate with its smell anything it crosses, even a sealed bottle of wine.

——SMALLEST MAMMAL ON EARTH. The house shrews are found in many parts of eastern and southern Asia and also in southern Europe. Most of them are rather small; the Etruscan Shrew, of the Mediterranean region of southern Europe, is the smallest mammal in the world. Its head and body measure only one and one-half inches, and its tail is about one and one-eighth. It is one-half inch shorter in body length than America's smallest shrew and weighs less than two grams.

The Hero Shrew, or Armored Shrew, *Scutisorex,* has been heard of far outside its native Congo and Uganda. It owes its fame to an unusually strong, reinforced backbone. The animal is large for a shrew.

with a head and body length of almost six inches and a tail three inches long. It has thick fur, dull brownish black in color.

——Congo Natives Show Off Its Strength. The Mangbetu natives of the Belgian Congo, whenever they get a chance, take delight in showing before a fascinated crowd the extraordinary resistance of this shrew to weight and pressure. Usually after a hubbub of invocations a man—he may weigh about 160 pounds—steps barefooted upon the shrew, and balances himself on it on one foot. He continues his eloquence for several minutes in this position.

Upon release, the shrew, after a few shivering movements, continues on its way none the worse for the mad experiment. Any other shrew or small rodent submitted to such treatment would be instantly killed.

——A Mighty Backbone. What makes this animal so strong? The backbone of the hero shrew is strikingly different from that of other shrews. It has more than twice as many vertebrae as they, and these bones are enormously enlarged and staunchly interlocked. The great strength of the backbone together with a strong curve of the skeleton behind the shoulders protects the heart and other vital organs from being crushed. These physical traits may be of value in shielding the animal when it crawls under loose rocks in search of insects and grubs.

——Magical Powers. It was the Mangbetu natives who originally named this creature a "hero." They believe that the hero shrew's charred body, when prepared by their medicine men, transmits heroic qualities. Accordingly, they wear it as a talisman or take it as medicine. Those engaging in warfare or setting out upon an equally dangerous mission, such as hunting elephants, are eager to carry along the hero shrew's ashes.

SHREW MOLES, DESMANS, AND TRUE MOLES

All the true moles and their relatives, the desmans and shrew moles, make their home in the Northern Hemisphere—we do not meet them in Africa and Central or South America. They are fairly small animals, with a long, pointed head, soft thick fur, tiny eyes and ears, and rather large forefeet. They feed mainly on insects and worms. Most live underground.

Of these animals, the moles, with their powerful claws and forelimbs, have made the best adaptation to a life of digging beneath the surface. The shrew moles, in their physical traits, are in between the moles and the shrews. For example, the American Shrew Mole, or Gibbs' Mole, as it is also known, has the long face of a shrew, but its muzzle is naked like a mole's. Its forefeet are larger than a shrew's and stoutly clawed, but they have not quite reached the extreme development we find in the broad front feet of the true mole.

Although, like the mole, the shrew mole tunnels in search of worms and burrowing insects, it spends a good part of its life on the surface, a habit it shares with the shrew. The American shrew mole inhabits a narrow strip along the Pacific coast of North America. Across the ocean, in Japan, lives its cousin the Japanese Eared Shrew Mole. This little animal is unusual in that it has a distinct external ear.

The desmans are the aquatic members of the mole family (Talpidae). However, they, too, make their homes underground.

THE DESMANS—SLOW SWIMMERS IN WEARY RIVERS

The Russian Water Mole or Desman, *Desmana,* is not a true mole, although it resembles one in a general way. It has thick, close, blackish-brown fur (like a mole's), but this is overlaid with long oily guard hairs to shed water. One of its outstanding features is its long, tubular muzzle, which extends far beyond the margin of the lower lip, forming a proboscis. Its hind feet are broadly webbed, and it has a long, scaly tail—almost half the animal's over-all length of sixteen inches or so. The tail is flat on the sides, like the blade of an oar, and forms a powerful instrument for propelling the animal through the water.

——SURVIVOR OF A BYGONE AGE. Though possessing many of the qualifications for an aquatic life, the desman is neither very swift nor quick in the water. Its inferiority in this respect is due to its descent from ancestral mole stock. The molelike body of this survivor of a bygone age just has not changed enough to permit it to make the most of a life in the water. Thus it favors slow-moving streams or still lakes. As it swims, only the tip of its long, flexible snout is out of the water; the snout is constantly in motion when the animal is on the move.

The desman feeds on leeches, frogs, freshwater crustaceans, mollusks, insects, and fish. It prods in the mud with its proboscis, searching for animal life, and can strike a fair blow with it. It will kill and eat a large carp.

Early spring is the desman's breeding season. The young are born about May, and number from two to six. A second litter may come later in the year. The desman is a rather sociable creature, and seven or eight fully grown individuals have been found in one den.

——THE DESMAN'S HOME. It is in the bank of the same sluggish stream or river it swims in that we can look for the home of the desman. In a spot reinforced by the interlocking roots of trees and shrubs, the animal begins to dig in the bank at water level. A foot or more from the entrance, it excavates upward, hollowing out the nest chamber close to the surface; it pushes the excess earth up through the roof, which produces a raised dome. From the entrance the desman keeps canals open through the muddy shallows for a safe journey to deep water.

The home is a more or less permanent abode. A strong odor surrounds it, arising from the rotting bones of fish dragged into the nest. Here the desman stays when it is not hunting; we usually see it about the time of the ice breakup in the spring, when high waters flood it out of its den.

The Russian desman is a native of northern Europe and Russia. A related animal, the Spanish Desman, has a smaller body and a rounder tail, but its habits are much the same.

TRUE MOLES—REMARKABLE DIGGERS

Most people think that they know what a mole is, but few have ever seen one, and these would probably not recognize it if they did. What does this remarkable animal actually look like?

The mole is virtually an underground bullet. It is cylindrical in shape and tapered to a point at the front end. It has no visible neck. Its limbs are short; the forelegs, highly specialized for digging, are broad and tremendously powerful. They are armed with stout claws, with which the mole is capable of excavating a hundred-yard tunnel in twenty-four hours. Six inches (including a one-inch tail) is about the average length of this industrious, hard-working creature.

The true moles live in the northern temperate regions of both the Old World and the New World. They do not penetrate into the extreme north because there the ground freezes to too great a depth. They have not invaded the tropics because the soil is, for the most part, too dry to support sufficient underground animal life to compensate for the labor of excavating.

Moles, like other forms of wildlife, must get a "living wage." As they dig, they must secure enough food to produce again the amount of energy they expend. Each day they eat their own weight in insects. No other mammals put in so many hours of hard manual labor as the lowly moles.

How the Mole Serves Man. Although the mole raises unsightly mounds of earth on lawns and in pastures, and is often accounted a general nuisance, it plays an important part in developing the soil and keeping it suitable for farming.

In low-lying plains, where too much water would normally turn the soil sour, mole runways drain off the excess. In dry pastures the runways convey the rain underground and distribute it where it is needed most, before it can run off over the hard parched surface.

Then, too, by transferring the subsurface soil to the top, the moles till the land, mixing it with dead leaves or rotting vegetation. In this way they help to produce the rich loam man needs to raise fine crops.

Life Under the Ground. Moles never leave any outside door open to their labyrinth of subterranean highways. From time to time a pile of excavated earth is pushed up through a hole, but once the job is done the exit is firmly plugged. They probably have some sort of community life, since they have passageways in common; where the traffic is too heavy there may be "one-way streets," too. These animals are as pugnacious as shrews, and two moles confined in a small space will fight until one is killed. They give no quarter and apparently expect none.

Danger in the Daylight. In the course of their underground existence, moles have almost completely lost their sight; at best they can only distinguish between day and night. Rarely do they emerge from their tunnels. In the spring, for example, the garden mole comes out to collect leaves and dry grass for a nest in which to raise its young. Overhead, soaring hawks are on the watch for the poor blind mole, which is not aware of its danger until too late.

Once the nest-building period is over, the mole is reasonably safe for another year. Under the ground, its exquisitely sensitive snout is more helpful than the sharpest of eyes.

Valuable Fur. Moles have one of the finest grades of fur. In the wholesale fur market, dealers' quotations are in the hundreds of thousands of pelts, but it is only in Europe that moles are sufficiently abundant to produce such quantities for the trade.

There are many different kinds of true moles, showing interesting variations from the general stock. In Japan there is the Furry-snouted Mole, a smaller-than-average species, that has a very long, pointed snout covered with short, velvety fur like the body. In southern Asia, the Club-tailed Mole has a tail enlarged at the tip; the Spindle-tailed Mole, of Burma and Yunnan, gets its name from its unusually thick tail.

EUROPE'S COMMON MOLE

The Common European Mole or Oont, *Talpa europaea,* inhabits the temperate regions of the Old World, from England and France to Japan. Five and one-half inches long, with a naked tail of about one inch, it has uniform black velvety fur, sometimes with a grayish or brownish tinge. Occasionally, there is an albino or piebald mole, but more often the off-colored ones are buff or steel-gray.

The European mole's normal life is spent underground. Twice a year, once in the spring and again in the fall, it deliberately breaks the surface and ventures out in the open air. In the spring it is for bedding to make a nest. In the fall, when the ground is hard and dry from the summer heat, the animal must go in search of water.

Interestingly enough, this subterranean dweller is a good swimmer. Occasionally it crosses rivers, and it has been seen swimming strongly in a lake one hundred yards from shore. But such excursions are unusual.

——UNDERGROUND SPEEDSTERS. The European mole is sociable to a degree. In a given area the moles dig main community highways. These thoroughfares, about a foot below the surface of the ground, are connecting arteries between the favorite hunting grounds. They may be used by forty or more moles.

In their underground tunnels these animals are credited with a speed of two and one-half miles an hour. They are as much at ease in the earth as the fish is in the sea.

——MATING OF THE MOLES. The mating season begins in March and lasts until May. The moles fight fierce battles for possession of the females. The female, either with or without the assistance of her mate, builds a regular fortress for her family far off the beaten track.

This fortress is a molehill, larger than usual and raised above possible high-water level in marshy areas.

In the molehill, at about ground level, or higher, the female hollows out a cavity one foot through, for the nest chamber. Here she weaves an elaborate, compact nest, like a ball, from leaves and grass. She provides an emergency exit at the bottom of the nest chamber, which she often surrounds with an intricate labyrinth. The actual entrance is from below. There is no regular opening to the surface, though the hungry weasel would no doubt welcome one.

Four weeks after mating the female gives birth to a family of from two to six. At first the young are quite naked and helpless, with wrinkled little pink bodies. But they grow very rapidly; at five weeks they are ready to leave the nest and show what good diggers they are. A second litter may come in the fall.

————The Mole in Folklore. There are many quaint notions about the European mole. Superstition would have it, for example, that the mole possesses only one drop of blood. According to folklore, too, the mole leaves the ground once a year to take a little fresh air in the daylight. In reality, the mole finds its air in the earth; thirst is more likely to bring it to the surface, as we have seen.

MOLES OF NORTH AMERICA

The Common American Garden Moles, *Scapanus* and *Scalopus,* each have their own particular territory in the United States. The Western Garden Mole, *Scapanus,* restricts itself to the region west of the Rocky Mountains. The Eastern Garden Mole, *Scalopus,* dwells from Massachusetts to Nebraska, and as far south as the Gulf of Mexico.

Superficially these animals look alike, with their thick, close coats, almost black in color, but the western mole is the larger of the two. Indeed, with its seven- to nine-inch length it is the largest mole in America. (The eastern mole measures seven inches.)

The common mole prefers open country for its activities: it favors low-lying meadows and lawns, where the soil is soft and moist, but it may live on hillsides. In these places it digs its two sets of tunnels— one a deep set and the other near the surface.

The creature's deeper runway is from one to two feet under the ground; here the mole spends the greater part of its time and has its living quarters. The surface runway is where the mole finds most of its food. It is used only occasionally, and sometimes only once—when the food supply is gone, the mole digs onward and elsewhere. Some of the passageways extend half a mile or more.

——THE MASTER TUNNELERS. The mole is a superb digger. It feels its way with its sensitive snout, then drives its shovel-like feet into the earth and scoops the soil, one handful at a time to the rear. By pressing its body first against one side, then against the other, it makes the walls compact.

A REMARKABLE DIGGER

There are two common American garden moles—the eastern garden mole and the western, which is shown above. Both are talented diggers and can hollow a tunnel out at the rate of fifteen feet an hour. The animals' underground activities have great value in keeping the soil fertile. Commonly, nothing is seen of the moles except their molehills; however, moles may be glimpsed aboveground in the spring, which is their mating season.

When sufficient soil has been excavated, the mole turns around and pushes the load up through a hole in the roof, forming a heap or "molehill." For the observer, these heaps, piled at intervals on the surface, mark the course of the mole's upper runway.

The animal has a sense of direction for its tunnels. Under hollows and over ridges it keeps approximately the same depth. It can excavate tunnels, shoveling away the dirt, at a rate up to fifteen feet an hour.

——THE WAY OF A MOLE WITH A WORM. Earthworms are the principal food of the American garden moles, but they will eat almost any kind of insects or larvae they find in the runways. The western mole will eke out its diet with roots or tubers and may eat tulips and iris bulbs. Such depredation cannot be charged against the eastern mole.

The way of a mole with a worm is an interesting one. The mole first grabs the victim, then works along until it comes to one end, usually the head; it commences to devour it like spaghetti, straightening out the kinks in the worm with its forefeet and at the same time scraping off the loose earth.

——FAMILY LIFE AMONG THE MOLES. The common mole makes its nursery in a lower-level tunnel. The chamber is about eight inches in diameter, and the female lines it with dry leaves or dead grass. She bears only one litter a year.

The mole babies come in March or April, after being carried in their mother's womb for thirty days. There are six to eight of them, and they are naked, completely blind, and helpless at birth. They are almost fully grown when they are two months old. Ten months later, in the following spring, they are ready to breed. Barring accidents, a garden mole will die of old age in its third year.

The male mole is not a "family man"; he may assist in building a nest during the courtship period, but even this is doubtful. Yet some cooperation from the male would really seem necessary. The mother must not only nurse and keep her naked babies warm (for it is still cold in March and April), but she must frequently make extremely long trips in search of food for herself. Deprived of sustenance for a few hours, she would be on the verge of death by starvation.

The Star-nosed Mole, *Condylura,* of northeastern North America, is the least molelike of all the American moles. It is an exceedingly strange-looking creature, and leads one to think, as the study of living things often does, that nature has left no experimental fields of development unexplored. For here is an animal with a naked fringe of twenty-two feelers, rose colored and highly sensitive, symmetrically arranged in the shape of a disk on the tip of its nose.

This mole has a fat, scaly tail about three inches long, which is equal to its body length. Like other moles it has well-developed claws for digging. It wears a thick, jet-black coat of fur without luster or sheen.

——FEELING ITS WAY. The star-nosed mole favors marshes and damp fields. It is as much at home in the water as in the soft earth, and can swim and dive like a muskrat. The feelers on its nose doubtless aid it in catching and identifying waterborne sounds and are used by the animal to feel its way about when submerged or underground and to detect the worms and insects on which it feeds. This species, like the rest of the moles, has practically lost the sense of sight; its sense of smell is weak.

THE MOLE THAT IS DIFFERENT

The star-nosed mole of northwestern North America looks somewhat different from its run-of-the-tunnel relatives. This odd-seeming creature gets its name from a fringed disk on its nose tip. This peculiar nose helps the animal to locate worms and insects, its chief food. Sometimes, in the cold winter months, we are afforded a fleeting view of the star-nosed mole when it emerges briefly from the tunnels which it has hollowed out in the snow.

The star-nosed mole is the most sociable of the moles; it lives in small colonies from Labrador to Manitoba, and south to Georgia. Breeding time comes in the late fall or early spring. During the mating season the animal's tail swells to at least twice its normal diameter. The first litter of young are born between the middle of February and May. There are from four to six babies in a family, and possibly a second litter is produced late in the summer. The baby moles are well-developed at birth, and at two months are out foraging for themselves.

The **Hairy-tailed Mole, or Brewer's Mole,** *Parascalops,* is quite different from other moles in that it inhabits upland wooded country. Most others favor low plains and meadowland. A little smaller than the eastern garden mole, this animal is black in color and has a short, well-haired tail.

For no obvious reason, the hairy-tailed mole frequently ventures on the surface of the ground and becomes an easy prey for hawks, owls, and other flesh-eaters. Not only is this mole practically blind like other moles, but it does not detect airborne sounds any better. However, it is very sensitive to sound variations in its own element, the earth. It digs its tunnels nearer the surface than do moles of the common garden variety. The passages follow along shady ridges and stone walls and are rarely marked by the usual unsightly molehills.

Hairy-tailed moles are scarce, and we know little about them. There is only one kind; its range is restricted to a strip in eastern North America from New Brunswick to southern Ontario and south in the Appalachian Mountains to North Carolina. A full-grown individual measures five inches from the nose to the tip of the one-inch tail. These animals are of little importance to man, either for good or for bad, since there are so few of them.

Flying Lemurs—Gliders of the Jungle

THE FLYING LEMUR, *Cynocephalus,* is a curious, exotic creature, found from the Malay Peninsula and Thailand to the Philippine Islands, Burma, and Java. Normally about the size of a large squirrel, it looks much bigger when it spreads the furry membranes, or sails, attached to its long limbs, and takes to the air.

In spite of its name, the flying lemur does not actually fly—it glides or volplanes. Usually the animal launches itself on its aerial expeditions from the top of a tall tree and glides evenly and smoothly forward to another one. Even when there is no breeze it can travel as much as seventy yards with little loss in altitude. With a breeze it can cover a surprisingly greater distance. Moving in for a landing, it steers toward the desired tree and comes softly to rest, head up.

So thoroughly is the flying lemur adapted for soaring, that it is at a disadvantage when it has to do other things. It cannot stand erect; it is practically helpless on the ground. It can climb, but only in a clumsy sort of way.

FLYING LEMURS

The flying lemur, about the size of a squirrel, is at home from the Philippines to Siam. It doesn't really fly—it glides, but can cover seventy yards or more in a single trip. Neither a squirrel nor a lemur, but a member of a family all its own, this odd-looking animal has a thin, furry flight membrane on either side of its body. The creature represents a transitional type—the first "birds" on earth were probably gliders like this one, before they acquired true wings. Seldom, if ever, does the flying lemur descend to the ground.

The colugo or caguan—that is what the natives call the flying lemur —is active solely by night. It passes the daylight hours sleeping. In a roosting position, it often hangs by its four feet, body down, like a sloth. Sometimes it may sleep wrapped around a branch; you may look directly at it and fail to see it, for it blends in perfectly with the bark of the tree.

The flying lemur is a slow breeder. As a rule it bears only one naked young each year, and it is not physically equipped to care for more than two. Like other animals that do not have a nest or a regular place to return to, the mother carries her baby wherever she goes. The baby clings to her breast in spread-eagle fashion as she journeys through the trees, feeding on fruits and leaves.

THE FLYING LEMUR'S STRANGE APPEARANCE

The flying lemur is extremely curious in appearance: it looks as though it were wearing a fur coat that reaches down to its toes. This is because on each side of its body the thin, furry flight membrane extends from the side of its neck to its thumb and between its fingers, down from its wrists to its ankles, and from the tip of its long outer toes to the end of its tail. When the animal is at rest, the membrane hangs in loose, voluminous folds. Covering its body is a coat of fine, soft fur that varies in color from grayish to chestnut, irregularly broken with silvery-white spots and blotches.

As we might expect in an animal that is strictly a night-prowler, the flying lemur's eyes are large and prominent. But they are hazel in color, which is rather surprising, as yellow pigment in the iris is usually for seeing in bright sunlight. The creature's four front teeth are unique among the mammals; each is compressed into a fine-toothed comb. Some say the animal uses them to brush its fur.

The flying lemur is not really one of the lemurs, although for many years scientists considered it a relative of those monkey-like creatures of Madagascar. Actually it is not closely linked to any other living mammal; it belongs in an order all its own, the Dermoptera ("skin wings"). There are only two living species.

The Bats

THE BATS we of the western world most often encounter have cunning pug faces and bright eyes—these little animals seem dreadful only to those who do not know their innocent habits. But there are other bats with enormous ears that fold like a concertina when not in use—bats with long, pointed faces—with flat faces—or with weird fleshy outgrowths on their muzzles. Some look fantastic, and a few can be described as hideous. No wonder superstitious people in all ages and lands have feared the bats and linked them with evil spirits.

There are bats with tails like mice; some have no tails at all. There are white bats, red bats, gray bats, piebald bats, black bats, and bats of many variations in color. On their feet some species have suction disks which they use for clinging to smooth surfaces. Bats come in such enormous variety that it is easier to say what they do not have than what they do have; there are no bats with actual trunks, quills, or shells.

The bats are built for flight. They are the only mammals that have real wings—wings not like the feathered pinions of a bird, but real wings nonetheless. Actually they are elastic membranes. Supported and spread by the bat's very long front limbs and fingers, these webs of skin extend all the way down to the animal's hind feet. (The bats' scientific name, order Chiroptera, means "winged arms," and in truth the wings are no more than modified forearms. The "thumb" is the only part of the hand that is the same as in other animals, and it bears a hooked claw.)

In most bats the membranes are also spread between the hind limbs and encase the tail, making it easier for the animal to float in the air. The bat's muscles and body structure are specially formed to support and operate the wings.

MYSTERY OF THE BATS' ORIGIN

These flying mammals have a very ancient lineage. In the dim ages of past geologic times, when the earth was tenanted by primitive land mammals such as the tiny four-toed horse, the bats were much as they are today. When they left the ground and took to the air, we cannot guess: there is a link missing between them and all other mammals. We know of no in-between types, no semi-fliers. Still, the flying lemurs and flying squirrels can travel a considerable distance in the air by gliding; they have no true wings, and are not capable of sustained flight. It may be that the first bats were gliders like these, and went on to develop into fliers.

WHERE WE FIND THE BATS

In the modern world we have found and named about two thousand different kinds of bats. Though certain kinds are restricted to certain regions, we encounter bats in all climates and countries from the Arctic to the Antarctic, except the polar regions. Those in the colder parts of the world are active only during the summer months—for the winter season they either hibernate or migrate to a warm climate.

BATS AND THEIR FOOD

In general, there are two main kinds of bats—insect-eaters and fruit-eaters. The latter favor the tropics, where, incidentally, bats exist in the greatest numbers and tend to grow larger. The insect-eaters are smaller than the fruit-eaters, as a rule, but there are more of them. In size, bats vary from the enormous flying foxes, with a wingspread of five feet, to tiny creatures no bigger than a hummingbird.

The diet of bats is not limited to fruit or insects. There are bats that eat meat, bats that go fishing, bats that draw the nectar from night-blooming flowers, and vampire bats that subsist on the blood they drain from the veins of birds and other animals. All, however, drink water regularly. They do not stop to lap it up like the cats and dogs, but skim the surface of the water like swallows and take their drinks in flight.

A NATURAL "RADAR" SYSTEM

Bats are supersensitive to sound waves. This capacity enables them to maneuver about in the dark as efficiently as a bird can in broad daylight. In fact, the bats already possessed a natural system of "radar" when man was still living in caves. In flight, a bat's mouth is open; it utters a continuous rhythm of sounds, pitched in a key too high for the human ear to recognize. These sound waves are thrown back to the bat by objects around it. By the use of its sensitive sound-perception ability, it can accurately determine its relation at all times to these objects, whether they be fixed or moving.

The author once had a striking experience with this ability when he disturbed a colony of several hundred bats in a small dark cave in the West Indies. All immediately took wing, swirling around in every direction, yet at no time were there any collisions. The orderliness of the seething, seemingly disorganized mass was incredible. Apparently each bat can recognize its own sounds, and not confuse them with those of its neighbors.

THE WEIRD NOSE LEAF

Certain bats have an outgrowth of skin and muscle on the muzzle and lips, generally referred to as a nose leaf. It varies in detail with different groups. Some entire families have only the slightest trace of a nose leaf, while on others it is long and lance-shaped, projecting straight up from the tip of the nose.

The use of the nose leaf is not yet well understood. Probably it acts as an antenna for the reception of air vibrations created by flying insects—it seems to be well developed in both fruit- and some insect-eating forms. Most bats also possess an extra spear-shaped flap growing in front of the ear opening. This flap, called a tragus, likewise helps the bat to detect sounds, we believe.

CREATURES OF THE NIGHT

Bats make no pretense of building any kind of nest. They usually have a regular place to roost, though—some dark or shady retreat such as a cave, a crevice in the rocks, a hollow tree, or just a shady tree, and they are not averse to taking advantage of human habitations as resting places. In tropical America there is a bat that actually makes its own shelter by scoring palm leaves, causing the sides to fold over and form a little tent. Bats sleep hanging head down, holding on with their feet.

Night is the time when bats are active. "Blind as a bat" is a meaningless phrase, however—contrary to popular belief, most bats can see perfectly well in bright light. The author has tried to catch one of the Kenya (African) species at noon as it clung to the bark of a great tree, but it scurried around the trunk in the sunlight, moving now slowly, now fast, and skillfully dodged every move made to capture it.

FAMILY LIFE AMONG THE BATS

Most bats are social. They live together in communities sometimes numbering as many as several hundred individuals. The peculiar thing about their social life is that normally the sexes do not intermingle in the communities. A colony of roosting bats is generally either all male or all female, although there are exceptions.

Most mammals go through some phase of courtship during the mating season, and among social animals a male will gather a harem of females. But not so with the bats. So far as we know, there is no segregation of mating pairs, no males collecting harems. There is free love among the bats—both sexes may have several mates.

Most bats mate only once a year. In tropical countries bats may mate in the early spring, but some pair off in August and September; these are the few that possibly breed twice a year. In temperate climates the mating season is in the fall, but the embryo does not develop until the spring.

BAT BABIES AND MOTHERS

The bat mother usually produces one baby at a time; a few species have twins and one or two of the migrating bats bear up to four babies. The members of the female colony bear their young at approximately the same time, about 110 days after mating.

Baby bats, though tiny, naked, and blind, are well-formed, with well-developed wings. The baby opens its eyes for the first time when it is five to nine days old. From the very first it gets a feeling of flight;

it is carried about by its mother wherever she goes for the first thirteen days or so. When she roosts upside down, it clings to her breast and she supports it with her wings.

The female bat is an affectionate mother. The care and tenderness she shows her baby are as great as any we see among the other mammals. One of the classic stories about a mother bat's love for her young was recorded in *American Natural History*, 1826. It concerns a boy who had caught a baby bat and taken it home with him. Later that evening he was carrying the bat in his hand, on his way to a museum, when he passed the place he had captured the tiny animal. Its mother made her appearance and flew round and round him. Finally she alighted on his breast and both the mother and baby were taken to the museum, the young clinging to its parent. There are many stories like this on record.

At the age of two weeks, the baby bat is often too big a burden for the mother to carry with her. Now it is old enough to be left hanging by itself. But often this period of confinement is short. Within a few days the young bat is on the wing, learning all the tricks and aerial maneuvers necessary to get its own living.

MOST BATS ARE USEFUL CREATURES

By and large, bats are useful creatures, and, for the most part, quite harmless. They do not habitually get into a person's hair, and they do not carry lice or bugs that might be troublesome to human beings. In the tropics some species wreak considerable havoc on fruit plantations, but most are insect-eaters and are of considerable economic importance in destroying mosquitoes and other insect pests.

Bats have a comparatively long life expectancy. Large fruit bats live about ten or twelve years, with a top age of twenty years or so. Some of the common Little Brown Bats are known to have lived twelve years and may have a maximum of fifteen years or more. They have few natural enemies; owls and hawks in particular prey on them.

BATS IN OUR FOLKLORE

Bats loom large in our folklore. They have a strange likeness to human beings which even primitive man noticed. Some of the ancients believed the bats were once a sort of bird; dissatisfied with their lot, they flocked to sacred places to pray to be made like man. In answer to their petitions, the bats underwent a change in part: they gained the faces of men but their bodies remained birdlike. Ashamed to meet the birds in daylight, they are abroad only at night. But they still gather in the sacred places, temples, and churches by day, and pray that they may be changed back into birds.

Among the Finnish people we encounter the belief that during sleep the soul often takes the form of a bat—hence the disappearance of bats by day. Should a bat fly near anyone, it is held to be the spirit of someone dear. According to a similar tradition, at death the soul usually takes the form of a bird and flies to heaven, but if the death was violent the soul becomes a bat and remains on the earth for such time as God may determine. The ancient Mayas of Central America worshiped a bat god whom they considered a most powerful deity, and in Mexico there was a city by the name of Tzinacent Lan— "Bat City."

BATS AROUND THE WORLD

We find eight families of bats peculiar to the Old World, six to the New World; three families are common to both hemispheres. Of the Old World bats, two families are represented by a single species— the Short-tailed Bat, *Mystacina,* one of the only two land mammals native to New Zealand (the other is also a bat); and the Sucker-footed Bat, *Myzopoda,* of Madagascar. They are both the sole survivors of ancient lines of bats that have found safety on these island refuges, but they are now reaching the verge of extinction.

The Old World fruit bats and flying foxes are the first group which will claim our attention here. This family (the Pteropidae) lives in the warmer regions of the earth and includes some genuine curiosities like the long-tongued fruit bats (the Dawn Bat is one of the best known), which use their extendible tongues to lick out the pulpy juices of ripe fruit or the nectar of flowers, and even have a lower jaw shaped like a spoon. Another oddity is the Tube-nosed Bat— this strange denizen of the South Pacific region gets its name from its peculiar breathing apparatus, fleshy tubes extending beyond its mouth.

In their tropical and subtropical home, the fruit-eating bats are a distinct bother to plantation owners.

OLD WORLD FRUIT BATS AND FLYING FOXES

The Dog-faced or Rousette Bat, *Rousettus,* is a fruit and berry feeder. When the fruit on one of a grove of trees is ripe, the dog-faced bats are there in hundreds, whirling and squabbling over the choicest fruit. Some they eat on the tree, especially if the fruit is small, but they may carry large pieces away to convenient hang-ups, to be consumed at leisure. At the zoological gardens at Giza, near Cairo, large numbers of these bats feeding in the fig trees are a common nighttime spectacle. Many are caught and eaten by barn owls.

In the daytime great numbers of these bats gather in the darkest corners of large caves, where they generally hang by both feet and spend much time in quarreling among themselves; they are extremely noisy in the early morning. When the colony is disturbed, the screeching is suddenly hushed; then, with a rush of wings, the entire assemblage takes flight and streams out of the cave, whirling round and round outside until the disturbance is over.

The dog-faced bat is a large, short-faced creature, dull brownish or grayish brown in color, with a wingspread of twelve to eighteen inches, and a short tail. Like most other bats, it has a claw on its index finger to hook onto a branch or cave wall when alighting. There are numerous species of dog-faced bats spread throughout Africa and the Indo-Australian region, including the Solomon Islands, but none dwells on the mainland of Australia.

In Africa the natives add dog-faced bats to their black boiling pots to help out their meager fare. Many of the natives have a particular cave that they visit regularly to keep their larder supplied with bats. However, they are reluctant to admit it, perhaps for reasons of a tabu.

The Flying Fox, *Pteropus,* is the biggest bat on earth. In flight, at close quarters, it presents an awe-inspiring appearance: it has a wingspread of two to five feet and its body may be twelve inches long. The animal is dark gray or black, with a bright yellow or tawny mantle marking its shoulders. It possesses a face like a fox's—the muzzle is long and slender.

The flying foxes love company, often associating together in great multitudes during the day, in giant trees in the forest or overhanging a river. Colonies of several hundred individuals may sometimes occupy a single tree. They have a well-marked roost, where the branches are marred by constant use; the upper limbs of the same trees may be used year after year for generations, until they become quite bare of foliage.

——FLYING FOXES ARE INDIVIDUALISTS. At sundown all the bats leave the roost and wing their way in search of ripening fruits and berries. Such a raiding party may steal a considerable amount of fruit from a plantation.

If the home roost is on a small island offshore, in the evening the entire colony flies in mass to the mainland before dispersing in search

THE BIGGEST BAT ON EARTH

The flying fox, largest of the bats, may have a wingspread of five feet; forbidding though the creature looks, it feeds mostly on fruit. The flying fox hunts by itself, and, although it roosts in colonies, each bat must have enough space so it does not touch its neighbors.

of food. But, though many may fly together in one direction, they do not travel in regular flock formation. Except when roosting, these bats are highly individualistic and pay scant attention to each other as they pursue their separate inclinations.

Returning to roost, each tries to get the most favorable position. There is much commotion and quarreling as newcomers fight for places already taken. It seems that the bats must be evenly spaced or have sufficient room so that they do not touch each other. The bickering continues into the day—it is a wonder that they get any sleep at all. Eventually most of them quiet down, hanging either by one or both feet with their heads bent down on their breasts and partly covered by the folded wings.

Flying foxes often supplement their fruit diet with small fish. The bats hover over the water and catch the fish in their feet. Then they make off to a nearby tree to devour the catch.

The social habits of these creatures vary with the seasons. From September to January both sexes flock together. When the mating season in February and March is over, the females leave the regular roost. The males stay on for a while, but they too soon seek other fields. In June the females, now heavy with young, return to the roost. There the single young is born in August or September—a few come earlier or later.

——WHERE WE FIND THEM. The flying fox is found in tropical Asia, eastern Australia, Madagascar, and the islands of the South Pacific, but not in China or Africa. Near the southern limits of their range, the flying foxes make regular seasonal migrations, moving north or south in large bodies. There are also local migrations governed by ripening fruits.

The flying fox has no tail. Like this animal in general appearance, except that it does possess a tail, is the Bare-backed Fruit Bat of the Celebes and Queensland. It is also known as the Spinal-winged Bat because the wing membranes are attached along the middle of its back (incidentally making the back look bare).

The Hammer-headed Bat, *Hypsignathus,* is Africa's largest bat; it has a head and body length of ten and one-half inches and a wing-spread of forty. The head, with its swollen face and pendulous upper lip, appears to be cut off short. Grotesque ruffles of skin surround the warty snout and the split lower lip.

——A POWERFUL VOICE. The hammer-heads dwell in large flocks in the forest. At sunset the whole colony takes off, not in a flash but as individuals. On entering the trees, the males start to utter resounding calls, each repeating the sound at intervals of half a second, until midnight. To produce this call, they have an enormous bony larynx, or sound box, that fills one-third of the body cavity and crowds the heart and lungs backward and sideward.

In no other mammal is every other organ so entirely subordinated to the voice. Females are normally constructed, and have little or no vocal power.

The specialized means of communication of the male hammer-head is interesting and must have some significance. Since it is peculiar to the males, it could be for the purpose of attracting females. But, on the other hand, the males frequently gather in one particular place for their choruses.

Like other social species, the hammer-headed bat might be expected to breed at one season of the year, but females have been found with a single young in May as well as December, suggesting that they do not have a fixed breeding season. The mother carries her young until it is about one-third grown.

——CLASS DISTINCTIONS AMONG THE HAMMER-HEADS. This bat seems to observe some sort of class distinction. As usual, the adult males congregate in one roost and the females in another. But the immature males and females may associate together, forming a third group, separate from the adults. When hanging at rest, the hammer-headed bat folds its wings over its abdomen and breast and makes a rainproof cover for the body.

The hammer-headed bat is a fruit-eater. It feeds on ripe guavas, mangoes, figs, and other fruits in season. After picking the fruit, it carries it to a convenient perch to hang from. Here the animal munches away at leisure, spilling all but the soft pulp on the forest floor.

The Yellow-haired Fruit Bat, *Eidolon,* a native of Africa's tropical forests, has a wingspread of thirty inches, a small free tail, and a pointed head like the flying fox's. Its soiled yellowish coat has a sunburst of orange-tawny hair on the front of the neck.

——A NOMAD RACE. The yellow-haired fruit bat is a nomad race and moves in mass from one region to another where the fruit is ripe— instinctively it knows when and where to go. During migration, flocks estimated at one thousand to fifteen hundred have been seen in flight. In search of food, these bats will climb freely among the branches of trees. They can assimilate only the soluble juices contained in ripened fruits, and do not seem to take any solid food; seeds and fleshy pulp are rejected.

For an interesting picture of how these bats behave we may turn to the field notebook of Herbert Lang and James Chapin, who wrote: "At Avakubi, November 19, 1909, a flock of perhaps one hundred had taken shelter for the day beneath the limb of a large tree, some sixty feet above the ground, where they were shaded by a mass of epiphytic ferns and orchids, and formed one great squirming mass. Ever and again one seemed to lose its hold in the crowd, took wing and hooked itself up anew. All the while they kept up a chorus of snarling and scolding noises that could be heard a hundred yards away."

This animal is eaten by the African natives, who are adept at capturing or killing it. In the markets at Leopoldville, in the Belgian Congo, you can see large numbers of yellow-haired fruit bats on sale, tied together in bunches, dead or alive.

SAC-WINGED BATS, SHEATH-TAILED BATS, AND TOMB BATS—TROPICAL INSECT-EATERS

These bats are a family of insect-eaters. Creatures of the tropics, they dwell in the Old World as well as the New. In general they are small, slender animals with long, slim leg bones. In most other families the wing membrane between the hind legs encloses the tail, but these bats have the tip of the tail free.

The sac-winged bats of tropical America are peculiar in that they have a large pouch or gland in the wing membrane; it is present in both sexes, but more conspicuous in the males. By a muscular action the bat can open or close its pouch. When it is open, an odor escapes from the gland. This odor is most apparent during the breeding season and no doubt is helpful in attracting the opposite sex. It also suggests a well-developed sense of smell in these bats.

The Sheath-tailed Bat, *Emballonura,* for which the entire group was named (family Emballonuridae), has no special peculiarities. Its face is furred, typical, and without a nose leaf. Plentiful in southern Asia, the South Pacific, and Madagascar, it frequents forested country, and roosts by day in small groups, clinging to palm trees.

The Black Tomb Bat, *Saccolaimus peli,* roosts in a hollow tree or an old tomb. The largest insect-eating bat of the African continent, it has a wingspread of twenty-seven inches that dwarfs the head and body of six inches. When not in flight, it not only folds its wings like an umbrella but turns them back in a curious manner. Now, with the wings shortened to nearly half their length, the animal can climb about with considerable ease.

In the air, this creature is one of the most skillful of its kind. It is able to shorten or lengthen the membrane between its hind legs like a sail, so that it enjoys a high degree of control over its movements as it flies along. Indeed, the insect-eating bats as a group are the best fliers of all the bats.

Shortly after nightfall a dozen or more black tomb bats may be seen traveling at a height of about thirty feet or more toward their feeding grounds, usually the open spaces about human habitations. Like the falcon, they make rapid swoops at their prey. In half an hour they have eaten all the insects that they can consume, and retreat to their roost. They are out again a few hours later to continue the feast. This bat, by the way, never enters occupied human dwellings.

——A NOISY FELLOW. The black tomb bat is a very noisy fellow. Rarely does it fly without exercising its vocal powers to some extent. The sounds it produces are particularly noticeable when it is wounded and lying on the ground. Then it will make a squeaking cry which attracts others of its kind. They come swooping down to within a foot of the ground, circling round and round, all uttering the same shrill sound.

The tomb bat may breed twice a year: females have been found with young in June and December. It dwells from the Gold Coast and the Cameroons to East Africa, with several species in South Asia, Africa, and Australia.

The Ghost or White Bat, *Diclidurus,* found roosting between the leaves of coconut palms and canes in tropical America from Guatemala to Brazil, presents a curious commentary on the value of camouflage. A medium-sized bat—about three inches in length—it is covered with snow-white fur, to which it owes its name.

There is nothing remarkable about animals being so colored in countries where snow lies on the ground for long periods, nor is a white coat a great handicap to animals that live in total darkness underground—but a pure-white animal that flies in the semidarkness of the tropical night, as this one does, is a most conspicuous target for its night-flying enemies.

BULLDOG BATS—NIGHTTIME FISHERMEN

The Bulldog Bat, *Noctilio,* of tropical America and the West Indies, is better known as the Fish-eating Bat, though it is also an insect-eater. A comparatively large, tawny creature (about the size of a starling) with a light stripe down its back, it has a face like a bulldog: its powerful jaws are armed with formidable teeth, its ears are tall and erect. It is a strong, fast flier, with long wings.

The bulldog bat will often choose a roost on a small, uninhabited island—as a precautionary measure, no doubt—and fly to the mainland to hunt. Caves and hollow trees are its favorite roosting places. Usually we can detect the roost from a distance as great as one hundred yards: it has a strong, unpleasant smell. Still, the colonies are not large. For example, in a cave on Puerto Rico the author found just five bulldog bats hanging from the roof.

These bats, like most others in the tropics, leave their roost shortly after sunset and troop over the sea by twos and threes, or more. They soon have gorged themselves on insects; after a drink of fresh water they return to the roost for a while to digest their food. Then they go out hunting again. In the dark you may hear their teeth crunching on crisp, horny-covered beetles.

——A Close-up View of the Bulldogs. Dr. G. H. Kingsley, brother of Charles Kingsley the novelist, visited Trinidad and watched some members of this bat family (Noctilionidae, or "night bats"). He wrote:

"They came out in the gloaming and fluttered and splashed and somehow or other caught tiny fish. I floated about many an evening to see how it was done; but though I was close to them—close enough to be nauseated by their detestable scent—I could never quite make up my mind on the subject. On the whole, I was inclined to accept the native idea that they scoop them off the surface with the inter-femoral membrane [the flying membrane stretched between the hind limbs].

"However it was done, they certainly did catch fish, and eat them; for I found fish scales and bones in their stomachs and had micro-scopical slides prepared to prove it."

The author has personally verified Dr. Kingsley's findings—also the fact that the bad odor of these bats is noticeable only when they have been feeding on fish. One bat the author captured left a smell on his hands that was more nauseating than that of a skunk and lasted for days; this creature had been feeding on fish. Thirteen others, caught on St. Thomas, had not even a suggestion of an unpleasant odor; these had been on an insect diet. It was also interesting to see how some bats, knocked into the water, swam with remarkable ease and managed to get into the air again.

HOLLOW-FACED BATS AND FALSE VAMPIRES

We find the hollow-faced bats in Africa and Malaya. On the face these incredible-looking creatures have a deep groove that literally splits it. (They are sometimes called "slit-faced bats.") The nostrils open into this groove. On the tip of the nose they have an erect arrow-head of skin, the nose leaf. Their ears are large, their eyes minute. Their bodies are only about two or three inches in length—comparatively small for bats—and covered with long, soft brownish or grayish brown fur. Encased in the membrane between the hind legs there is a long tail. (One genus, *Nycteris,* makes up the family Nycteridae.)

In contrast, the false vampires are large bats. They have a well-developed nose leaf and big ears that are joined together over the top of the head; they have no tail. Because of their size and certain other traits they have been connected with the genuine vampires, and hence their name. The tragus, the peculiar fleshy outgrowth projecting upward in front of the ear opening (a prominent characteristic of most bats), is forked in the false vampire.

Flesh-eating Bats. The false vampires dwell in tropical Africa, Asia, the East Indies, and Australia. A leading member of the family (Megadermatidae), the Carnivorous Bat makes its home throughout southern Asia and Malaya. Larger than the average, it has a head and body length of about three and one-half inches. It is actually carnivorous and cannibalistic in its habits of feeding on other bats, small rodents, frogs, and fish as well as insects. It is noteworthy that both sexes live together the year round with the young.

Another flesh-eater is the Lyrate False Vampire, a grayish-brown bat of India and southern China, about the size of the carnivorous bat. It kills and eats birds and other bats smaller than itself, and has been accused of sucking blood from human beings but we have no positive proof of this.

The Yellow-winged Bat, *Lavia,* fantastic yet strangely beautiful, haunts the forests of tropical Africa. Curious and unusual tints of orange, yellow, green, and brown are spread harmoniously over the enormous ears that tower above the head with its tall, spear-pointed nose leaf. Out of each ear comes a long, slender projection shaped like a finely tapered dagger—the tragus. Mixed shades of orange, yellow, and green, splashed over the broad wings and flying membranes, are also in brilliant contrast to the modest slate-gray of the long-haired body.

A fair-sized bat, *Lavia* measures a little over three inches in length and has a wingspread of fifteen inches. However, because it lacks a tail, it appears small. It favors an outdoor life and roosts in the warm sun, hanging from the open branches of a thorn bush. Sometimes it is active by day—more so than most bats—and indeed it seems wide awake at all hours of the day as well as the night. It does not wait until dark to feed but forages for food before the sun has set.

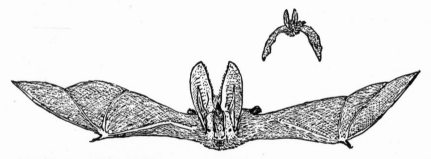

A BAT THAT LIKES FRESH AIR
The yellow-winged bat has enormous ears and broad wings beautifully shaded in hues of orange, yellow, green and brown. This creature is sometimes seen abroad by day, and will roost in the open. It does not eat while in flight, but consumes its insect victims on some convenient perch. Note the tragus in each ear—it is part of the bat's "radar."

This bat eats relatively large insects. Theodore Roosevelt was greatly interested in it, and writes of its feeding habits:

"In catching insects it behaved not like a swallow but like a flycatcher, except that it perched upside down. Each bat hung from its twig until it spied a passing insect, when it swooped down upon it and after a short flight returned with its booty to the same perch."

In its habit of not feeding on the wing, this animal is different from most insect-eaters.

Like other bats, the mother yellow-winged bat carries her baby during flight. She will continue to carry it until it is able to fly alone or is almost as large as she is. Then she leaves it hanging when she goes off. On her return the baby quickly scrambles to its accustomed place on her breast to nurse. If anything frightens the mother, her precious young is never too heavy for her to carry away from danger.

HORSESHOE BATS AND CYCLOPS BATS

Most of us would find it hard to tell these two families of Old World bats apart, so much alike are they in appearance. They are close relatives, too.

The horseshoe bat gets its name from its large nose leaf—it is not pointed, but shaped like a horseshoe or a tombstone, with the nostrils in the center. Above and behind the horseshoe there are folds of skin, probably used by the animal to receive air vibrations and guide itself about.

Some of the horseshoe bats are tiny creatures, little more than an inch long (head and body); the giants of the family (Rhinolophidae, a term meaning "nose crest") are over three inches in length. Most are brownish or reddish in color and all have large, pointed ears and moderately long tails. They live in both temperate and hotter regions, a large number of different kinds being found in Europe, Asia, Africa, and Australia.

The second family, the Cyclops bats (sometimes also called horseshoe bats—the family name, Hipposideridae, means "horseshoe"), range throughout the warmer regions of the Old World. They have horseshoe-shaped nose leaves, too, and in general differ little from the bats of the first family in color.

The bats of both these groups are for the most part cave-dwellers. But they will take up residence in the dark attic of an abandoned house or in old castles, where they hang from the roof or walls. In India one species is known to frequent the burrows of the crested porcupine. Some of these bats are solitary and roost either singly or in pairs, while others are extremely sociable, congregating in colonies of several hundred individuals.

SKILLFUL FLIERS AND HUNTERS

The horseshoe bat is a late flier, and does not leave its roost until some time after sunset. It hunts thirty to forty feet above the ground.

In flight it exhibits unusual grace and power, often arresting the motion of its wings and sailing along thirty or forty feet like a sea gull. It is remarkable in that it recognizes glass as a barrier, and will not try to fly through a closed window. When alighting, it does a rapid somersault in the air and comes to rest hanging by its hind feet.

——Horseshoe Bats of the Himalayas. This bat, like others, is a skillful hunter. In Asia there is a large horseshoe bat that is especially partial to a giant cicada or harvest fly which is abundant in the forests of the Himalayas. As the sun sets, this insect pours forth an almost deafening, discordant song. The horseshoe bat, apparently attracted by the sound, whirls around the trees, scanning each leaf until, detecting one of the unfortunate minstrels, it snatches it still screaming from its lofty perch.

HOW BATS SLEEP THROUGH THE WINTER

The horseshoe bat, *Rhinolophus ferrum-equinum,* of Europe, one of the largest species, roosts in caves the year round but goes deeper into them, below frost line, in winter. Here it will hibernate, often from October to March or April.

While the bat is active in summer, its normal body temperature is as high as 104 degrees; when the animal roosts for the winter, its temperature drops to that of the surrounding air.

The bat becomes torpid when its body temperature goes down to 50 degrees, and a low of 42 degrees is possible. But when its blood warmth sinks much below this, as in an unusually cold season, the danger point is reached; at 30 degrees the bat will die.

As the bat enjoys its long winter nap, its breathing slows down. It will take only about ten breaths an hour now. Sometimes it does not breathe at all for as long as eight minutes.

As spring approaches, the air becomes warmer and the bat's temperature begins to rise. Gradually its breathing speeds up until, at two hundred respirations a minute, the animal is ready to take wing.

AMERICA'S NOSE-LEAF BATS AND LEAF-LIPPED BATS

Perhaps we should name this family the American bats, as we find them only in the warmer parts of America—North, South, and Central. They are an impressively large group, with an unbelievable va-

riety of strange and contrasting creatures, among them a Ghost Bat
and a White Bat. In size they range from the Great False Vampire,
with a wingspread of thirty inches, massive jaws, and powerful teeth,
to tiny, long-tongued bats with teeth so minute that they could not
crush a beetle.

Many of these creatures have large ears, but the ears are by no means
their most striking feature: almost all the bats in this family (Phyl-
lostomatidae—"leafy mouth") possess a big nose leaf or else, as in
the case of the leaf-lipped bats, an extensive leafy outgrowth on the
lips, giving them a most hideous expression. These growths, we have
observed, probably keep the animals informed of air currents and
enable them to find their way about, not only in dark caves but in
the open air as well.

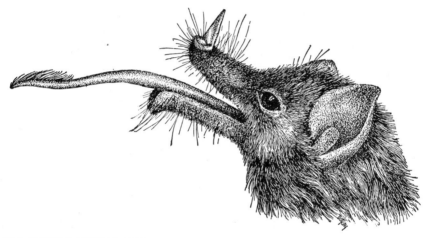

THE NECTAR-LOVING BAT
The Mexican long-nosed bat is one of the most interesting and bizarre members of the
entire bat order. Its very long muzzle ends in a short nose leaf. The animal has rounded
ears, minute teeth, and a long tongue. This tongue can dip deeply into the flower of the
night-blooming cacti, which furnishes nectar for the bat to consume.

The Long-eared Bat has carried the development of the nose leaf
to the extreme. The animal itself is only two inches in length and its
big ears one inch, but the lance-shaped nose leaf is as long as the ears
and head combined.

Most of these American bats are fruit-eaters but some feed on insects, and some on the pollen and nectar of flowers. They may have
long, extendible tongues specially adapted for lapping up the juices

of ripe fruit or lancing into the heart of a bloom. A number will eat flesh—the two giants of the group are noteworthy for this habit.

America's Biggest Bats. The Javelin Bat, *Phyllostomus,* and the Great False Vampire Bat, *Vampyrum,* are the two largest bats in America. The larger of the two, the great false vampire, has a wingspread of thirty inches, as we have seen, and a head and body of five or six. Both animals are blackish in color. Their homeland stretches from Mexico to the Amazon region in South America.

——A Hideous-looking Animal. The great false vampire, now known to be harmless, was formerly thought to be a blood-sucker; that is how the name "vampire" came to be applied to it. Its great size and repulsive appearance no doubt added strength to this error. This diabolical-looking animal has been aptly described by the naturalist Bates, who visited the Amazon many years ago:

"Nothing in animal physiognomy can be more hideous than the countenance of this creature when viewed from the front, the large leathery wings, the large leathery ears standing out from the sides and top of the head, the erect spear-shaped appendage on the tip of the nose, the grin, and the glistening black eyes all combining to make up a figure that reminds one of some mocking imp of fable."

Strangely enough, Bates found that a church was the local headquarters of these bats and adds: "I used to see them as I sat at my door during the short evening twilights, trooping forth by scores from a large open window at the back of the altar, twittering cheerfully as they sped off to the borders of the forest."

The javelin bat, like the false vampire, is a large and sturdy animal with powerful jaws and strong teeth. Its staple food is ripe fruit, but it will kill and eat small birds, mice, frogs, and bats, devouring the entire animal and grinding up the bones with its massive jaws. It never molests human beings.

——A Visit with the Javelin Bats. The javelin bats, too, have been observed at close quarters. The naturalist Goldman tells us of a visit he paid them in Panama: "In one of the Chilibullo caves, near Alhajuela, I found thousands suspended from various parts of the vaulted roof in the total darkness of the principal chamber. More than one hundred were seen in a single spot over which they were so densely massed that their bodies seemed to be touching.

"There was much loud squeaking, but I was allowed to approach within twelve or fifteen feet, when they vacated the place almost in a body. In flying through the resounding passages of the caves, the noise of their wings resembled the thunderous roar of a waterfall when heard at a distance."

The Leaf-chinned Bat, *Mormoops,* of the warmer regions of the Americas, is a fantastic-looking animal. The extremely developed skin growths on the lips are almost impossible to describe. Tiny, sparkling eyes peer out from the weird mass of contours, folds, and papillae that surround the small mouth and nostrils and block out the rest of the face. Large, rounded ears with intricate accessory folds that bonnet the face give the impression of an open flower rather than the head of an animal.

Like other leaf-lipped bats, this one has a large tail encased for most of its length in the flight membrane between its hind limbs. The animal, though, is comparatively small, with a tawny-olive head and body about two and one-half inches long.

——LOVERS OF HEAT AND DARKNESS. Surprisingly little is known about the habits of this creature. It favors dark, warm caverns near the surface, where the tropical sun raises the temperature to an uncomfortable degree.

On Mona Island, off Puerto Rico, the author, flashlight in hand, followed one of the long, winding passages of a cave that began at the foot of a cliff. The air became more and more humid and stagnant as the passage wound its way upward, deeper into the cliff. Eventually it led into an open chamber just below the surface of the ground. The heat in here was intense.

Hanging in pitch darkness from the high roof of this chamber were half a dozen leaf-chinned bats. They objected to the beam of the author's flashlight and quickly flew to darker corners. Unless there was another entrance, the animals had to fly underground at least half a mile to get out.

This bat must have a keen sense of time because each night, at exactly the same time, just after the sun had set and as the tropical night was closing in, they came winging out of the cave entrance one after the other.

The Flat-faced Fruit Bat, *Artibeus,* is the common fruit bat of Middle America, the West Indies, and northern South America. A medium-sized, robust creature, it feeds on all kinds of ripe fruit in season, a habit that does not endear it to fruit growers.

Almost any kind of a retreat will suit the flat-faced fruit bat, so long as it is shaded from the bright sunlight. Colonies will roost in caves, empty water cisterns, abandoned houses, and hollow trees. The author has seen them clustered in tall trees like a swarm of bees; here they cling together in a ball suspended from the topmost branches, each trying to hide its head in the compact mass. They certainly are not such lovers of darkness as most of the family.

Still, these creatures are very much at home where the light never comes. Encountered in their black caverns, bats do not turn out to be quite the demons of the dark that writers of fiction would have you believe. On the contrary, they will treat a visitor with respect, as this personal experience shows.

——FRUIT BATS AT HOME. On St. John's Island, American Virgin Islands, the author crawled through an opening into a large dark cave at the edge of the sea. (At high tide the opening was under water.) Inside the cave, on the vaulted roof, were hundreds, probably thousands, of these fruit bats. The entire ceiling was a black, swaying mass above his head. There was a low, rumbling sound that can best be described as the shuffle of an innumerable host of miniature umbrellas.

The roof was too high for a close view. To get some action, the writer fired a pistol. At once it seemed as if the entire roof pitched downward in one black mass, and then came to life in a thousand whirling forms churning about him in all directions. The fluttering of those leathery wings as they billowed past the author's head was like the wind in the treetops before a tropical storm.

Though the air was thick with bats there was no disorder. They never collided with one another and with the exception of a slight touch from the tips of their wings, did not annoy the unwelcome intruder in the least. One even hung up on the rim of his hat.

The Little Fruit Bat, *Artibeus watsoni,* and the Yellow-eared Bat, *Uroderma,* are perhaps the only bats that attempt to build a house or den. These ingenious animals cut the ribs of a palm leaf so that the fronds bend over at a sharp angle to form a tent as a shelter from the sun, rain, and flesh-eaters on the prowl. It is done with genuine engineering ability.

VAMPIRES—BATS THAT DRINK BLOOD

Vampires are no myth. They are bats that feed on the warm blood drained from the veins of living creatures, including man. Their teeth are especially adapted for cutting through skin; their stomachs are modified to digest blood in particular. They are not known to eat anything but blood.

Charles Darwin, it is generally supposed, was the first European to discover the vampire bat's bloody habits. Actually, a Spanish naturalist, Felix de Azara, had already studied the animal in Paraguay, in 1802. But long before the day of either of these gentlemen, tales of blood-sucking vampires were current in Europe. These were said to be corpses that rose from their graves at night and drank blood to renew their vitality.

THE BAT OF LEGEND

The true vampire bat is a creature of the tropics, and makes its home from Mexico south to Brazil. It lives on nothing but blood, and man is one of its victims. Its razor-sharp teeth are especially adapted for slicing through blood vessels. The animal is not a danger because of the small amount of blood it drinks, but because of the germs it may leave in the tiny wound it makes. On occasion, a dangerous case of rabies may be the result.

Bats and other eerie creatures were associated with the deeds of the living dead, and it was natural that the name "vampire" should be transferred to the tropical blood-drinking bats, the Desmodontidae, when they became known. In obscure corners of the Balkans, a belief in human vampires still lingers on.

The True Vampire, *Desmodus,* is encountered from Mexico to Brazil. Despite its evil reputation, it is not a fearful-looking creature. Barely over three inches long, its body is covered with drab gray or brownish short, close hair. It has no nose leaf, the feature that makes some bats seem frightening to us, and its ears are low and pointed.

The true vampire lives in colonies of perhaps a dozen or more, roosting in fissures and cracks in the walls of caves. It can run along vertical walls with its long legs, and dart into crevices with remarkable speed. With its wings folded, it walks like a four-footed animal or hops like a frog.

——An Expert Surgeon. The bite of the vampire is almost painless; in fact, literally it does not bite. Its back teeth are undeveloped, but the animal has razor-sharp front teeth, which it uses to slit a vein of the victim. So deftly and cleanly does this expert surgeon make its incision that it would not waken even a light sleeper.

On occasion, vampires have been seen hovering over an intended victim so that they appeared to be fanning a particular spot prior to the "operation." Some people would have us believe that the cool air stirred up by the bats' wings helps to make the incision painless.

——The Danger of Disease. The bat stands on its victim as it drinks. A vampire does not suck the blood but laps it up with the tongue as it flows from the wound. The victim suffers no discomfort, and the wound heals readily. What is worse than unpleasant, however, is the fact that the little vampire transmits germ diseases, such as rabies. Horses, cattle, and human beings have suffered seriously because of the activities of the vampires.

Fortunately, these bats are not a big family. All told, there are only three species. By and large, the vast bat order is often of great service to us in the enormous work of insect control.

TRUE INSECT-EATING OR COMMON BATS

Most of the bats you see flying on a summer's evening along country roads and village greens are the true insect-eating or common bats. They are really quite attractive, and charming in their ways, once you get to know them. None is very large—some are extremely small. The common bat's tiny face, with its sparkling little eyes and snub nose, is covered with the finest fur. The teeth are too tiny to puncture even the skin of a child. Consuming insects in vast quantities, these creatures help make the earth a safer place for man to live.

The common bats dwell throughout the world but favor temperate latitudes in particular. Over much of their range they are at the mercy of drastic changes in climate; when the weather turns cold, too, the flying insects they feed on disappear. Under these circumstances, some provision must be made to survive, and so a number of the common bats hibernate, retreating to underground caverns below frost line to sleep away the months of famine. Others journey south with the swallows in the fall and spend the winter in a warm, sunny climate.

NATURE'S OWN RADARMAN
Long before man invented radar, the bat had a perfect system of its own. It is super-sensitive to sound waves, and the sounds it utters in flight, thrown back to the bat by the objects around it, give it a very good idea of its surroundings in the dark. The delicately formed little bat shown is the butterfly bat. This creature is noteworthy because its artistic wing tracings and exquisite color tints fade quickly after it dies.

A Resourceful Bat. Of special interest is the resourceful way the Silver-haired Bat, one of the few migrators in North America, may combine both these habits. Though more or less solitary during the summer, in the fall it congregates in flocks, often numbering thousands, and makes its trip to the southland. But occasionally winter overtakes one of these little creatures before it has left its northern home; forced to break with custom, the bat selects a comfortable hollow tree or similar roost and falls asleep till spring.

"UNCOMMON" COMMON BATS

A Bat Like a Butterfly. There are many other oddities among the common bats. Some members of the group are distinctly uncommon, like the Butterfly Bat, a delicately formed animal with artistic tracings on its wings. They are exquisitely tinted with color when the bat is alive, but when it dies they quickly fade.

The Jackass Bat. Another "uncommon" common bat is the Jackass Bat of the southwestern United States. Although all of its family possess prominent ears, this one has outclassed the rest in headdress. Its tiny face is surmounted with ears so gigantic that the proportions of a rabbit's ears to its head seem almost normal by comparison. The black livery of this fantastic creature is splashed with large blotches of white that bear a strong and startling resemblance to a death's head.

Smallest of all Bats. We have said the common bats are not large. As a matter of fact, what is perhaps the smallest of all bats belongs in this family—the Little Bamboo Bat, of southeastern Asia. This reddish-brown creature is no more than one and three-eighths inches long—it is so small that it can crawl into a mere crack in a bamboo stem to roost. Apparently built to live amid bamboo, it has a flattened skull that enables it to use such a narrow entrance, and, on its thumbs and feet, adhesive disks to cling to smooth surfaces.

Admittedly, these animals are curiosities—they are by no means the most familiar of the common bats. The "common" common bats are the Pipistrelle, the Little Brown Bat, the Red Bat, the Long-eared Bat, and the Hoary Bat; we shall come to their interesting ways in a moment. We often call the common bats "vespertilionids," for they belong to the family Vespertilionidae (a name connected with our word "vesper"). They lack the nose growths that make some other families so nightmarish a sight, but they do show quite a bit of variety in their appearance as well as their habits.

"COMMON" COMMON BATS

The Little Brown Bat, or Mouse-eared Bat, *Myotis,* is the common bat of North America. On that continent, when you glimpse a small bat on the wing, the chances are that it is a little brown bat. This animal lives as far south as Mexico and as far north as trees will grow.

Do not suppose, however, that all little brown bats are the same or that they live only in North America. There are about eighty different kinds, and we encounter them in almost every part of the globe. Most are small—about two inches long, with a shorter tail. They are dainty animals, usually dark brown in color, with a medium-sized ear about as long as the head. All are furred except for the wings and feet. Several larger species are found in southern Asia and the islands of the South Pacific; some are bright orange or reddish with black wings.

Despite its size, the little brown bat has probably frightened more people than any other species for the simple reason that it is common around human habitations. It is the bat you are likely to find flying about your head when you are walking in the country. There is no reason to be disturbed—it is picking off the mosquitoes that are trailing you. It is extremely sociable and has little fear of man.

——A Good Sense of Time. The little brown bat sometimes roosts in the eaves of a house in the country, in caves, hollow trees, rocks, and crevices. As many as thirty or forty may crawl into one tiny crevice and settle there.

Just after sundown they begin to pour out. At waking time they start to shuffle around and squeak as if impatient for the right moment to come so they can leave their stuffy quarters and soar in the clean air. They are very exact about time in this respect, though it may take fifteen or twenty minutes for the colony to get on the wing. Their departure coincides with just about the instant the last chimney swift has gone to roost. In full flight, they are interesting to watch. They can suddenly turn at right angles in any direction, and have much greater agility than most birds.

The little brown bats are not so precise about the time they retreat in the morning—some stay out until broad daylight. All have a well-developed homing instinct. Marked specimens have found their way back to the home roost over a distance of seventy miles in six nights. Others, released 180 miles away, also eventually found their way back.

——The Hungry Little Brown Bat. This little creature has a big appetite. Within an hour after leaving its roost it will devour a quarter of its weight in insects—half its weight during the night!

The little brown bat eats its food on the wing; sometimes on a still night, one can hear its tiny teeth crunching a beetle or clicking away as the animal attempts to capture a moth. When the prey is large, it is carried to a nearby roost to be eaten.

In some localities bats devour enormous quantities of insects. Those in the Carlsbad Caverns of New Mexico—their number is sometimes estimated in the millions—consume several tons of insects a night. The droppings of these bats (guano) are considered an excellent fertilizer.

——A LIGHT SLEEPER. On an average, a little brown bat spends almost half its life hanging from the roof of some cave. It is a winter sleeper, hibernating in a cave below frost line. When the temperature drops to 40 degrees above zero, the bat falls into a lethargy. Its sleep is not so very profound—the bat breathes at five-minute intervals, and colonies sometimes move their positions during the winter.

——MATING AND MOTHERHOOD. This bat's mating season is generally the late fall. Females usually have one young at a time, but the baby is slow in coming. During the winter sleep of the mother-to-be, the development of the embryo is completely suspended. In May or June, after the female has awakened, her offspring finally arrives. It is small, naked, and blind, and about one-third her size.

The mother is devoted to her baby, and bestows on it a considerable amount of affection for the short while it must depend on her. In two weeks, however, the young bat is half-grown and now she leaves it on the roost. At three weeks of age it is learning to fly and feed itself.

In general, the little brown bat has few enemies, and knows how to cope with most of them. The average individual may live to a ripe old age of ten or twelve years.

Much like this bat in its habits is the Big Brown Bat, or Serotine, *Eptesicus*—big only in comparison to the little brown bat. It is a fastidious creature, and spends considerable time cleaning and combing its fur, once it has appeased its hunger.

The Fish-eating Bat, *Pizonyx,* is the champion of bat fishermen. Much has been written about the bulldog bat and the flying fox because of their fondness for fishing, but *Pizonyx* is a better angler by far. Another surprising thing about it is the limited area it has chosen for its home: the animal is rather common over a radius of a hundred miles or so on the Gulf of California, but you will look in vain for it elsewhere. It has never strayed farther afield either to the north, south, or east.

Lewis Walker, the California bird expert, has provided us with much of our basic information about the fish-eating bat and its habits. On a visit to the island of Pescadora in the Gulf, he saw what he at first thought were petrels flying just above the surface of the water. After watching their erratic flight for a while, he perceived his mistake. These were not birds but brownish bats with a sixteen-inch wingspread (they are some three inches long, with a tail almost the same length) and they were catching fish. As the daylight faded, the bats became bolder. They rose from the water, headed for the cliffs on the island, and passed close by him, uttering high-pitched squeaks.

A BAT THAT FISHES

The best angler of the bat tribe is the fish-eating bat. In flight it resembles the petrel, close to which it sometimes roosts. Its victims literally seem eager to surrender to this bat; as it passes over the water, the fish surface, jump into the air, and are caught.

For an hour Walker watched the bats fishing but he could not determine exactly how they did it. Sometimes as a bat skimmed the surface, leaving a ripple in the form of a V, there would be a slight agitation ahead and a small crustacean or fish jumped out of the water and was caught by the flier. Perhaps the white underparts of the bat, reflected in the water, somehow stampeded the schools of these tiny creatures into breaking the surface and leaping into the air.

——A STRANGE ASSOCIATION. On Cardonosa Island, Walker observed this bat by the thousands roosting in rock slides, caves, and even in old turtle shells. There, from May to June, you will find a strange association of animal mothers—the Least Petrel brooding on a single white egg and, only a few inches away, the fish-eating bat nursing an only child. In the evening, like other bats, she leaves her baby to go in search of food—the small fish in the warm waters of the Gulf.

The babies appear to grow very rapidly. When Walker visited the islands in April, he found no evidence that the females were carrying young. A month later some of the babies were almost as large as the adults. The largest of the young were seen clinging by their hind feet to the roof and walls of a cave, beating their wings vigorously in the air as they learned to fly.

The Pipistrelle or Flittermouse, *Pipistrellus,* has had an opera named for it—*Die Fledermaus* ("The Flittermouse"), by Strauss. This small creature is famous for its habit of dancing aerial ballets; it continually twists and whirls in its flight.

Like the little brown bat, which it fairly closely resembles, the pipistrelle lives in colonies concealed in caves or hollow trees or barns. By day the Old World species of pipistrelles roost in companies of half a dozen to a dozen or more. They do not hang up like most bats, but cling to the walls with feet and wing claws, usually head downward.

The pipistrelle is on the wing early in the evening, leaving its retreat at about the time the sun dips below the hills. It does not fly high or fast, and its flight, as we have seen, is very erratic. As it twists and turns, it keeps up a constant shrill cry. When the evening closes in, the bat ascends higher in pursuit of the flying insects that rise to capture the last rays of daylight. Sometimes it will alight to devour its prey; sometimes it makes a pouch with its tail and the membrane between its legs and holds the insect there and consumes it in the air.

——A DEVOTED MOTHER. We do not know much about the breeding habits of the pipistrelle, but that the mother has a strong feeling for her young can be vouched for. W. A. Phillips, who in 1924 visited Ceylon, records an incident where a baby bat too small to fly was brought to him in the daytime. That evening a pipistrelle, apparently its mother, came into his room, suckled the baby bat, and carried it off clinging to her breast.

——LATE TO BED, EARLY TO RISE. The pipistrelle is common in North America and in most of the Eastern Hemisphere; it is found in almost as many different parts of the world as the little brown bat, and is well known in England. Its body varies from a little over an inch in length to over two inches. American species are brownish in hue; in the Old World they may be brown, red, or blackish. In the northern latitudes the pipistrelles are torpid in winter; they are the last bats to go into hibernation and the first ones out in the spring.

——THE NEAT NOCTULE. A bat that looks like a large pipistrelle is the Old World Noctule, *Nyctalus,* the biggest bat in Britain. It is one of the few bats that fly in mass formation. Meticulous about its toilet, it spends considerable time cleaning and combing its fur. Every part of its body, head, and wings is carefully groomed.

The Red Bat, *Lasiurus borealis,* not only seems to raise the largest families in the bat world—it is by far the most attractive and interesting of the bats found in the United States. Unlike many other species, the sexes show a remarkable difference in coloring. The males are a bright orange red frosted with white, while the females are a delicate shade of chestnut.

The red bat is a creature of the sunlight. It does not seek a dark shady nook or a dingy cave in which to roost. Instead, it hangs during the day among the open leaves of a tree, usually an oak. To a passerby it resembles a fading leaf and is unnoticed. It is one of the first bats on the wing in the evening, and its first object is to find water and scoop up a drink as it skims the surface like a bird.

A migrating species, the red bat lives in the north during the summer and passes the winter in the warm south. Although normally a solitary species, it may travel south in flocks of a hundred or more. Like many of the migrating birds, it favors the coast line, and has gone aboard ships to rest, sixty miles from shore. The migration southward is a perilous voyage. The animal flies partly in daylight and is an easy prey for the migrating hawks that follow the same route. No doubt jays, crows, and sea gulls also take a serious toll of its numbers.

——BIRTH AMONG THE BATS. To its good fortune, the red bat is able to make up these losses by producing a fairly large number of offspring. Twins are common; sometimes there are three young, and occasionally four. Red bats do their courting on the wing, but after mating the male, like other bats, has no further interest in domestic affairs.

Birth among the bats is an interesting process. When the young are to be born, in the warm days of June, the mother attaches herself to a branch by her feet and also hooks onto it with her thumb hooks. Suspended in this wise, she spreads her wing and tail membranes, forming an apron to catch the baby. It comes into the world head first —in some species feet first—squeaking at the top of its shrill voice. Like other bat mothers, the red bat carries her naked, tiny babies with her during the early days, but parks them in some secluded spot when they become too great a burden for her to take along on her nightly searches for insect food.

The red bat is found in North and South America, the West Indies, Bermuda, and the Galápagos Islands. A small bat, it is noteworthy for the fact that it has some fur on its flying membranes.

The Long-eared Bat, *Plecotus,* a native of Europe and northern Africa, has ears that are not merely long—they are, relatively speaking, enormous. Picture a bat less than two inches in length, covered with long, soft fur—and possessing ears that may be only a half-inch shorter than its body! Such a creature is Mr. Long Ears. When he is at rest, they curl up like the horns of a ram.

——Long Ears Well Used. Animals have a way of putting to good use every physical feature they possess. Mr. Long Ears and his huge, oval-shaped appendages are no exception to this rule. He is very fond of moths, for example. Now moths' wings are covered with down, which serves to deaden the minute sounds they make as the insects move about in the night air. This silencer is of little help to them, however, when Mr. Long Ears is in the vicinity.

The long-eared bat flies with its great ears directed forward to catch any sound. Suddenly it becomes aware of the flutter of the insect. The bat's delicate butterfly-like flight is immediately halted and it hovers like a hummingbird over a suspicious clump of leaves. Then it pounces into the clump, grabs the moth hiding there, and devours it, resting on the foliage. It uses the membrane stretched between the hind legs as a pocket to hold the meal until it is finished.

Though fortified with such an excellent hearing device, the long-eared bat is not endowed with the ability to detect rebounding sound vibrations. In England, the author saw one of these bats fly into a room through a partly open window. It fluttered vainly to get out again through the glass. Almost any other bat would without any hesitation have flown out the way it came in.

——A LEISURE-LOVING ANIMAL. The long-eared bat appears to be the only species in Europe that believes in fresh air and sleeps during

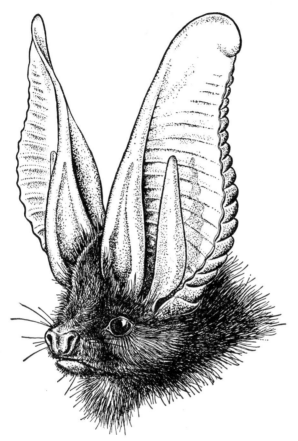

A BAT WITH BIG EARS
The long-eared bat dwells in Europe and neighboring Africa. Its ears are huge, only half an inch shorter than its body. When the animal is at rest, the ears curl up. This bat is an insect-eater, and its acute hearing detects even the moths, though they fly with muffled wings. The large spearlike growth in the ears (tragus) also seems to help detect them.

the day in open places—on the bark of trees or in wide-open hollow trees. It is a late flier and never leaves the roost until at least thirty-five minutes after sunset. It threads its way through thick forest trees with perfect rhythm, seeming to float through the air rather than fly.

It is active all night and feeds leisurely; there is none of the hustle characteristic of so many of its relatives.

When fall comes and the nights begin to get cold, the long-eared bat changes its habits: it enters a cave to sleep out the winter. All summer long it has lived a solitary life in the trees, but now it becomes more sociable, and eight or twelve may hang up in a cluster. It is not a deep sleeper, and when the temperature goes up to 45° F. it will be on the wing. February is the month of awakening, and the bat leaves its winter retreat and seeks summer quarters. The female gives birth to a single young in June.

The Great Northern or Hoary Bat, *Lasiurus cinerea,* is the largest bat found in America's northern latitudes, where it lives, for the most part, among evergreen trees in the mountains.

You can distinguish the hoary bat from all its kind by its irregular flight, its long, pointed wings, and its great size. The wings spread out to about fifteen inches—three or four times the length of its body. It has a white frosting on its coat—hence the name of "hoary bat"—and has a darker and deeper color than the smaller red bat, which it resembles otherwise. All in all, it is a handsome creature, and harmful only to insects.

——A SOLITARY FELLOW. The hoary bat lives alone in the solitude of the northern forests. One of the last bats to leave its retreat in the evening, it soars far above the tops of the tallest trees, where the great Luna moths and Cecropias fly. These and large beetles are its favorite food.

In autumn, the hoary bat turns migratory, like other species of the genus. Even now, it is somewhat solitary. During migration there is a gathering of the nomads but this is more a matter of all following a definite route at a given time than a social gathering. It is everyone for itself, and let the hawk take the hindmost. In September these bats have been seen in company with flocks of swallows moving south. During migration, individuals get lost in big cities and fly into open windows, or are often picked up hanging to bushes around suburban houses.

Courtship is brief for the hoary bat. It takes place in the summer. The prospective bridegroom must catch the not-too-reluctant female on the wing, then both come to earth. The young are born in May or June and may number up to four in a litter, a large family for a bat.

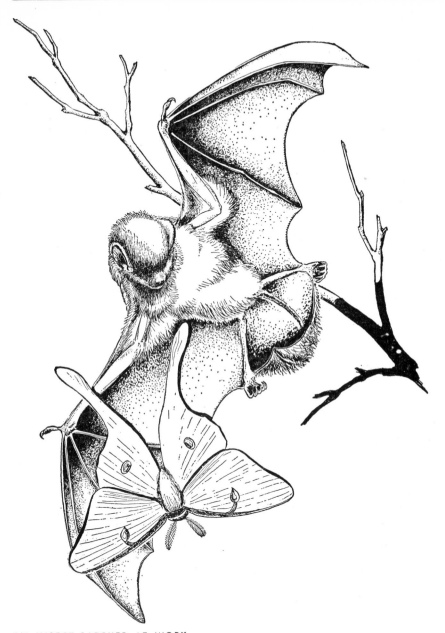

AN INSECT-CATCHER AT WORK

The hoary bat of the mountains of North America is one of that continent's largest bats, having a wingspread of fifteen inches. Its coat is frosted with white, like foliage on a winter morning. This flying mammal is fond of eating large insects, and is shown here in the act of capturing a Luna moth.

The mother does not make a nest, but has her roost in the thick branches of an evergreen tree or in an old crow's nest. At about one month of age, the youngsters are on their own.

We find this species over most of North America, northern South America, and the Hawaiian Islands.

FREE-TAILED BATS: MASTIFF BATS, WRINKLED-LIPPED BATS, AND BONNETED BATS

To find the free-tailed bats, we must go to the warmer regions of the earth. They are strong, muscular animals with long, narrow wings built for high speed. Thick, leathery ears extend well forward to frame the face like a bonnet.

Why do we call these bats "free-tailed"? Most others, we have seen, have the tail enclosed in the flying membrane, between their hind legs; in bats of this family (Molossidae), however, the lower half of the tail is free. By muscular action the bat can slide the membrane up or down the tail at will. This gives the free-tailed bat fine control over its movements when it is in the air.

Mostly, the free-tailed bats feed on insects. Fast and erratic fliers, they hunt their prey with consummate skill and play an important role in keeping in check the hordes of harmful insects in the tropics. From time to time the number of insects in an area will vary. When their food supply gets smaller, the free-tailed bats must move on. Thousands have been seen in mass migrations to better hunting grounds.

Free-tailed bats usually roost in colonies of tightly packed masses of individuals that apparently enjoy high temperatures. They have been known to congregate under a galvanized iron roof where the tropical African sun makes the heat unbearable to human beings. They also like to hide in cracks in rocks just wide enough to crawl into.

When subjected to low temperatures, most tropical bats do not hibernate but maintain their body warmth by shivering and being continuously active. Some of the free-tailed bats, in the northern part of their range, do sleep the winter away, however, generally about the time the temperature drops to 50 degrees. At the Carlsbad Caverns, in New Mexico, they stay dormant until March, but when the temperature goes up to 60 they awaken slowly and become active.

GREAT GUANO DEPOSITS

The free-tailed bats are also known as the guano bats, though Guano Bat, as a proper name, belongs to one species, *Tadarida*. Where caves have been used by these bats for centuries, vast quantities of guano have accumulated. It is in great demand by agriculturists for fertilizer, and many tons have been removed.

At the Carlsbad Caverns, mentioned in connection with the little brown bat, bat guano was deposited for over a quarter of a mile, one hundred feet wide in places, and up to a nearly equal depth. Over a period of fifteen years, 120 tons of guano were taken daily from these caverns and sold at from twenty to eighty dollars a ton. Replacement takes place at about one inch a year.

Earlier, during the American Civil War, bat guano was utilized by the Confederate States in making niter for gunpowder. The best deposits known then were in Texas, and were guarded by a regiment of soldiers.

BATS IN WAR

The Civil War was not the only human struggle that bats have been connected with. Do you know that thousands of bats were inducted into the Armed Forces of the United States in World War Two? They were enlisted in a most dangerous branch of warfare all their own, the bat suicide squad, designed to carry incendiary bombs into enemy territory for the purpose of setting fire to industrial centers and ammunition dumps. The project was carried on with great secrecy and with the full approval of President Roosevelt and top military officials in Washington.

The free-tailed bats proved ideal for this purpose. There were and still are eight million of them in the Carlsbad Caverns of New Mexico. Each bat proved capable of carrying a bomb load three times its own weight. A one-ounce time-bomb was strapped on the bat's chest and was actually larger than the animal itself. When exploded, the bomb produced a twenty-two-inch flame that burned for eight minutes.

In tests, the bats were packed individually with their bombs into crates, much the way eggs are packed. As long as the crates were kept under refrigeration at 40 degrees, the bats remained dormant and required no food.

These crates were carried in planes and dropped by parachute, which gave the bats time to warm up and be ready to fly at one thousand feet. When a crate opened (an automatic mechanism took care of this), it spread from one thousand to five thousand bat-bombs over an area of twenty miles in all directions.

Usually, when released, the artful little bats crawled into a narrow crevice of some building, chewed off their harness, and continued on their way, leaving the bomb to do its deadly work as planned.

THE BAT WITH A BONNET

This engaging-looking creature, not known to many Americans, is a member of a group known as the free-tailed bats. They are denizens of warmer regions, and some of them roost in the Carlsbad Caverns in New Mexico. The thick ears, of a leathery texture, frame the bat's face like a bonnet. This particular species, which is not found north of southern Mexico, is the domed-palate mastiff bat, *Promops*; its fearful-seeming teeth are used to attack nothing larger than insects. Like most bats, it does much good and little—if any —harm.

In preliminary tests, a village was burned to the ground and a couple of bomb-equipped incendiary bats which escaped burned up the auxiliary air base at Carlsbad, New Mexico. At about this time, the Navy took over the bat brigade and dubbed it "Project X-ray."

When the atom bomb was nearing completion in 1944, Project X-ray, costing two million dollars, was suddenly dropped, either before or soon after it was put into practice in Japan. Silence has shrouded its end.

Dr. Lytle Adams of Irwin, Pennsylvania, who surveyed the bat caves for the Army estimated that there are one hundred million free-tailed bats in the southern United States.

When great concentrations of these bats begin to leave the caverns in the evening, there is at first a muffled sound in the darkness which gives way to a rumble like the sound of many waters. As the main body of millions swings by on the wing, the volume of sound increases to the roar of a cascading torrent. As the hosts emerge into the open air, they pour forth like a great, circling column of black smoke, shooting one hundred feet into the air before dispersing.

HIDDEN BAT CITIES

One of the most interesting and bizarre of the free-tailed bats is the African Crested Bat, *Chaerophon*. On top of its head it has a rather jaunty tuft of long silky hairs that can be raised and spread out like a fan in a thin half-moon fringe. When the animal is resting, the crest is laid neatly back.

Lang and Chapin, the noted naturalists, found the crested bats inhabiting the hollow trunks of the half-dead giant forest trees in the Congo.

"They populate them in such numbers," these authors wrote, "that one might speak of hidden bat cities. From the narrow gate they fly out in even more ghost-like fashion than the bats of temperate climates; because behind the vapor veil of damp equatorial atmosphere they disappear instantly.

"The free-tailed bats indeed are swifter in flight, and though several may be seen passing about at one time, each one by itself chases in dexterous swoops the insects it is most fond of, often some two hundred feet from the ground above the dense canopy of the forest, or else lower down about the clearings."

SOME CURIOUS FREE-TAILED BATS

Some bats have been described as fantastic, and others as grotesque and terrifying, but the Naked Bat, *Cheiromeles*, a native of Malay and Indo-China, is just plain ugly. What hair it has is so short and thin that the animal is virtually naked, a fairly rare thing among mammals. Its long piglike head, small ears, and the fleshy fold of skin around its neck add to its repulsive appearance.

The Mastiff Bat, *Eumops,* has exceptionally thick, leathery ears that join at the base of its forehead and extend forward to hang over its nostrils. The California Mastiff Bat is the largest bat found in the United States, and the largest of the family. A high flier, it has narrow wings that spread out eighteen inches—about four times its entire body length. Most of the time this bat selects a roost that is a considerable distance from the ground; it appears to have trouble getting on the wing from low elevations. The animal possesses powerful jaws armed with strong teeth capable of inflicting a fatal bite on smaller bats and birds.

THE BAT FALCON

Bats, we have said, have few natural enemies. However, in tropical Asia and Africa the Bat Falcon, *Machaerhamphus,* feeds to a large extent on the free-tailed bats. In his field notes James Chapin writes concerning this bat-catching hawk:

"A few words about this remarkable bird of prey may not be out of place here, especially as it seems in so many ways adapted just for the capture of bats. Its unusually large . . . eyes suggest at once its nocturnal habits. By day it seldom appears but it becomes extremely active at dusk. Falcon-like, it pounces upon even the most rapid fliers among bats, striking them, we believe, with its long talons. Its small, sharply hooked, laterally compressed bill may help to kill them, and its wide gape [mouth] of course can dispose of a dead bat at once. From our observations we feel inclined to think that it swallows its prey in full flight."

The Clever Ones—An Introduction to
the Monkeys and Their Relatives

IN ALL the groups of animals we have looked at so far, one feature could not fail to impress us: their variety. Almost every order of living things has its giants and its midgets, its common types and others so curious in appearance and behavior that we find it hard to believe they are related. Of few groups is this truer than the present one, whose members range from little marmosets and tiny lemurs no more than five inches long, to monkeys, chimpanzees, and great gorillas which may weigh six hundred pounds. It includes man, too.

If you open a natural history published in the last century or earlier, you will generally find this group at the start. Because man belongs to it, it is known as the order Primates, a term that means "first" or "foremost." The primates are first, however, only in one respect. Certain parts of their brain are particularly well developed, especially the cerebrum (the portion that, in man, controls the ability to reason). In other respects—in sight, hearing, smell, general strength, and physical development—many other animals surpass them.

In their mental powers, the members of this group vary greatly. The lemurs, for example, show little more intelligence than the average mammal, whereas a certain amount of forethought—and even reason—may be seen in the apes, as when they pile object upon object to get at food hanging above them. The orangutan's brain is most like man's, but does not equal it in size or weight. Ounce for ounce, the smaller monkeys have more brain weight compared to body than most other living mammals.

137

AGILE CLIMBERS

Most of these animals live in the tropics. As a rule, we do not meet them much farther north or south than the belt of land that surrounds the Equator. In this warm region dwell the four great apes— the chimpanzee, the orangutan, the gibbon, and the gorilla.

QUICK IN UNDERSTANDING AND ACTION
The monkeys are native to Asia, Africa, and the hotter parts of the Americas. For the most part, these creatures feed on fruit, nuts, leaves, insects, small birds, and birds' eggs. Usually they have long tails, and this feature, as well as their smaller size, distinguishes the monkeys from the apes.

Except for a few animals like the baboon, and the old gorilla that has grown too heavy to climb, the greater number of the members of this order spend most of their time in the trees. Here agility and good coordination are at a premium; the brains of the apes and monkeys seem to have reached their fine development partly in connection with the high degree of mobility they have achieved in the trees.

Some time, when you visit the zoo, look closely at the hands and feet of a monkey, an ape, or one of their relatives. You will then see very clearly how they come by this freedom of motion and superb ease when aloft.

On each limb the primates usually have five fingers or toes, with flattened nails quite like man's, to protect the tips. (Exceptions are the lemurs and marmosets, which still have claws.) Most have the thumb and great toe set apart from the other fingers or toes, making it possible for them to get a vise-like grip on things. The animals can swing their arms freely, either forward or backward. Although the typical member of the group moves on all fours, the higher-ranking ones show a marked tendency to stand erect and walk on two feet, like man.

EATERS OF LEAVES AND FRUIT

Look at the monkey's face, too. Note how short faced and short jawed the animal is. The higher monkeys have a mouth much like man's, with only thirty-two teeth. The teeth are not so specialized as they are in many other creatures. The primates are vegetarians, on the whole: the majority feed on fruit, leaves, flowers, and the like. But some will eat animal food such as eggs, insects, and possibly birds.

A number of these animals are fond of water and can swim and dive with great skill, but they are not aquatic in the full meaning of the term. The monkeys and apes are active by day, using the night to rest and sleep, but the lemurs, loris, and galago conform to the more normal animal scheme: they are about at night and rest or sleep during the day.

SHARP EYES

For an animal that lives in the trees, good vision is of surpassing importance. The lemurs, monkeys, and apes often possess large eyes. These are usually set more forward in the face than is the case with other mammals, so that the primates can look straight ahead and see through the tangle of jungle vegetation before them.

The monkeys and apes are able to get a single image through both eyes, with a good perception of depth. Some have color vision and doubtless see things much the way we do, unlike the rest of the animal kingdom. The sense of smell is less vital to these tree-dwellers, and so we are not surprised to discover that their snouts are generally reduced. The ears, although well developed, lack lobes.

REMARKABLE TAILS AND VOICES

The apes have no tail (except in embryo, like man). Almost all the rest of the group possess one, however, and usually it is long and well developed; they use it to help balance themselves in the trees. In most South and Central American monkeys the tail is prehensile—that is, it can take a firm hold on things—and they use it as an extra hand. We do not find such a tail in the Old World monkeys.

There are many other interesting features to be observed among the primates, high and low. At a zoo, when you look at the baboons and drills, you can hardly fail to notice the remarkable rough, callous patches on their buttocks. Often they are brilliantly colored at certain seasons of the year. These patches, which go by the ponderous name of "ischial callosities," do not seem attractive to us, but no doubt they have their charms for the big Old World monkeys. Some of the primates grow beards, and all are hairy, to say the least.

These creatures have quite a range of vocal powers. Their voices vary from the guttural roar of the gorilla to the gruff, barklike tone of the chimpanzee. The gibbon and howler monkey have really remarkable voices—their volume is so great they can carry a distance of a mile or further. Most monkeys emit a whistling note, often plaintive.

SOCIABLE CREATURES

In general the monkeys and apes are clannish folk. They form family groups or whole troops but they do not join forces and no outsiders are accepted. There is, too, always the "lone wolf" that prefers his own company to a crowd.

The males are not domestically inclined and take no part in raising the family. This role is left entirely to the female. The babies—generally there is one at a time—are born helpless, and the mother carries them wherever she goes, clinging to her breasts (normally she possesses two teats) when they are very young. Often they ride on her shoulders as they grow older. The male, though, is not entirely relieved of his family responsibility, and is on the job when danger threatens his womenfolk.

THE "RACES" OF MAN

Although man is a primate along with the monkeys and the apes—
his bones, his nerves, his glands, his muscles, his tissues, and his organs
are almost identical with theirs and he possesses tail bones—he is not
descended from them. Rather, he comes from the same apelike stock
they do; all represent offshoots in different directions.

Only One Species. All living men—black, brown, yellow, and white—
belong to just one species. It is *Homo sapiens,* or "clever man." The
final test of what makes a species is this one: can its members inter·
breed and produce fertile young? Certainly all the so-called "races" of
man can do this.

It is difficult to label any group of men a "pure race"—none exists,
and very likely never did. A term such as "Aryan," often heard in our
times, only describes a group of Indo-European languages, not the
varied kinds of people who speak them: Russians, Persians, Asiatic Indians, as well as western Europeans and Americans.

MAN'S FORERUNNERS

Diggers into the past have turned up the remains of a number of
man's forerunners. It is impossible to prove that man is descended
from any of them in a straight line. Some of these prehistoric creatures
are so markedly different from people today that scientists may place
them in separate families; others, although placed in the same family
as man—the Hominidae ("man and his relatives")—belong in different genera. Their fossil record is incomplete, for they were relatively
scarce. But in time more finds will surely be made and we shall be
able to see the prehistory of man in a somewhat clearer light.

MEN OF THE OLD STONE AGE

The earliest form of primitive man discovered—perhaps he should be
called a manlike ape—is known as *Pithecanthropus erectus* ("erect
apeman"), or Java man, because it was in Java that his remains were
first found. He had a receding forehead and chin much like a gorilla's,
but a brain capacity 50 per cent greater. (Modern man's brain capacity
is more than double the gorilla's.) This man roamed the earth about
a half-million years ago. He has sometimes been regarded as the "miss-

ing link," but there is no reason to consider him the ancestor of modern man. He belonged to another genus altogether.

Another manlike form with a better-developed brain, *Sinanthropus*, or Peking man, lived in the same period or later. On the basis of where the remains of this creature were found, it is likely that man or truly manlike creatures had their beginnings in the Eastern Hemisphere.

The earliest type of man in Europe was for a long time believed to be *Eoanthropus*, the Dawn man, also called the Piltdown man, because his remains were discovered at Piltdown, in Sussex, England. He supposedly existed probably two hundred thousand years later than Java man, but the date was necessarily uncertain. He had a well-developed brain, yet resembled the apes in being chinless, it was thought. Late in 1953 scientific investigations cast strong doubt upon the authenticity of the only specimen known.

The Neanderthal man, the next important type, was a cave-dweller of Europe and the Mediterranean area between 200,000 B.C. and 100,000 B.C. and probably later. He was short and walked with stooped shoulders, but had a brain capacity much like that of man today. He made stone implements, was a hunter and user of fire, and there is reason for thinking he believed in a life after death. In time he was conquered or absorbed by an important figure in the world about fifty thousand years ago, Cro-Magnon man. This fellow was a handsome creature, closely resembling the modern type, and possessing a large brain. An artist and a craftsman, he left, on cavern walls, realistic drawings of animals of his day like the mammoth and rhinoceros. Experts term them true works of art, though their purpose was undoubtedly magical.

MEN OF THE NEW STONE AGE

Cro-Magnon man was the last of the races of the Old Stone Age, or Paleolithic period, the era when man used simple stone tools and caught or gathered his food in the wild. Next came the peoples of the New Stone Age, or Neolithic period (it began about ten or twelve thousand years ago, and lasted till the dawn of history, loosely speaking). They ground and polished their stone tools, began to practice agriculture, domesticated animals, and developed such crafts as pottery and weaving.

The bones of New Stone Age man tell us that he was virtually identical with modern man. In the past ten thousand years man's body has undergone no significant evolutionary changes.

Now that we have had a glance at the most advanced of the primates, we may turn to the simplest. The contrast is great indeed.

Tree Shrews, Lemurs, Pottos and Other Half-Monkeys

TREE SHREWS—THEY LOOK LIKE SQUIRRELS

THE TREE SHREWS, natives of southeastern Asia and the neighboring larger islands, are among the most primitive of all mammals but are still more advanced than the egg-layers and the marsupials. They climb trees like squirrels and look like them, right down to the long, bushy tail. As a rule, however, they are smaller, and possess four fingers on each limb. They were taken for squirrels by the first Westerner to report them, a surgeon who traveled to China with Captain James Cook, the explorer, in 1780.

The typical tree shrew, *Tupaia,* is the best known member of the group. It is a simple little creature, never still, always seeking its food —fruits and insects, not nuts like the squirrel—among the leaves of trees or on the moss-covered ground, poking its long slender nose into every nook and cranny. Feeding, it sits up on its haunches like a squirrel, and holds the food in its forepaws. After each feast it licks its hands and then washes its face with them. It is fond of water, not only as something to drink, but to bathe in.

HOME LIFE OF THE TREE SHREWS

When night comes, the tree shrew retreats to a rudely constructed lair of moss in the highest branches of trees or into a hollow bamboo, or to a hole in the ground. This animal does not like intruders and will fight to the death any fellow shrew that invades its own particular domain. When angry, it will utter a shrill, protracted cry. Pleased, it expresses its emotions with a peculiar tremulous whistling sound.

While the tree shrew is seemingly rather solitary in its habits, breeding pairs live part of the year together; sometimes the male may assist in raising the family. The mother bears her one or two babies at practically any season of the year except December. Some species produce more young; the number of teats varies from one pair in certain forms to six in others.

TAME TREE SHREWS

Confined in a cage, the tree shrew will not survive very long. On the other hand, taken young and raised as a household pet, it becomes quite domesticated, although it does not like to be handled.

A tame tree shrew will come forward at mealtimes for choice bits of food, and shows some attachment for the people who take care of it. However, it evinces disquietude—expressed by a chattering-like noise—whenever a stranger enters the house. If it is given freedom to run out of doors, it will not try to escape.

The typical tree shrew is grayish or olive in color but some are mixed yellow and black or reddish brown. They are about six to eight inches long, the tail a bit shorter. All told, the tree shrew family (Tupaiidae) has six genera. The smallest of the group, the Bridled Tree Shrew, is the size of a small rat; the largest, the Borneo Tree Shrew, has a body length of nine inches.

The oddity of the family is the Pen-tailed Tree Shrew, a native of Borneo, Sumatra, and the Malay Peninsula. It has a lengthy tail, horizontally feathered toward the tip with long, stiff hairs like the web on a tail feather of a bird.

Originally naturalists classified the tree shrew with other shrews as an insectivore. But then it was discovered to represent the earliest type of the primates, and so was shifted into their order.

A MAMMAL WITH A TAIL LIKE A FEATHER

A curiosity, even among its own tribe, is the pentailed tree shrew—the end part of its long tail looks like a feather. This animal climbs trees like a squirrel, and will sit on its haunches to feed, holding the food in its five-fingered forepaws. Its home is in the Malay Peninsula, Borneo, and Sumatra.

LEMURS—THE FOX-FACED "MONKEYS" OF MADAGASCAR

The word "lemur" means "ghost." And ghostly indeed is the impression created by these strange, monkey-like animals as they move swiftly from branch to branch, from tree to tree, in the dark. When they descend to the ground, some stand erect on their long legs and walk or hop, carrying their slender arms aloft, while others walk on all fours. Their eyes, large, dark, and expressionless, look forward over a sharp, foxlike muzzle.

Although they once dwelled in many other places, most of the lemurs today live in the forests of Madagascar; some dwell on nearby islands. We do not find many kinds of animals on Madagascar outside the tenrecs and the lemur family (Lemuridae); the lemurs' situation here reminds us of that of another group of animals isolated on a great island, the marsupials of Australia.

The lemurs, however, have not overrun their homeland the way the marsupials did. Since Madagascar is, or was, more or less covered with dense forests, the majority took to the trees. A few spend part of their time on the ground; none has gone all the way and become a bur-rower like so many of Australia's smaller native animals. Fossil re-mains tell us that in prehistoric times some lemurs, like the ancient marsupials, were much larger—perhaps about the size of the great apes.

A fair number of the marsupials are meat-eaters that prey on other animals, limiting their spread. Not so the lemurs. Timid, gentle, and inoffensive creatures, they have habits that could hardly be called predatory. Most of them feed on insects, fruit, and the like. Only a few have been known to touch meat.

It is chiefly during the hours of darkness that the lemurs go about the business of food-getting. They prefer to pass the day sleeping in the trees. A few may be seen at large during daylight hours, but even these are most active in the early morning and evening. One of them, the Common or True Lemur, *Lemur,* rests perched in the branches during the noonday heat, its head beneath its arms, its long bushy tail curled about its neck. Awake, it travels about in troops of six to twenty or more that let out a chorus of loud, shrill cries every now and then. Occasionally one will descend to the ground to retrieve a fallen piece of fruit.

SOME INTERESTING LEMURS

There are a number of colorful true lemurs, each about the size of a house cat with the face of a fox and the body of a monkey. Like most night prowlers, they are covered with soft, silky fur. Only one kind, the Ring-tailed Lemur, is not a forest-dweller; it lives in the dry, rocky regions of western Madagascar, which are practically destitute of trees. The animal is well adapted to its circumstances—it possesses leathery palms and soles which allow it to get a firm hold on the slip-pery rocks.

The ring-tailed lemur, by the way, is one of the most distinctively marked and best-known animals in captivity. Look for it at the zoo some time: its body is a delicate shade of gray, its long tail is banded with alternating rings of black and white. The tails of all other lemurs are solid in color.

Still handsomer—and bigger—than the animals we have been talking about is the Ruffed Lemur. It has a conspicuous ruff on the sides of its neck, black and white markings on its body, and a bushy black tail almost as long as the animal itself (two feet).

The ruffed lemur is considered sacred by some of the natives, who claim it worships the sun. And so it seems to. When the first rays of light appear above the horizon, the ruffed lemur sits up on its hind legs and remains erect, opening and extending its arms toward the sun as if in supplication, its eyes fixed on the ball of fire. At the setting of the sun, a troop of ruffed lemurs will utter their plaintive cries in unison.

From the human point of view, almost as odd are the habits of the Fruit-eating Lemur, a pretty, reddish-gray inhabitant of northern Madagascar. It makes its den in a hollow tree, and does not seem to care a bit that a swarm of bees may share its dwelling. Since the bees are active during the day and the lemur at night, there is no congestion in traffic.

LEMURS THAT SLEEP THROUGH THE SUMMER

In the summer in Madagascar, it becomes extremely hot, and in some places the insects and vegetation the lemurs feed on may dwindle. Some species, such as the Mouse Lemur (it is not much larger than a rat) and the Fat-tailed Lemur, become torpid and sleep throughout this time of the year. Before they go into their lethargy, their tails grow exceptionally fat and become a reservoir of energy upon which they can draw during their long rest.

The summer den is a hole either in the ground or a hollow tree. The lemur packs it with dead leaves and dry grass till the chamber is just large enough to hold its body. After retiring, the comfort-loving creature covers itself completely with its bedding.

Lemurs breed once a year. The mother bears only one young at a time. She cares for it tenderly, carrying it in spread-eagle fashion, either on her back or her breast.

The natives of Madagascar hunt the lemur with mongrel dogs. Its agility in the trees makes it hard to follow with the eye, and almost impossible to shoot, at least when it is in motion. Also, the animal has a habit of dropping suddenly to the ground from lofty trees as if dead, and then making off through the underbrush to a distant tree. Besides man, its only enemies are the civets.

Lemurs, in general, are considered delightful pets, though they lack the intelligence or relatively even temper of monkeys. W. S. Gilbert, of the world-famed Gilbert and Sullivan operetta-writing pair, was a noted lemur fancier, and kept a number on his estate.

THE WOOLLY LEMURS

With their long hind limbs and small thumbs, the woolly lemurs of Madagascar are rather different from the lemurs pure and simple. A small brownish-gray woolly lemur with a bullet-round head, the Avahi, *Lichanotus*, gets about only slowly, and impresses us as an unsociable creature. Much more appealing is the Sifaka, *Propithecus*—a handsome, long-tailed near-monkey, remarkable for its diversity of color (usually white varied with yellowish red and black). It dwells in all sections of Madagascar, in the open spaces as well as the dense forests, and is never killed by the natives, who revere it.

Inoffensive and peace-loving, the sifaka goes about in groups of half a dozen or more, feeding on fruits, leaves, and flowers. It is most alert during the early morning and evening; the hot hours of the day it sleeps away. On the ground it does not run on all four feet but stands erect. It throws its arms about its head and proceeds in a series of extremely agile and fantastic leaps.

The Indri, *Indri,* is the largest of the woolly lemurs and the most famous, although it is rarely seen in captivity. It lacks a tail, but otherwise is very close to the monkeys. In motion this creature presents an extraordinary sight: usually it stands or walks erect, steadying its swaying body with its long arms and hands or waving them aloft like an apprentice acrobat on a tight-rope. From nose to rump it is some two feet long, but it seems much larger with its arms extended.

——THE INDRI'S PROTECTIVE COLORING. The indri is well protected from enemies in its home forests. On its hairy body, black and white meet in sharply contrasting and extremely variable color patterns.

Amidst rich vegetation, with sunlight shooting through, the indri can hardly be seen at all as it goes about in friendly troops nibbling on fruit and leaves.

——How It Got Its Name. Some people find it odd that the natives of Madagascar, the Malagasy, never call this creature an indri—to

BIGGEST OF MADAGASCAR'S LEMURS

The indri, the best known of the woolly lemurs, is remarkably human in appearance. It is a skillful climber, although it does not possess a tail to help it in the trees. Often it walks upright. The natives of Madagascar credit this strange-looking animal with magical powers, and will not slay it.

them it is a "babakoto." In the language of the Malagasy, "indri" means "look." That is what they said when they first pointed out the animal to the early Europeans on the island, but the newcomers took the natives' exclamation for the local name. This misunderstanding is very much like the one by which the kangaroos got their name.

——THE INDRI OF LEGEND. To the natives the indri is a hero and full of mystery. They free it when they find it in captivity, and bury its dead; they would consider it a sin to kill an indri. Many are the curious folk beliefs they hold concerning it. For example, they say that the trees in which this animal lives supply a sure remedy for all forms of illnesses and they gather the leaves and use them medicinally. They also believe that the indri can be a dangerous enemy if attacked. The Malagasy claim that if a spear is hurled at it, the spear will be caught in flight before reaching its mark, and will be hurled back at the thrower with deadly aim—the indri, they say, never misses its target.

One story would have it that at birth the indri is put through a severe trial. As soon as the young is born (the female indri, like most lemurs, bears a single baby) the mother takes it in her arms and throws it to her mate, who is stationed some distance away; he in turn throws the baby back to its mother. Thus they pass it back and forth a dozen times or more. If the baby falls to the ground, the natives declare, it stays there and the parents make no effort to recover it. But if it passes the test without falling, it is tenderly cared for.

There are other tales told about the indri, all making it a creature of might and magic. Naturalists place it and the sifaka and avahi in one family, the Indridae.

AYE-AYES—MYSTERY CREATURES OF MADAGASCAR

The Aye-aye, *Daubentonia,* is yet another mysterious creature of Madagascar. Although it is a relative of the lemurs, it has two pairs of chisel-like gnawing front teeth very much like a rodent's. But these are by no means the most peculiar feature of this bizarre animal.

——THE AYE-AYE'S STRANGE FINGERS. The aye-aye is about the size of a house cat. It has coarse, shaggy dark brown hair, and a very lengthy bushy tail. Its hands are long and its clawed fingers incredibly spider-like. Longest and thinnest of all is the middle finger. It is said that the animal feeds on tree-boring insects and uses its chisel teeth to cut through the wood; with the claw on the wirelike middle finger it is supposed to reach into the cracks and hook out the insect larvae. We are also told that it uses this finger for tapping on the branch of a tree; that by listening to the sound the aye-aye is able to determine just where a boring bug is located.

How much of this is fact it would be hard to tell, for the aye-aye (it is named, incidentally, from the cry it utters) is a fairly rare creature—many of the natives on Madagascar say they have never seen one. We do know that in zoos the aye-aye turns up its nose at insects, but is glad to eat fruit; it chews wood readily but does not eat it.

HALF-MONKEY WITH A BUSHY TAIL

The aye-aye is another of the curious animals of Madagascar. This weird-looking creature, roughly the size of a cat, has extraordinarily long, slender hands and fingers and sharp nails—plus front teeth like a rat's. A relative of the lemurs, it is different enough to be placed in a separate family.

The aye-aye will, however, use its all-purpose middle finger to comb its hair, and clean its face, nose, mouth, and huge, leathery ears. It also employs it to bring water to its mouth: the animal will sweep the finger through a pan of water and between its lips a good forty times a minute.

————THE AYE-AYE IN THE TREES. In its broad face this strange creature has big eyes that help it to see its way in the bamboo forests as it prowls solitarily under cover of darkness. Here its opposable great toe (a feature it shares with the lemurs) helps it to maintain its hold.

All day the aye-aye sleeps high in the trees with its single young. Its nest is made of dry leaves and twigs, and is shaped like a ball, about two feet through, with an entrance at the side. The Malagasy, who believe that touching an aye-aye means death, nevertheless say that a twig from this nest will bring good fortune. The animal, we are told, favors the traveler's tree in particular; the leaves have a clear, watery sap that the aye-aye is reputed to drink.

Particularly because of its gnawing teeth, the aye-aye was for a long time a puzzle to scientists. Some considered it the most primitive of the primates. Nowadays it has been placed in a family by itself (Daubetoniidae) quite close to the lemurs. The teeth seem to be a special tool it has evolved, rather than a clue to its origin.

LORISES, GALAGOS, AND POTTOS

The Slender Loris, *Loris,* believes in making haste slowly. Proceeding in a deliberate, slow-motion crawl through the trees, it creeps up on its unsuspecting prey like a chameleon. On the ground it will walk like a monkey, but without the speed of one. It has to have a very good reason before it will snap up its pace.

We meet the slender loris only in Ceylon and southern India. A primate in miniature, it is about five inches long, with slender arms and legs, well-formed hands and feet, but no tail. A coat of short brown fur clothes this creeper. Its ears are small and rounded, but its eyes are gigantic. Placed close together at the front of the animal's face, and accentuated by a large black patch above each, they are easily the animal's most impressive feature.

They are beautiful eyes. Often they seem to have a haunted, melancholy look. The iris is chestnut in color, and in bright light the pupil contracts to a vertical slit; at night, when the slender loris awakens from its daytime lethargy, the pupils expand and the orbs shine with a golden coppery light. The Singhalese villagers sometimes treat this harmless creature with great cruelty; they extract its remarkable eyes and use them in love potions or for the healing of eye diseases.

The slender loris spends much of its time aloft, but not in high trees like more active animals. Amid the low branches and bushes, it has an odd habit of swaying its head to and fro. It is quite incapable of jumping even a short distance, and does not swim in the wild.

A sluggish animal cannot prey on speedsters: it hardly comes as a surprise to us to learn that the slender loris is fond of snails. Into its diet, too, go insects, lizards, small rodents, and birds that it can sneak up on unawares. It makes a hearty meal of them: everything is consumed, including the horny wings of beetles, the scales of the lizards, and the bones and feathers of the birds.

The breeding habits of the slender loris are something of a mystery. Usually the female bears a single baby, but now and then there are twins; they come about six months after mating time. Mother loris has been seen nursing a newborn baby while her back was bowed under the weight of another young one (from a previous birth) half her own size.

The Slow or Gray Loris, *Nycticebus* ("night monkey"), is a snail compared to the slender loris. It moves at a singularly measured, exasperatingly unhurried pace. On horizontal branches it inches its way along in an inverted position like a sloth. "Sloth," incidentally, is just what its name means in the language of the Dutch colonists of Malaysia, who baptized this strange creature. It dwells only in the Philippines, the East Indies, and the warmer parts of southern Asia.

——The "Bashful Cat." To the Bengali, this slowpoke is the "bashful cat." It is more than twice the size of the slender loris, and robustly built. Its typical coat of thick woolly fur is silver gray, with dark brown markings on the head; no doubt it puts this warm covering to good use during the chilly evenings in the trees. It has practically no tail. Its eyes are fairly large, a rather common thing among animals that hunt at night, we have seen.

Slow loris sleeps by day rolled up in a ball, its head and hands buried in the fur between the thighs. At dusk it begins to stir, and rambles through the trees in search of its evening meal: insects, fruits, and probably bird eggs in season. Rarely does it descend to earth. On the ground, it can, if necessary, move along with an awkward wavering gait, the limbs held out at right angles.

——Safety First. Slow loris tracks its victims softly and stealthily. When it is within range of a succulent moth, beetle, or grasshopper, it raises itself on its hind legs, hurls itself on the unfortunate insect, and grabs it between its fingers. It always takes care, however, to have a secure hold on a branch with its hind feet. Its thumb and great toe are very large, so it can get a tight grip on things.

This animal has some of the coy habits of its relative the monkey. For example, it will often hide its face in its hands. The natives say it does this because it is continually seeing ghosts.

THE ANIMAL THAT WON'T HURRY

The slow or gray loris moves very leisurely, to say the least. It literally inches its way along the branches of a tree, like a sloth. It hunts at night, quietly tracking moths, beetles, and other insects through the trees. Sometimes it covers its face with its hands. According to the natives, the loris does this because it sees ghosts and is afraid.

Many strange powers are attributed to the slow loris in its homeland; almost every event in the lives of men, women and children is supposed to be influenced by it for better or worse. A Malay native found guilty of a crime will claim that an enemy buried a particular part of a loris under his threshold, which compelled him to commit his transgression. Contrariwise, the Malays will tell you that the fur of the loris has healing powers and that a ship with a live loris on board will never be becalmed. The Burmese, on the other hand, believe the animal's bite is poisonous.

The Common Potto, *Perodicticus,* is unique among mammals in having its backbone partly outside its body! The vertical spines of the vertebrae actually are not covered with skin. On this loris-like creature's back, they form a ridge of bare dry bone tips an eighth of an inch high.

Nature's strange gift is not wasted by potto—the animal uses it aptly in self-defense.

When danger threatens, the potto will face the enemy, rise up on its hind limbs and, with fists clenched, suddenly double up, bringing its head in between the hind legs. As it does this, the row of sharp bony spikes sticking out down its neck and back rips its adversary brutally. Interestingly enough, the potto can raise the fur around these spiny protuberances at will, to hide them, or spread it to expose them.

——Like a Little Old Man. Poor potto, no one has yet described it in flattering terms. The old Dutch traveler and naturalist, William Bosman, when he saw it well over two hundred years ago, called it a horrible, ugly creature—the most disagreeable-looking animal found on the whole earth.

It is not so hideous as he would have had us believe. Potto rather resembles a little old man, with its large hands and feet turned outward and its big head hung down. Its face is round and it has big, peering eyes. A little over a foot long, potto possesses just a stump of a tail. The soft, thick fur on the animal's sides is grizzled, and the back is shaded with honey-yellow.

——A Powerful Hand Grasp. This little tree-dweller is quite a bit like the loris, not only in appearance but also in its motions; these are extremely slow and deliberate.

Often the potto travels upside down like the sloth. It always keeps a very firm hold with its hands and feet (they are lined with a large pad, and the thumb and great toe are enormous) when climbing, and never releases one hand until the other has secured a firm grip. In fact, potto has the strongest hand grasp of any creature its size; the West African natives claim that it is impossible to break its hold on a tree even in death.

The natives have said, too, that once potto climbs a tree, it will stay in it until all the fruit and leaves are devoured. (Potto feeds on these and probably some insects.) They also claim that if the next tree is some distance away, potto will die of starvation while crossing the space between, but this, of course, is sheer fantasy.

A CREATURE WITH A UNIQUE WEAPON
A couple of centuries ago, a naturalist named Bosman saw his first potto and declared it to be the ugliest animal on earth. This tree-dweller, although not actually so unpleasant a sight, is unique among the mammals in that it has part of its backbone outside its body. This provides a row of sharp bony spikes which the potto uses to slash an enemy.

Potto has no established nest or home, but sleeps during the day curled up like a ball, hanging to a branch of a tree hidden in the foli-age. It lives its entire life in the forest, and seldom comes to the ground. Nighttime is when it is active.

The sluggish potto seems to lead a solitary life, except at breeding time. The single baby will cling to its mother's under side until almost two-thirds grown. Very much like the common potto is the Golden Potto of Old Calabas, West Africa. Its spines, however, are not so prominent, and it has a thick, golden coat of fur and webbed fingers and toes.

The Bush Baby, Ojam, or Galago, *Galago,* an interesting, attractive little animal of southern and equatorial Africa, is as nimble as the potto is slow—it will bounce about like a rubber ball on the ground or in the trees.

STRANGE CRIER IN THE NIGHT
The bush baby, a native of Africa, is a charming creature that can leap with remarkable agility on the ground or among the branches, thanks to its long hind legs. The bush baby has a cry that sounds much like a human baby's. One of the larger species, the thick-tailed galago, is shown above.

The bush baby's long, slender toes and fingers are equipped with flesh pads at the tips, which act like suction cups, enabling the animal to walk or run up a tree without the use of its claws. It seems literally to gallop through the trees, with both fore and hind feet together— not just leaping from branch to branch but going forward at a fast rate and in a straight line.

——It Can Look Directly Backward. The bush baby is clad in thick woolly fur, and its bushy tail may be a little longer than its body. It has singularly beautiful large eyes of rich translucent brown. The odd thing about these eyes is that the bush baby cannot move them in their sockets as we can. It must turn its head when it wishes to look at something a little out of the way. What is more, it can turn its head far enough to look directly backward, an ability we might well envy.

——A BALL OF BUSH BABIES. Like most lemurs, little bush baby lives in the trees and sleeps by day. It has a sociable nature and loves company, but not large crowds. Bush babies will sleep huddled together in groups of three or four, their limbs twined about each other, making one big ball. At this time the large, thin, hairless ears on their round heads are turned backward and folded up. The sleeping place is some hollow tree or amidst dense foliage.

——WHEN THE BUSH BABIES CRY. One rarely sees bush babies unless they are disturbed during the hours of sunlight, when they nap. At sundown the members of the small band come alive and utter a peculiar haunting cry, which they repeat at intervals throughout the night, as they rush about in quest of food. It is because of this cry, we are told, that they are called "babies." They are mainly vegetarian in diet, but are very fond of birds' eggs. In the dim light of the jungle night, the agile creatures can jump and land with accuracy on a branch twenty feet away. Although they are quite pugnacious—a quarrel among them may be the beginning of a fight to the death—they have been tamed and are reputed to make docile pets.

There are many kinds of bush babies. The largest is about the size of a house cat and the smallest not much bigger than a large mouse. They dwell in the forested parts of Africa south of the Sahara, and belong to the family Lorisidae, with the lorises and pottos.

The Tarsier, or Spectral Tarsier, *Tarsius,* is just a handful of an animal, but it has enormous owl-like eyes, set close together. In bright sunlight the pupil contracts to a narrow slit, as we see in the eye of the cat, but at night it expands to cover nearly the whole iris.

Vision in the dark is important to this small night prowler of the trees. Insects move fast, and the insect-eating tarsier must move faster. Adhesive pads on its fingers and toes permit it to cling firmly to smooth branches, as it progresses nimbly from branch to branch in a series of leaps and hops that bring to mind the kangaroo and the frog. It travels much the same way on the ground.

——THE TARSIER'S QUAINT EATING HABITS. From John Whitehead, who obtained living specimens of the Philippine tarsier, which is known as the Magou, we have the following interesting picture of how tarsiers eat:

"They feed on grasshoppers, sitting on their haunches. When offered an insect, the magou would stare for a short time with its most wonderful eyes, then slowly bend forward and with a sudden dash would seize the insect with both hands and instantly carry it to its mouth, shutting its eyes and screwing up its tiny face in a most whimsical manner." Afterward it opens its eyes and consumes the tiny prey in a leisurely manner. It seldom makes a sound but when it does its cry is a sharp, shrill one, something like a monkey's.

MITE OF AN ANIMAL
The tiny tarsier can actually be held in your hand, for it is only six inches long. Its most prominent feature is its huge eyes, which remind us of an owl's. The animal is a hopper, and jumps about in the trees with great nimbleness as it pursues the insects which make up its diet.

The natives have a strange belief that this woolly-furred animal eats charcoal. When they capture it—it is not too hard to find, for it has a strong musky smell—they attempt to feed it on burnt wood, to the animal's misfortune. It has little fear of man if approached slowly, but a sudden movement will send it leaping off through the thickly wooded regions it inhabits. A male and female are generally seen together.

———THE TARSIER FAMILY. The tarsiers rank a step above the lemurs and their relatives in the primate world, forming a family, the Tarsiidae. They get their scientific name from their very long ankle bone, or tarsus. Other noteworthy features of these half-monkeys are the ears, which are comparatively large and rounded and set on each side of the short face (it is not foxlike, as in the lemurs) and the flat nails—rather than claws—on their fingers and toes.

Tarsiers live in the East Indies, from Sumatra to the Philippines and the Celebes, but not on the mainland of Asia. They bear a single young. An adult is no more than six inches long, with a ten-inch tail rather like a rat's but tufted at the tip.

Monkeys of the New World

THE NEW WORLD MONKEYS haunt the dense tropical forests of Central America and northern South America. Compared to their Old World relatives, they are fairly small creatures, have more teeth, and are more lightly built. Most possess a grasping tail, thanks to which they are talented acrobats.

Another striking thing about the New World monkeys is that they are flat nosed. The openings of the nostrils are usually widely separated. Like monkeys round the world, the members of this family (Cebidae) tend to be vegetarian, though most eat a certain amount of insect life. Almost all are creatures of the warm sunlight—they sleep away the hours of darkness.

These monkeys, like others, have a nervous, high-strung temperament, and seem to understand a great deal more than they actually do. At times they wear an almost human expression.

The Night Monkey, Douroucouli, or Mirikina, *Aotes,* is a strange little creature, the only monkey that is out after dark. During the day this night prowler hides in thick foliage or in a hollow tree, where the bright light of day cannot hurt its sensitive eyes. It is a bit larger than a squirrel.

Douroucouli is usually a light sleeper. The least noise will serve to arouse it. It is fairly sociable, and several families may live together in the same hollow tree; often a male and female share one den. If a person passes by the tree where the family makes its home, the little striped faces pop out at the opening in the hollow trunk to see what is going on.

THE MONKEY THAT TRAVELS BY NIGHT

Silhouetted against the moon in its South American homeland is the night monkey, or douroucouli, the only monkey that stays out at night—all others prefer to remain at home during the hours of darkness. This monkey has an eerie cry that often startles the Indians in the tropical forest. The douroucouli is gentle and makes a nice pet, when tame.

In the evening and at night, douroucouli becomes increasingly active and most noisy. As it roams through the trees after insects, its favorite food, it utters a reverberating, caterwauling cry, so bold it sounds like a challenge. Perhaps it is for this reason that the Indians call the animal the "devil monkey."

Nonetheless, douroucouli has a gentle disposition. Kept as a pet in tropical South America, where it lives, it is said to free houses of giant spiders, cockroaches, mice, and centipedes. It is much appreciated because of its clean habits and its charming ways. When visitors call, it dives for refuge inside its box, but then turns and gazes curiously at the strangers. If it is not handled gently, it may spit and bite in a fury. It does not live long in captivity.

Sometimes these animals are called "owl monkeys." The head is round and the eyes are saucer-like. A ruff of long hair surrounds the short face, which is marked by three converging jet-black lines and a band of white; a coat of rusty brown or reddish gray fur covers the body. The furry tail, slightly longer than the one-foot body, has a tufted tip; unlike most other New World monkeys, douroucouli cannot use it for grasping. The ears, short and concealed in the soft, fluffy fur, prompted the name *Aotes,* or "earless." All in all, this animal may be considered an American facsimile of the lemur.

A close relative is the Titi Monkey, *Callicebus,* which is a little larger but has smaller eyes. It hunts by day in the jungles of Brazil and most of equatorial South America.

The Uakari, *Cacajao,* is the only short-tailed monkey in the New World. It shows a remarkable resemblance to the orangutan in general appearance. The short face and the front of the head are bare, the ears are naked. It has an almost human expression. This monkey is quite an intelligent animal, possessing a well-developed brain.

Uakari lives in the forests of the Amazon basin. It is only about the size of a house cat, and has long hair, which forms a cape on its arms and shoulders. Although the short tail might lead one to believe uakari is a ground walker, it prefers to stay in the trees. Its highway through the woodland follows interlacing branches, along which it runs. Uakaris often wander in small bands among the tops of the highest trees, and feed on fruit; a mother will carry her baby on her back. They have few enemies in this lofty home—mainly vultures, snakes, and eagles.

——CAPTURING THE UAKARI. In Brazil, uakaris are in great demand for presents and fetch a high price. The Amazon Indians have devised a curious way of capturing them. They shoot the uakari with a poisoned arrow and catch it in their arms when it falls. Then they put a pinch of salt, the antidote for the poison, into the monkey's mouth, and the animal revives quickly. But few uakaris last long in captivity (the Brazilians call them *mortal*—that is, delicate in constitution) unless they have been taken young and kept in their native climate. They are fairly silent animals, whether in the jungle or as pets in somebody's home.

Two species are remarkable for the coloring of their faces. The Bald or White Uakari has a scarlet face and a gray body; the Red Uakari has a vermilion face and a bright chestnut-red body. In anger or excitement their faces glow like fire. A third, the Black-headed Uakari, is black in limbs and body, except for its chestnut-hued tail and back.

A SMART AND AMIABLE FELLOW

The uakari, a cat-sized monkey, makes its home in the region of the Amazon. The animal has superior intelligence, and physically resembles its Old World relative the orangutan; it even has a shorter tail than most monkeys. The uakari is popular as a pet, but generally it is not long-lived away from its jungle haunts.

The Saki, *Pithecia,* is a queer-looking but affectionate creature, bearded and bundled up in a great coat of coarse, unkempt, shaggy hair that looks as if it were badly in need of a trimming. The tail (not used for grasping) is quite bushy and at least as long as the body. The long hair on top of the head is parted in the middle and hangs down, partly covering the face.

The saki is a comparatively small monkey, but the heavy coat of long hair makes it look much larger. It varies in color from golden brown to black.

——INTELLIGENT AND FRIENDLY. This animal is not lacking in intelligence. The naturalist Bates observes that, although dull and cheerless, the saki exceeds other American monkeys in its capability of attachment to man.

According to Bates, a neighbor went out one morning, leaving his pet saki behind. The monkey, missing its friend, made its way to Bates' house to see if its master had come there as he often did. Failing to find him, the saki climbed onto the table and sat down with an air of quiet resignation to await his return. When the owner entered the Bates home, the monkey at once jumped to its usual perch on his shoulder.

In general, the saki is a delicate and timid creature. Once tamed, as Bates' story shows, it is likely to refuse to leave its master, but clings to him the way a child does to its mother. Seldom does it survive long in captivity. It is native to tropical South America.

The Howler Monkey, Aluata, or Caraya, *Alouatta,* is the largest monkey found in the New World. A thickset, heavy-bodied animal, it is about three feet long, with an even longer prehensile tail. Its head is pyramided to a round top. A heavy beard hangs from the chin beneath the otherwise naked face.

——THE HOWLER'S REMARKABLE HOWL. Sullen-tempered and comparatively untamable, the howler is considered low in the scale of intelligence. Its chief claim to distinction lies in its ability to produce a deep roar, so far-reaching that it can be heard for a distance of three miles through the forest. The howler can roar this way because it possesses a "sound box" in its throat, formed by a modification of one of the throat bones. A strong, muscular "bellows" drives the air over the mouth of the reverberating bony soundbox.

The howler utters its cries most frequently just after sundown. But often you will hear it late in the evening, before sunrise, at intervals during the day, and also at the approach of rain. The sound is a wonderfully impressive one, best described as a series of deep growls, becoming a prolonged roar when several howlers join in what has been termed a "community sing." Often the animals seem to be trying to howl each other down and convince a female that each has better vocal powers than the rest. Many times, despite the tremendous volume of sound heard by travelers, it is only the old male of a party that is giving voice to his feelings. He always starts and ends abruptly.

LOUDEST OF THE JUNGLE CHORUS

The biggest monkey of Latin America is the howler, which weighs up to twenty pounds. It has a sullen disposition, and its hideous roar can be heard at a considerable distance; there is an enlarged "sound box" in the howling monkey's throat which gives the voice added depth. Note the animal's long grasping tail, curled about the tree trunk.

——FAMILY LIFE OF THE HOWLERS. Howlers live in family groups of five or six individuals and sometimes as many as twenty. Most active in the early morning and evening, these parties roam slowly through the tops of the tallest trees. For food they choose the terminal twigs of trees, but they will also eat some fruit.

A group will occupy a definite and limited territory and will avoid meeting other clans of howlers. It seldom travels more than a hundred yards an hour, or about eight hundred yards a day. An old male usually takes the lead, and the females with their young follow in the rear. Midday, from eleven o'clock to two, is the rest period, or siesta.

The howler breeds throughout the year. The female is promiscuous in the breeding season, and may have relations with several males, who seem unconcerned about sharing her. She carries her newborn clinging to the under side of her body. Later the baby climbs onto the back of the mother and rides aloft as she journeys through the trees. Often it will coil its tail around hers for a surer hold.

——THE WONDERFUL "MONKEY CHAIN." One of the most famous bits of "monkey business" is the so-called "monkey chain." Although we see it pictured in today's cartoons, it has quite an old history. For example, in 1720 a traveler named Lionel Wafer wrote of the howler monkeys in Panama, that when they came to a crossing from treetop to treetop a little too far for leaping, they would sometimes hang down by one another's tails in a chain. Swinging in this manner, the lowest would catch hold of a bough of the next tree and draw up the rest of the band. We are told that troops of monkeys have crossed rivers in this manner. These are good stories, but they would be still better if they were true.

Still, there is no question that the howlers have powerful tails. In his *Voyage of the Beagle*, Charles Darwin relates that he killed a howler that was hanging to a branch by its tail. The animal did not fall to the ground, and the tree had to be cut down for the naturalist to get his specimen.

There are a number of different species of howlers—the main difference among them is in color. Most howlers are black, but quite a few are bright golden red, and there are various shades in between. The male of the Black Howler is entirely black, and the female golden brown. These animals have a wide range, from Vera Cruz, Mexico, south through Central America to Brazil, Peru, and Bolivia.

The Capuchin, or Ring-tailed Monkey, *Cebus,* is the most intelligent monkey in the New World and the one we most frequently see in captivity. Although it has only one-sixth the brain weight of a chimpanzee, it can learn to use sticks to bring food within reach, tell some colors apart, recognize differences in weight, and in general wins distinction as a circus performer. It is one of the monkeys most often trained to work with the organ grinder.

The capuchin is South America's commonest monkey. Scarcely as large as a house cat (it weighs only two to four pounds) it is a robust creature with fairly long arms and legs and a lengthy hairy tail which it can use to take hold of things. It has a round head and a flat flesh-colored face that is alert and full of spirit. The hair on its head forms a peak rather like that of a monk's cap, whence the animal's name. Black or brown hair covers the body; often it is yellowish or golden buff on the chest, shoulders, and sides of the face.

Troops of wild capuchins may number thirty or forty individuals. They often travel in single file through the trees in their tropical homeland, which extends from British Honduras to Paraguay. For the most part they feed on fruit, but they are also forever on the search for insects in the crevices of tree trunks. Birds' eggs and nestlings hold an irresistible appeal for them. Tempted by the luscious morsels to be found in barnyards, they are a source of considerable worry to poultrymen, who trap them with baited gourds.

——FULL OF PRANKS. The capuchin is as mischievous as it is intelligent. The actions of one captive specimen provide an excellent example of how the animal blends the two traits. This little creature had ingenuity enough to hold out a piece of bread in its hand to young ducks on the water; when a duckling was lured within reach, the monkey would grab, kill, and eat it.

Capuchins will also pick a person's pocket and keep anything edible. If a dog gets in this monkey's way, it arches its back and spits and barks so ferociously, the intruder is likely to flee in terror. But, in general, capuchins are gentle, good-natured animals, and popular as pets. There is quite a traffic in them in South and Central America.

There are many species of capuchin; except for color, little difference exists among them. The White-throated Capuchin is typical. It has a body length of eighteen inches, a tail a little longer. Its face and chest and shoulders are white, in marked contrast with the rest of its body, which is jet-black. These animals are known by a variety of names: sapajou, caiarara, cebi, cai, and camail are the more common ones.

The Squirrel Monkey, *Saimiri,* one of the commonest of New World monkeys, is a small, interesting animal that haunts the forests from

Costa Rica to Bolivia and Peru. It resembles a squirrel in more than a preference for the trees: it possesses an inquisitive little face with rather large eyes and small ears. On its head it may have a crown of gray or black; its back, hands and feet are a vivid orange-yellow; its shoulders, legs, and other parts may be a yellowish gray. This, at any rate, is a picture of the Costa Rican squirrel monkey, a colorful fellow indeed.

Choosing the sunlit scrub woodlands rather than the gloom of the deep forest, this little monkey (it is only a foot in length, with a hairy, tip-tufted tail a few inches longer) feeds on insects, fruit, lizards, eggs, and small birds. It is a companionable creature, and travels in small bands that may scrimmage in the trees when a particularly tasty bit of food is sighted. Often father squirrel monkey will carry his baby on his back, turning the infant over to mother when feeding time arrives. Male and female and young and old look much alike.

The squirrel monkey has more than its share of curiosity and intelligence. As a matter of fact, in proportion to its body, it has one of the biggest brains of all the monkeys, and its skull is quite long. It is well liked as a pet.

In the woods, a band of squirrel monkeys will journey along with a traveler for quite a distance, intently watching every move he makes. W.W. Brown, a museum collector who rambled through the foothills of Panama, says that troops of this beautiful little creature with its long, tasseled tail (the monkey cannot use it as a fifth hand) would follow him about the underbrush chattering. They allowed him to come so near that he could almost put his hand on them.

Sometimes people refer to the squirrel monkey as the titi monkey, but that name more properly applies to a different genus (Callicebus).

The Spider Monkey, *Ateles,* is the champion acrobat of the New World. You can quickly recognize it by its light, slender body, its long, spidery limbs, and its extraordinary lengthy tail, which is better developed for grasping than that of any other monkey.

The spider monkey's tail deserves more than passing mention. It has twenty-three vertebrae and is over two feet in length—a little longer than the animal's rounded head and short body. The extremely sensitive tip is naked and can grasp with unshakable firmness anything it may touch. The tail fulfills the purpose of a fifth hand. With this remarkable appendage the monkey can suspend itself in the air, leaving all four limbs free, or it can grasp fruit that is out of the reach of the hands.

Normally the spider monkey travels along the upper surfaces of branches, using all four feet, carrying the tail arched over its back. When the animal wants to cross from the limb on which it finds itself, it may bring the powerful tail into play as a suspending arm, and swing itself till it can get a grasp on the next branch.

——A LEAP OF THIRTY FEET. The spider monkey's arms are longer than its legs, and its hands are nearly as long as its feet. It has no thumbs, and so the hands cannot help it much in grasping. Swinging is another matter again—speed and the spider monkey are synonymous. In a flying leap it can cover a distance of thirty feet or drop twenty feet straight down. Its normal pace through the trees is about four miles an hour; not many monkeys can match it in agility.

Spider monkeys are clannish folk and live in small groups, such as several females with their respective young, a male with several females and their young, or it may be a group of males only. The bachelor group consists of as many as ten individuals. Sometimes the smaller bands join up to form a group of males and females that may include thirty-two or more.

A large proportion of the spider monkey's food is fruit, but it also consumes birds, flowers, and insects in small quantities. Wading into a stream, it will catch fish. It is busiest just before dawn and before the sun sets in the evening. As soon as one area develops a scarcity in food, the colony moves out.

Although the spider monkey has a sad face, it is an amiable creature and not deficient in intelligence. But it is not overfond of intruders. It has been known to drop dead branches eight or ten pounds in weight on travelers that pass beneath it.

——FAMILY LIFE AMONG THE SPIDER MONKEYS. The spider monkeys have no fixed breeding time, but more young may be born during certain seasons of the year than others. For about the first month the baby spider monkey is carried on the belly of the mother; after this it rides on her back. When traveling, the infant curls its tail around the mother's, close to the base.

The mothers are very careful of their young. When danger threatens, a female will catch up in her arms an infant resting on a branch, place the baby on her back, and carry it away. The young are dependent on their mothers until ten months old.

At times a spider monkey will help adolescent companions across difficult places by pulling together separate vines over which they are

CHAMPION MONKEY ACROBAT

The spider monkey has an unusually long tail, which enables it to qualify as one of the great acrobats of the monkey world. This slender, spidery creature moves with great rapidity, and can jump ten yards in one leap. The youngsters love to wrestle; they often engage in this sport while hanging by their tails.

crossing. On one occasion a spider monkey drew a vine close to a tree trunk while five animals passed from the vine to the tree—without this assistance they could not have made the crossing.

Young spider monkeys love to sport and play. One of their chief games is wrestling. Their favorite position for their mock combat is hanging by their tails; sometimes four will play together in this fashion.

We come upon the spider monkeys in the tropical forests, from southern Mexico to Bolivia. The different species are much alike. Some are entirely black, while the coarse, woolly fur of others is golden yellow or reddish brown. Rather like them in many ways is the Woolly Spider Monkey, or Miriki, *Brachyteles,* of Brazil; although it is not brightly colored, its face is often a brilliant red, which becomes intensified when the animal gets angry.

Quite a different creature is the Woolly Monkey, *Lagothrix.* One of the biggest monkeys in the New World, this attractive fellow has dense woolly fur and a round bullet-like head topped off with a "crew hair-cut"; Darwin thought it looked most human. The woolly monkey lives mainly in the upper Amazon basin, where it is valued by the Indians as an article of food. It has a curious habit of making a hammock of itself; attaching its feet to one branch, its long tail to another, it rests on the tail and swings back and forth in the trees.

MARMOSETS AND TAMARINS—SOUTH AMERICA'S "NEAR-MONKEYS"

In South America we find a curious group of near-monkeys called marmosets and tamarins. These tree-dwellers are all under a foot in length, and their long tails are not developed for grasping. Instead of having nails like the monkeys, they possess hooked claws, except for the great toe, on which there is a true nail. These animals appear quite clumsy when they come down to the ground.

Some of the marmosets and tamarins are totally indifferent to their fellow beings, whereas others are very sociable, traveling in troops through the trees, where they feed on insects and fruit, especially bananas. Not only do they carefully comb their own hair but they pay equal attention to a neighbor's toilet—to the extent of picking and cleaning each other's teeth.

——A FIFTY-FOOT FALL. Rambling from branch to branch, occasionally a marmoset will lose its hold on the tree. The nature writer Bates describes an incident of this sort. While walking along a forest pathway, he observed how one of these little creatures, which was passing with a number of its kind, lost its hold and fell head first some fifty feet to the ground. Somehow it managed to alight on all four feet and then stared perplexedly at Bates before scampering up the nearest tree.

THE MONKEY WITH A RUFF
The lion monkey is an alert and fragile tamarin, or marmoset. This tiny animal's neck is encircled by a ruff, and the tail is as long as the body. A father tamarin will carry his young about—a rarity in the monkey world. In general, tamarins are amiable and engaging as pets.

——Marmoset Pets. Another author, Bartlett, tells us an even odder tale of a species found in the Peruvian Amazon region. He states that the Indian women make pets of them and allow them to hide in the long hair on their heads. From this retreat the little animals emerge to capture spiders and insects and then scamper back to devour them at leisure in their owners' luxuriant tresses.

Both tamarins and marmosets are credited with little intelligence, but, treated kindly, they become tame, friendly, and playful as kittens. When their curiosity is aroused they have a captivating way of tilting the head to one side with a knowing expression. With strangers they are sly and apt to bite.

There is quite a bewildering array of species, with a surprising range of variegated colors. Many are vivid, others a somber and drab color. They form a big family (Callithricidae) that is spread over a vast area in the equatorial forested regions of South America.

We can, however, separate these creatures into two principal groups—the somewhat larger species, with long canine teeth (*Leontocebus*); and the slightly smaller ones with short canine teeth. This second group we sometimes call the true marmosets (*Callithrix*) and we place with them some of their relatives, such as the tufted-eared, bald-faced marmosets and the mico or naked-eared, pink-faced species.

The True Marmoset, *Callithrix,* is an engaging, shy, and delicate creature, smaller than the average squirrel. It has soft, thick, silky fur, a rather long, bushy tail, a round head, and large eyes. The face and large ears are naked, the neck is often encircled with a ruff.

The true marmosets vary greatly in color. One form is white (strange for an animal that lives in the tropics), some have ringed tails, and others are clothed with gay colors. They have larger families than most primates—the female marmosets may bear two or three young instead of the usual one.

The Common Marmoset, or Ouistiti, is yellowish-gray and has its tail banded alternately with black and white; tufts of long white fur are found behind its ears. Smallest of all the primates in the world is the Pygmy Marmoset of Brazil, a speckled dark-brown and yellow creature about six inches long, with a tail a little longer.

The Lion Monkey or Maned Tamarin, *Leontocebus rosalia,* is one of the most brilliantly colored of the mammals. This resplendent, golden-yellow little monkey has a conspicuous ruff or mane of long hair around its face and neck. The face, hands, and feet are purple. It is average-sized, having a length of seven inches; the tufted tail is equally long.

The French naturalist, Isidore Saint-Hilaire, said that when one of this species was shown figures of a cat and a wasp, it was frightened;

but when it saw pictures of a grasshopper and a beetle, it tried to seize and eat them. In any event, this is a high-strung creature, much given to playful quarreling with its fellows. Both parents are credited with taking turns carrying the young, which are full grown in about six months. The species is native to Brazil. The Mustache Tamarin, belonging to the same genus as the maned tamarin, has a curling mustache of long white hairs on the upper lip that extends beyond the face to the ears.

Old World Monkeys

THE TAILED MONKEYS of Asia and Africa have in some ways developed far beyond their cousins in the New World. Although the differences may seem slight to you if you are simply watching monkeys in a zoo, to the student of animals they have great meaning.

For one thing, the Old World monkeys possess fewer teeth—thirty-two, the same number as man. The nostrils, too, are more manlike, being closer together than in the American monkeys. The Old World monkeys seem to have some degree of color vision, but none has a grasping tail.

This family includes all the Old World primates except the lemurs and the great apes. We commonly divide it into two groups. The members of the first group possess cheek pouches in which they store food. Among these animals are some of our common zoo monkeys, like the Mona Monkey and the Green Monkey (these are Guenons, the most abundant type of primate) and other little dwellers in the trees. Some of the largest, like the baboons and the drills, live on the ground. This group feeds on a varied diet of fruits, vegetable matter, insects, crabs, small birds, and eggs.

The second group prefers leaves as a diet. They have no cheek pouches, but, to digest vegetable matter, their stomach is more involved, rather like a cow's in some respects. In this group we find the Langur, Guereza and the curious Proboscis Monkey, which has a nose longer than man's. They spend most of their lives in the trees, trips to the ground being rather rare.

Because of their canine walk, this Old World family (Cercopithecidae, or "tailed apes") has been called the "doglike monkeys." Their arms and legs are nearly equal in length. They proceed on all fours, with their fore and hind quarters pretty much on a level. In moving about, the palm of the hand is placed flat on the ground, but the heel of the hind foot is raised. In the trees these animals get about rapidly, using the great power of their hind legs for springing. Their hands and broad nails are strikingly human.

The female has a regular menstrual cycle and possesses a "sexual skin," located at her rear, which swells when she is fertile. The greater the swelling the more attractive is she to the male.

MACAQUES—DWELLERS IN ASIA AND THE EAST INDIES

The Macaque, *Macaca,* is the hardiest of all monkeys. Some of its great clan (there are about fifty species, including the famous Rhesus Monkey and the Barbary Ape) can live in climates where the temperature is quite cold in winter. Others, however, are at home in the hottest parts of India and Burma. Most of these strong, sturdy animals dwell in Asia and the East Indies.

The average macaque is about the size of a small fox terrier, but some may be smaller or even much larger. Drab brown or yellow hair covers its heavy body (though a few of these animals are brilliant or gaudy in color). Its head is fairly large, with naked, pointed ears; long hair may extend down the neck or shoulders to form a mane. Overshadowed by heavy, prominent eyebrows, big eyes, placed rather close together, stare with interest and intelligence at all that goes on about the creature.

The macaque has cheek pouches in which it temporarily stores leaves and fruit. On the bare buttocks there are large callous patches, occasionally bright red in color. Some macaques have rather long tails, others practically none at all.

MONKEY MARAUDERS

The macaques usually congregate in troops which may number from a half-dozen to over one hundred monkeys. They spend as much of their time on the ground as in the trees, and are very much at home in rocky, treeless wastes. Although abroad at all hours of the day, they are most active in the early morning and evening and are fearless enough to raid an orchard or garden on moonlight nights.

BULLIES AND UNDERDOGS

Each monkey troop has its bullies and its underdogs. The social arrangement is extremely interesting to observe, for it much resembles that prevailing in human groups.

A dominant macaque may monopolize the food available, and keep its followers in a constant state of hunger. It does not necessarily achieve its position because it is a better fighter, stronger, or bigger than its companions, although these factors certainly count; it is a creature that under most circumstances appears surer of itself, more ready to take what it wants, and more inclined to greet rival claims with a quick series of blows. We see the same thing in groups of children, where a small, cocky individual may dominate others who are bigger and older but perhaps lacking in self-assurance.

Often the young bachelors form their own band, or else there are troops in which males and females travel together. It is not unusual to find that a female has the upper hand in a troop; if she is more aggressive than the males, she will have no great difficulty in bringing them to heel. We observe various ranks of superiority in the males, who are treated with fear and respect by those inferior to them. With high rank goes priority of access to the females. A female will accept a number of mates when she is in heat.

Macaques are not merely pugnacious—they exhibit more than a little intelligence and curiosity as well. In captivity they will learn to manipulate tools in a crude manner; one report tells us of a macaque that was able to hammer nails and use a saw. These animals can distinguish among colors, weights, shapes, and sounds with a fair amount of accuracy.

A macaque is fully adult when it is some four or five years old, but it may breed a year before this. There is no particular breeding season.

The female bears a single baby, which comes about seven months after mating time. The baby weighs a pound or so, and clings to its mother or climbs about her body when she is at rest. Not long afterward it apparently begins to wonder about its world, and will leave the mother for brief periods. But she must never be too far off.

A BOLD AND STURDY FELLOW
There are many different kinds of macaques found from Asia to North Africa. They are as smart as they look, and display considerable curiosity and intelligence. Shown above is the rhesus, the species that was used in experiments that established the blood types Rh negative and positive.

THE RHESUS MONKEY

Probably the best known of all the macaques is the Rhesus Monkey, *Macaca mulata,* a merry fellow that has earned a reputation as an organ-grinder's monkey, like the capuchin. At the present day it has come to the fore particularly because it was used in experiments to establish the nature of certain blood types, Rh negative or positive. The "Rh," as a matter of fact, is taken from the beginning of the monkey's name.

The rhesus is quite common in northern India, where it may dwell high up in the mountains. About two feet in length, it has a thirteen-inch tail, and is pale brown in color. It is popular in zoos because it is so active and playful. In its homeland, however, it is not regarded as a funmaker. The Hindus hold it sacred, and give it free access to all their temples. At Benares, India, you will often see it practicing impudent tricks with its cousin the langur monkey in the temple of Hanuman, the Monkey God. No one may interfere with it; it is under the special care of the priests, who provide it with food.

EUROPE'S ONLY MONKEY

The only monkey at large in Europe is the Magot, or Barbary Ape, *Macaca sylvanus*. This large, powerful, light brown creature is also at home in North Africa, but how it got there we cannot say—it is the only member of its tribe on that continent. In Morocco and in the south of Spain one frequently sees it tame, a pet at lodging places and stores. It is often trained by showmen.

Many, many years ago, the Barbary ape was introduced on the great Rock of Gibraltar, and roamed wild over it under the genial supervision of the British. There is a tradition that the animals warned the Rock's garrison in advance of a surprise attack by the Spaniards and so saved the day. It was also said that if the apes ever left Gibraltar, the day of the English there would be over. In any event, the apes were allowed to roam where they wished, and were supplied with medical care.

But too many times the monkeys upset the calm order of the garrison, or wreaked havoc among the livestock. Nowadays they do not enjoy the freedom once permitted them; their numbers have thinned out. Winston Churchill, in World War II, ordered that some should always be maintained on the Rock, so that it would be certain to remain in the hands of the British, in accordance with the old tradition. Food is provided for the apes on Gibraltar.

In the wild, most, if not all, of the macaques are social and travel about in bands like the baboons, and the Barbary ape is no exception. It frequently robs native gardens of fruit and vegetables.

The name "ape" is rather misleading as applied to this monkey and some others. It suggests a relative of the great apes, whereas the

Barbary ape resembles its higher anthropoid cousins more than other monkeys only in the absence of a tail.

SOME OTHER INTERESTING MACAQUES

At one time or another, all of us must have seen the "three wise mon-keys"—the little statuette portraying a trio of humorous-looking monkeys, one of which will hear no evil, another that will speak none, another that will see none. They originated in Japan and are quite common in Japanese art, being modeled after the Japanese Ape, a macaque with a brilliant red face and gray hair.

Another interesting monkey is the Pig-tailed Macaque, a native of Malaya, India, and China. A cheerful, friendly animal about two feet long, with brown hair, a naked, flesh-colored face, and a wiry tail, this monkey is easily tamed if taken young. It is well liked by the natives, who teach it to climb coconut trees and drop the nuts down to them below.

Not so likable is the Lion-tailed Macaque of southern India, a majestic monkey with a thick, somber gray mantle of long hair about its head, neck, and shoulders, and a jet-black body. It gets its name from its tufted tail, and it also seems to share the lion's disposition. Although sociable enough with its fellows, the lion-tail is likely to make trouble for people who approach it. On a number of occasions it seems to have slain young native children in the forests.

The Crab-eating or Long-tailed Macaque, found in Burma and many of the South Pacific islands, haunts the mangrove trees near the shore line and combs the beaches at low tide in search of crustaceans, its favorite food. It is fond of bathing and can dive and swim under water with admirable proficiency. This macaque often swims from island to island or across a bay, and is the only monkey found on some of the more isolated islands. About two feet in head and body length, it has a tail of eighteen inches.

One of the most colorful of this group of monkeys is the Toque Macaque of Ceylon. This long-tailed fellow has a black band over its eyes and temples; a bright reddish ring circles the top of its head. The sides of the neck are yellowish white and the sides of the body are splashed with red-brown. Yellow-ochre arms and hands, and reddish thighs complete the multihued portrait.

THE WILY BLACK APE

A related animal, the Black or Celebes Ape, *Cynopithecus,* almost the size of a baboon, belongs in a separate genus. It is famous for its quick wit, and the folk of the Celebes tell many tales about it.

One such story concerns the time an ape was trapped on a rock in the water by a crocodile. Just when the crocodile was preparing to eat it, the ape persuaded the large reptile to invite its scaly relatives to the feast. When they came, the monkey requested them to arrange themselves in a line, one behind the other, so it could count them.

The crocodiles obliged, and the wily black ape ran to safety across their backs.

MANGABEYS—NAMED FOR A PLACE THEY NEVER LIVED IN

The Mangabey, *Cercocebus,* gets its name from Mangaby, a place in Madagascar—but the animal has never lived on that island! The misnomer is due to an error of the early naturalists, who so often had to rely on faulty second-hand information rather than on facts that reputable observers had seen.

Although we are not very familiar with the mangabey's habits in a state of nature, we definitely do know where it dwells. The home range of this slender, long-tailed monkey extends from the east to the west coast of tropical Africa, from the Congo basin to Kenya Colony. It lives in large bands in the dense forests, where it patrols the treetops.

Like the macaque, the mangabey has large cheek pouches in which it stores food for a while. In some other respects, it parts company with its Asiatic cousin—its fingers and toes are webbed at the base, and its upper eyelids are white. It seems unlikely that the animal uses them to transmit a kind of "blinker" code to other monkeys, as has been suggested by fanciful observers.

FOND OF MAKING FACES

This monkey is less belligerent than some of its clan. Taken captive, it is soon transformed into a gentle pet with a very amiable disposition. It has a habit of making faces and will show a liberal display of teeth to those who watch it; probably this grin is due to a nervous tension in the animal, rather than the friendliness for which it is noted. The mangabey is an extremely active monkey, in any case. Its vocal powers are limited; the loudest noise it can make is a shrill call that ends with a gasping sound.

The mangabeys are not very common, but still there are two distinct groups of several species that can be recognized by whether or not they possess a prominent crest of hair on the head. Those without the crest are the brightest in color; the ones with the crest have a more subdued hue. Some of the better-known species are the Sooty Mangabey, the White-crowned Mangabey, the Black Mangabey, and the Crested Mangabey. These animals are about two feet long, with a tail six inches shorter.

BABOONS—BIGGEST OF THE MONKEYS

The Baboon, or Dog-faced Monkey, *Papio*, is about the size of a mastiff. It possesses great strength and a savage, ugly disposition when molested. Leopards and lions may attack a female or a young baboon, but a group of males will tear such a marauder to shreds with their powerful jaws and long, pointed canine teeth.

The baboon is a large monkey that has left the trees and adapted itself to a life on the ground. It has a long muzzle and, unlike so many other monkeys, an excellent sense of smell. Its eyes, which can distinguish colors, are set in front of the face and directed downward, so that when the animal wishes to look up, it must lift its heavy, overhanging eyebrows. The skin of the face may have a brilliant color.

CLEVER FOOD-GETTERS

Baboons travel in bands and favor open rocky country. Only once in a while do they enter dense forests, where, however, they can climb the loftiest trees. Walking on the ground, they set their horny patched hands and their feet flat on the surface; they can run fast on all fours in a sideways gallop, though a dog is easily able to overtake them.

In their search for food in the barren places where they usually live, baboons must frequently cover great distances. Almost anything edible is grist for their mill—fruits, roots, reptiles, and insects. Looking for insects, they will sit for long periods of time sifting sand through their hands, or move about with speed, ceaselessly turning over stones and bits of wood under which the insects may hide. Like the mangabey and the macaque, they have cheek pouches in which to store their food.

Honey is a favorite sweet of the baboons. No one can fail to be struck by the skill with which they obtain it. For one thing, they make a point of swooping down on the hive very early in the morning, before the insects are truly astir. They do not sit down to their meal until they have carefully pulled the honeycomb through the grass, thus shaking off bees that may be attached to it.

HERDS OF BABOONS

Besides being among the most intelligent of the Old World monkeys, the baboons are among the most sociable. Herds that number several hundred animals are not unusual. They are polygamous, and spend much time grooming their own fur or that of a mate.

Much has been written about the baboons' habit of posting sentinels. We are told that when a troop of baboons is searching for food, one or two sentries keep watch from a high point, where they can view the surrounding country and give warning of the approach of danger (baboons bark, grunt, or scream, and each call appears to have some meaning).

On the other hand, travelers have time and again wandered over an outcropping of rock and suddenly found themselves in the midst of a baboon band. The animals seemed just as surprised as the human intruders, so probably we should dismiss the story of the baboon watchers as a good tale—if true.

BABOON PESTS

Although baboons do not molest other animals as a rule, but will peaceably share the same feeding grounds with them, they have managed to make pests of themselves near human habitation. They will often raid orchards and steal eggs from birds' nests. Prowling about, they will break down fences.

There is an account of a troop of baboons that invaded a farmhouse in South Africa to investigate the premises. While they were inside, the door slammed accidentally, sending the animals stampeding off by way of the closed windows and the chimney. They made good their escape, but not much was left of the dwelling.

When baboons have made a nuisance of themselves in a vicinity, drastic measures are taken against them. The use of strychnine in fruit is generally of little avail, for the animals appear able to detect the poison. Accordingly, regular drives are organized to exterminate them. Native beaters locate the band of offenders, and then, with the help of shouts, noisemakers, and guns, proceed to drive them to some high spot where they may be readily surrounded. Afterward, the hunters close in and make short work of the baboons with rifles.

THE HELPFUL TAME BABOON

For all this, a tame baboon is an affectionate and intelligent pet when young. (It may grow morose and dangerous as it gets on in years.) In South Africa, baboons have been trained to find bulbs which are used as food; these monkeys have also done yeoman duty in locating water beneath the soil, after a good thirst has been raised in them with salted food. Indeed, they seem to be natural water-finders, wild baboons having the habit of excavating holes in the sand at the bottom of gullies in order to assuage their thirst in the dry season.

There have been many famous tame baboons, but one in particular stands out in the annals of trained baboondom for its ability to make itself useful. This creature belonged to an injured railroad signalman in South Africa toward the end of the last century. The animal used to sweep out the signalman's shack, carry water for him, and performed many other tasks. When the driver of an approaching train blew his whistle, the baboon took down a special key needed on the railroad, and carried it out to him. The animal labored faithfully in this wise for almost a decade, until it was stricken with tuberculosis.

Baboons are the biggest members of the Old World family of monkeys. We find three general groups of the dog-faced baboon, *Papio:* the dark-colored ones, the lightish yellow ones, and the maned gray baboons. One of the best known is the Chacma, a brownish black creature at home in South Africa and often observed at zoos. The baboons have tails of different lengths, but on the average they are fairly long and carried arching upward. Except for the Hamadryas Baboon, another genus, all the baboons are strictly African animals, found south of the Sahara.

THE HAMADRYAS BABOON

The Hamadryas Baboon, *Comopithecus,* was the sacred baboon of the ancient Egyptians, who often pictured it on their monuments. They found it, as we do, around the Red Sea. (It is a native of Ethiopia, but a smaller species lives in Arabia.) Like the dog-faced monkey oi baboon, this fascinating creature sticks close to the open country and rarely turns up near woodlands.

FIERCE-TEMPERED BABOON

Among the most intelligent of the Old World monkeys, as well as one of the most sociable, is the hamadryas baboon. The more aggressive male keeps a harem, which he guards quite zealously. If a female attempts to share her affections with a male other than her regular lord and master, such fickleness may cost her life.

We know much about the behavior of the hamadryas in captivity, thanks to a careful study of two large groups made by Dr. S. Zuckerman. At the London Zoo and the Munich Zoo, enclosures were established that aptly copied the situation in which these animals find themselves when they are at home—rocks, caves, and all. Dr. Zuckerman watched the way they comported themselves here, and discovered many interesting things about their habits.

The hamadryas lives in troops, each dominated by a powerful male. whom we may call the overlord. He has a number of wives, sometimes as many as seven, and keeps them in his possession by virtue of his greater weight, size, fighting ability, or general self-assertiveness. He will not share a wife with other males, and may beat her to death if she dallies with someone else. If he has the strength for it, he considers it quite proper to steal the mate of another male.

BABOON BATTLES

Rarely does a simple fight take place between two baboons for the possession of a female. The battle may start between two, but it does not end that way. One lord begins by showing his teeth in a savage grin, then beats the ground and works himself into a fury, jumping back and forth and striking at his opponent. Others soon join in, almost as though they had been itching for a fight.

The female is the pawn in the battle; she may pass from the ownership of one male to another as the frenzied, short-lived struggle continues. So brutal are the combatants that the female who provoked it seldom lives to see its end. No matter—her corpse is an object of value to the victor, who will watch over it jealously when peace returns again. These animals cannot recognize the signs of death, and at zoos the removal of a body such as the one mentioned is quite a problem to the keepers.

In this monkey world, the female's lot, then, is hardly an enviable one. Even should there be no fighting, her master grudges her what she eats, preferring to take it for himself. He is likely to share a meal with her only when she is ready for mating (the condition is shown by a swelling of the sexual skin at her rear, a regular occurrence at the midpoint of the menstrual cycle), provided he momentarily desires her. If she offers herself to him and he does not desire her, she will get a severe beating. About six months after mating, she bears a single baby, which clings to her belly hair or rides on her back. During the pregnancy and while she is nursing the baby, she has no sexual relations as a rule.

In the wild, packs of two or three hundred hamadryas baboons of all ages are not uncommon. The oldest males are always in the lead when the troop is moving, the younger large males make up the rearguard. Often bachelors live in troops of their own.

These animals have lengthy, pointed muzzles, bright, pink faces, and their fur is reddish brown or grizzled. The male has a long, loose mantle of heavy hair covering his shoulders and back. Not to be confused with them is the Gelada Baboon of southern Ethiopia. This handsome, sturdy monkey much resembles the hamadryas in its habits, and even wears a mantle of black hair on its shoulders. It is less aggressive than the hamadryas, which will fight a leopard and is said to attack man.

MANDRILLS AND DRILLS

The Mandrill, *Mandrillus sphinx,* a sturdy baboon of West Africa, is a colorful creature, no matter from what end you look at it. Its sitting-pads are violet in hue, surrounded by crimson. The face is like that of a clown in a nightmare—a monstrous daub. The top of the long nose is bright red, the tip is scarlet, and the side ridges a vivid blue. There is a black spot on the forehead, and a yellowish-white patch above each ear extends around the neck. As a finishing touch, the beard is yellow.

The rest of the mandrill's body (the animal is about three feet long, with a stump of a tail) is mostly black, which serves to set off emphatically the weird hues of the fantastic head and rump. Females are not so massively built as males, and like the young have colors of a more somber hue and less prominent ridges on the face.

In their eating habits, the mandrills resemble other baboons. They will feed on almost anything edible, and their usual menu includes fruits, roots, eggs, insects, reptiles, and amphibians. With their inch-long canine teeth they are capable of killing quite a large animal, but they are not habitual mammal-eaters and do not make unprovoked attacks on man.

The mandrills inhabit dense forested country—indeed, they are the most forest-loving of the baboons. Still, they spend the greater part of their lives on the ground, climbing up into trees only occasionally. They travel in troops, and have no fixed abode, although a company of mandrills usually has its own home territory.

A close relative and neighbor is the Drill, *Mandrillus leucophaeus,* a strong, thickset monkey with a heavy body and nothing more than a stub of a tail. Somewhat smaller than the mandrill, the drill lacks that creature's gaudy colors: the face is black and the lower lip red, the sides of the head are greenish brown, and the body brownish black.

ONE OF THE ODDEST OF ALL MONKEYS

A strange-looking fellow is the mandrill of West Africa. Not only does this creature have a very prominent muzzle, but hues of red, blue, yellow, black, and white meet on its face. The mandrill loves deep forests, although much of its time is spent on the ground.

GUENONS—AFRICA'S COMMONEST MONKEYS

The Guenon, *Cercopithecus*, is the commonest monkey of Africa. The number of different kinds of guenons far exceeds that of any other group of primates. We now recognize about eighty forms, each with distinct color markings. Included are the Grivet, Talapoin (the smallest of all), Osok, Avem or Avembo, Green Monkey, Diana Monkey

(Linnaeus named it that because it is so attractive), Mona Monkey, and the Vervet.

The name "guenon" is an exotic one. Supposedly, it originally meant a maker of faces, and was applied to these creatures because of their fondness for showing their teeth and grimacing at observers. Be that as it may, we can generally identify the guenons by their

HANDSOMEST OF THE GUENONS

There are about eighty different forms of guenon, each distinctively marked; the prettiest, pictured above, is the Diana monkey. The guenons are Africa's most typical monkeys, and travel about the trees in small bands. The mother guenon is devoted to her baby, and even if wounded to the death will try to protect it.

slender body, long legs, very lengthy straight tail, and short face. Most are about the size of a house cat, though some are quite large.

The guenons are charming creatures and coy in their ways. They spend their days in the trees, seldom coming to the ground. Their troops are small—rarely do they number more than twelve—and an old male is their leader. Most of the time he is the only one that utters a loud sound, and when he calls they follow. The members of the troop hardly ever seem to rest, one graceful movement rapidly dissolving into another as they race through the trees, hunting for such favorite dainties as fruit, bird eggs, insects, and wild honey, some of which they may stow away in their cheek pouches.

A traveler passing by cannot resist watching these colorful monkeys —they may be hued with a blend of green and gray or blue, or yellow and brown or black, with brilliant head markings daubed with other shades from nature's palette. The guenons feel an equal curiosity about a man, and will halt their activities and scrutinize him closely, shaking their round, whiskered little heads in wonderment. Mostly, however, they keep to themselves. When night comes, they curl up on a convenient branch and sleep away the hours of darkness.

MONKEY MOTHER LOVE

We have spoken often of the affection that many mammals lavish on their young; the mother guenon is no exception. As she travels through the trees, her baby clings to the hair on her breast, and frequently she will hold it there with one arm. In the face of danger she will fight staunchly to protect the infant, often first taking the precaution of passing it on to a neighbor. Should she be fatally wounded, she will still attempt to preserve her baby, either by hiding it with her body or entrusting it to the care of one of her associates.

A "SICK" MONKEY

At the zoo, the guenons will delight you for hours with their quaint antics and grimaces. Some of their "monkeyshines" are remarkably human. For example:

A certain sick guenon once was placed on a prescription of spirits. This pleasant medicine was given at set hours by order of the veterinarian and the animal soon developed a liking for it—medicine time could not come soon enough to satisfy Mr. Guenon. However, when the creature recovered from its illness, the spirits were discontinued. The monkey showed its unhappiness by putting its hands to its belly and moaning and grimacing as though in the direst misery, whenever the hours of its former treatment came around again.

The guenons are strictly African monkeys. We find them throughout the entire continent except in the extreme northwest along the Mediterranean Sea. They are not native to Madagascar.

RED MONKEYS

Closely related are the Red Guenons, or Red Monkeys, *Erythrocebus,* which dwell in equatorial Africa. These are considerably larger and have coarser hair than the typical guenons we have just been considering.

The red guenons do not climb trees but live on the open plains and prairies, moving about on all fours. They can achieve a good speed, for their arms and legs are longer than those of the typical guenons; indeed, their limbs make us think of stilts. Often it takes a good horse to overtake these animals, which travel in small companies that are commanded to some extent by the older males. One well-known species, the Patas Monkey, has a black nose; another, the Nisnas Monkey, has a white one, but both are alike in possessing handsome fox-red coats.

LANGURS—COMMON MONKEYS OF THE ORIENT

The Leaf Monkey, or Langur, *Presbytis,* also known as the Holy Monkey or Wanderoo, is the common monkey of the Orient. We meet about fifty-six different kinds of these creatures from China and India all the way across to the East Indies. Some live at great heights; the Himalayan Langur braves the cold twelve thousand feet up in the mountains.

The langurs, or leaf monkeys, resemble Africa's guenons in a general way. With long, narrow hands and feet, a lengthy straight tail, and a slender body, these creatures are well fitted for a life in the trees. We can tell them apart from their African relatives by their shorter great toe and thumb. Also, they have no cheek pouches in which to tuck away their food.

In the dense forest the langur can travel at great speed, making long leaps with perfect ease and rhythm, aided by the remarkable grasping power of its hands and feet. A single leap may cover distances of twenty or thirty feet between trees, or forty or fifty feet from a treetop to a branch below. The animal jumps like a human being, with feet foremost and hands outstretched to grasp the next branch.

Mother langur bears one infant at a time. For the first month or two it clings close to her breast, holding on to her hair with its tiny hands and feet. In this manner it goes with her wherever she travels, clinging tightly as she leaps from tree to tree; sometimes the mother will steady her child with a protecting hand, the way the guenon mother does.

EATER OF LEAVES

The snub-nosed langur, shown above, is a leaf monkey; there are over fifty different kinds of these creatures in the Orient, where they are the commonest of the monkeys. They are notable climbers and leapers, and in India, where they are protected as "holy," show considerable boldness.

Community life among the langurs is in general well regulated and polite. They are not quarrelsome nor do they squabble over food. Generally they eat leaves (hence the name "leaf monkey") but they will also dine on fruit, flowers, and seeds. Around villages they will accept gifts from perfect strangers with all the confidence of old friends. They have a rather musical, joyous call when pleased. Fright-

ened, they utter a harsh, guttural note as a danger signal, especially
to warn their fellows of the presence of their most-dreaded enemies,
the leopard and tiger.

THE HANDSOME LANGUR

Some of the langurs are exceedingly handsome. The Douc, for one,
has a pink face, black hands, white arms, white cheeks and throat,
and a black collar. It is average in size—about two feet long, with a
tail the same length. The Wanderoo, or Purple-faced Langur, a resident of Ceylon, is mostly black, finely mixed with white, and has a
distinctive ruff extending under its chin from ear to ear.

In general, the colors of the langurs range from black to brown,
red, yellow, gray, and white. The hairs on top of the head sometimes
radiate to a central high point so that the monkey looks as though it
were wearing a dunce's cap streaked with colored stripes.

THE SACRED MONKEY

Most renowned of all the langurs is the Hanuman, *Presbytis entellus*.
This large monkey has a pale yellowish body; its hands, feet, and face
are black. It carries its long tail arched over its back, and may proceed
waving it disdainfully wherever it will in its native land, Central India.

The hanuman is sacred to the gods. One of its ancestors (his name
was Hanuman, and he was the son of the wind and a monkey nymph)
did the deity Rama a good turn when he was trying to conquer Ceylon; the Hindus have carried the langur on a pension ever since, feeding it and protecting it. Hanumans travel back and forth over India,
often in the company of the country's strolling saints or holy men.

The hanuman feeds on fruits, seeds, and leaves and impudently
raids gardens and orchards in broad daylight, taking advantage of its
immunity as a sacred animal. Having nothing to fear from man, it
wanders around country villages in large and small groups and has
free access to the temples. It is an important figure in local quarrels.
As an act of revenge or spite, a native will throw a handful of rice on
a neighbor's roof during the rainy season. The monkeys will tear the
tiles off to get at the grains of rice that have fallen into the cracks.

Such creatures can make incredible pests of themselves, yet anyone who molests them does so at the risk of his life. When the British ruled India, from time to time pious Hindus would ask them to rid their towns of the hanuman plague—they would not touch the animals themselves. Accordingly, large numbers of monkeys were taken prisoner and released in cities some distance away. This act hardly pleased the residents in the monkeys' new home, who took prompt steps to get them returned whence they had come.

OTHER OLD WORLD MONKEYS

The Proboscis Monkey, *Nasalis larvatus,* is the oddest-looking monkey on earth. It has an extraordinary nose, perhaps three inches long: the tip, in the male, droops down below the chin. Not only is the nose large and mobile—a furrow down the middle makes it seemingly

THE SIMIAN CYRANO

The proboscis monkey has a remarkable nose; sometimes it is all of three inches long, and may hang below the chin. A native of Borneo, this animal will take to the water and swim with great skill, should the need arise.

double. When the monkey utters its call (it sounds like "honk" or "kee-honk"), it is drawn out and deeply resonant.

This quaint fellow dwells in Borneo and is quite large. About two and one-half feet long, he is reddish in color, with some gray on his limbs and lower back. The Malays call him a *blanda*. The word means "Dutchman," a name that may raise the animal in its own esteem but can hardly prove pleasant to the ears of the colonists from the Netherlands.

The proboscis monkey is a tree-dweller, and especially favors parts of the forest near the water. It knows how to swim, and paddles along doughtily in dog fashion. If fired at, it will dive for safety and come up half a minute later some feet ahead, whereupon it will try to make a getaway.

Like the langur, the proboscis monkey is a vegetarian, feeding on leaves and fruit. It travels in small troops. It is not so given to activity as many other monkeys; for long stretches of time it will sit calmly on a branch, at ease with the world.

The Guereza, Colob, or Bishop Monkey, *Colobus,* in the flowing "robes" of its silky fur, is the aristocrat of the monkey world. Peace-loving and gentle in its habits, it spends its life in the tops of the tallest trees in the dense forests of equatorial Africa.

——GREAT DESTRUCTION OF THE GUEREZA. The guereza's long coat has suggested a bishop's robes to some. When, on rare occasions, this large, slender, langur-like monkey comes to the ground, and moves about on all fours, its mantle may trail a foot from its body. The hair closely resembles the white lichen that hangs from the boughs in the animal's homeland. Contrasting color patterns of dark and light shades—they render the animal hard to discern in the tree-tops—attractively mark the fine, satiny hair. Most often these monkeys are black and white, but one group of guerezas favors red.

Although the guereza's coat keeps it warm during cold nights in the trees, and provides an effective shield against stinging insects, it has almost proved to be the creature's undoing.

Toward the end of the last century guereza fur became extremely popular for trimming ladies' hats and coats. Close to two hundred thousand guerezas were slain each year to appease a fashion-hungry civilization. Finally, when approximately two million of the animals had been destroyed, the style changed, just in time to save the guereza from extinction. Its fur is still sought by native witch doctors, however.

In spite of its heavy robes, the guereza can achieve remarkable speed in the trees. By day, family groups of these monkeys hunt for leaves to fill their stomachs, or feast on buds, fruits, flowers, and seeds. Like most other animals, each little band has its own domain, a certain section of the forest over which it travels periodically. These creatures have no regular home or nest.

A MONKEY ARISTOCRAT
The guereza or bishop monkey has a long coat of silky fur that reminds us of a bishop's robes. The popularity of the fur for trimming almost led to the animal's extinction; some two million guerezas were killed around the turn of the century. Fortunately, the vogue waned, and the animals now dwell in comparative peace in the African jungle.

Mother guereza will bear a single baby at a time; there are no twins. When her infant is small, she carries it in her arms, and it holds tightly to the fur on her breast with its little hands and feet. As it grows older, it gains confidence and rides courageously on her back. It likes to climb up on her shoulders when she is sitting at rest.

We can easily distinguish the guereza from the langur by its extremely small thumb. Some of the guerezas also have a tuft on the tip of the tail. Neat, clean, and well-groomed, the guereza is pleasing to look at in spite of the sad expression on its little black face.

Giants of the Monkey World—
The Great Apes

IN SPITE of what you may see in motion pictures, the great apes will not adopt human waifs, nor do they steal native women. It seems likely such false notions arose because a number of these creatures are so manlike in appearance. That, in any event, is why they are sometimes referred to as anthropoid ("manlike") apes. The great apes include the gorilla, chimpanzee, orangutan, the long-armed gibbon, and the siamang.

The behavior of the great apes, as we shall soon see in detail, is almost human. They are quick to learn, and show an instinct closely akin to reasoning. In this respect they go far beyond the monkeys. In appearance, too, there is a greater difference between the great apes and the monkeys than between man and the great apes.

The great apes—they are members of the family Pongidae— are more robust and sturdily built than most monkeys. They lack a tail, and have long arms that can easily support the weight of the body. Arms and shoulders are greatly developed, compared to the legs, which are shorter. The legs are too weak to launch the weight of the animal in a long jump, but it can swing from branch to branch by means of its arms.

Like the monkeys, apes are creatures of the warm sunlight. Generally they are vegetarian in their choice of food, but most eat a certain amount of insect life.

Apes love comfort. Often they will build a nest as a temporary abode or overnight sleeping place. Each animal makes its own—there are no family retreats, although a female will naturally take her nursing baby into her shelter. Some of the nests are no more than a rude platform; others are covered overhead as a protection against

196

the weather. Even the heavy-bodied gorilla has a comfortable nest, although it has to make it on the ground. Few other members of primate society are accustomed to provide a bed for themselves the way this group does.

Some of the great apes will occasionally walk erect, or nearly so. When they proceed on all fours, they do not apply the hands (which are never shorter than the feet) to the ground in the manner of monkeys. Instead, they support the weight of the body on the bent knuckles of the fingers and the outer edges of the soles of the feet. Their thumbs are freely jointed at the wrist as in the human hand.

The great apes cannot swim. If they accidentally fall into deep water, they will drown. A gorilla that recently tumbled into the moat at the New York Zoological Park made no attempt to save itself— watchers were amazed to see it drown without a struggle in just a few feet of water. It is possible, however, that these animals could learn to swim if they were taught when young.

GIBBONS—THEY RACE THROUGH THE TREES

The Gibbon, Hoolock, or Wau-wau, *Hylobates,* has such long arms that the tips of the fingers actually touch the ground when the animal stands erect. The slender hand is noticeably longer than the foot. The animal is the smallest of the great apes (it stands three feet high, and has a weight under fourteen pounds) and is regarded as the lowest in the scale of intelligence.

On the ground, the lithe, slender gibbon appears awkward and out of place. It moves along with difficulty, holding its long arms over its head and hurrying forward to keep its balance. But it is well named *Hylobates* or "tree-walker." Once in the trees, it proceeds with facile rhythm and grace as it speeds through the forest, swinging from branch to branch. It can walk erect along a horizontal limb, gripping it with the great toes. No other ape or monkey can travel through the trees with the speed of the gibbon.

The gibbon frequently gathers its food as it hangs from a branch by one arm. Gibbons subsist largely on fruits, leaves, and the tender shoots of plants, but they will eat insects, too, and are especially fond of spiders. They also, no doubt, rob bird nests of eggs and nestlings. Often they loot orchards, and, when surprised, swing away through the trees, carrying the fruit with their feet. Forewarned, the speedy gibbon is safe from any of its foes. The leopard is its archenemy; on the ground occasionally a big cat will surprise it in an unguarded moment.

TREMENDOUS VOICE OF THE GIBBON

This ape has a tremendous voice that it is fond of using in the early morning. When feeding, it lets out a succession of low, staccato, almost whistling, cries followed by a prolonged series of ear-splitting shrieks that make the forest ring. You may hear these cries a mile away. The story is told that at the London Zoo the sounds produced by a gibbon once brought a police officer from a considerable distance —he was convinced someone was being murdered and wished to prevent the crime.

THE GIBBONS' FAMILY LIFE

Gibbons travel about in groups ranging from a few individuals to a dozen or more. They raise a considerable noise that disturbs their fellow inhabitants of the jungle. The family appears to be fairly monogamous. The mother produces a single baby about seven months after mating time (not nine months, as is the case with the chimpanzee and other great apes). The infant develops slowly. For the first half-year of its life it clings to its mother's body, only very gradually learning to walk and look after itself. When the young male shows signs of sexual maturity, he is usually forced to leave the family group. Males are more pugnacious than females.

In intelligence tests, gibbons have not proved much smarter than monkeys. Still, with their large eyes, they can distinguish among colors and sizes. These animals quickly learn to operate the catches of wire containers in order to get at food within them, and will use rakes to reach food that is outside their zoo cages. They are rather docile, gentle creatures, and will often make affectionate pets.

WHERE THE GIBBONS LIVE

There are two main groups of gibbons. *Hylobates* is exclusively oriental, being found only in southeastern Asia; the western limits of its range are the hills of Bhutan, between India and Tibet. Many species are black or brown, but one sees notable differences in color and size among these animals, as indicated by their names: the White-handed Gibbon, Black-crested Gibbon, Dark-handed Gibbon, Dwarf Gibbon, and Gray Gibbon. The Hoolock Gibbon of Assam and Yunnan may be black or a yellowish or reddish buff.

The Siamang, *Symphalangus syndactylus,* the largest of all the gibbons, is native to Sumatra and the Malay States, where it lives at altitudes of two thousand to six thousand feet. This black creature has a tremendous reach, with an armspread of five feet, yet the head and body length is only three feet. It is peculiar in that its second and third toes are combined in a web. The siamang also has a great voice —an inflatable sac in the throat is probably responsible for its volume.

THE ORANGUTANS—"MEN OF THE WOODS"

The Orangutan, or Orang, *Pongo,* a native of the forests of Borneo and Sumatra, is truly a big ape. A full-grown male will weigh between 150 and 200 pounds. It has an armspread that will reach seven and one-half feet (greater than either the chimpanzee's or gorilla's) but the body does not exceed four and one-half feet in height. The orang can easily be recognized by its large size and coat of long, loose brick-red hair. Its common name means "man of the woods."

Only the thickest and most luxuriant forest growth is frequented by the orang. Here it swings by its great, long arms from limb to limb and tree to tree. The pace is not rushed but even and deliberate. Yet, though seemingly slow, the orang travels faster than a man can run over the forest floor below; in a single swing it covers a distance of seven feet.

THE ORANGUTAN TESTS EACH BRANCH

The mias or mawas, as the orang is known to some of the natives, also walks with measured tread along the heavy branches in a semi-erect position. It is obliged to proceed this way because of the great length of its arms and the shortness of its legs, and because it leans on its knuckles instead of the palm of the hand as it walks.

The animal never leaps or springs; this would hardly be safe, as even large branches might snap with the sudden application of a weight of two hundred pounds. Careful observations reveal that the orang instinctively tests each branch before trusting its full weight on it. It favors a life in the trees more than does the chimpanzee or gorilla.

THE ORANGUTAN IN PEACE AND WAR

The orang is a "home body" of a sort. It builds a nest to sleep in—a rude sort of platform composed of slender boughs, branches, and leaves. Usually it places the platform not more than twenty-five feet

AS HEAVY AS A MAN

The orangutan is one of the giants of the monkey world. When grown, the male weighs as much as a man—up to two hundred pounds. It is among the most tree-loving of the great apes and builds a nest among the boughs, in which it passes the night. It may live for twenty-five years in a zoo, and very likely longer in the forest.

from the ground; higher, it would be too exposed and windy for comfort. Each orang builds its own nest, which is only a temporary shelter and may be used but once. During the rainy season the animal covers itself with leaves.

Having prepared such a comfortable nesting place, the orang is loth to leave it in the morning. It does not get up until the sun has dried the dew upon the leaves. Once arisen, it feeds all through the day.

The orang seems to prefer unripe fruit, especially the very sour and intensely bitter kind such as the red fleshy arillus. The durian, another favorite, is a large fruit with a delicious custard-like pulp and a thick, spiny rind. However, more fruit is wasted than eaten.

Natives say that the orang has no enemies; only the crocodile and the python dare attack it. It is said that when the crocodile does attack, the orang will kill it with brute strength by pulling open the crocodile's mouth and tearing out its tongue and throat. When the python attacks the orang, the ape bites the snake in two—or so the natives declare. Certainly the adult male is a formidable fighter, and possesses long canine teeth.

A CHEERFUL AND INTELLIGENT ANIMAL

Although the orang wears a mournful expression, it does not have a sluggish disposition. In fact, in captivity the animal is most cheerful and quick to learn new tricks. Some orangs can manage to ride a tricycle after three lessons, and to drive nails into pieces of wood with a hammer. They even learn to dress themselves—to put on trousers, sweater, cap, and adjust suspenders. An intelligent orang can not only use a key in a lock but can pick the right Yale key out of a half dozen or more with a little practice.

At least one orang in the New York Zoological Park conceived the idea of how to use a lever without any prompting from the keepers. For some time it had been showing it was annoyed because it could not put its head through the bars of the cage and look about. Using its trapeze bar, the orang inserted one end of it between the bars of the cage and very deftly pried them wide enough apart so that it could thrust its head through and look around outside. This orang can also plait and twist straw into a rope and use it to swing on.

The orang has a long life expectancy; one lived twenty-five years in captivity and probably would have lived longer under natural conditions. The female has only a single young at a time, about nine months after mating. Adults are rarely seen together.

CHIMPANZEES—SMARTEST OF THE APES

The Chimpanzee, *Pan*, at home in equatorial Africa, is probably the most intelligent of all the apes. Its face is very mobile; the mouth, lips, and eyes are capable of expressing emotion to an almost human degree.

An enraged chimpanzee is hardly a fellow to fool with. A large male stands about five feet in height and weighs about 150 pounds. It is not so powerful as an orangutan but is more than a match for the strongest man.

The chimpanzee is sturdily built, with a rather stout, heavy body, a large head, and big ears. The legs are long, and the foot is shorter than the hand, while the great toe is opposable for grasping. The long arms reach just below the knee when the chimpanzee stands erect. It can and does stand up on its hind legs and walk upright but more often this ape travels on all fours, the hands folded so that it leans on its knuckles.

Chimpanzees enjoy their privacy. Each has its own individual nest or house, a shelter made with branches of trees twenty-five or thirty feet above the ground. Branches are collected and tied together with wild vines to make something like an umbrella, beneath which the chimpanzee rests on a horizontal branch. The animal feeds on fruit and vegetables; when these become scarce in one locality, the chimpanzee moves to another, where it builds a new house.

CHIMPANZEE FAMILIES

As a rule, the male chimpanzee occupies one tree and the several ladies in his harem the trees close by. Social gatherings are limited to family groups. Solitary chimpanzees are not unusual; the head of a family will fight off any ambitious strangers that try to steal his mates.

About nine months after mating, the female bears a single baby. It is all of a year old before she weans it, and the youngster stays on with the family until half grown. The chimpanzee reaches maturity in its tenth or twelfth year. The normal life span is shorter than man's and may not exceed twenty-five years. After the first seven or eight years this ape is not to be trusted; it often becomes bad-tempered and temperamental with age in captivity.

Tests have shown that the chimpanzee takes more readily to training and learns more easily than any of the other animals. But one thing it cannot learn, and that is to speak. Give the chimpanzee the power of speech, then what would be the limit of its progress?

AN EDUCATED CHIMPANZEE

One star performer named Peter learned to do fifty-six separate acts in sequence. Peter removed his cap, hung it up, and seated himself on a chair at a table. He unfolded a napkin and fastened it under his

IT DOES EVERYTHING BUT TALK

The chimpanzee, with a brain about one-third the size of a man's, is the most intelligent and teachable of all the apes. As a circus performer, a chimp will ride a bicycle, do carpentry work, and dress or undress itself. In the wild it is quite shy, and will run away when human beings approach.

chin. Using a fork, he speared slices of banana and ate them with relish. Uncorking a bottle, he poured himself a drink in a glass and recorked the bottle.

In his next act Peter poured a cup of tea, added sugar and cream, sampled the mixture with a spoon, and drained the cup. Putting a cigarette in his mouth, he struck a match, lit the cigarette and puffed smoke from the corner of his mouth, and then spat into the cuspidor.

In still another act Peter brushed his teeth with a toothbrush. He brushed his hair and powdered his face with the aid of a mirror. He also undressed himself, lit a candle, got into bed, and blew out the light. He put on his own roller skates, and enjoyed the fun of skating. Peter could mount and ride a bicycle and did so without any practice. While riding around the stage he would wave his cap to the audience, pick up a bottle and drink from it, and finally dismount and bow, clapping his hands.

The nervous strain of such an act on any chimpanzee is enormous and cannot be endured for long. Poor Peter did not last.

HE KNEW WHAT HE WAS DOING

Dr. Lightner Witner, professor of psychology at the University of Pennsylvania, who tested Peter's mentality at the laboratory of the university, stated that the chimpanzee knew what he was doing and delighted in doing it. Dr. Witner expressed his belief that Peter's proficiency was not entirely the result of training but was partly due to self-education. The animal showed marked intelligence in his actions. For example, before using a hammer to nail wood, Peter examined both ends of the tool and used the flat side instead of the round end.

Peter, like many other trained chimpanzees, understood language and followed vocal instructions. Although he was able to say "mamma," he could not converse nor did he try to learn how.

CAPTURING THE CHIMPANZEE

There are three different forms of chimpanzees found in the tropical forests of West Africa: the Bald-headed Chimpanzee, the Long-haired Chimpanzee, and the Pygmy Chimpanzee. All are attractive creatures with glossy coats. The common practice in capturing these animals is to fell the trees around them until they are isolated on a single one. Then they are driven into nets. However, they resist savagely, and are quite capable of taking a life with their long canine teeth.

GORILLAS—GREATEST OF THE GREAT APES

The Gorilla, *Gorilla,* is the largest of the great apes. It is heavily built, with enormous arms that reach the middle of the lower legs when the animal stands erect. A very big male may weigh up to six hundred pounds (few actually exceed four hundred), stand five and one-half feet high, and have an armspread of eight feet. Even a lion would not dare to provoke a row with such a mighty creature, and indeed the gorilla has no natural enemies.

In spite of its great size and formidable canines, the gorilla is not dangerous unless attacked. It feeds on fruits and vegetables and never kills to eat. This ape will not kidnap women and children—rather, it carefully avoids all human contact.

At the least sign of trouble, the female gorilla beats a hasty retreat. The male, if he is present, rises to his feet with a fierce snarl on his face, glares at the intruder, and beats his breast with his clenched fists. Then, lifting his head, he lets out a mighty roar—sharp, snarling barks at first, and then a long, deep, guttural rumble. Hearing this, most animals decide it is wiser to look for other game.

THE GORILLA BAND

A band of gorillas includes only the immediate members of a family—the adult male, one or two females, their babies, and several adolescent young—about six in all. The band does not accept outsiders, although a few groups may find themselves brought together in search of food. Nomads, every evening the gorilla folk make camp, only to move on the next day.

Preparing to sleep for the night, the gorilla builds a rude nest. The young and some females can climb trees, and that is where they make their sleeping place. Old gorillas, especially adult males, are too heavy to climb, and so they usually sleep on the ground upon a nest of leaves and twigs, with their backs against a tree.

In the daytime, the gorillas are likely to spend as much time on the ground as we do. As a rule they walk on all fours, leaning on their knuckles. Occasionally, they will stand upright and walk a short dis-- tance. In running, they pace—that is, the leg and the arm on each side move together, as we see in the hyena.

JOHN GORILLA

Gorillas in general are considered a poor third in the rank of mental ability. (The chimpanzee is first, and the orang a good second.) There are exceptions, and John Gorilla was one.

John, a young ape secured by Major Rupert Penny, in 1918, was educated by a Miss Alyse Cunningham, in England. According to her report, he was hardly the monster people expect a gorilla to be. For

STRONGER THAN IT IS SMART

The giant of the great apes, although not the most intelligent, is the gorilla, which may weigh over five hundred pounds. So big an animal has little to fear in its native jungles, and the gorilla is much more likely to stand and fight an intruder than is its cousin the chimpanzee. The habits of the gorilla, in the wild, are not well known, for the creature is rather scarce, but in captivity it proves to be gentle and amiable, as well as bright.

example, it was impossible to leave John alone at night because he shrieked from loneliness and fear, and this affected his health and appetite. He would never run into a dark room without first turning on the light. He was fearful for people in high places and would push away anyone who stood near a high window.

John, Miss Cunningham reported, was a playful fellow. He loved to stand on the rail at the bottom of a bed and jump onto the springs, head over heels, like any child. For that matter, he was especially fond of children, and would play for hours with Miss Cunningham's niece. The gorilla delighted in the game of hide-and-seek and would giggle and laugh while being chased.

A case of original thought was demonstrated one day when John was given a piece of the coarser meat from a beefsteak. Handing it back, he took Miss Cunningham's hand, put her finger on the tender part of the meat, and accepted a piece of it.

THE MYSTERIOUS GORILLA

It seems odd, with the enormous publicity the gorilla has received in motion pictures and at circuses, that it was hardly known one hundred years ago.

Mention of the animal appears in ancient literature, but it was not until 1847 that the first gorilla skull was examined in the United States. Even decades later, the appearance of the living creature was quite unfamiliar to the experts, and when genuine gorillas were shown in captivity they were mislabeled as chimpanzees. The London Zoo did not receive its first gorilla until 1887. The famous writer of some generations ago, Paul du Chaillu, is said to have been the first white man to kill a gorilla and show its skin, but he, too, appears often to have confused the animal with the chimpanzee.

The gorilla has a large mouth and a receding chin; its lips are thin. Its ears are relatively small compared to those of the chimpanzee. Its neck is short, and the large head sits close on the broad shoulders. On its clumsy hand it has a short opposable thumb. The female is markedly smaller than the male.

There are two distinct types of gorillas. The Mountain Gorilla is black, and lives in the forested mountain regions around Lake Kivu and in the mountain ranges that extend from the Belgian Congo eastward to the border of Uganda. The Lowland or Coast Gorilla is iron gray, and lives in the rain forests along the west-coast region of equatorial Africa. Old gorillas turn gray. An age of twenty-two years in a gorilla is said to be roughly the same as seventy in a man, but some of these apes may live for twenty-eight years or more.

The "Toothless" Ones—Anteaters, Sloths, and Armadillos

NATURE has its pacifists as well as its battlers. The "toothless" mammals are peace-loving, inoffensive creatures that in the main deserve our gratitude for the work they do in destroying harmful insects, especially termites. They dwell, for the most part, in the warmer regions of the New World.

In this group you will find some of the oddest and strangest-looking mammals on earth. A number of them wear coats of hair: the slow-moving sloths, which move upside down in the trees of tropical America, and the American anteaters, which live both on the ground and in the trees. Yet also a member of the group is that living armor-clad, the armadillo, a burrowing animal abundant in South America and sometimes found in the southern United States.

MOST OF THE "TOOTHLESS ANIMALS" HAVE TEETH

Seemingly, these creatures have little or nothing in common. What is more, although they are brought together in the order Edentata or "toothless animals" (edentates), the name is inaccurate.

Of all the animals in the group, only the anteaters are really without teeth. Some others, such as the armadillos, have as many as twenty-four teeth, but these are primitive and peglike, deficient in enamel and without roots. All lack canines and incisors, the teeth that make flesh-eating mammals such formidable foes. As a rule their body temperature is extremely low, rising and falling with the climate in which they live.

Add to these features the fact that the edentates have fairly small brains, pretty much on the underdeveloped side, and you get a picture of a rather primitive sort of creature. Yet each type of edentate is highly specialized to a certain kind of life and shows such an extreme in form that it might well be placed in a separate order. Indeed, the edentate order has been reorganized from time to time since it was first set up in 1798 by Cuvier. For example, the pangolin and the aardvark, once considered edentates, are now placed in separate orders; more about these later on.

A WANING GROUP

At the present day the edentates are a waning group. But hundreds of thousands of years ago they filled a prominent place on the earth, and had a much wider range. In those times, some of them were as large as cattle, but even then they do not appear to have lived by aggression.

For the sake of convenience, we may divide the edentates into two groups: those with hair and those with shells. To the first belong the American anteaters (family Myrmecophagidae, a name meaning "anteaters"), including the ant "bear." All lack teeth, have a little mouth with a long, extendible tongue by means of which they capture their tiny prey, a long tail, and strong, hooked claws that are also an essential part of their food-getting equipment.

AMERICAN ANTEATERS

The Great Anteater, or Ant "Bear," *Myrmecophaga,* is not a bear that feeds on ants, but an anteater that is the size of a small bear. It is about two feet high and eight feet long—far and away the largest of the American edentates.

Close up, there is nothing bearlike about this remarkable animal. No one can fail to be struck by the curious appearance of its long, nozzle-shaped head; it is over a foot long and is very narrow. The mouth, merely a hole at the end of the muzzle, is no bigger across than the blunt end of a lead pencil.

After the animal has torn down a termite nest with its powerful claws (the middle claw on the forefoot is greatly enlarged) and the insects are swarming out, the anteater draws them into its mouth with its lashing tongue. This whiplike organ—it may reach nine inches out of the animal's mouth—is smooth and rounded, and is kept moist with a sticky saliva that traps great numbers of the termites at one time.

——WHEN ANTEATERS TURN SAVAGE. A peace-loving denizen of the swampy savannas in tropical America, the great anteater never looks for trouble. It will make off as fast as its legs can carry it (at about the speed of a man) on the first intuition of danger.

Yet the animal is far from defenseless, and when cornered will put up a terrific battle. Raised up on its haunches in the defense position, with its well-armed forefeet posed ready to strike, it presents a front that few animals dare to face. The saber-like front claws will slash gaping wounds in an attacker. Injured, the anteater utters an exceedingly loud and ferocious roar for a creature with such a small mouth.

AN ANT "BEAR"

The great anteater is truly a big fellow—from the tip of its long snout to the end of its hairy tail it may measure eight feet. Despite its large size, the great anteater is a pacifist; it has no teeth, and prefers the diet that its name suggests. Wounded or cornered, however, the animal may prove extremely dangerous.

A collector of scientific specimens relates that his party once came upon a pair of giant anteaters. They shot and killed the male, which was in front, but a second shot only wounded the female. A native boy accompanying the collector tried to strike the wounded animal with his machete. The blow was but a slight one, and the anteater seized the youth and drew him into her embrace. With her tremendous claws she succeeded in killing him while the collector stood helplessly by, unable to shoot for fear of hurting the boy.

——Peaceful Moments Are More Usual. To dwell on such acts of ferocity, however, would be to present the great anteater in a false light. The animal is not ferocious as a rule, and prefers to give battle to nothing larger than ants.

During the day, this creature sleeps curled up in some secluded spot with its brush of a tail (about two feet in length) protecting the odd tubelike head and nose. At this time it resembles a heap of dried grass. Late evening and night find it most active. (This fact is somewhat surprising, for the great anteater has the very small eyes that we generally associate with creatures active by day.) In walking, it places just the outer portions of the forefeet on the ground, holding the claws doubled under, and carries its tail projecting straight out behind it. Although it is a land-dweller, it can and does swim across large rivers.

——Only One Baby in a Litter. Once a year the great anteater female bears a single baby. It develops only slowly, remaining with its mother for a year. Much of the time she carries it around on her back, perhaps even until her new baby comes.

We know little about the home life of these animals, beyond the obvious devotion the mother shows her offspring. We get a graphic picture of it from one writer (George Tate), who relates how he and his group happened upon a male and a female that was carrying a young one. He says the male made off but the female stayed awhile, swinging her head slowly from side to side with her long snout pointed at the men as though she were testing the wind; somehow she resembled an elephant with its trunk extended to catch the scent of strangers.

——Where We Find It. The great anteater is a native of Central and tropical South America; it is now quite rare north of Panama. Its coarse fur is grizzled and marked with a distinct broad black stripe or collar, bordered with white, extending from the throat over the shoulders and ending on the back. The hairs on the tail are very long— some measure fifteen inches—but the tail is not used to sweep up ants, as people once supposed. In captivity (at the London Zoo), one great anteater lived over fourteen years.

In the tropics, the natives occasionally eat the flesh of this animal, but readily admit they do not find it especially tasty.

The Silky or Two-toed Anteater, *Cyclopes,* is an attractive little tree-dweller at home from Mexico to Bolivia, where the climate is reasonably warm. Like Cyclops, in the old Greek tale, it cannot see very well. It is further handicapped in having a dull sense of hearing, so it must depend largely upon touch to find its way during its nightly wanderings, which are necessarily slow.

——A CAPTIVE SILKY ANTEATER. The naturalist Van Tyne observed the actions of this little anteater (it is only about fifteen inches long, half of this being the tail, which it uses for grasping) at Barro Colorado, Panama. His specimen was captured as it climbed slowly through the top of a tall bush. Never was it active during the daytime. Sunlight was repugnant to it and it usually kept its eyes closed to mere slits during the day, even when forced to move about. Left alone, it would immediately curl up and go to sleep.

——A GENTLE ANIMAL. When startled, the anteater uttered a peculiar little sneeze and would suddenly let go of the branch with its forefeet and straighten out stiffly. Clinging to the perch only with its tail and hind feet, it held the forefeet stiffly on each side of the nose, partly covering the eyes. After a while, however, it would relax. Even though it was handled a good deal, it was very gentle and never made any attempt to strike.

This animal gets one of its names because of its pretty coat of fur, which is soft and silky. It has a delicate golden yellow color, with an iridescent silver gloss; a narrow dark-brown line runs down the back.

Like the rest of its family, the silky anteater feeds on termites. Moving about in the trees, it uses all four feet and the tail to maintain a firm grip on the branches. At rest, it will sleep curled around a branch or clinging to the inside wall of a hollow tree. Its most dreaded enemies are the big cats, which it may encounter in the forest at night.

The Three-toed Anteater. Quite a bit larger is the Three-toed Anteater, *Tamandua.* About half the size of the great anteater, Mr. Three-Toes spends most of his time in the trees, a kind of life for which his grasping tail well suits him, though he comes down to the ground now and then. Attacking termite nests in the branches, this creature will consume about a pound of insects at a meal.

On his forefoot, Mr. Three-Toes actually has four toes, but the fourth is very small; there are five on the hind feet. The fur is a golden or reddish yellow, varied with black. The animal lives from southern Mexico to Paraguay, and has habits much like its big cousin's. A female at the London Zoo lived for five years, but these creatures may live longer in the wild.

AN ANTEATER THAT LIVES IN THE TREES
The three-toed anteater, or tamandua, is another primitive type of mammal that lacks teeth and feeds on insects. Its digging claws are not so big as those of its large ground-dwelling cousin, the great anteater. This animal has a prehensile, or grasping, tail, and lives in the trees. The female bears a single baby, which she carries about on her back.

TREE SLOTHS—SLOWEST MAMMALS ON EARTH

No other warm-blooded creature shows such a disinclination to action or movement as the sloth. It is so languid and lethargic that a green alga, which looks like moss, actually grows in its coarse hair. In the rainy season, when the sloth's hirsute "garden" is well watered, its fur often has a distinct greenish tinge due to the luxuriant growth of algae. (When the hot dry season comes around, the "garden" dries up.)

THE SLOTH'S TOPSY-TURVY WORLD

The sloth sees the world upside down. At the ends of its toes it has long, hooked claws. The animal habitually hangs by them from the upper branches of a tree and moves along hand over hand in this inverted position. It passes its waking hours slowly picking and munching leaves, especially the leaves of the Cecropia tree.

GOOD SWIMMERS, FIERCE FIGHTERS

No attempt is made by the sloth to construct a den or shelter in the trees as a protection against the weather; but it will return to a particular crotch in a tree to roost. It normally sleeps on a vertical branch, keeping a firm hold with all four feet, and the head hangs down and rests between the front limbs. In this manner the sloth spends about eighteen hours each day in peaceful slumber. Still, when it awakens, it hardly seems to have enough energy for its limited activities.

The sloth is not entirely helpless on the ground; given time enough, it can manage to cover a considerable distance. In the water, strange to say, the sloth can travel faster than in the trees and occasionally crosses lakes a mile wide. Most of the swimming is done with the forelimbs, which swing alternately on each side.

Sloths are solitary creatures and are never found together except during the breeding season. If put together in an enclosure, they will fight and kill each other.

THE "FAST" SLOTH AND THE "SLOW" SLOTH

There are two main kinds of sloths. The Three-toed Sloth or Ai, *Bradypus* ("slow foot"), is a slender-bodied animal about two feet in length, that looks heavier because of its long, thick, coarse hair; as its common name suggests, it has three toes on each foot. The head is small and round, and the eyes and ears are little—the animal can neither hear nor see well, but depends on its sense of smell and touch.

The three-toed sloth has a long neck (it possesses nine vertebrae, two more than the ordinary mammal) and is drab brown or gray in color, with patches of white. An extremely odd thing about the males is the bright-yellow spot, about the size of a silver dollar, on the back. In this one spot the hair is short and glossy; so far no one has come up with an explanation for this strange feature.

Somewhat larger is the Two-toed Sloth or Unau, *Choloepus* ("lame foot"). Much more animated than its lethargic cousin with the three toes, it can walk carrying its body clear of the ground (Three-Toes cannot stand upright) and can turn around on a tree trunk and come down head first, whereas Three-Toes must descend tail first.

In eating, Two-Toes will draw leaf-bearing branches to its mouth and even hold a broken twig in its paw while feeding.

The young sloth comes during the summer months; there are no twins. During the early stages it clings flat to the mother's belly, with arms and legs spreadeagled. It begins to feed itself when about five weeks old. Slow-breeding animals usually have a long life span, and a male lived for eleven years at the London Zoo.

SPEED IS HARDLY ITS FORTE
The tree sloth is built for a life in the trees—a life upside down, at that. This creature hangs languidly by its long hooked claws or moves along slowly by day. When the tree sloth is at rest, it keeps its head upright, as shown; only when the creature moves is the head actually upside down.

GIANT SLOTHS OF YESTERDAY

Nowadays the sloths (family Bradypodidae) live in suitable localities from Honduras to Bolivia. In the past, however, there were many more of them, in different varieties, roaming the Americas from New Mexico to Patagonia. They ranged in size from animals no bigger than a fox up to the Giant Ground Sloth, *Megatherium,* which was twenty feet long and considerably larger than a full-grown elephant.

The ground sloths were leaf-eaters like the modern tree sloths. We believe that the big fellows uprooted and pushed over trees so that they could get at the green shoots on the upper branches, in much the same fashion as elephants are known to do in East Africa.

The discovery of the remains of a giant sloth in Patagonia, in which the animal's rolled-up dried skin and hair were found along with cut grass and traces of early humans, suggests that these beasts may have been kept in herds by primitive man, or at least that they existed on the earth at the same time as he did. A bear-sized sloth, discovered in the crater of an extinct volcano in New Mexico, was in such well-preserved condition that it apparently could not have been dead for much more than two thousand years.

ARMADILLOS—ENEMIES OF THE WHITE ANT

When the Spaniards came to the New World, they were much struck by the marvels of animal life they discovered there. One of the quaintest creatures they found was impressive to them because of the heavy coat of mail in which it was clad. They called this animal the "armadillo," or "little armored thing."

The armadillo looks like a forerunner of our own war tanks, in a manner of speaking. A shieldlike shell encases its back. This shell is not a part of the skeleton, as it is in the case of the lobster, but is actually a development of the skin. It is made up of numerous bony plates securely welded together and covered with horny scales. It is flexible, too—pliant bands across the middle of the shell act as hinges and allow the armadillo to bend and twist and scurry with some freedom.

But this is not all the armor plate worn by the well-protected armadillo. It also has an armored shield over its head. Many armadillos, too, have the tail encased in an armored sheath. Superficially, these creatures seem built for a life of active warfare.

Nature's ways are not always what we might expect, however. It is an odd fact that when we find an animal sheathed in this manner, it is almost sure to be unaggressive.

W. Pedersen—Australian Official Photo

ONE OF AUSTRALIA'S STRANGE ANIMALS

Many odd, primitive kinds of mammals survive in Australia, but the duckbill platypus is one of the strangest of all; it lays eggs like its reptile ancestors, but it nurses its young just as modern mammals do. The platypus is at home in Australia's quieter streams and rivers, dwelling in a burrow in a bank. An able swimmer and diver, it feeds on tadpoles, worms, and small fishes.

Australian Of

SPINY ANTEATERS — PORCUPINE-LIKE DIGGERS OF AUSTRALIA

Spiny anteaters, or echidnas, are natives of Australia, too. Like their relative the duckbill platypus, they lay eggs. Slow of foot, the animals are likely to go underground when very frightened.

SPINY ANTEATER ON ITS WAY DOWN

The spiny anteater's forefeet are armed with powerful claws, and the creature can dig its way out of sight with great rapidity. It does not dig at an angle, but sinks a shaft straight down.

New York Zoolog

ONLY ITS BACK IS VISIBLE NOW

Burrowing, the spiny anteater thrusts away the dirt with flying claws, but never relaxes the guard of its bristling spines. The soil seems almost to bubble up from around the animal; in a few minutes it is completely out of sight. Of course, the firmer the ground the longer it takes.

ALMOST TOO BIG FOR COMFORT

The female kangaroo carries her baby about in her pouch until the young "joey" is well-developed; inside the pouch, the baby feeds at a teat. Kangaroos are herd animals and eat vegetable matter. They move about on all four feet when feeding, placing their front limbs on the ground and pulling their hind limbs forward. They are famed for their talent as jumpers,

Australian Official Photos

KOALA AWAKE
The koala — Australia's "native bear" — is about two feet long and has a prominent snout This harmless creature spends its life in the trees. It eats leaves, but only certain kinds, and is active principally after dusk.

KOALA ASLEEP
With its limbs tucked in, the koala naps securely in the trees. Earlier in the century it was almost wiped out for its fur, but today it enjoys government protection.

Australian Official Photos

THE WOMBAT OF AUSTRALIA
The wombat looks like a small bear in its coat of long, coarse fur, which may range in color from buff to almost black. A vegetarian, the wombat uses its lengthy claws mainly for digging.

THE TASMANIAN DEVIL
The Tasmanian devil has earned the farmer's enmity for killing sheep and poultry. By contrast, most other Australian marsupials are timid and inoffensive.

A STARTLED CREATURE OF THE NIGHT

The Tasmanian brushtail possum is only one of a number of Australia's possums, which are among the commonest of all marsupials. The long, bushy tail, together with the pointed face and large ears, makes it look somewhat like a fox. This animal is very much at home high up in the trees.

Frank M. Blake—U.S. Fish and Wildlife

AN OPOSSUM MOTHER AND HER YOUNG

The Virginia opossum is about the size of a house cat and has a long, naked, grasping tail. It is the only marsupial found north of the Rio Grande but it has some close relatives in South America. The young, very tiny when born, are carried about for a while in the mother's abdominal pouch, and later on her back. They may look forward to an average life span of eight years.

THE OPOSSUM LOOKS MUCH FIERCER THAN IT REALLY IS

With its mouth open, the opossum is a savage-looking creature; confronted with danger, however, it is likely to fall into a coma. Although it will dine on almost anything edible, the opossum feeds largely on small animal life such as rodents, frogs, and insects, and also dines on fruit.

A BAT THAT FEEDS
ONLY ON INSECTS

Only a few inches in length, this little brown bat of the eastern United States belongs to the great group of insect-eaters. (The other major group of bats feeds on fruit.) Note the enlarged claw at the end of each forelimb; it is used in climbing. Bats are the only mammals that can fly.

THE FEMALE BAT IS A DEVOTED MOTHER

This striking photograph shows a female bat with her wings spread apart, revealing a baby clinging to her underside. Like most other mammal mothers, the bat is devoted to her young, carrying it with her on her flights until it becomes too heavy.

A ROCKY CREVICE IS THEIR RESTING PLACE

The outstanding fishermen of the bat tribe are the fish-eating bats — small, brownish creatures that dwell only along the Gulf of California. Like the herd animals, male and female bats live apart, in separate colonies; only at mating time do the sexes come together. The fish-eating bat often raises her young in close association with a bird mother, the least petrel.

THE SLENDER LORIS HAS EXTRAORDINARY EYES
The slender loris, a lemur of southern India and Ceylon, has large eyes which reflect light with a coppery shine at night. The animal is only about five inches long and has remarkably well-formed fingers and toes. It passes the greater part of its time in the trees, but it does not jump and is slow in its movements. It feeds on insects, small birds, lizards, and rodents.

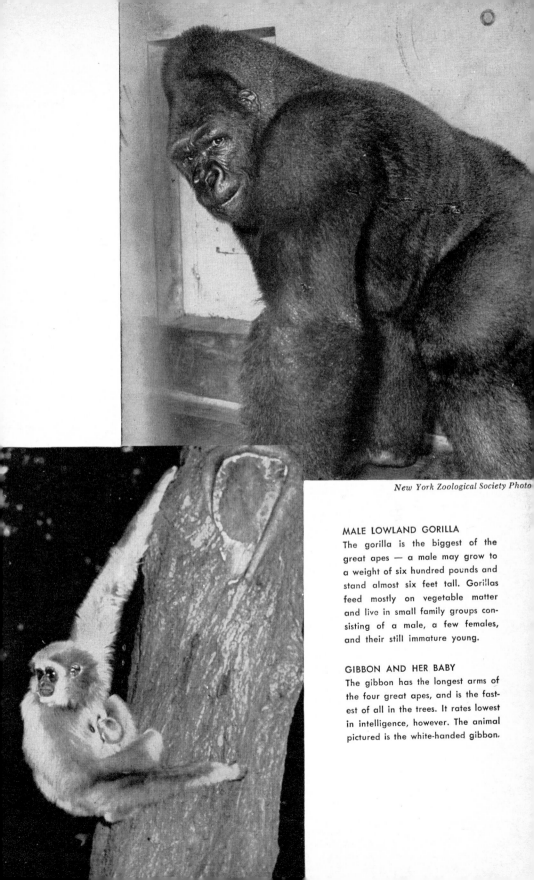

MALE LOWLAND GORILLA
The gorilla is the biggest of the great apes — a male may grow to a weight of six hundred pounds and stand almost six feet tall. Gorillas feed mostly on vegetable matter and live in small family groups consisting of a male, a few females, and their still immature young.

GIBBON AND HER BABY
The gibbon has the longest arms of the four great apes, and is the fastest of all in the trees. It rates lowest in intelligence, however. The animal pictured is the white-handed gibbon.

THE GIANT ARMADILLO DIGS FOR ITS FOOD

The giant armadillo, a South American species, is the largest of its tribe. Like other armadillos, it feeds mostly on insects, termites in particular. A night hunter, it has an acute sense of smell which enables it to locate its prey in the earth. With its enlarged claws the animal quickly digs the insects out and then catches them by means of its long, extendible tongue.

A QUNFIDHA OR ARABIAN PORCUPINE
Only a handful of an animal, the qunfidha lives in the desert, where it feeds on insects. Although sometimes known as the "Arabian porcupine," it is not really a porcupine at all, being more closely related to the hedgehog. Hedgehogs are found in many parts of the Old World — in the Mediterranean region, in western Europe, Malaya, India, and Africa. They are insectivores.

TWO FLYING SQUIRRELS INVESTIGATE AN OLD STUMP

Of all of North America's squirrels, the flying squirrels are the only ones active at night. During the day, these large-eyed rodents remain hidden in a hole in a tree, or in a nest made of shredded bark. Flying squirrels do not actually fly, but use the furry membranes at their sides to support themselves as they glide soundlessly from a high place in the trees to one lower down.

Paul A. Moore—Tenn. Conservation Dept.

THE GROUND HOG IS A WARY ANIMAL
The ground hog, a large, ground-dwelling squirrel or marmot, makes its home in a burrow. If an enemy approaches, it seeks shelter underground. Normally the ground hog feeds on green vegetation, but when winter comes it retires to its den, where it sleeps away the cold months, drawing sustenance from the thick layer of fat that covers its body.

THE PRAIRIE DOG
The prairie dog is another ground squirrel. It is active by day; its nights are spent in a den which is part of an extensive series of burrows beneath the plains of western North America.

MARMOT PEERING FROM ITS DEN
Hoary marmots, like the one pictured below, are quite at home high up on a mountain side.

D.A. Spencer—U. S. Fish and Wildlife Service

J.S. Dixon—U. S. Fish and Wildlife Service

La. Dept. of Wildlife and Fisher

THE COYPU — IT EASILY FILLS A CHILD'S ROCKING CHAIR

The coypu, a water-loving rodent native to southern South America, may weigh more than nine pounds and measure three feet in length, including its thick, foot-long tail. Its hind feet are webbed for swimming. The coypu is now raised in Louisiana and New Jersey as well as in Europe. Known as nutria, its fur, brown to black in color, is valued by the fur trade.

THE MUSKRAT — AN OVERGROWN MEADOW MOUSE

The muskrat, a close relative of the meadow mouse, is another rodent very much at home in the water. Its hind feet are webbed, it has thick fur that sheds moisture, and a vertically flattened tail which it uses as a rudder. The muskrat lives in a hole in the bank of a stream, or builds itself a dome-shaped house of mud and rushes. This animal possesses glands which emit a musky odor.

BIRTH OF A BOTTLE-NOSED DOLPHIN

Marine Studios, Marineland, Fla.

In the photograph above, the birth has already begun — the tail of the baby may be seen protruding at the left from the mother's body. In the lower picture, the infant has almost completely emerged. Final delivery is swift or the young would drown, though the actual birth, from beginning to end, may take considerable time — possibly two hours.

THE BABY IS NOSED TO THE SURFACE BY ITS MOTHER
Dolphins are mammals, and they must breath surface air if they are to live; they do not, like fishes, have gills to extract oxygen from the water. In the top picture, the mother is nosing the baby to the surface immediately after birth, so it may draw its first breaths. (Ninety minutes later she was nursing it.) The lower picture shows mother and her growing baby swimming together.

Marine Studios, Marineland, Fla.

THE RED FOX — IT HAS SHARP EYES AND WITS

Even after several generations of captivity, the red fox is seldom very tame. Generally it is only the immature or inexperienced fox that gets caught — the adult animal will detect its pursuers when they are far away and throw them off the scent by such tricks as backtracking, or entering a stream. Black, cross, and silver foxes are color variations of the wily red fox.

E. R. Kalmbach—U.S. Fish and Wildlife Service Pho

THE COYOTE SINGS ITS MOURNFUL SONG

The coyote, famed as the evening singer of the American West, here appears to be celebrating its kill, a rabbit. A swift-footed animal, capable of a speed of more than forty miles an hour, the coyote is the only mammal in its range that is fast enough to bring down the jack rabbit. The male coyote is a good parent, and keeps his mate and growing family supplied with meat.

THE SWIFTEST OF ALL LAND MAMMALS STALKS ITS PREY

The cheetah, a big cat of Asia and Africa, can cover a distance of one hundred yards in four and one-half seconds, but it cannot keep up this pace for long. In India for hundreds of years tame cheetahs have been used to bring down game.

THE FEROCIOUS BOBCAT
NEED FEAR FEW ENEMIES

A skillful climber and a speedy runner, the bobcat can generally protect itself against most natural enemies. It hunts mainly by night, taking an extensive toll of rabbits, squirrels, mice, other small game.

Paul A. Moore —
Tenn. Conservation Dept.

HIS FATHER IS A LION, HIS MOTHER A TIGER

This young animal, known as a liger, is one of the great rarities of the animal kingdom. Such a hybrid generally has stripes, and may grow a mane when it is mature. The lion is the typical big cat of Africa; only a scant number of lions are found in Asia, home of the tiger, so that the two big cats seldom meet and never interbreed in nature.

THE BLACK BEAR LIKES TO CLIMB TREES

Black bear cubs are fond of climbing trees in search of honey and fruit. They travel in the company of their mother, who protects them and teaches them the rudiments of bearcraft. Black bears grow fat as winter approaches, sleep away the cold months in a hollow tree or cave.

LITTLE CAN ESCAPE THE ALERT EYES OF THE RACCOON

The raccoon, a friendly and inquisitive animal, frequently approaches human dwellings. It makes a docile pet if captured and trained when young. Wooded country, with water in the vicinity, is favored by the raccoon, which feeds on almost anything edible — fish, frogs, small mammals, insects, fruit, and the like. A good climber, the animal often makes its home in a hollow tree. In the winter, it may sleep for long periods in the colder parts of its range.

UNGAINLY ON LAND BUT A CHAMPION IN THE WATER

Long ages ago, the ancestors of the fur seal had legs like other land mammals, but these limbs developed into flippers when the animals took to the water. Ungainly on land, the fur seal is exceedingly graceful and swift when it swims. The animal shown here is a young male.

A FUR SEAL FAMILY ENJOYING THE OCEAN BREEZES

The Alaska fur seals spend their summer on the Pribilof Islands of the North Pacific, where they mate and bear their babies. The sizable bull at the rear of this group watches jealously over his harem of six females and their young. More aggressive, powerful males may have a harem over ten times as large as this one and often fight savage battles to preserve it

AN INDIAN MONGOOSE SURPRISED WITH HIS PREY
The mongoose is one of the commonest flesh-eaters of Africa, southern Asia, and the Pacific islands. A long-tailed, weasel-like animal, it preys extensively upon rodents, but is most noted for its talent as a destroyer of poisonous snakes. Mongooses are generally not immune to venom; they depend upon their very sharp vision and agility to avoid a fatal snakebite.

BIG, WATER-LOVING COUSINS OF THE PIGS

The hippopotamus, a relative of the pig, is common along many of the waterways of tropical Africa, where it has been known to overturn small boats. If undisturbed, however, it is a peaceful animal; it is quite sociable by nature and is often seen in large herds. At night the hippo frequently wanders several miles across country in search of food.

CAMELS DRINKING AT AN OASIS TROUGH IN SAUDI ARABIA

The Arabian camels pictured here are taller, faster animals than their cousins the Bactrian camels, and have only one hump. Camels are particularly well adapted for life in the desert: they have special cavities in the stomach which store water, the fatty hump serves as a food reserve, and the feet are broad and cushioned, which makes walking across the sands easier.

NOT A FIGHTER

The armadillo is no fighter at all. It cannot even bite. Its teeth are peglike structures (there may be up to thirty-two of them) and they are placed in simple rows well back in the mouth—there are none in front, where they might serve a defensive purpose. Mostly the armadillo eats white ants, or termites; it is of great importance to man in controlling them, for they are among the most destructive foes of timber in tropical countries.

The armadillo also devours scorpions and other injurious insect pests. Occasionally it varies its diet with snakes, mice, eggs, carrion, and vegetable matter. It does most of its food-getting at night, though sometimes we see it abroad by day. When traveling, it moves along at a jaunty gait. The animal's eyesight and hearing are poor, and so it is somewhat at a disadvantage in detecting the approach of an enemy.

When threatened with danger, the armadillo goes the other way. Most armadillos make off as fast as their short legs can carry them in an attempt to reach the burrows in which they live. The shell permits them to pass with ease amidst the cacti in their surroundings, while the plants' sharp points may bar the passage to the pursuer.

When a hungry flesh-eater is about to overtake an armadillo, it will quickly bury itself if the ground is soft. Failing this, it tries to crouch under the shell, drawing in its legs; some species roll up in a ball. To the armadillo's sorrow, flesh-eaters like the wild dogs and foxes have learned that they can roll their prey over and get at the exposed parts underneath; they will also push it into water to get it to open up.

HOME LIFE OF THE ARMADILLO

The armadillo, we have seen, dwells in burrows. Sometimes the den is at the end of a tunnel a good twenty feet long, but usually the passageway is shorter than this. Inside the nest chamber, dry grass and leaves provide a soft bed. The animal may have several other dens as well, for use in time of emergency.

Both sexes look and act very much the same. Although adults generally live alone in separate dens, some armadillos are sociable. On occasion four or five have been found in one nest chamber, and fifty nine-banded armadillos (we shall come to this species soon) have been seen hunting their food together. The female shows a warm affection for her babies.

There is a surprisingly large number of different kinds of armadillos (family Dasypodidae) living today. South America is their
home, but some have invaded Central America. One species has
crossed through Mexico and penetrated into the United States.

ANCIENT GIANTS

In prehistoric times, many strange armored creatures dwelled in
South America, among them the Glyptodons, ancient relatives of our
armadillos. Some of the Glyptodons were giants that measured fourteen feet in length and five in height. They had shells that were thick
and strong but not hinged. Compared to the armadillos, they were
well armed, a number carrying a formidable spiked club at the end
of the tail.

ARMADILLOS OF TODAY

The Nine-banded Armadillo, or Peba, *Dasypus,* is the common armadillo, and the only member of the edentate group found north of

ARMORED, BUT NOT WARLIKE

    Latin America has armadillos in plenty, but only one—the nine-banded armadillo, pictured
above—has made itself at home in the United States. The animal cannot see well, and
you may come quite close to it without being detected, if you are quiet. When disturbed,
the armadillo runs off at a good rate in search of cover.

the Rio Grande. It lives south as far as Argentina and in recent years has extended its range into Louisiana, Alabama, and eastwards. In many places it is called the "poverty pig" or "poor man's pig" as it is used for food; its flesh is delicate, white, and tender, and tastes rather like pork.

——THEODORE ROOSEVELT AND THE ARMADILLO. It is one thing to say that the meat of this animal tastes good, and quite another to get to taste it. In spite of its clumsy armor and short legs, the nine-banded armadillo is extremely agile. Theodore Roosevelt, writing of his Brazilian experiences in 1914, graphically tells of the creature's ability to elude a pack of hounds:

"Early one morning," he says, "we came across two armadillos . . . We were riding with the pack through a dry sandy pasture country . . . One headed back for the nearest patch of jungle, which it reached. The other ran at full speed—and ran really fast, too—until it nearly reached the other patch a hundred yards distant, the dogs in full cry immediately behind it. Then it suddenly changed its mind, wheeled in its tracks, and came back like a bullet right through the pack.

"Dog after dog tried to seize it and turned to pursue; its wedge-shaped snout and armored body, joined to the speed at which it was galloping, enabled it to drive straight through its pursuers, not one of which could halt it or grasp it, and it reached safety in thorny haven of refuge."

——IT CURLS UP FOR SAFETY. The nine-banded armadillo is much like others of its kind in appearance. About the size of a house cat, it has nine movable bands (sometimes only seven) about its middle, separating the front of the body casing from the rear section; this arrangement permits the animal to curl up and protect its soft under parts when it is in danger. Long, pointed ears project from the tapered head. The tail is long, too, and covered with horny rings that interlock.

——IT SWIMS LIKE A DOG. A rocky terrain, with some grass and cacti about, is favored by the nine-banded armadillo. Often water is scarce in the places where it lives. However, it is not averse to drinking, or, for that matter, to swimming. The armadillo can swim vigorously, propelling itself along much in the manner of a dog. Frequently it will walk under water across the bottom of shallow ponds.

——POWERFUL FEET AND CLAWS. Ants and beetles are a mouth-watering sight to this animal. It seeks its food at night as a rule, and finds it with the help of its keen sense of smell.

Having detected the small prey in the ground, the armadillo loses little time in going after them. Rapid, powerful strokes of the front feet and claws lay bare the insect feast. In goes the muzzle, probing; the extendible tongue works back and forth, catching insects and earth on its minute papillae. As the animal digs and feeds, a low grunting noise comes from its mouth.

——BABIES OF ONE SEX. The armadillo begins to breed at the end of July, but the young do not come until March or April. A great curiosity about this creature's births is that all the babies in one litter —about four are born at a time—are of the same sex. They develop from a single cell, but it does not begin to divide until fourteen weeks after mating time. The babies are born 120 to 150 days later, in the underground nest.

Young armadillos are exact miniatures of the adults, and can move about a few hours after birth. Their shells do not harden completely, however, until the young are nearly full grown. The mother nurses them for nearly two months; she possesses four teats, so nobody goes hungry. When she moves about, her babies trail behind her.

In Texas, the nine-banded armadillo is fairly common nowadays. (So common, that it is often called the "Texas armadillo.") Frequently we find it at the rate of one to each ten acres, and occasionally one to three acres. The adult males are generally larger than the females, and measure in total length about thirty-two inches, with a weight of thirteen pounds or so. It seems unlikely the animal will travel much further north than it has gone; its shell will not keep it warm the way fur does other mammals.

——VULTURE INTO ARMADILLO. Despite the strange form of this weird beastie, it plays a fairly minor role in native folklore. The Maya Indians of Yucatan used to believe that the black-headed vulture, in old age, turned into an armadillo.

According to this myth, when a vulture gets on in years, it notifies its companions it is ready for the change and alights before a hole in the ground. The other vultures bring it food and the old one remains earthbound a long time. Gradually its wings disappear, and it loses all its feathers. When the change is complete, the animal enters the hole and starts life as an armadillo.

As proof of this story, the Indians point out the similarity between the bald pate of the vulture and that of the armadillo.

The Giant Armadillo or Tatuasu, *Priodontes,* is like something from a past age. It is not only a giant among armadillos but is a large animal in its own right. Full grown, it will measure five feet over-all; the shell alone is about three feet long. The middle finger on the forefoot is armed with a vicious-looking sickle-like claw four inches long and one and one-half inches at the base. It can be used effectively

A GOLIATH OF ITS KIND

The giant armadillo measures five feet, the shell being three feet long. A dweller in the tropical forests of South America, this animal has peglike teeth, like the sloth, and feeds on termites for the most part. Note the enlarged claw on the forefoot—it can rip apart a termite nest with great efficiency.

as a defensive weapon but its primary use is to tear down termite nests and to dig in the ground. This giant is at home in the tropical forests of South America from Venezuela to Argentina.

The Fairy Armadillo. The smallest of the edentates is the Fairy Armadillo, or Lesser Pichiciago, *Chlamyphorus,* a dainty, pink-shelled little creature only five inches long that lives in the ground like a mole. It is native to Argentina and differs from all other armadillos in having the shell attached not on the sides but only along the line of the backbone; its rear end is protected by a separate circular disk—a very useful provision for an animal that burrows in the earth and is subject to attack from the rear. It has a larger burrowing cousin, the Greater Pichiciago, which has a somewhat wider range.

THE ARMADILLOS HAVE A PYGMY

This dainty five-inch creature provides such a contrast to the other members of its family that it is called the fairy armadillo. For all its small size, the fairy armadillo has big claws on its front feet; it uses them in digging and burrowing. Very odd is its straight, armored rear. The shell is pink.

The Three-banded Armadillo. Another unusual member of the family is the Three-banded Armadillo, *Tolypeutes,* also known as the Apara and Mataco. This South American species does not bury itself in the ground when in danger; it prefers to roll itself up in a tight ball, leaving no vital parts exposed. The armored crown of the head fits snugly into a notch in the shell, and the tail and feet are all tucked away inside, too, so that the animal presents an unbroken, invulnerable surface to any potential enemy.

There are several other armadillos that go under the name of Peludo and are generally considered to be carrion-eaters. In general, the armadillos are long-lived; a Hairy Peludo, *Chaetophractus villosus,* was still living at the Rotterdam Zoological Gardens after eighteen years in captivity.

COUNT THE BANDS

It is easy to recognize the three-banded armadillo—three narrow plates of armor run across its back, connecting the front and hind shields. When menaced, this armadillo rolls itself into a ball, like a hedgehog. A clever dog will, however, tumble the animal into the water so that it must uncurl itself and become vulnerable again.

Old World Anteaters and Aardvarks

PANGOLINS OR SCALY ANTEATERS

THE PANGOLIN, or scaly anteater, is a native of Asia, Africa, and some islands in the Pacific. Superficially it bears a remarkable resemblance to a huge pine cone.

Look at the pangolin more closely, however, and you will see that its covering is not so innocent as it seems. Linked mail just about describes it.

From the head to the tip of the tail the pangolin is clad (except for the under side) in large, overlapping, and rather pointed scales. They are horny in texture and sharp at the outer edge. Not only does this coat of mail permit the creature freer body action than the plate armor of the armadillos—it can be used as a weapon of attack against an aggressor.

MASTER OF THE ART OF SELF-DEFENSE

The pangolin is a master of the art of self-defense. Its name, in Malayan, means "roller." When the animal sees danger at hand, it assumes an on-guard position by rolling itself into a ball. This protects the naked under parts. At the same time the pangolin erects its scales, presenting an array of knifelike blades that bristle at the foe.

Should the attacker not take heed of this warning and the loud hissing that accompanies it, the pangolin will slash its tail out at him with unexpected speed, and drive the sharp blades deep through skin and flesh. If the enemy attempts to seize the pangolin by the body, the erect blades snap down with a cutting bite. Pangolins are pacifists, but, if they must fight, they will, and with singular effectiveness.

Although not closely related to the American anteater, the pangolin resembles it in some ways. It is an eater of ants and termites, and has no teeth. Its head is small and the face pointed; from the tiny mouth the long, sticky string of a tongue can be extended several inches to pick up the insects. The body is streamlined and tapered at both ends.

HOW PANGOLINS GET THEIR FOOD

Strong claws on the pangolin's forefeet serve it well in ripping open termite nests, which it seems to detect by means of its sense of smell (it cannot see or hear very well). In feeding, it favors ants' eggs more than the ants themselves and is especially fond of the big leafy nests of the red ants, containing millions of ants and eggs. These large red ants will bite the pangolin on the abdomen and face so that it must pause to scratch them off.

TREE AND GROUND PANGOLINS

On the ground the pangolin has a peculiar way of walking, made necessary because the third claw on the front foot is so long. The pangolin has to double the claw under, so that, as the animal moves, only the sides of the foot touch the earth.

Some of the pangolins spend their entire lives on the ground, while other kinds, particularly a number of the West African species, pass most of their time in the trees. They can and do drop down from considerable heights, using the elevated scales to break the fall.

The Asiatic pangolins, although ground-dwellers, will climb on occasion. They are the most typical of the pangolin group (there is only one family, the Manidae, making up the order Pholidota), although not so strong and heavy as the African ground pangolins nor so slender as the tree pangolins.

Slow Breeders. Pangolins are not fast breeders. One baby is about the average for a litter, and twins are quite rare. At birth, the infant's scales are soft and flexible, but they harden in a few days. Mother pangolin soon takes it traveling with her; she carries it riding precariously on the upper surface of her tail, to which it clings with all its might. When she is alarmed, she folds her tail and head under her body, and the baby finds itself in the sheltered cavity thus formed.

When taken young, the pangolin makes an interesting pet. One lived in captivity for two years, which seems to be the only known record on longevity. In the natural state the pangolin may live much longer.

Largest of all the pangolins is the Great Ground Pangolin, *Smutsia gigantea,* of equatorial Africa. This huge, mighty fellow measures up to six feet in length, with scales five inches across and three inches long. Too heavy to climb, it lives on the ground, with a self-dug burrow for its den.

The Common Ground Pangolin, *Smutsia temminckii,* is almost as large as its big cousin, and is also possessed of great strength. This ground-dweller of eastern, central, and southern Africa has enormous gripping power when it is curled up—no two men can unroll it by hand while it is still alive. The brown-scaled covering on the back will resist a .303 bullet fired point blank at one hundred yards.

——A DANGEROUS TAIL. Rolled up in a ball, the common African

pangolin is by no means defenseless. It does not remain inactive in this position, but keeps slapping and grinding its tail against its body. It will try, this way, to entrap the leg or foot of an attacker— say a cat or a dog. Once it succeeds in doing this, it begins to saw back and forth with the tail; so sharp are the scales that they may completely sever the assailant's limb.

Still, as its mighty defensive armament suggests, the pangolin is not normally a ferocious creature. It prefers to direct any aggressive inclinations it possesses against the termites on which it feeds.

AN ANIMATED PINE CONE
> The common ground pangolin of Africa is protected by scales on the upper part of its body and on its tail. Its soft belly is its weak spot, and so this animal will roll into a ball when endangered; the tail is wrapped around the body, or lashes out against the foe. The pangolin has a long tongue and feeds on termites, like America's anteaters.

——SEARCHING FOR FOOD. During the day the common pangolin sleeps in a hole in the ground; it does not begin prowling until darkness sets in. Usually its movements are slow and deliberate as it travels across the open sand veldt, or through the thick bush and forests in which it lives. The heavy tail drags behind on the earth.

Being cautious and timid by nature, the animal frequently pauses to raise itself up on its hind legs and survey the neighborhood for possible danger.

——THE ENERGETIC COMMON PANGOLIN. Once the pangolin finds

an anthill, it abandons its clumsiness and goes to work with furious energy. The speed with which its claws can drive a shaft in the heart of the antheap is truly astonishing. Its tongue shoots forth a full foot beyond the snout and mops up dozens of the insects at a time.

This large pangolin, we have seen, is very strong. It can, as a matter of fact, raise almost anything under which it can force its nose. Although very much a ground-dweller, it has remarkable ability as a climber, should climbing be called for; it can scale the krantzes or cliffs of South Africa even when they are almost vertical. To make it a still more impressive creature, it possesses anal glands capable of ejecting jets of repulsive-smelling liquid, rather like the skunk's.

——"SUPERNATURAL POWERS" OF THE PANGOLIN. With all these strange powers, it is not surprising that Africa's natives are inclined to regard the pangolin as having supernatural attributes. The bushmen and others use its scales as charms.

In South Africa the pangolin is credited by the natives with having some strange influence over their cattle. When a pangolin is captured, the poor beast is burned at the stake in the cattle pen—a sort of sacrifice to preserve the health of the cattle and improve the fertility of the herd. This practice is perhaps one of the reasons why the pangolins are becoming increasingly rare in that part of the continent.

West Africa's Tree Pangolins. We find two tree-dwelling pangolins in West Africa. The Soft-scaled Tree Pangolin, *Phataginus*, has very thin scales but they are far from soft, being more like fine-spun steel. This animal is almost all tail: out of its thirty-six inches only fifteen are head and body.

The Long-tailed Tree Pangolin, *Uromanis*, has an even longer tail, which is serviceable to a tree-climbing animal. While it cannot jump from one branch to another, it can reach across with the tail or else suspend itself from a bough by the tail and climb across. The scales on the underside of the tail also act as climbing irons.

Ground Pangolins of Southern Asia. The pangolins of southern Asia, though they live on the ground, can and do climb trees, chiefly with the help of the tail. The Common or Chinese Pangolin, *Manis*, is typical of the group; it measures eighteen or twenty inches without the twelve-inch tail, and large individuals will weigh up to seventeen pounds. The Chinese esteem it for its flesh and use its scales as "medicine."

Tigers often eat pangolins, and the natives invade the tiger haunts for the scales. The Burmese, on the other hand, consider it unlucky to meet a pangolin.

AARDVARKS—AFRICA'S "EARTH PIGS"

The Aardvark, *Orycteropus,* is a large, donkey-eared animal that makes its home underground. To the early Dutch colonists of South Africa this long-snouted creature with the fat, rounded body covered with scant brown or gray hair looked much like a porker and so they put together their words for "earth" and "pig" to name it. That is the simple way the strange word "aardvark" was born.

THE AARDVARK IS AS ODD AS ITS NAME
In South Africa, where termites abound, this large, donkey-eared creature is fairly common. It is a rather uncommon sight, however, since it spends its days underground, emerging only after dark to hunt its insect prey. The aardvark has stout digging claws, and can tunnel its way into the earth at an amazing rate of speed.

The aardvark is one of the world's great diggers. Its short, thick legs (there are four toes on the front feet, five on the rear ones) are armed with powerful claws. With them it excavates the extensive burrows in which it dwells. Since it is an animal of considerable size —it weighs about one hundred pounds and is on an average about four feet long, with a heavy, tapering tail half as long again—the burrows are large enough to allow a small man to enter without much difficulty.

HUNTING THE AARDVARK

African natives relish the aardvark's meat. Often they will track the earth pig to its lair, and pay it a most unwelcome visit.

A young member of the tribe enters the burrow armed only with a short-handled spear or a long knife. If lucky, he will reach the animal before it has had time to save itself by digging and throwing up a wall of earth between itself and him.

Having killed the creature, the native indicates his position to his fellows by tapping on the roof of the tunnel. Then they sink a short shaft and lift out the trophy and the valiant hunter, both being seldom more than five feet below the surface.

The tribesmen make use not only of the aardvark's flesh but of its teeth as well, which they wear around their wrists to ward off ill fortune.

A PRODIGIOUS EATER OF ANTS

This kind of charm, or at least the manner in which it is obtained, may in the long run bring about the reverse of the natives' desire. The aardvark is of considerable economic importance in keeping the great hordes of termites in check; if they are not controlled, they do serious damage. Fortunately the numbers of termites consumed by the big-bodied aardvark in a single night are staggering.

The aardvark does its hunting under cover of darkness, either alone or with a single companion, so it is rarely seen by man. With its doughty claws it can quickly demolish termite nests of hard-packed clay that may be five or six feet high.

Either to defend their home or repair it, the white ants rally about in large numbers at the point of destruction. Then the anteater sets upon them in earnest. Its sticky, foot-long tongue is broader than that of the typical anteater or pangolin, and it can retrieve more termites in a shorter period of time than either of these.

HOW THE AARDVARK DEFENDS ITSELF

Man is not the aardvark's only enemy. In the vast territory it in-habits—from Ethiopia to the Cape of Good Hope—the larger flesh eaters such as the lion, leopard, and ratel (a fierce, badger-like ani-mal) frequently prey upon it.

When attacked, the aardvark will roll over on its back and use its chisel-pointed claws in self-defense. Like other eaters of ants, it is not pugnacious in its habits, nor does it have the sharp teeth of more aggressive creatures. As a matter of fact, it lacks teeth altogether at the front of its mouth; those on the sides of the jaw are simple, peg-shaped affairs.

Aardvarks bear only a single young, in May, June, or July. In captivity they do not last long. The London Zoo did, however, have one that survived for almost ten years. We place the animal in the family Orycteropodidae, a name meaning "digger-foot," which is well applied to this creature with the big claws. It belongs in an order of its own (Tubulidentata), since it is in so many ways different from the edentates or typical anteaters. Its ancestry and relationship to other mammals remains a total mystery.

The Shy Ones—Hares, Rabbits, and Pikas

Proverbially among the most harmless and peace-loving of animals, the hares, rabbits, and pikas are seldom if ever detected in an act of aggression. We find neither ferocity, savagery, nor resentment in the makeup of these small creatures. Though they have stout, strong teeth, they rarely bite, even when danger threatens their lives. Because of the gentle disposition of these animals, a number are popular as pets.

Everyone knows the outstanding traits of the rabbit and the hare— the large hind limbs and feet which they use in hopping, the small tail, and the big ears. Telling a hare from a rabbit, or either from a pika, is another matter. The first two, in the main, are larger. The major difference between them is that rabbits bring their babies forth naked and sightless, while the hares' young are better developed at birth, have a coat of fur and good vision. Pikas, on the other hand, are smaller, with shorter ears, front and hind limbs of about the same length, and no tail at all. The name "cony" or "rock rabbit" is often applied to them.

In the United States, little distinction is made between hares and rabbits, both generally being called rabbits.

WHY RABBITS ARE IMPORTANT TO US

Rabbits are of considerable economic importance. Though in some instances they are harmful to crops and vegetation, as a source of food as well as clothing they are quite beneficial to man.

Rabbits have been domesticated for a long time. It is generally supposed they were first raised on the Iberian peninsula. As far back as the beginning of the Christian era, Strabo wrote that ship cargoes of these animals were brought to the Roman markets from Spain. All domesticated rabbits are descended from the Common European Rabbit, *Oryctolagus*.

There are now many varieties developed for different purposes. The so-called Belgian Hare, Flemish Giant and New Zealand White are some of the breeds used for food, particularly in Europe. About ten thousand tons of rabbits are imported annually to England. Rabbit flesh is white, fine grained, and palatable.

All rabbit skins have commercial value and are used extensively by the fur trade, being substituted for more valuable furs. A large part, if not most, of the felt used in hats is made from rabbit fur. The Chinchilla Rabbit has been widely exploited as a better-grade fur producer.

A comparatively new phase of the industry is raising rabbits for wool. Angora Rabbits produce a wool five to eight inches long which is fully replaced a year after shearing. One rabbit yields twelve ounces of wool a year. The wool is warm and light when made into garments.

In North America wild rabbits have always been an important source of food during the winter season. The lowly Cottontail represents big business—over twenty million are killed annually by hunters in the United States. The Snowshoe Rabbit is edible in season, but its flesh is not very tasty during the summer.

RABBITS IN FOLKLORE

Rabbits and hares have played a large role in folklore in many different lands and times. Our Easter Rabbit probably comes down to us from pre-Christian times. There is an old Teutonic legend that the hare was once a bird, and was transformed into its present shape by Ostara, the goddess of spring. (Our word "Easter" is derived from her name.) In grateful recognition of this service, the hare laid eggs at the festival of its patroness, in April. It seems logical that these fertile animals should be associated with nature's rebirth at winter's end.

The South American Indian revered the Great Hare as the original creator of the universe, looking upon it in much the same way as the North American Indians did the Great Beaver. The devout Hindu sees the outline of a hare in the spots on the moon. And old Sanskrit fables tell of a hare that lived on the moon and was king of all earthly hares.

Among certain European peasants, tradition once had it that the hare was the spirit of corn. The last of the harvest was "the hare" and the man who cut it was said to have "caught the hare." The last sheaf of corn reaped at the harvest was shaped into the form of a hare and used in rituals.

The hare has not always been regarded in a favorable light, however, and many people still think it unlucky if a hare crosses their path.

RABBITS ARE NOT RODENTS

There are two families in the rabbit order, Lagomorpha (the name means "hare-shaped"). The pikas form the family Ochotonidae, and the rabbits and hares form the family Leporidae. In earlier days, they were often classified with the rodents. While they share with these some traits such as chisel-like front teeth, actually they have followed their own independent line of development; any resemblance between the two orders is a coincidence rather than the sign of a relationship.

We find the rabbits, hares, and pikas commonest in the Northern Hemisphere, with North America having a large share of the species. However, these animals are native to most parts of the world except Madagascar and the Australian region.

In Australia, twenty-four European rabbits set free in 1859 multiplied so rapidly that today the rabbit population threatens to nibble the Australian plains bare. The country now loses about a hundred million dollars a year to the rabbits through damage of this sort, apart from expenditures in an effort to control these pests. Foxes were brought in to check the plague of rabbits, but they became a plague themselves.

Better success is looked for through the use of a virus deadly only to rabbits. Numbers of the animals are inoculated with it and released to wander forth among their kin and infect them.

PIKAS, OR WHISTLING HARES

The Pika, *Ochotona,* has no lack of common names. Little chief, whistling hare, cony, rock rabbit, mouse hare, and haymaker are some of the better-known ones applied to this sturdy little mountaineer.

Smaller than a guinea pig, the average pika is only about six inches long; the largest measures nine inches at the most. It looks just like a miniature rabbit but its ears are not so lengthy, its hind legs are nearly as short as its forelimbs, and it lacks a tail. It has even finer and softer fur than most rabbits. Its voice varies from a sharp, shrill whistle to a bleat like that of a lamb.

The pika is at home in the mountains of eastern Europe, Asia, and western North America, but its range does not extend west of the Ural Mountains in Europe nor east of the Rocky Mountains in North America. Its favorite dwelling place is among tumbled rock piles near the summit of bleak mountain ridges; its den is an impregnable fortress underneath slabs of massive rock.

Still, not all pikas are strictly cliff-dwellers; some Asiatic species live in burrows in the ground, and others are foresters that dwell among thickets and scrub. They are sociable creatures, and live in colonies. They spend the daylight hours abroad, returning to the security of their dens at night.

THE HARE THAT "BLEATS"

The pika or whistling hare looks like a tiny, short-eared rabbit, but resembles a guinea pig in its lack of a tail. It utters a peculiar "bleat" that is unmistakable, but the animal is difficult to detect because it lives among rocks and rock slides.

THE SPEEDY PIKA

The color of this little "mountain chief" blends closely with the reds, grays, and browns of the lichens and mosses that grow on the rocks about its den. Posed on some high peak or rock, the pika loves to bask in the warm sunshine and watch the valley below. Once in a while it will yawn and stretch lazily or utter a shrill ventriloquial cry which is repeated by another pika in the vicinity. The animal's actions are swift and sudden. One moment it is there, the next moment it is gone—quicker than the eye can see—to reappear on another rock, frozen motionless as if it had never moved.

BUSY LITTLE WORKERS

The pika is an eater of green vegetables. Since it does not sleep through the long, cold winter that visits its mountain home, it must make provision for the lean days of famine. Even the bitter icy winds and severe frosts that split the rocks about its den cannot drive the pika from its lofty realm to the sheltered valleys below.

When the days begin to grow short in the fall, the little harvester gathers its crop of green vegetation and grass and spreads it out on the rocks to dry and cure in the sun. Should an unpredictable storm threaten to wet the drying harvest, the entire colony of pikas will turn out in force, gather the hay into bundles, and lug it away to the safety of their dens.

If necessary, these busy little workers will stay on the job until far into the night. The harvest means life to them, and full well they know it.

Spring comes late in the land of the little pikas, and it is May or June before the first young are born. Three or four are about the average number in a litter, and litters continue to arrive until the beginning of September.

PIKAS AROUND THE WORLD

In North America we find three principal kinds of these little mountaineers; they are mostly grayish or buff in color. The Rocky Mountain Pika dwells in the mountains from British Columbia to Arizona, while the Gray-headed Pika occurs at high elevations in California, Oregon, Idaho, Nevada and Utah. The Collared Pika is a grayish animal occupying the cold, bleak mountain ranges of Alaska and the Yukon.

Of the Old World species the Himalayan Pika is the largest. There are many other pikas at home in the Altai Mountains of Siberia, in China, Mongolia, and northern India.

TRUE HARES AND RABBITS

Large, long ears, a short tail, very long hind limbs and feet, thick soft fur—it is by these features that we recognize the hares and the rabbits. Yet how can we tell the two apart? Earlier, we saw there is more than a little confusion in the use of the names "rabbits" and "hares." "Rabbit" was originally applied to a European species that lives underground in communal burrows, or warrens, and brings forth its babies naked, blind, and helpless. On the other hand, in the true hares of the genus *Lepus,* the young (they are called leverets) have their eyes wide open, are fully clothed in soft, warm fur, and are active at birth. They are born (kindled) in a "form," or surface nest, and never go underground as adults, unlike the true rabbits. Hares are larger than rabbits.

Still, these distinctions are not generally known. A number of animals, such as the jack rabbit and the snowshoe rabbit, are really hares; some, such as the cottontail, are neither rabbits nor hares, strictly speaking. But once a name has grown popular with laymen, it becomes practically impossible to eliminate it from common usage.

Hares average about twenty-five inches in head and body length, and often have very big ears; sometimes these are seven inches in length. The animals have a fairly long tail, which, but for the white on the underside, is more or less concealed in the fur. The exceedingly long hind limbs and feet enable the fastest of them to travel at forty-five miles per hour. The true hares make their home in Europe, Asia, Africa, and North America.

HOW TO RECOGNIZE THEIR TRACKS

Rabbit and hare tracks are distinctive and can never be confused with those of any other animal. Moving slowly or at full speed, a hare or rabbit never walks, but travels in a series of leaps. The hop may be lengthened but the pattern of the tracks is always about the same: in front are two large imprints side by side; centrally lined up at the rear are two smaller prints, one behind the other.

THE ANCIENT RABBIT

With an ancestral lineage dating back some thirty million years, wild rabbits have spread over most of the large land masses of the earth. They have not reached southern South America, which is surprising, since introduced European rabbits and hares have become well established there.

Despite their great antiquity, the rabbits conform closely to a general standard pattern throughout their wide range, though they may vary in size from the great Alaska Hare to the Pygmy Idaho Rabbit. Only the Hispid Hare, *Caprolagus,* from the Himalayan foothills, has comparatively harsh, coarse fur. They are all vegetarians and live on land, some dwelling in burrows in the ground.

The probable length of life for rabbits in general is not more than ten or twelve years with full protection. Few wild rabbits live for more than three or four years; cottontails are old at three years.

GREAT WHITE HARES

It is odd that we should find the largest of all the hares in a most forbidding climate. Weighing up to nine pounds or even more, and two feet long, the Arctic, Polar, or Snow Hare makes its home as far north as the snow-sheeted, treeless wastes bordering the Arctic icecap. In northern Europe and Siberia its range extends south into wooded regions at all seasons of the year, but in America it travels below the timber line during the winter only.

The Arctic hare is well adapted to its life in the Far North. All winter long its fur is snow white, except for black tips on its moderately sized ears. A prowling enemy would have to be very sharpsighted to spot it on the icy plains; even the hungry wolf and fox and the snowy owl are often deceived. The hare changes its coat with the seasons, wearing one brownish or grayish in color during the short summer months when the snow has left the tundra. It makes this change by molting and not by altering the pigment of the hair.

Battles at Mating Time. Springtime, bringing new energy, also brings enmity and distrust among the Arctic hares as the mating season begins. After a winter of friendly relationships, the males now snap angrily at each other; often, with their teeth and claws, they rip chunks of hair from their neighbor's throats. Standing on their hind legs, they will box furiously. When the two-weeks' mating period is over, the bands of hares break up, dispersing in ones and twos over the Arctic tundra. The doe has only one litter, with about four young on an average, and they come a month or so after mating time.

The Arctic hare does not sleep in a hole in the ground: its bed is out in the open on the wind-swept Arctic wastes. Only during a blizzard, severest of all weather, will the animal seek the friendly shelter of a willow or alder thicket.

There are three principal groups of polar hares: the American Arctic Hare, *Lepus arcticus,* the Greenland Hare, *Lepus groenlandicus* and the Eurasian Varying Hare, *Lepus timidus.* The latter is known in Europe as the Mountain Hare or Blue Hare. In Greenland the Arctic hare joins in social gatherings of thirty to forty individuals.

AMERICAN JACK RABBITS

The White-tailed Jack Rabbit, or Prairie Hare, *Lepus townsendii,* second in size only to the Arctic hare, is a heavy-bodied hare (not a rabbit!), usually with a white tail at all seasons of the year. In the summer it wears a coat of yellowish buff; in winter it is pure white except for the black tips on the great ears. It lives in the Rocky Mountain region up to ten thousand feet in altitude and from the great plains of Saskatchewan to the border of New Mexico.

The white-tailed jack rabbit is one of the fleetest animals on the western plains; it can easily outrun a fox or coyote. Twelve feet is a single normal running hop, but if necessary the leap can be lengthened to eighteen or twenty feet. The jack rabbit lopes along at an evidently easy gait of thirty-five miles an hour; forty-five miles an hour is top speed.

Jack rabbits almost never dig shelters in the earth: normally they rest in depressions in the surface of the ground. In the north they will make a burrow in the snow to escape the winter's extreme cold. They are not particular about what they eat: anything will do, so long as it is green vegetation. They are great destroyers of alfalfa crops.

——ENEMIES OF THE RABBIT. White-tailed jacks are talented leapers. They have a high jump of at least five and one-half feet. Not all of these leaps are due to exuberance. Some are definitely observational— the creature's purpose is to get a view of the surrounding country and spot possible foes.

Many animals prey on this rabbit. The coyote used to be one of its worst enemies. However, for years now, open warfare has been waged on the coyote, and, as its numbers have dropped, those of the jack rabbit have multiplied.

When an overabundance of jacks threatens crops, every man, woman, and child of a district may be enlisted in a rabbit drive. Long lines of beaters sweep forward to herd the jack rabbits into corrals, where they are destroyed by the hundreds or even thousands.

A rabbit drive in North Dakota netted 7,550 of these creatures from an area of thirty square miles.

——Fighting for a Mate. Jack rabbits are famous for the combats they engage in at breeding time. The mating season begins in early spring and lasts until midsummer in the north and from January to September in the south. There is considerable fighting between the bucks for possession of the does, and many of the males show scars and ripped ears. The young come about six weeks later. They are born in a scraped-out depression, lined with the mother's fur, under an overhanging bush or tall grass.

Newborn jack rabbits weigh from two to six ounces and broods may contain from one to eight young; four is near the average. They are clad in mottled brownish fur and have their eyes fully open. Five minutes after birth they are ready to nurse.

When the mother leaves her babies, she covers them with the grass and fur of the nest. She returns merely to nurse them, and then only under cover of darkness. When the babies are but a few days old, they begin to forage for themselves—in three or four weeks they are independent of the mother. Several litters are raised each year.

——Rabbit Dances. The white-tailed jack rabbit likes a social gathering. On moonlight nights in midwinter, when unseasonably warm weather has melted the snow, the author has seen ten or twelve of them together, enjoying what seemed to be some sort of ritual or social dance. Their frolicking apparently followed a regular pattern. They gathered in a great circle that gradually grew smaller as they closed in, when they would suddenly bounce high in the air and disappear in all directions. In a matter of minutes another circle would form and vanish again in similar manner.

Migrations are rare among the jack rabbits. One has been recorded where thousands were seen together moving down from high country to the lowlands into the face of a heavy snowstorm.

The White-sided Jack Rabbit, *Lepus callotis,* is perhaps the strangest hare on the North American continent. It owes this distinction to a curious trick that it can play with its coat.

This creature, otherwise brown, has ears that are totally white— there are no black tips, as in so many other jack rabbits. It also has a whitish area covering the lower sides of its body. The astounding fact is that the animal can shift the white area on the lower sides around at will by the contraction of certain skin muscles. Thus it can transfer the brown fur on the back to one side or the other and replace it by white side fur, even when the animal is traveling at a fast pace.

When an enemy approaches, the white area is always pulled onto the side that faces the intruder. As the jack rabbit zigzags on its course, the coat is correspondingly switched from side to side. In bright sunlight the white side flashes a brilliant signal that can be seen from afar, possibly a warning to other jack rabbits of approaching danger.

The territory of the white-sided jack rabbit extends from southern Arizona to Oaxaca, Mexico.

Other Jack Rabbits. The handsomest of the jack rabbits is Allen's Jack Rabbit, *Lepus alleni*. It has very long legs, and enormous ears, larger than those of any other hare or rabbit; they measure seven inches in total length. Its head and body length is two feet; its tail

THE RABBIT FARMERS HATE

The black-tailed or California jack rabbit causes more trouble than any other hare. Farmers all up and down the West hunt it relentlessly, and one Oregon county, in a single year, paid bounties for a million tails. The California jack's cousin, the white-tailed jack rabbit, or prairie hare, has been seen dancing in circles on moonlight nights.

is two and one-half inches. Its range extends from southern Arizona to Tepic, Mexico.

The most widespread and troublesome hare in the western United States is the Black-tailed Jack Rabbit, or Gray-sided Jack Rabbit, *Lepus californicus.* The black-tailed jack often builds up its numbers to enormous hordes; the county of Harney, Oregon, alone paid bounties for one million tails in one year.

There is no mistaking the black-tailed jack. Its buff-brown coat, its large ears tipped with black, and its black tail distinguish this species from all other rabbits and hares. It ranges from the state of Washington east to Nebraska and south into Mexico. An even more distinctive member of the group is the Espiritu Santo Island Jack Rabbit, which has a glossy, pure black coat.

SNOWSHOE RABBITS—THEY CHANGE THEIR COATS

The Varying Hare, or Snowshoe Rabbit, *Lepus americanus,* is well described by either name. It varies by changing from a reddish brown coat in summer to a white robe in winter. (The change is made by the calendar, not by the temperature.)

"Snowshoe" is equally appropriate as a name, especially when the snow is on the ground. The hairs on the animal's feet thicken and lengthen in winter, greatly enlarging the size of the feet and forming "snowshoes" for support on the soft snow.

As this hare walks or hops, it spreads its long toes wide. This gives them a firm grip on the ice. The creature is hardly ever slowed down, whether it is rushing over the softest snow or the most slippery ice.

The varying hare, like the rest of its family, is a vegetarian, feeding on succulent herbs and growing twigs. The daylight hours it spends mostly at home in the damp, marshy woodland. Its nest is a small depression made by its resting body in a safe place, usually overhung by shrubs and tall grasses. Through custom it uses a network of trails with a main road leading from its nest to the feeding ground. An adult weighs about five pounds, is one and one-half feet long.

——Varying Hares Mature Early. Courtship and its battles begin in early March: it may be all of two weeks before a pair have mated. The father takes no interest in his young, which come thirty-six days later, usually about six of them in a litter. (There are from three to five litters in a season.) At birth the babies weigh about two and one-half ounces each, and are fully clothed with close brown fur, the proper garb for the time of year. They can move about as soon as they are dry; when a week old, they are out feeding themselves under their mother's watchful eye. The following year they are ready to mate.

——CYCLES OF THE VARYING HARE. These fertile little creatures have a life expectancy of about eight years, yet few live more than half that time. Often there may be five thousand of them to the square mile in their range, which extends from the northern tree limit of Canada and south in the mountains to Virginia and New Mexico. Sometimes, however, the hunter will search for them in vain throughout many parts of this area.

The varying hare, we have found, passes through cycles of great abundance and great scarcity. The reason for the extreme low can be explained but the cause for the fast multiplication is a mystery.

Over a number of years the hares build up their numbers with increasing rapidity. When the peak has been reached, a plague will always spread with incredible speed through the thickly populated areas. The hares die by the tens of thousands. After the snow melts in the spring, their shriveled bodies, strewn thickly over the forest floor, leave mute testimony to the relentless scourge of death that has passed through the hordes of hares.

Still, some have escaped, and so the cycle can begin again.

OLD WORLD HARES

The European, Brown, or Eurasian Hare, *Lepus europaeus,* is the common hare of Europe, making its home in the many parts of that continent, as well as in Great Britain and the temperate regions of Asia and Asia Minor.

A big, heavy-bodied fellow, this leaper and springer is over two feet long, and has large ears, a long tail for a hare, and a curly brown coat. Since it does not encounter intense cold and long, snowy winters in its homeland, it does not turn white in winter.

The European hare is typical of the race, and frequents the open downs, moors, and grasslands. It takes readily to the water and is a good swimmer, often crossing from island to island off the coast of Scotland. It does still better on land: a full-grown hare in its prime has a top speed of forty-five miles per hour, as checked by speedometer. It can make good use of this speed, for it is a natural prey of the hunter, because of its size. It was classed as game in England long ago, by the Normans, and has ever since been protected as game.

——"MAD As a MARCH HARE." Like their cousins in other lands, the "jack" hares fight furiously with their claws and teeth for possession of the does at the height of the mating season in March. Our old expression "mad as a March hare" owes its origin to their seemingly senseless behavior as they leap into the air in combat.

During the breeding season, which extends throughout the summer, the doe has from three to five young, or leverets, at a time. They are born with their eyes wide open and fully furred.

The European hare lives on the surface of the ground, and its den is, as you might expect, nothing more than a depression on the ground in tall grass. Though the animal is usually silent, it will call its young to feed by uttering a low bugle call, which it repeats once or twice. On a still night you can hear it three hundred yards away.

Hares in Asia and Africa. We find relatives of the European hare in most of Asia and Africa. Generally speaking, they are not very different in their ways and appearance from the animals we have just been looking at, but we may single out a few species as particularly noteworthy. For example, one, the Woolly Himalayan Hare, likes to live high up. This silvery gray creature makes its home at altitudes from ten thousand to sixteen thousand feet.

There are at least twenty-eight species of true hares native to Africa, the South African Gray Hare and the Cape Brown Hare being the commonest. The Grass Hare, *Poelagus,* a distinct genus, ranges from Uganda to the Anglo-Egyptian Sudan. This small-eared hare is of particular interest because it closely resembles the European rabbit, *Oryctolagus,* in its general appearance.

The Red Hare, *Promolagus,* found in central and South Africa, is another large form that should be mentioned. In addition to being rather colorful for a rabbit, it lives among the rocks and barricades the entrance to its den with a pile of sticks. It is the least rabbit-like of the African hares.

AMERICAN COTTONTAILS AND PYGMY RABBITS

The Cottontail, Molly, or Briar Rabbit, *Sylvilagus* ("forest rabbit"), is the common rabbit of the American woods. It gets its most popular name from the white-tufted under side of its tail. The animal is not a hare, nor, strictly speaking, is it a rabbit—but try convincing an American child of that!

The cottontail, about fifteen inches long, is small compared with hares and rabbits in general. Caring neither for the gloom of the deep forest nor the glare of the open plains, this animal chooses the borderland or brush country. Although its favorite feeding time is twilight, there are no time limitations on the cottontail's activities; it is abroad day and night. It feeds on plants, and is in disfavor among farmers because of the damage it does to crops. Millions and millions of cottontails are killed every year.

THE RABBIT THAT ISN'T ONE
The cottontail, molly, or briar rabbit, most common of all American rabbits, is not a true rabbit at all, nor even a hare! A gadabout, it is abroad both day and night. It is preyed on by most flesh-eaters, but, as it is prolific, there will always be cottontails. These animals are spread all over the United States, as well as Mexico and northern South America.

——A COURAGEOUS MOTHER. In startling contrast to its normally timid behavior, there are times when the cottontail burns with hot fury, and justly, too.

Whenever a snake threatens her brood, the female cottontail

opens the attack with marvelous courage and strategy. So quick and fast are her actions that even a large snake will turn and seek safety in flight to avoid being ripped to ribbons by claws and teeth. Still, a great number of wild cats, foxes, coyotes, weasels, raccoons, hawks, and eagles take a large annual toll of the cottontail. Though its life expectancy is two or three years, it seldom dies of old age.

Cottontails are prolific creatures. Five or six young are not unusual in a litter, and there may be three or four litters a season. Each litter has a different father. The mother is an expert at her trade. Often she prepares the nursery—a depression in the ground—a week or two before her babies come, lining it with her own fur.

The newborn infants, naked, helpless, and blind, weigh about three ounces. Ten days later their eyes are wide open; in fourteen days, though still tiny balls of fur, they are out sporting and playing tag together.

Mother Cottontail visits the nest only at night, to nurse the youngsters. When she leaves, she covers them with grass and wisps of her fur, so that her babies will be hidden from enemy eyes. But even by day she never seems to be far from the nursery; if the babies call, she comes quickly to drive off the marauder if she can. As we have seen, she is a staunch fighter.

——Where We Find Them. We find the true cottontail over practically the whole of the United States and Mexico, and south to Costa Rica and northern South America. Actually, its range extends from the Canadian border south to Patagonia, but the Central American and South American species differ considerably from the typical North American cottontail.

There are five distinct groups of North American cottontails—the Mountain Cottontail, the Eastern Cottontail, the Desert Cottontail, the Brush Cottontail, and the New England Cottontail.

More American Rabbits. Other kinds of American rabbits worthy of mention include the Forest Rabbit, the typical rabbit of Central and South America. The Swamp Rabbit and the Marsh Hare of the southeastern United States are cottontails that have left the dry land and taken to the water, a rather surprising development in the race. They swim with remarkable ease and are as much at home in the water and the wet marshes as on dry land.

The Idaho Pygmy Rabbit, an underground dweller, is of particular interest because it is not only the smallest rabbit in the Americas but the smallest in the world (six to eleven inches long). The Mexican Pygmy Rabbit is more like a pika than a rabbit and averages about half an inch longer than the Idaho pygmy. We meet this little Mexican only on the Mexican volcanoes Popocatepetl and Iztaccihuatl, at altitudes of ten thousand to twelve thousand feet.

OLD WORLD RABBITS—INCLUDING THE ORIGINAL RABBIT

The Rabbit, *Oryctolagus,* is the "true" rabbit—the animal to which the name "rabbit" was originally applied. Native to central and southern Europe and North Africa, it was introduced into England at an early date, possibly by the Romans. It was from the stock of the true rabbits that our domestic rabbits were derived.

The true rabbit, in the wild, is a hardy, fast-breeding creature. Its somber hues—it is grayish brown in color—aid it in concealment. About sixteen or eighteen inches long, it will average about three pounds in weight; a large one will weigh up to six pounds. The animal's ears are moderately large.

In contrast to the hare, which nests on the surface, the rabbit lives in underground communal burrows, or warrens. These are connected by well-worn runways to the feeding grounds. Hundreds of rabbits may dwell together this way.

While living a community life in the warren, the doe digs a separate den in the ground some distance away for breeding purposes. She lines this nursery with dry leaves or dead grass mixed with her own fur. The breeding season extends from February to September; the young come a month later, five to nine of them as a rule. Their story is much like that of the cottontails.

——THE RABBIT'S FOES. With such a high rate of reproduction, the rabbit is a serious pest. Its human and animal enemies do not find it an easy animal to destroy.

The rabbit knows full well that the best way to escape detection is to remain motionless. When caught in the open, away from a safe retreat, it will flatten itself out on the earth and "freeze." Even on a plot of bare ground it is by no means easy to detect a crouched rabbit; it will stay there until almost stepped on, and then it will spring up and race for the nearest shelter.

Mother Rabbit, like Mother Cottontail, will put up a fight to defend her young. On one occasion a gamekeeper at Tunbridge Wells, England, saw a stoat (the weasel, or ermine) playing with a young rabbit just as a cat will play with a mouse it has caught. Suddenly a full-grown rabbit—probably the doe—rushed up. It sailed into the stoat, knocked it over, and made off with the young one in its mouth. Recovering itself, the stoat followed in hot pursuit but was soon seen in a hasty retreat, chased by two adult rabbits.

Foxes and badgers are also mortal enemies of the rabbit, but the ferocious stoat is responsible for more rabbit deaths than either of these. Once on a rabbit's trail, a stoat will follow the particular individual underground. It will hound its chosen prey through a warren full of rabbits and eventually run it down, we are told. (This case, certainly, would be hard to prove.)

Apparently there are still stranger goings-on in these warrens. J. A. Millais, the British naturalist, tells of an occasion where a ferret was sent down a rabbit hole. A little while later, out came a few rabbits—a fox—a stoat—and a cat!

——A Colorful Relative. Like the true rabbit, most of its relatives have a somber color, without any characteristic markings. In Asia we do, however, meet one with a very striking color pattern. This creature, the Sumatra Rabbit, *Nesolagus*, presents an attractive combination of grayish yellow, mahogany brown, and black. Starting at its nose, a black strip runs the length of its body.

The Rodents—Mammals That Gnaw

A rodent is an animal that gnaws. To most people the name suggests only rats and mice. But it describes, just as accurately, legions of other creatures—squirrels, beavers, woodchucks and marmots, prairie dogs, chipmunks, gophers, muskrats, hamsters, lemmings, porcupines, and many others whose astonishing habits we shall soon have a look at.

There are more kinds of rodents—6,400 in all—than there are members in any other order of mammals; in actual numbers they may exceed the combined total of all other mammals alive on the earth today!

WORK OF THE RODENTS

The rodents represent a mighty force in the world, and their strength lies in numbers. You may be surprised to learn that the combined efforts of these industrious creatures play an important part in making and keeping the earth habitable for us.

How do they help us? The rodents clear out excess forest growth and replant denuded areas; they contribute to the creation of vast forest areas and aid greatly in natural conservation of our water supply. Digging and burrowing, they transform barren wastes into fertile soil.

On the debit side of the ledger, rodents have been instrumental in taking the lives of more people than all the wars this world has ever known. Many rodents carry lice and fleas that are disseminators of various plagues such as typhus, trichina, infectious jaundice and numerous other serious diseases.

THE RODENTS HAVE TRAVELED FAR

The rodents have entered most fields of animal activity and have literally covered the face of the earth from the border of the Arctic ice fields to the last tip of dry land in the Antarctic. Somehow, rodents even bridged the impassable gulf between Australia and the mainland of Asia—a feat that all other placental land mammals, except the bats, had failed to accomplish.

Rodents have entered the water, climbed into treetops, burrowed underground; some, while not actually able to fly, have learned to volplane. Most of the smaller rodents are of the scurrying type, but there are fast runners, hoppers, and highjumpers in their ranks, as well as some that are slow-moving.

Rodents build the finest nests of any mammal, breed the fastest, and probably live the shortest lives. They are harvesters and hoarders. Vegetable matter is their food, but they are not all vegetarians;

they supplement their diet with insects and other forms of animal life. One interesting mouse is credited with devoting much of its efforts to hunting scorpions.

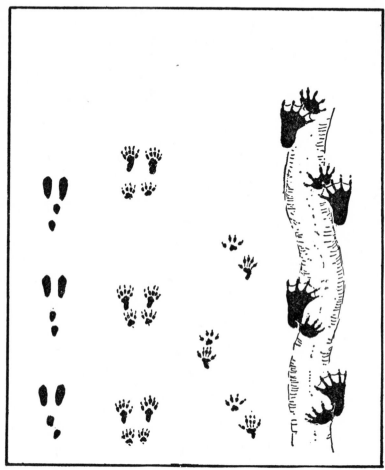

FOOTPRINTS ON SNOW AND WET GROUND

    Often you will see animal tracks in the snow or wet ground. At the far left there are footprints made by a cottontail rabbit. Next to them you see the imprint left by a bounding gray squirrel. Next is the track of a field mouse, and at the far right is the trail left by a beaver. Notice the prints of the webbed hind feet and the mark left by the broad dragging tail. All of these animals, except the rabbit, are rodents.

ALL KINDS OF RODENTS

One thing you will not find among the rodents, and that is monotony. The texture of the rodent hair varies from the soft, downy fur of the chinchilla to the barbed quills of the porcupine—yet both are rodents. The body structure of these animals varies amazingly, too.

Some of the groups of rodents are distantly related, and other than the fact that they are classified as rodents, seem to have little in common with the rest of their order (Rodentia). Others, though seemingly wide apart, are closely allied in descent. Anyone can see that the tree squirrel and the beaver are very different animals both in appearance and habits—yet the beaver is a close kin of the squirrel.

TEETH LIKE CHISELS

The chief feature by which we can tell the rodents from all other mammals is the pair of large, chisel-like incisor teeth they have at the front of both their upper and lower jaws. They use these front teeth constantly in gnawing.

Subject to severe wear, the incisors would soon be mere useless stumps if they did not continue to grow throughout life. A precious possession, they often mean the difference between living and dying to the rodent. If it damages one, it can no longer feed properly, or the opposing tooth may grow right through the bone of the other jaw and kill the creature.

The rest of the rodent's teeth are placed well back in its mouth, and a wide space separates them from the incisors. The hares and rabbits are often mistaken for rodents because they have a similar dental arrangement, but they possess another pair of teeth behind the upper incisors.

RODENTS OF TODAY AND YESTERDAY

All in all, we find that these animals fall into three main groups, or suborders. The first contains the squirrels and their relatives (Sciuromorpha), the most primitive of the rodents.

The second group is much larger—it would take a six-hundred-page book just to list the members of the 186 genera here. They include the typical rats, mice, voles, lemmings, and like creatures (Myomorpha).

The last group is the most specialized—in it we place the porcupines, guinea pigs, and their kin (Hystricomorpha). To this third division also belong such isolated curiosities as the mole rats and gundis.

Rodents are a very ancient order—their history dates back to the beginning of the Age of Mammals. Well-formed rodents existed on the earth sixty million years ago, and at that early date they had already learned to climb, as the squirrels and so many others still do today.

Squirrels, Chipmunks, Beavers, and Their Relatives—Important for Flesh and Fur

MOUNTAIN BEAVERS—NOT BEAVERS AT ALL

THE SEWELLEL, Mountain "Beaver," Boomer, or Whistler, *Aplodontia*, is the last survivor of a primitive race of rodents; it has no living relative. A short, chubby animal (it is about a foot long and has the thick, dark fur and the small eyes and ears of a burrower), it more nearly resembles a tailless muskrat than a beaver.

The sewellel is an odd little creature, and so are its names. First of all, "sewellel" is a Chinook Indian name, originally not for the animal itself but for a robe the Chinooks made from its skins. "Boomer" is the name used for this animal in Oregon, but the mountain boomer does not boom; neither does it whistle, as its other name implies.

The sewellel has been called the "silent one" since it is rarely known to utter a sound other than a singular rasping noise made by grating its teeth when angry. However, it is not mute, and is reported to utter a curious quavering note resembling that of a screech owl.

Furthermore, the sewellel is not a typical mountain animal. Its favorite haunts, aboveground, are among the dense underbrush in wooded country that affords concealment and shelter from flesh-eaters on the prowl. One of the remarkable things about it is its limited range—we find it only in a narrow strip along the Pacific coast of North America, from the southern border of British Columbia to central California.

THE SEWELLEL'S "SUBWAY SYSTEM"

The sewellel lives underground in colonies. It excavates extensive tunnels in the earth, not, like the moles and gophers, to get at food in the soil but to provide an integrated "subway system" for the sewellel colony. By these "subways" the sewellel can travel in dark safety from one surface feeding ground to another.

A LITTLE-KNOWN RODENT OF THE AMERICAN WEST
The sewellel, at home along the western coast of the United States, is really not a beaver at all. It lacks the tail characteristic of that animal, and in general looks more like a muskrat. Sewellels live in colonies in the earth and travel by underground routes to reach their feeding ground on the surface.

This chubby rodent leaves all doors to the outside world wide open, for ready use. Once a sewellel has arrived at the exit to the feeding ground it wants to visit, it speeds out of the tunnel, hurriedly gathers its loot, and retreats underground to feed. The underground passageways form a virtual labyrinth with enlarged chambers here and there for storage of food.

A SAFETY-MINDED CLIMBER

All manner of succulent vegetation has an appetizing look to the sewellel. It does not limit itself to what is growing on the ground, but will even climb small shrubbery to get at the choice green shoots on top. Here, as always, it is safety-minded—on the way up it will cut the branches off with its teeth a few inches out from the main stem, leaving a series of pegs as footholds for retreat.

The mother sewellel bears a litter of three to five young. They are believed to be born in June. We place the mountain beavers in a family by themselves, Aplodontidae.

SQUIRRELS OF THE TREES

The squirrel family (Sciuridae) is a very great one. It includes all tree squirrels and flying squirrels, and many animals that people do not commonly think of as squirrels at all—the squirrels that live on the ground, such as the woodchuck, marmot, chipmunk, and the prairie dog.

The tree and flying squirrels are mostly small, slender-bodied creatures, a foot in length or shorter, with bushy tails often as long again. The greater number are dwellers in the trees; for this kind of life their tails are essential equipment, as we shall soon see. Their relatives, the ground-dwelling squirrels, are bigger as a rule, but have smaller tails.

The squirrels are equally at home in the Old World and the New—we meet them in Europe, Asia, Africa, North America, and South America, but not in Australia or Madagascar.

The Tree Squirrel, *Sciurus* (the scientific name means "shadetail," and from it our word "squirrel" is derived), like the rabbit and the fox, is one of childhood's first picture-book animals. Every man, woman, and child in the civilized world is at least vaguely familiar with the squirrel, its long, bushy tail, and its habit of hoarding nuts. Its nervous movements, its rapid flight, its sudden appearances and disappearances are famous; these probably gave rise to the old Scandinavian legend that the squirrel is a messenger of the gods and carries news of what is going on in the world to animals in distant lands.

All true tree squirrels have a showy tail, and in some it is magnificent. The squirrel is proud of its graceful appendage and never forgets to keep it well groomed. But, for all its beauty, the tail is not solely used as a decorative feature; it is a vital necessity, and its purpose is to maintain and correct the balance of the animal in its daring leaps from branch to branch.

——THE INCREDIBLE JUMPER. The accuracy with which a squirrel can leap from one swaying bough to another and never fail in its estimate of the distance to be covered is miraculous. In a leap, the squirrel first fixes the direction, judges the space, and hurls itself in the air with feet extended forward, body flattened, and tail held straight out behind as a rudder to keep the course. At the end of the jump, the animal lands with its head up, ready to scamper away.

The author has never known a squirrel to miss its aim. Still, he can recall an occasion when a red squirrel made a long leap to a rotten branch and both came crashing to the ground. After regaining its dignity, the very annoyed creature soundly scolded everyone and everything that it could blame for its humiliating experience.

Not all squirrels climb trees in exactly the same manner, but, in general, squirrels go up at a gallop, the fore and hind feet being used in pairs alternately. Coming down, the squirrel travels head first and is more careful as it moves, setting its feet individually.

——A CAREFUL HOARDER. The tree squirrels are active by day. They are habitual hoarders of nuts, seeds, fruits, and other types of vegetable food. Often they have a number of storage places, making their caches in holes in trees or underground, or next to logs or rocks. To conserve storage space, they usually shell the nuts and take the seeds and the corn from the husks. Edible mushrooms and toadstools are first sun-dried and cured in the fork of a tree before storage.

The squirrel appears to find its way back to its cache by memory, but it also has a keen sense of smell. Some of its hidden food it never locates again; it is a great planter without knowing it.

An individual pair of squirrels usually have their own particular section of woods, an area of about two hundred square yards, which they defend with vigor from thieving and enterprising neighbors.

——BABY SQUIRRELS. In the northern temperate and cold regions, many squirrels sleep, but do not truly hibernate, during the severest part of the winter. They usually mate about February; the young are born in March or April. A typical nursery, that of the gray squirrel, is the winter den—a hollow tree will serve if there is one available.

At first the young are furless, sightless, and helpless; it is five weeks before their eyes open and they are fully clothed. Once they gain their sight, the young squirrels are soon out in the spring sunlight. By the time they are old enough to eat solid food, they must vacate the den, for squirrels are not the tidiest of housekeepers. Now an airier, more sanitary home is built—a summer nest of dried leaves in the forked branch of a tree.

Tree squirrels are spread over the world in a rather surprising pattern. They are perhaps best represented in Central America and Mexico; the rest of North America is a good second. South America has a fair share of tree squirrels, but Russia, Siberia, and most of Europe have but a single species, the so-called European pine squirrel.

TREE SQUIRRELS OF EUROPE AND NORTHERN ASIA

The European Pine Squirrel, *Sciurus vulgaris,* is a dweller in the pine trees and evergreen forests. Though not arrayed in gaudy colors, this little fellow is one of the most attractive of all squirrels. Long tufts on the tip of its erect ears and a thick, bushy tail curled up gracefully over the back add accents of elegance to its spruce, well-groomed appearance.

The pine squirrel is one of the very few really wild creatures that the casual observer may still see in the European woodlands. The gleam of its red coat (the color commonest in Europe) as it streaks through the gloom of the evergreen trees relieves the monotony of the ever-increasing stillness of the forests. Its brilliant little eyes glitter in the sunlight while it leaps and bounds from branch to branch. It is fascinating and delightful to watch this comely, small red-furred squirrel frolicking and playing with the falling autumn leaves.

——IT CHANGES ITS COAT. The pine squirrel is deceptive in appearance when seen in the treetops, giving the impression of being considerably larger than it really is. The head and body length is not more than about eight inches for a large male, and the female is only six and one-half inches. The superb bushy tail is seven inches long in both sexes.

In Europe, the animal's color varies with the seasons. In October it puts on a long winter coat of grayish brown. In May the full, lengthy dress is shed and in its place grows a shorter and redder coat, but the extensive ear tufts remain until they are renewed in the fall.

——FIGHTING FOR A MATE. The European pine squirrel mates early in the year, about March. This is a time of great activity. The males fight like game cocks. Often, locked in each other's embrace, they fall biting and scratching to the ground and roll over and over in their fury. But in a moment they separate and both go scampering after the fleeing female.

——HOW THE BABIES ARE LOOKED AFTER. Both male and female take part in building the drey, or nest, which is composed of sticks and moss and is lined with shredded bark. The drey, usually placed high up in the small top branches of a tree, looks something like a crow's nest, but it is roofed over and has an entrance on the side.

There are usually about three or four babies in a litter, born a month or so after mating time. They are naked, blind, and quite dependent at first. The pine squirrel makes a good mother. When her babies' safety is threatened, she gets highly excited. One at a time she bears them away, as a cat carries her kittens, to a safer nest in a nearby tree.

——A HOARDER, BUT A WASTER, TOO. The pine squirrel greedily eats beechnuts, chestnuts, hazelnuts, mushrooms and seeds of pine cones. It also cuts and eats flowers. In true squirrel fashion it sits up on its hind legs holding the kernel of a nut in its fore paws.

Unfortunately, this likable animal is not quite without fault. It loves bird eggs and in the spring it robs birds' nests and even eats their young. This extremely wasteful creature will scatter a whole treeful of nuts, taking scarcely a nibble out of each. In October and November the pine squirrel fills its storehouse with ripe nuts and seeds and sundried mushrooms, in preparation for the barren winter.

This squirrel is not out of place in the water—it can swim several hundred yards without tiring. Wisely, it prefers to cross a stream the easy way over a bridge.

The only representative of the squirrel family in Europe and northern Asia, the pine squirrel is spread over the forestlands from the Atlantic coast of Europe east to the Pacific coast of Siberia. Other tree-dwelling squirrels occur in the same area as the pine squirrel, but are not true tree squirrels. Africa has tree squirrels, but no typical ones.

The forty varieties of the species, adapted for varying kinds of climate, range in coat color from the subdued red type common in Europe to the black pelage flecked with white typical in eastern Siberia. Only one typical species, the Iranian Tree Squirrel, is found in southern Asia. Though not very different in general from its European cousin, it is bright yellowish red and lacks the attractive ear tufts.

——HUNTING THE SQUIRREL. Squirrel hunting was once a common practice in England and on the continent of Europe. It used to be the custom to fell the animals with sticks weighted at one end. While the pelt of the red squirrel is not valued by the fur trade for wearing apparel, it was traditional for the Scots to wear pine squirrel on the occasion of marriage. The black Siberian pelts were popular in the fur trade until the enforcement of restrictions on the fur trade with Russia.

——FOLK TALES ABOUT THE SQUIRREL. As might be expected, the little redcoat bobs up in many different chapters of European folklore. In Germany people used to believe there was an alliance between the squirrels (the little people of the trees) and the elves of the grass and flowers. For its bright red coat, Norse mythology associated the pine squirrel with the great god Thor. The Edda places this excellent climber in the biggest tree of all—the ash tree Ygdrasil, whose branches embrace the world. On top, it relates, sat an eagle and among the roots dwelt a serpent. Between the two the squirrel ran up and down, seeking to sow the seeds of dissension.

NORTH AMERICA'S TREE SQUIRRELS

The Red Squirrel, *Sciurus (Tamiasciurus) hudsonicus,* is the noisiest and most rollicking creature in the northern evergreen forests; it is always ready to chatter and scold at any stranger that passes along. It can utter a seething monologue of rage, often sputtering, stamping its feet, and jerking its tail in fury. When not disturbed, it also has a long, vibrant, rolling call, which may be answered by another red squirrel in the distance. These vocal accomplishments have tagged it with such names as chickaree, boomer, and barking squirrel.

——THE RED SQUIRREL'S HOARD. The red squirrel is on the move during daylight hours throughout the year; one sees it about during the coldest days of winter. It feeds largely on the seeds from pine and spruce cones. When the seeds are ripe in the fall, it busily harvests large quantities and then carries them to a carefully guarded storehouse, along with mushrooms and toadstools which it has first sun-dried and cured.

The red squirrel is charged with occasionally robbing a bird's nest—and has been caught in the act—but there are no other black marks against its name.

——AVOIDING ENEMIES. The home territory of one of these little rodents covers an area of about two hundred square yards. By and large, in the evergreen forests, the average population is about one squirrel to each four acres but the number will vary with the abundance of food. The range of these animals extends from the forestlands of Labrador to Alaska and south into the eastern United States to Pennsylvania and Tennessee.

Through custom, the red squirrel knows every branch and tree in its restricted domain and will fight any intruding squirrel that dares to trespass upon it. It not only has a domicile in a tree, but also a labyrinth of underground tunnels and runways in which to elude pursuers such as hawks, owls, and martens.

In its own territory, the red squirrel can easily outmaneuver its archenemy, the marten; but once the marten succeeds in edging it off its home ground, there is one red squirrel less. The red squirrel may live to the grand old age of ten years, yet it begins to show signs of decline after its fifth year.

——MOTHERS AND BABIES. Red squirrels mate in the early spring, beginning about February; the height of the season is in March. The mother-to-be prepares a bulky nest among the branches of a tree or simply settles in a hollow tree trunk. About forty days after mating, she bears from two to six young, in a comparatively immature state.

Although in a few days a downy fur appears on their bodies, the babies do not open their eyes until about the twenty-seventh day, and they are not able to care for themselves until fully five weeks old. They can count on their mother to nurse them and watch over them up to this age and longer.

In winter the pert little red squirrel displays a broad rusty-red band down its back, contrasting with its olive-gray body color and white under parts; in summer a black stripe appears on its sides. Its head and body length is six and one-half inches, and the tail is about an inch shorter.

——OTHER RED SQUIRRELS. The Chickaree replaces the red squirrel in the evergreen forests west of the Rocky Mountains. It is very similar to its more northern cousin, but has no rusty-red band on its back, and is reddish brown instead of white underneath. Fremont's Pine Squirrel is like the chickaree except for white under parts and a white fringe to its tail. It is found in southern Wyoming and in the southern Rocky Mountain states.

The Eastern Gray Squirrel, *Sciurus carolinensis,* is a familiar figure in eastern North America. It is a resident of groves of oak, maple, chestnut, and hickory trees from the Atlantic Ocean to the Great Plains and from southern Canada to the Gulf region of the United States.

——STRANGE SQUIRREL MIGRATIONS. Up to comparatively recent times, the gray squirrel engaged in curious, inexplicable migrations. When its numbers reached their peak in one region, some unknown influence would urge them to move out.

At first, the migrants would be a comparatively small group, but as the company moved along, others would join up and the army increased rapidly. Two such armies, actuated by the same impulse, would join forces, and the combined legions would be joined by still other marching hordes.

The stories of such migrations told by pioneers and homesteaders of a hundred years ago seem almost incredible. According to these accounts, the great gray squirrel migrations recruited armies a hundred thousand strong. They seemed possessed with an unswerving desire to travel in a straight line.

What the strange attraction was at that point of the compass toward which the squirrels headed, no one will ever know. But on they went. They crossed open prairies, climbed precipitous mountain crags, and swam roaring torrents. The bodies of hundreds of dead squirrels strewed the countryside or floated in streams, grim testimonials to the determination of the travelers.

——Old Squirrel Tradition Revives. These mass migrations are a thing of the past, but old squirrel "tradition" revives. In the fall of 1933, the squirrels in eastern Connecticut seemed to be up to something. Upon investigation, the author found that a thousand gray squirrels had already swum across the Connecticut River on September 24. Seventy-five were counted crossing a lake, and another indefinite number were seen moving in the same direction.

A FAMOUS TREE SQUIRREL

The eastern gray squirrel is a well-known animal in the eastern half of the United States. Generally it is gray in color, but black "gray" squirrels are seen in some places. These animals are extraordinary leapers, and balance themselves in the air with the help of their large, bushy tails.

They reached the Hudson River on December 10. Hundreds crossed the Bear Mountain Bridge, but the majority swam the Hudson. A few boldly marched on board the ferry boats at Yonkers, New York, and stole a ride across the river. Once on the New Jersey side of the river, they scampered ashore. Here all traces of the army were lost.

——TANGLED TAILS. The gray squirrels have other curious habits. Not the least remarkable is that on occasion they tangle their tails. Unable to separate them and escape, the animals may starve to death.

In December, 1951, a keeper at the New York Zoological Park noticed no fewer than seven squirrels huddled together in the Park grounds. Their bodies were extended in all directions but bound together by their tails. The hair of the tails was so twisted and interwoven that it had to be cut away in order to separate the animals. All were adult: two females were dead and another soon died; four recovered and were released.

——HUNTING THE GRAY SQUIRREL. Gray squirrel hunting has always been a popular sport with the country boy. The squirrel is well aware when the hunting season opens and it is no easy matter to pick one off with a .22 rifle in a leafy oak tree. Flattening itself on a thick branch, the rodent slides around to the opposite side as fast as the hunter moves to get a better view. Always the animal tries to keep the branch in between itself and the hunter. Should it fail, it makes a tasty dish, which is often served in the eastern states.

The gray squirrel mates late in the winter, about January or February. The nursery is usually built of dry leaves and twigs in the protected shelter of a hollow tree. After a period of forty-four days the young are born. Their life is much like that of the red squirrel. They are not full grown until about two years old, although they may breed at one year of age.

——EASTERN AND WESTERN GRAY SQUIRRELS. The eastern gray squirrel is a large squirrel with a head and body length of nine inches. Pepper-and-salt gray is its normal color, but it has a strong tendency to become black in some localities. Its life expectancy is not more than ten years, but few ever reach this age under natural conditions. In captivity, the gray squirrel may live for fifteen years.

The Western Gray Squirrel, *Sciurus griseus,* of the Pacific Coast region of the United States, is quite distinct from its eastern cousin. It is gray in color but larger, and with a handsomer tail and longer and finer fur.

The Tufted-eared or Tassel-eared Squirrel, *Sciurus aberti,* is a big, handsome, heavy-bodied fellow noteworthy for the elegant tall black tufts of hair that rise from its long ears. Its dwelling place is the great belt of yellow pine trees that stretches in a narrow strip along the Rocky Mountains from the southern United States to Mexico.

Naturalists distinguish three different but closely related forms of the tufted-ear—the Abert, Kaibab, and Durango squirrels. Among the gaudiest of the tree squirrels, they vary in color in certain regions. Still, their basic pattern is much the same: a soft lead-gray color, broken by a reddish-brown saddle, spreads over the back, while a coal-black line on the side sets off the snow-white under parts. The tail is large and bushy, with a graceful arch to it.

The tufted-eared squirrel usually builds a bulky nest of twigs and pine needles in the top of a great tree. It makes the nest about the size of a bushel basket and lines it with soft, shredded bark. From the outside it is a rough-looking, dome-shaped structure. But it is securely woven into the tree's branches, and is strong enough to resist high winds and winter storms. In it the tufted-ear remains day after day when the weather is not to its liking, venturing out only for food.

The tufted-eared squirrel does not store up a supply of nuts and seeds for winter food, but depends largely on the bark of the yellow pines in which it lives. (In summer, though, it feeds on much the same fare that other tree squirrels do.)

When the snow starts to melt in the Rockies, this handsome squirrel begins to lose the heavy winter coat it grew in the fall, but the stately plumes on its ears, one and one-half inches long, are retained until early in June. These grow back again, however, in time for the next winter.

Families of three or four baby tufted-eared squirrels arrive early in June. (It is possible there is a second litter which is born around September.) They are weaned on the inner bark of the tall straight pine trees and are taught to hunt mushrooms, bird nests, seeds and edible roots. Soon they are scampering about in the trees and chattering furiously with their elders. Under the protection of the United States Forest Service, the tribe leads a life of security in the Grand Canyon National Park, but in the wild forests of the American Southwest and northern Mexico it is cautious and wary of hunters.

Full grown, the tufted-eared squirrel is about twenty inches long, and weighs up to two pounds.

The Fox Squirrel, *Sciurus niger,* is the largest tree squirrel in eastern North America. It resembles the common gray squirrel in general appearance, but you can tell this one apart by its larger size and orange or brownish grizzled coat. It owes its name to its great, fox-like face.

If you are to see the fox squirrel at all, it will be in scattered localities in the eastern half of the United States; the animal is quite scarce nowadays. Usually it favors open upland groves of oak, hickory, and beech trees rather than the deep, unbroken forest. In the South it will be found in the cypress swamps and long-leaf pines. Because of its large size, it is not particularly nimble in the trees, though it is a fairly fast and graceful runner on the ground. Several fox squirrels may haunt the same wooded area, but they pay scant attention to each other. Old males stick strictly to themselves.

——A LATE RISER. Squirrels in general are early risers, but not the fox squirrel; on cold, frosty mornings it will "lie in bed" till noon. Its den, most often, is in a tree, and the floor of the chamber is covered with pieces of bark and dry leaves. In the summer it may weave a number of large nests of leaves and twigs; it is a frequent mover. In winter it builds more carefully, and makes a solid, durable dwelling.

A hoarder by instinct, the fox squirrel caches nuts fast and furiously in little holes in the ground. It is also an eater of insects, bark, berries, nuts, sap, and seeds.

——MATING AND MOTHERHOOD. The mating period begins in January, when the males utter an often-repeated low bark. About a month and a half after mating time, the young are born, generally in a hollow tree trunk or a leaf nest their mother has built. Up to five in number, at birth the babies are naked, pinkish little bundles of helplessness, weighing less than an ounce each. In two weeks they are clothed with the lightest beginnings of a fur coat but their eyes will not be open for a month yet. They stay babies for a long time.

Fortunately, the infants can rely on their mother's tender care. If she has to move from the nest, she carries her brood with her, taking them one at a time and holding them with her teeth. When eight weeks old, they are able to eat solid food and on about the seventieth day can crack nuts; it is not long after this that they set out to make their own way in the world.

There is some evidence that fox squirrels may pair for life. We do know that pairs frequently live together in some particular hollow tree for a number of successive years. When the time comes to raise the family, the male behaves like many of our old-fashioned fathers—he retires to a nearby solitary residence and does not return until the young have been weaned.

A full-grown fox squirrel weighs about two pounds and is roughly two feet long. Its average life is about six or seven years, but this is sometimes shortened by its enemies, the hawks, owls, foxes, raccoons, and man.

COLORFUL TREE SQUIRRELS OF SOUTH AND CENTRAL AMERICA

The rest of the world has its tree squirrels, and has them in plenty. We find a surprisingly large number of showy ones in Mexico and Central America. Especially interesting is the Fire-bellied Squirrel of Mexico, so named because it is bright red below, contrasting with the pale gray color of the back. The Canyon and Apache Squirrels are well-known Mexican species allied to the fox squirrels of farther north.

The Variegated Squirrel is perhaps the best known and the most widely spread of Central America's larger squirrels. It shows a remarkable variation in color pattern; its hues range with the locality, from almost white through combinations of bright red, buffy, yellow, brown to entirely black. Closely related, but smaller and less spectacular is Humboldt's Squirrel, an olive-gray creature with a wide range in Central and South America.

Flame Squirrels. The Flame Squirrels of South America are a flashy group of variously colored species. The name was first applied to one kind with fur of such brilliant red hue that it suggests a tongue of flame as it leaps through the dark tropical forests.

Pygmy Squirrels. In most groups of animals there is a pygmy and the American squirrels are no exception. In fact there are two midget squirrels here. The Common Pygmy Squirrel, *Microsciurus*, is widely distributed in the Andes of South America and north to Nicaragua. The Midget Squirrel, *Sciurillus*, is even smaller, having a head and body length of four and one-half inches. It is unique because it is not closely related to any of the American squirrels; its range is the Lower Amazon and Guiana region.

(However, the distinction of being the smallest squirrel in the world goes to a tiny, little creature, *Nannosciurus,* two and one-half to three inches long with a tail of equal length, found on the islands of the South Pacific. There are several species but none is much larger than a mouse.)

TREE SQUIRRELS OF ORIENTAL ASIA AND THE PACIFIC ISLANDS

The Indian Palm Squirrel, *Funambulus,* is the favorite squirrel of India. It is easily recognized by its small size and the three white lines that run down the back from the neck to the rump.

The Indian palm squirrel is commonly found in groves and gardens and often enters dwelling houses; though occasionally seen in palm trees, it is by no means partial to them.

In movement, this squirrel is quick and jerky. It is extremely agile in the trees, making astonishing leaps from branch to branch, often covering a distance of five feet or more. Well aware of the fact that when chased it is not safe in a small tree, at the first opportunity it will make for a larger one. The female has from two to four young in a bulky nest of twigs and grass built in the branches of a tree.

The palm squirrel eats nuts, seeds and fruits and is frequently seen on the ground feeding in company with parties of birds called Babblers. The squirrels and birds are apparently on the best of terms. Interestingly enough, the animal's cry is shrill and birdlike.

The palm squirrel is easily tamed and makes a very pleasing pet. Its attractive habit of sitting up when feeding, with a morsel of food held between the fore paws, and its lively and confiding ways make it most popular with the natives of India and Ceylon.

The Oriental Giant Squirrel, *Ratufa,* is a Goliath among the squirrels—it is the largest tree squirrel in Asia. Some species have a total length of over three feet.

The giant squirrel or "tree dog" is about only during the day and inhabits tall trees in heavy jungles. It is most active from dawn until about nine in the morning, and from four in the afternoon until dusk. It is exceedingly fast and agile. When alarmed, it makes off

through the treetops with almost unbelievable rapidity—it can easily cover twenty feet in one leap from tree to tree.

During the heat of the day the oriental giant rests lazily in a nest
built in the small branches and foliage of a tall tree. The animal
usually has several such nests, lined with green leaves: the natives
claim that it always builds seven. Not a sociable creature, it lives
either singly or in pairs. Its call is a startling, loud, shrill cackle,
often repeated in the early morning.

We know little about the breeding habits of the giant squirrel.
Usually there appears to be only one baby in a litter. Taken at an
early stage, the young are easily raised and make entertaining pets.
One lived sixteen years in captivity.

Second Only to the Rat in Numbers. Among the many other kinds of
Asiatic squirrels the Common Oriental Squirrel, *Callosciurus,* is especially noteworthy because it has the largest number of squirrel
species and the most variable ones. There are approximately 320
forms already named—this squirrel is second in number of different kinds of animals in any genus, the common rat being first. Some
of the orientals are striped, others have red bellies and many combinations and shades of colors.

Prevost's Tree Squirrel, from Malacca, is the most distinctive and
ornate of the entire group. There is no doubt that this particular
squirrel suggested the name *Callosciurus,* which means "beautiful
squirrel." It is black above, deep chestnut below with white bands
from the cheeks to the hips.

AFRICA'S TREE SQUIRRELS

Even though Africa is separated from the rest of the world by vast
expanses of water and arid, treeless deserts, it has its own particular kinds of tree squirrels. Spread over the entire continent, they vary
from large to tiny in size. A few are marked with ornamental stripes
like the American chipmunks, but most are colored in conservative
shades of red, gray, and buff.

The Oil Palm Squirrel, *Protoxerus,* is known as the giant squirrel of Africa. Over a foot in length, it has a bushy tail even longer.
This creature is remarkable because for some unexplainable reason
the underside of the body is almost naked.

Quite a contrast to this animal is provided by the Pygmy Squirrel, *Myosciurus* ("mouse squirrel"), of West Africa. With a head and body length of only three inches and a tail even shorter, it is the smallest squirrel on the Dark Continent. It is also of interest because there is only a single species, which does not vary throughout its range.

The "Sun Squirrel." The Isindi, *Heliosciurus* ("sun squirrel"), is almost as large as the oil palm squirrel but is found in more places and is better known: there are forty-seven varieties that range from coast to coast in equatorial Africa. The animal's scientific name was derived from its habit of basking in the tropical sun on the branches of trees; this also explains why its fur is often sun-bleached and faded.

The Tree Squirrel That Likes the Ground. Not all African tree squirrels spend their time exclusively in the trees. The Bush Squirrel, *Paraxerus,* for example, often hunts on the ground. This rodent is extremely variable, not only in size but in color and color pattern. An East and South African squirrel, it may be either striped, white sided, red bellied or just plain olive brown.

GROUND-DWELLING SQUIRRELS

WOODCHUCKS AND MARMOTS

The large, heavy-bodied animals known as marmots—the American species are called woodchucks or ground hogs—are ground-dwelling squirrels. Too big to climb trees with ease, they live in burrows in the ground or have their dens among rocks. Mostly, you will see them up and doing only in broad daylight during the summer months. Loving a life of comfort and ease, they sleep all night, and all winter, too.

The Marmot's Long Winter Sleep. When summer has gone, but before the air is chilled with the autumn frost, the marmot retreats to its deep winter den. It will not see the light of day again until the spring sunshine warms the earth. It packs a relatively small cache of green fodder into the underground chambers. Then it plugs all entrances to the burrow securely, with a foot or more of earth mixed with straw. Usually two to four marmots hibernate together, but as many as fourteen have been found in one winter den.

At the start of its long, continuous winter sleep, the marmot's breathing slackens and its body temperature drops, until a state of lethargy has been reached. The body temperature of a hibernating marmot ranges from 43° to 57° Fahrenheit; at this time the animal is insensible and to all appearances dead. It would take several hours in a warm room to awaken it from its winter sleep.

"Ground-Hog Day." American tradition has it that on the second day of February the ground hog comes out of its den for the first time in the year. If the sun is shining and the animal sees its own shadow, it will retreat underground for another six weeks of slumber. Accordingly, the forecast is for continued cold and a late spring. If the day is cloudy and the ground hog fails to see its shadow, it is a sign that the cold weather is over and there will be an early spring.

——TRUE OR FALSE? What is the truth of this tradition? Although the ground hog is not the most reliable of weather prophets, clear skies in February often come with cold weather; cloudy days usually are warm at this season of the year.

The source of the superstition of Ground-Hog Day is not known. It is generally supposed to have originated among Negroes of the middle-eastern states, but the legend of Ground-Hog Day is actually a remarkable example of the transfer of Old World folklore to the New World. In Europe the second of February is associated with Candlemas Day, but in this instance the hedgehog and the badger play the role of weather prophet.

Where We Find the Marmot. Despite its love of warmth and its dread of cold, the marmot does not live in tropical countries, and none has crossed the Equator. In fact, it favors the temperate regions of the Northern Hemisphere. Most of the United States and Canada is marmot or woodchuck country. In the Old World these rodents are found in the Alps of Europe and eastward in the mountains to China and northeastern Siberia.

The Woodchuck, or Ground Hog, *Marmota monax,* is common in the eastern United States. The smallest of the American marmots, it weighs eight or nine pounds. In the fall, however, when it is fat, it may weigh up to fourteen. When the woodchuck comes out in the spring, it is almost as fat as it was in the fall but soon loses its stored reserve; by April, the animal is quite lean.

——BABY MARMOTS. Mating begins in March, when the woodchuck comes out of hibernation. Four or five 1-ounce baby chucks are born a month later. At first they are quite naked and sightless. It is a month before they open their eyes, but they are then fully clothed and ready to scramble on their shaky legs to get their first view of the outside world.

The young increase their weight to about three pounds by August and are big enough to take care of themselves. They then leave home and seek their own fortune. This, on the whole, amounts to digging a den and getting fat.

THE ANIMAL FOR WHICH A DAY IS NAMED
Every American schoolchild knows that February 2 is Ground-Hog Day. The American marmot or woodchuck, better known as the ground hog, is considered a weather prophet—if it emerges from its burrow on the second day of February and sees its shadow, a long winter is predicted. Often this forecast turns out to be correct.

——THE WOODCHUCK'S HOME. The woodchuck usually provides its burrow with a nest chamber and several side rooms. It likes to have three "doorways" to the outside world. First there is the "front door," with a pile of dirt at the opening. A "back door" is hidden in the bushes as an emergency exit. The third opening is a drop hole that has no telltale soil around it and goes straight down for two feet or more.

When an intruder approaches, the chuck will sit confidently on

the edge of the drop hole to the last safe moment, then suddenly
drop out of sight down the two-foot shaft to the runway below.

The woodchuck is fastidious about sanitary conditions. When conditions are not favorable outside, it uses one of its side rooms as a
toilet and covers its feces with soil. In fair weather an outside mound
of earth is used, generally the pile of loose earth at the main entrance.

Every spring the chuck remodels and improves its castle in the
ground. New rooms are excavated, old ones enlarged and renovated,
and piles of fresh earth are shoveled out at the main entrance of the
den.

For some unexplainable reason the animal reverts to the proverbial
squirrel habit of filling its storehouse with food in the fall. On several
occasions the author has found caches of green grass packed in the side
tunnels of the woodchuck's den. In some of the pockets the grass was
moldy or mildewed and quite inedible.

——A Lazy Life. The woodchuck's life is one we might well envy.
While the day is still young—but not too early in the morning—the
chuck is out feasting on the fresh, tender leaves of grass, clover, and
other sweet, green vegetation. When the sun rises high overhead the
chuck, its belly now full, stretches out lazily on the shady side of some
cool rock or under a leafy tree. As the shadows begin to lengthen in
the afternoon, the animal feasts once more. At sundown it retires to
the seclusion of its warm nest for a night's sound slumber.

On one occasion the author surprised a woodchuck fast asleep on
a warm, sunny hillside. It would be hard to say which of us was the
more startled. With a whistle the animal suddenly sprang up and
bolted through the briars, making as much noise as a dozen animals its size.

While the chuck is too fat and lazy to climb, it can scramble up a
tree trunk. It rarely ascends higher than the first fork; one observer,
however, reports seeing a chuck fifty feet up in a tree.

——Where We Find It. In the United States, we find the eastern woodchuck from the Atlantic coast west to the Mississippi Valley, with the exception of the Gulf States. Its range stretches across
the continent in Canada and extends north to Alaska. When this
creature is full grown, its broad head and chubby body are about
twenty inches long. Its limbs are short, and so is its flat tail. The fur,
moderately long and coarse, is brownish gray in color. Another spe-

cies, the Yellow-bellied Marmot, or Rock Chuck, lives in the American West.

The Hoary Marmot, or Whistler, *Marmota caligata,* keeps strict watch over its home territory in the high mountains of northwestern America and northeastern Siberia. Whenever a stranger enters its realm, this big marmot sounds a danger signal—a shrill, high-pitched whistle that can be heard a mile away.

Seemingly, there is always a sentinel like this, "posted" on a high rock to keep watch and give warning. (Probably no marmot in particular is the sentry—any one will give the signal.) It is needed, for the hoary marmot is definitely social; the little communities of half a dozen or more use the same trails and retreats, and their enemies know it. Fortunately, the marmots also have far-reaching eyesight, as do most creatures that live high up in the mountains, and are constantly watching for the prowling bear, the hungry wolverine, and the fisher that may come along at any hour.

These are about the only animals that could kill an adult marmot. A golden eagle will take the young and probably could kill a full-grown marmot caught unaware. The marmot, however, is always ready for an emergency. No matter how far it seems to wander in search of the grass, flowers, and succulent plants on which it feeds, it is never too far away from a drop hole into which it can plunge as soon as it hears the alarm.

——THE HOARY MARMOT'S WHISTLE. The marmot's sharp whistle is not made with its lips, but seems to be formed in the throat; the mouth is not open nor do the lips move when the sound peals out. It has a piercing quality, especially clear in the rarefied air, far above timber line, in the hoary marmot's northern home.

Here, toiling up the steep, trailless slopes of the Mackenzie Range and the mountains of subarctic America, the author has seen, moving about in a silent summer paradise, small bands of caribou and white mountain sheep, solitary moose, climbing goats, and an occasional bear; but the only sound that ever broke the universal quiet was the shrill call of the great marmot, perched high up on some outstanding rocky crag.

——PROFOUND SLEEPERS. In the rocky wastes of the Northwest, you can hear this call for a brief season and no more. The winter **is** long, the spring breakup comes late and snow begins to fall again as early as August. The marmots in these remote outposts of nature are conscious for only three months out of the year. The other nine months they spend in profound sleep.

The hoary marmot weighs up to twenty pounds; it will stand seven inches at the shoulders. It measures about thirty inches from its snout to the tip of the eight-inch tail. Its fur, used by the Eskimos for making robes, is grizzled, with some mixture of reddish brown. White-tipped hairs frost the coat, and give the animal its name.

Other Well-known Marmots. The European or Alpine Marmot, *Marmota marmota,* a grayish-brown creature much like the American breed, is still found in the Alps and ranges east into the mountains of Asia. Tradition would persuade us that this marmot uses a living wagon to transport hay to its den.

——A TALL TALE. According to such ancient nature historians as Pliny, Topsell, and Gesner, the European marmots gather a great quantity of hay. Now one of them lies down on its back, lifting its feet toward heaven, and the hay is loaded on the animal's belly and kept in place by the four limbs. Next, the other marmots take the supine one's tail in their mouths and drag their brother home like a sled. As each takes a turn of service as a wagon some time or other, none has any hair on its back at this season of the year.

Topsell, however, concludes his account with this telling sentence: "I cannot affirm certainly whether this be a truth or a falsehood . . . but that some of them have been found bald on the back." A like tale is told about the rat.

——CHINESE AND KASHMIR MARMOTS. The Chinese Marmot, or Bobac as it is often called in China, is much hunted for its fur, which is used as a counterfeit marten. The creature is protected during the mating season by the Chinese but dug from the burrows at other times. It comes out of hibernation in the spring carrying a heavy coat of fat which it quickly loses. The Mongols of the Central Asian steppes are fond of this fat and hunt the animal for food when it first appears. Marmots are clean feeders and wholesome to eat.

The Red Marmot of Kashmir is one of the several other Asiatic marmots. It differs from all others not only in having a rusty red coat and black back but also in having an unusually long tail for a marmot—about half the length of the head and body.

PRAIRIE DOGS—AND THEIR DOG TOWNS

The Prairie Dog, *Cynomys* ("dog mouse"), of the midwestern United States, is not a dog but a ground squirrel. A fat little bob-tailed rodent, it was as much a part of the Old West as the Indian and the buffalo. Like the others, it has all but vanished. It did not fall before the guns of the frontiersmen; the cattlemen killed it off with strychnine, for it fed on the forage they needed for their herds.

In early pioneer days, the prairie dogs were famous for their "towns." These were actual underground cities, with miles and miles of well-worn tunnels and dens extending in every direction beneath plateaus and upland prairies. The horde of individuals in a big town was almost incalculable; a large one may have had millions. A few towns still persist in out-of-the-way places, but their numbers are limited.

Protecting the Entrances. Town building requires considerable skill; moreover, these industrious little animals must work constantly to keep them in repair. Mounds of earth are built high around the entrances to insure the safety of the home and to prevent flooding, a most serious menace to animals that live underground.

A Prairie Dog Secret. One of the riddles still to be solved about the dog town is how these resourceful creatures excavate the soil as they extend their burrows.

The entrance hole goes almost vertically down, ten or twelve feet, before it levels off to a horizontal subway. The prairie dog could hardly scratch the soil out behind it or push it up on its head and it cannot carry such a load in its arms or mouth. Yet somehow it does get a large pile of soil up this perpendicular chute.

Prairie Dog Lynchings. There are many strange stories told about the prairie dog. For example, it is reported that when one of their members has in some way transgressed community laws, a mob of dogs has lynched the offender; this practice of ganging together and putting some individual to death has been recorded more than once. Prairie dogs apparently bury their dead and they will cover up and bury any other small animal that dies in a dog town.

When Enemies Approach the Dog Town. The fat prairie dogs are hunted by badgers, coyotes, foxes, ferrets, and wild cats. Eagles and hawks swoop down to grab them from the air.

Rattlesnakes and small burrowing owls sometimes take up residence with the prairie dogs in their towns, but it must not be supposed they are really their friends or anybody's. Each of these predators will devour the other's offspring, and a baby prairie dog is a juicy morsel for them. It has been claimed, and not without some basis for truth, that the prairie dog will seal off and try to entomb a rattlesnake that is visiting a dog town.

At the first sign of a stranger, a prairie dog utters a shrill whistle of warning. All its fellows stop whatever they are doing and look about to see what the trouble is. If there seems to be any danger, they plunge to the safety of their underground home. Each individual has its own particular den, and makes a scramble for it.

No matter how grave the danger, none must enter the wrong den; if one is confused and tries to take refuge in a neighbor's retreat, the proprietor drives it away in self-righteous fury.

Eating, Sleeping, and Mating. Like the marmot, the prairie dog feeds on green vegetation. If this gets scarce, it digs down to the roots and devours them. When there is a plague of locusts or grasshoppers, the prairie dog will join forces with insect-eaters to eliminate the destroyers.

The prairie dog is not strictly a hibernating animal. At high altitudes and on the colder parts of its range, it will sleep through the winter, but in southern localities it is active the year round.

The young—they average four or six in a litter—come early in May, in an underground nest. Four weeks later they are getting their first glimpse of the upper world and seeing how plants taste in comparison to mother's milk.

Two Kinds of Prairie Dogs. There are two main kinds of prairie dogs. The Black-tailed Prairie Dog is about a foot long without its three-inch bobtail; it weighs three pounds or so. Its general color is buff or cinnamon. Except for its smaller size and the white tip it has on its tail, the White-tailed Prairie Dog looks much like its black-tailed relative.

The prairie dog's range is comparatively small, extending over the Great Plains and the Rocky Mountain region of the United States; they are also found in southern Canada and northern Mexico. Their life span is about seven or eight years.

CHIPMUNKS—FRIENDLY CREATURES
OF THE NORTHLAND

The inquisitive, pert little chipmunks, with their bright colors and friendly disposition, add a warm, cheerful note to the countryside. They are creatures of sunlit woods and open pastures. The shrill, lively call of one will bring responses from another and another until the woods ring with their merry chatter.

Chipmunks are bold and confident when there is a safe retreat at hand. Some even have courage enough to accept a proffered morsel of food from the hand of a total stranger. Often in the lonely forests of the Northwest, far from human habitation, when the author had paused to rest on a fallen tree, a chipmunk would climb up alongside in a friendly gesture that always brought a reassuring feeling of companionship.

Chipmunks do not live in the trees, neither do they choose to live on the ground; they favor stone walls, rocks, and fallen timber, especially naked branches bleached by the hot summer sun. Like most other ground squirrels, we find them only in the Northern Hemisphere; Asia and North America are the home of the chipmunk tribe.

The American chipmunks are separated into two distinct groups that have divided the continent between them. There is no overlapping of territory except around Lake Superior, in Canada.

The Eastern Chipmunk, or Hacker, *Tamias,* is a small ground-dwelling squirrel, nine or ten inches long; almost half of this is bushy tail. We can readily recognize this fellow by the five heavy black lines running down the back.

The chipmunk's home is underground. To build its den, it first sinks a sloping shaft down in the earth to a depth of about three feet. At the end of this tunnel, it makes a number of chambers, some for sleeping in and some for food storage. It does not leave the excavated earth in a telltale heap, but spreads it out in the bushes or tall grass. At times it will plug up the entrance to keep undesirable visitors away.

——HOME LIFE OF THE EASTERN CHIPMUNK. There is no doubt that the chipmunk likes company. Still, its social gatherings include no more than family groups—several individuals occupy the same den in winter and share a common store of food.

The chief foods sought by the chipmunk are seeds, grains, nuts, and berries. All summer long, and especially in the fall, these busy little squirrels are out gathering food and transporting it to their storehouses underground. They carry it in their cheek pouches. An individual can transport a tablespoonful of seeds or as many as seventeen hazelnuts at a time.

——LIGHT SLEEPERS. The chipmunk's storerooms often contain half a bushel of nuts, dried fruits, and seeds. This extensive storing of food clearly shows us that the chipmunks do not pass through a long period of complete hibernation during the winter; real hibernators fatten up in advance and live off the fat on their bodies, while they are asleep.

CHIPMUNKS ARE GROUND SQUIRRELS
The chipmunk is a ground-dwelling squirrel, and makes its home below the surface. The little fellow shown above in the act of consuming a tasty morsel is the eastern chipmunk. Note the typical dark stripes on the animal's back.

During part of the winter, however, the chipmunks indulge in a short, uninterrupted torpid sleep. At other times they are awake, but stay down under. They are out on bright sunny days very early in the spring in the middle United States.

——MATING TIME. Now begins the mating season, and the male

chipmunk sets out to pay his respects to a prospective female. Courtship is no haphazard affair. The female must be cautiously wooed—an overeager suitor may be tossed unceremoniously aside, to nurse the wounds inflicted by an unimpressed female.

By March most of the females have mated, and five weeks later about six young are born. From the very beginning the stripes are visible under the babies' skin. They can recognize sounds when three weeks old, and open their eyes at the end of the first month. At the ripe old age of three months, the young are well developed and able to look after themselves.

——THE CHIPMUNK CLOSE UP. If you look at an eastern chipmunk closely, you will see that the central stripe on its back is bordered on each side by a brownish line, while the two outermost stripes are separated by white. The head, with two white stripes on each cheek, is rather pointed for a squirrel. The ears are low and rounded, and the tail bushy and flattened. The warm rusty-red shades on the hips add to the colorful appearance of this little sun-worshiper.

The eastern chipmunk is spread over the greater part of eastern Canada, and the eastern United States except Florida. It is found west to the Great Plains, but here the range stops abruptly.

Other Chipmunks. The Western Chipmunk, *Eutamias,* is more slender than the eastern chipmunk, and has a relatively longer tail. The general impression is that it has many more stripes, but its normal pattern consists of five blackish and four whitish stripes, all approximately equal in width, and all but the outer pair extending from the shoulders to the rump; the middle line reaches the head.

This creature occupies all of North America, west of the plains regions. Its range extends from the Yukon south into central Mexico and overlaps the range of the eastern chipmunk in Ontario and Wisconsin.

——A SIBERIAN RELATIVE. Slightly larger than the western chipmunk is its Siberian cousin, the Asiatic Chipmunk, *Eutamias sibiricus.* Full grown, it is about ten or eleven inches long, half of this being tail. Uniformly reddish or grayish, the animal has on its back five broad black lines separated by four light-colored stripes. Its pelt is used by the fur trade under the name of Borunduki.

GROUND SQUIRRELS, SPERMOPHILES, AND SUSLIKS

We have already had a look at a number of ground squirrels known by other names. Now we come to those that are popularly called ground squirrels. They are robust creatures, and have a rounded head, short ears, and short legs. Their bushy tails do not match the magnificence of those of their tree-dwelling cousins', but are medium to short in length.

AN EATER OF SEEDS AND GRAIN
The golden chipmunk, a native of the American West, is one of the most attractive of the ground squirrels in its striped, rusty chestnut mantle. This active little rodent quickly seeks safety in an underground burrow when it detects the presence of its dreaded enemies, the hawk, fox, badger, weasel, and coyote.

In a characteristic pose, ground squirrels sit up on their hind feet when they want to look around. For this reason, they are often called picket pins. They will remain motionless in this position for quite a while, but when they suspect that the intentions of an intruder are harmful, they utter a shrill whistle and dive into their holes.

Most ground squirrels are social animals, and live in densely populated squirrel towns under the ground. They feed largely on green vegetation in the spring and early summer. Later in the year they devote their attention to seeds. They balance this vegetarian diet with grasshoppers, cicadas, and many other insects.

The ground squirrels hibernate during a great part of the year. They often enter their winter dens as early as July and August and rarely come out before winter is over, late in January or early February. Their families, born about thirty days after mating time, are usually large; seven to ten are not unusual in a litter, and occasionally we find twelve or thirteen babies. There is not time to raise more than one litter a year, which may be one of the reasons for the large families.

The different species vary greatly in their size and color pattern. Many of them follow a uniform scheme of yellows, grays or browns dotted with white, but some are outstanding in their color pattern of dots and lines. They range from the size of a chipmunk to that of a gray squirrel.

We find the ground squirrels in many different parts of the world. In North America these animals occupy a large portion of the continent from the Arctic coast to Mexico; however, they are conspicuous by their absence in both the eastern parts of Canada and the eastern United States. In the Old World, we meet ground squirrels in southeastern Europe, central Asia eastward into Siberia, as well as in the warmer parts of Africa. Many are known as Spermophiles (genus Citellus—"little quick one"—and its relatives).

The Thirteen-striped Ground Squirrel or Spermophile, *Citellus tridecemlineatus,* is an ornate little squirrel that dwells on the plains and prairies of the Middle West. Its remarkable coat is decorated with thirteen to fifteen alternating stripes and lines of "stars." Because of this décor, it is often called the "federation squirrel"; the name "striped gopher," sometimes applied to it, is a misnomer.

The striped ground squirrel is up and about when the sun rises, and remains out on the midwestern prairies during the heat of a midsummer day. It has departed from a strict vegetarian diet—half of its daily rations consist of grasshoppers, insects, and field mice, and it will also devour bird-eggs and fledglings.

While common in some localities, this creature is not sociable, and lives a fairly lonesome life. Its voice is a birdlike trill, or trembling whistle—a long, drawn-out "chur-r-r-r" in a high key.

Other Ground Squirrels. In Canada's northland the Columbia Ground Squirrel, *Citellus columbianus,* ranges north onto the Arctic tundra and in the mountains of the Northwest up to altitudes of eight thousand feet. It is an inquisitive squirrel, always showing up when least expected.

Its relative, the Antelope Squirrel, reminds us of the antelope as its white tail flashes against the dun-colored body. It is a chunky little squirrel with white stripes on its sides. A lover of warm sunshine, it is one of the few ground squirrels that do not hibernate.

CREATURE OF THE BARREN WASTES
The Asiatic ground squirrel is at home in the sandy country and on the steppes of Asia. In such barren surroundings, it leads a gay, carefree life, but it always keeps an eye open for the approach of a foe. This rodent feeds on seeds, vegetable matter, and some insects. Its retreat is a burrow in the earth.

The Golden-mantled Ground Squirrel, with its brightly colored coat of both dark and light stripes, is the most talkative of its kind. It has quite a large vocabulary of chirps, buzzes, grunts, and sometimes fairly screams when in a rage during a fight. It also makes a low ticking sound accompanied by flicks of its tail. This handsome fellow favors open woods on the mountain slopes of western North America, from six thousand feet above sea level up to thirteen thousand feet.

The California Ground Squirrel and the Rock Squirrel, of the Rocky Mountain region, from Utah to Mexico, are the largest of the ground squirrels. Though typical ground-dwellers, they often climb oak trees in the fall to get the acorns and other nut-bearing trees in search of food.

——THE SUSLIK. The European Ground Squirrel, *Citellus citellus,* is generally known as the Suslik, or Souslik. We find this yellowish-brown animal from Silesia and Bohemia east across central Asia. It loves the wide-open spaces of the earth, and the drier the climate the happier it is. A great digger, it dwells in deep burrows; generally it prefers sandy wastes for its home, but all the steppe country of middle Asia is friendly to it. (It is, however, not so common here as another species, Eversmann's Ground Squirrel.)

Susliks must have many enemies for they are never off guard. They take every precaution for their own safety. Still, at the same time, these jolly little desert dwellers are independent and impertinent. They sit up and whistle at you, cocksure of their safety on a sand dune eighty yards away, and they never let you get any closer. They move lizard-like with well-spread legs and make a wide track over the soft sand.

Many susliks do not hibernate. For their rest they choose the summertime, when the heat is intense. They retire to the cool earth and stay below, taking a long siesta, sometimes until fall.

Africa's ground squirrels, found in most of the warmer parts of the continent, are much like some of the American ground squirrels.

FLYING SQUIRRELS—THEY DO NOT FLY

Despite their name, the flying squirrels of the Northern Hemisphere are not really fliers, but gliders. Their "flying" equipment consists of thin, loose furry membranes extending on each side of the body between the fore and hind limbs.

As the animal, perched on some lofty bough, launches itself into the air, it spreads its legs, drawing the membranes taut. This wide expanse gives the squirrel enough support to permit it to glide in a downward course for a considerable distance. Before landing, the squirrel checks its speed by manipulating its tail, and comes to rest head up on the trunk of a tree.

The flying squirrel cannot sustain its flight for any long period of time: it lacks propelling organs like the wings of a bat or bird. Still, it can glide through the air up to a distance of eighty yards or more.

Its driving power is really the pull of gravity, aided by the muscular effort it makes when it leaps from a high position. However, this animal can control its direction and speed.

GLIDING THROUGH THE NIGHT

Flying squirrels are active only during the night, and their large eyes are modified for seeing in dim light. They leap from tree to tree in the dark forest as the true squirrels do in the daytime. Without their sharp vision and their ability to control their flight, they could hardly do this, since they cannot see their landing point clearly until they are quite close to it.

HOME LIFE IN THE TREE DEN

During the hours of daylight, the flying squirrel rests and naps. Its bedroom may be the hollow limb of a tree twenty or thirty feet above the ground or an outside nest, made of shredded bark. If

IT GLIDES BY NIGHT

The flying squirrel, as you may observe, has no true wings, and is not a flier in any sense of the word. But it can travel for many yards by gliding, with the assistance of the furry membrane it has on each side of its body.

the squirrel is small enough, a hole abandoned by a woodpecker will suffice. When the squirrel moves in, it cleans out the old nest and installs a soft bed of finely shredded bark and lichens. Now the animal has a home for many years to come.

In the flying squirrel's tree den—or in the leafy nest in the tree-tops—the young, numbering from one to six, are born about April, forty days after mating time. They are naked and pink at first, with their eyes and ears sealed tight. Their flying membranes are already well developed, but at this time are fine, transparent webs of skin.

The babies open their eyes at the twenty-sixth or twenty-eighth day, and are nursed for about five weeks in all. The mother will bravely protect them from almost any danger, gliding off with them to another tree if necessary. When three months old, they have changed their baby coats for the thick fur of the adult, and by now have learned to climb and glide.

Family ties are not easily broken. The young of the year may continue to live with their mother until the following spring. Some are ready to breed at the end of the first year, but others are two years old before they raise families of their own. They have a life expectancy of about six years.

HOW THEY GET THEIR FOOD

Flying squirrels feed on much the same kind of food as the typical tree squirrels. Nuts, seeds, berries, and insects constitute the bulk of their diet. In the winter and early spring they dine off the buds and shoots of trees. Since these creatures do not hibernate, they collect a good supply of imperishable provender and store it in "warehouses" for winter use.

Though really not carnivorous, flying squirrels will never pass up an opportunity to feast on meat or fat. They will on occasion kill and eat sleeping birds, and also eat bird eggs. They must have water to drink, especially in hot weather. The author has frequently found flying squirrels drowned in water tanks, especially in the woods.

Trappers in the North Woods often find these rodents troublesome. The animals fly into the traps after the bait, thus interfering with the capture of valuable fur bearers. Otherwise the feeding habits of the flying squirrels are not injurious to man and may be of some use in insect control.

WHERE WE MEET THEM

Flying squirrels are spread far and wide over the Northern Hemisphere. We encounter them throughout the forested regions of Europe, and in Asia from eastern Siberia south to the Malay region. In North America they range from the limit of tree growth in the north, south to Honduras in Central America. All in all, there are thirteen genera (they make up the subfamily Petauristinae).

There are no flying squirrels in South America and none in Africa or Australia; the so-called "scaly-tailed flying squirrel" of Africa is not a squirrel at all.

Giants and Pygmies. These gliders reach their greatest development in the warmer parts of southern Asia, the home of the Giant Flying Squirrel, *Petaurista*. There are many variations of this creature, colored from fox red to white or black; it may be all of three feet in total length. At the other extreme is Borneo's Pygmy Flying Squirrel, a little over seven inches long (some four inches are the tail).

North America's Flying Squirrels. The North American Flying Squirrel, *Glaucomys,* is spread over the continent as far south as Honduras. There are two species: the Greater or Northern Flying Squirrel (it is a foot long, over-all) frequenting the wooded parts of Alaska and Canada, and south in the eastern United States to Massachusetts, and in the mountains of the west to California; and the Lesser or Southern Flying Squirrel (nine inches long), which is found in the eastern northern states west to the Great Plains and south into Central America. Both have long, soft, fine fur, varying in color from light to dark buff. The tail is flattened and feathery, and the eyes are dark and large.

POCKET GOPHERS—A LIFE IN TOTAL DARKNESS

The pocket gopher spends almost its entire life underground in total darkness. Not even a streak of light is permitted to penetrate its maze of subterranean passageways. It is a spectacular digger, like the mole—a single gopher can excavate a tunnel two or three hundred feet long in one night. At regular intervals, as it digs, it makes a temporary surface opening and forces the loosened excavated earth out through it, but promptly and securely plugs up the hole afterward, for safety's sake.

This mining machine of flesh and blood looks as though it had been designed for its work. Short-legged and thickset, the pocket gopher has no appreciable neck. Its ears are barely noticeable, its eyes minute and almost sightless. Its forefeet, armed with strong, curved claws, are first-rate digging tools, but where the ground is excessively hard, the animal brings its strong, chisel-like front teeth into action.

The pocket gopher is one of the few animals that can run backward as fast and as easily as it can move forward. Here its tail serves it in good stead. Fleshy and of moderate length, the tail is endowed with tactile organs, enabling the animal to feel its way around underground when it moves in reverse.

The pocket gopher actually has pockets, from which it gets its name. The pockets are large cheek pouches that open to the outside of its face and reach back to its shoulders. They are lined with fur, and the gopher uses them for one purpose only, to carry food—not dirt as has often been supposed. (The word "gopher," by the way, comes from the French *gaufre*, meaning "waffle" or "honeycomb," an allusion to the maze of tunnels the animal makes.)

It would be a mistake to think that the gopher never ventures above ground; quite frequently one will come out to get some green vegetation, but during the time it spends on the surface it is nervous and fidgety, as if fearful of being snatched up by some prowling beast of prey. Its food includes roots, tubers, and stems of grasses that can be secured below the surface of the ground, or drawn into the tunnels from below.

A SPACIOUS APARTMENT UNDERGROUND

Gophers are great hoarders and fill their storehouses with much more food than they can possibly consume. Hoarding is a necessity, as they do not hibernate in the colder parts of their range, and much of the ground where they secure their food is frozen solid during winter.

Each gopher has up to eight or nine storage rooms; all may be kept packed with roots and tubers. When the ground is covered with snow, the gopher may also use snow tunnels and feed on surface vegetation.

The gopher's nest is located close to the storage rooms. It is a round ball of finely shredded leaves and grass, about nine or ten inches through, and may be at various depths, depending on the temperature and moisture in the ground. In wet lowlands a gopher may even raise a mound of earth six feet in diameter and two feet high in which to have a comfortable dry nest.

Gophers, like many other underground dwellers, make toilets for their own use, and periodically close them off and dig new ones.

AN ANIMATED MINING MACHINE
The pocket gopher, with its long, sturdy claws, is a tunneler by nature, and spends much of its time hollowing out underground passageways that will bring it close to vegetable food. It may do great damage to crops and the roots of trees. Pictured above is the western pocket gopher of North America.

HATE AND LOVE AMONG THE GOPHERS

Gophers prefer their own individual company. There is never more than one gopher in a particular chain of runways. If two accidentally meet, they fight to kill. The only time in the year that one will tolerate another is in the spring; then, just the male leaves his den to court the female, who stays in her own, awaiting his coming. About four weeks later the young are born—from one to nine in a litter. The male has long since returned to his own labyrinth of subterranean passageways.

Only the female cares for the baby gophers. At birth they are naked, and weigh about one-fifth of an ounce. Their eyes and ears are sealed shut until their fifth week. However, these little creatures develop rapidly and are soon ready to eat solid food. After two months the family breaks up, the young gophers leaving the shelter of the mother's home to build their own nests.

The life of the pocket gopher, we see, is much like that of the mole, with one great difference: the gopher feeds on vegetable matter, and the mole on small animal life such as insects and worms. In the past, the gopher's digging, like the mole's, has done much to further the cultivation and preparation of the rich, fertile plains of western North America, that are today feeding the world. However, this rodent's activities under the ground are not entirely beneficial to agriculture, as we shall soon see.

WHERE THEY DWELL

Pocket gophers are strictly North and Central American animals. They range from the plains of Saskatchewan in Canada, southward to Panama, being most abundant in the western United States and Mexico. We do not find them in the region east of the Mississippi Valley except in the Gulf States, where they reach the Atlantic Coast in Florida.

DIFFERENT KINDS OF "EARTH MICE"

Though very much alike in general, there are many different kinds of pocket gophers. (They make up the family Geomyidae, or "earth mice.") In size these creatures range from six to twelve inches in head and body length. All have fairly short tails and legs.

Almost every mountain ridge marks the boundary of a particular kind of gopher's domain. Since they spend their lives in the darkness of their tunnels, they have not specialized in fancy colors. Although there are a number of distinct kinds and an extremely large variety of geographical forms (here we shall look at only a few) the fur of most is dull brown or soil colored.

North American Pocket Gophers. The common pocket gopher of the Western States is the Western Pocket Gopher, *Thomomys*. Although it is only about five inches long, it is a source of constant annoyance to farmers. Not only are the mounds raised by it a menace to the reaping machines cutting the alfalfa, but it destroys the crops by eating their roots. Its endless gnawing on bulbs, tubers, the roots of fruit trees and other economically important plants causes vast destruction.

In the middle states, east of the Rockies, from the Dakotas to the Mexican boundary and in the Gulf states, this animal is replaced by the Eastern Pocket Gopher, *Geomys,* a somewhat similar creature that differs, however, in having a deep groove down the front of each upper incisor.

Pocket Gophers of Other Lands. With the exception of the Chestnut-faced Pocket Gopher, *Cratogeomys,* found on the plains of southwestern Colorado and Oklahoma, all the larger gophers occur in Mexico and Central America. The Giant Costa Rican Gopher, *Macrogeomys heterodus,* is one of the largest—it has a length of twelve inches without its short tail. As can readily be imagined, this big fellow is very destructive to sugar cane, banana plantations and sweet potato crops.

Cherrie's Pocket Gopher, a smaller animal, is blue black in color and is one of the few kinds of gophers that have any distinctive color markings. One species has a characteristic white spot on the crown of the head while another has a distinctive white girdle about the hips. These decorative color patterns are probably an accidental development and seemingly have no value to an animal that lives in total darkness. However, since the markings in this case contribute little to the destruction of the species, they can be safely inherited by succeeding generations.

POCKET MICE AND KANGAROO RATS— NEITHER MICE NOR RATS

We generally find these little creatures in dry regions, often where there is no water whatever. Of course, no animals can live for an indefinite length of time without water in some form, but these, especially the little pocket mice, are able to extract whatever amount they need from their food. Even when the diet is limited to dry grain, they never drink.

Like the pocket gophers, the pocket mice, spiny pocket mice, and kangaroo rats are natives of North and Central America. Like the pocket gophers, too, all have fur-lined cheek pouches. Still, they are not squirrels or gophers, and, although they usually have a long tail, they are not mice or rats. Their hind limbs are longer than their front ones. Beyond these common traits, they are very different from each other in appearance, although they are close relatives. (Appropriately enough, their family name—Heteromyidae—means "different mice.")

POCKET MICE—NO HEAVIER THAN AN OUNCE

The Little Pocket Mouse, *Perognathus,* is a small, dainty underground dweller with long hind limbs for jumping. Its many species include the smallest rodent on the North American continent, the Pacific Pocket Mouse, which, when fully grown, weighs only one-third of an ounce; the largest of the group, the big California Pocket Mouse, will weigh an ounce. They are found only in Western North America and do not live east of the Mississippi River. The northern limit of their homeland is Ashcraft, British Columbia; the southern is Thalpam, in the valley of Mexico.

——LITTLE DWELLER IN THE DESERT. The life of the pocket mouse is spent for the most part in dry places, where there is often no water for many months of the year. The sun in a cloudless sky, day after day, burns up all the moisture in the ground, leaving it hot and parched. In these torrid surroundings the tiny pocket mice are born and live until their last, long sleep.

As the sun goes down, these little denizens of the desert open their doors and set out on their quest for food. Standing up on their stilt-like hind legs, they pluck seeds from the grasses and plants with their tiny white hands.

Each hand independently stuffs seeds from the grasses and plants into the fur-lined cheek pouches, and moves so fast that the motion becomes a blur. The cheek pouches swell to seemingly bursting capacity. (Each pouch actually holds from one-eighth to one-half of a teaspoonful of plunder, according to the size of the species.)

Their pockets filled, in the early morning the pocket mice return to their burrows and unload their spoils with a sweeping motion of their hands. They firmly "close the door" with soil behind them.

This habit of going abroad by night is particularly advantageous in a hot climate, where there is no water. In its underground burrow the little pocket mouse is protected from the heat of the sun during the day; after sunset the desert cools rapidly.

The gentle and inoffensive pocket mice live alone except when breeding. Each mouse has its own individual little burrow. The burrow may be a simple straight tunnel with a grass-lined nest chamber at the end or it may be a network of runways with numerous store-rooms, sometimes as long as seven feet. Normally the outside door is closed when the pocket mouse is at home, but should some predator break down the door and enter, the resourceful little mouse will put roadblocks in the way.

——POCKET MICE OLD AND YOUNG. Mating is not confined to any particular season over the entire pocket-mouse range. A female usually bears two families a year. Each comes between three and four weeks after mating; two to eight tiny babies make up the litter. A life of not more than a few months lies before them—there are too many hungry mouths waiting to devour the average pocket mouse. Its worst enemies are foxes, skunks, weasels, badgers, coyotes, snakes and owls.

In captivity, pocket mice do much better. Some have lived four or five years; one even tottered past its seventh birthday, but this was a very old mouse indeed when it died: its teeth were worn down almost to its gums.

——POCKET MICE SOFT AND SPINY. We have said there are a large number of different species of pocket mice. They fall into two well-defined groups. Those in the first group have fur that is fine and soft, while those in the second have an almost spiny coat. The general color is in varying shades of buff, with a greater or lesser admixture of black.

These creatures are all small to tiny in size. An animal of average size is about five inches long, and often the tail is almost half of this.

SPINY POCKET MICE—THEY HATE COLD WEATHER

Protected Against Cactus and Insect Bites. About the size of a large mouse or small rat, the spiny pocket mouse has a long, well-haired tail, and fur-lined cheek pouches like the pocket gopher and the pocket mouse pure and simple. The coat that gives it its name is made up of dark-brown hair mixed with stiff, flattened spines and helps us to tell it from its immediate relatives.

Why the spines?—they are no defense against the mortal enemies of the pocket mice: snakes, foxes, cats, weasels and the like. Still, they may afford some degree of protection against cactus thorns or insect bites.

Nighttime Foragers. Tropical and subtropical America, from southern Texas to Ecuador, is the home of these creatures. They dwell in warm, arid places—often in the open desert—but are also found in humid forests. Burrowers, they keep house in a series of underground tunnels, and make sure that the door to the outer world is always securely closed. They rarely open it before nightfall, when they go foraging for nuts, seeds, and grass. This quest takes them into cultivated fields sometimes, to the detriment of farmers.

A Habit Out of the Distant Past? While the spiny pocket mice always avoid bright warm sunlight, they abhor cold weather. This looks like a contradiction, but so do many mammal habits. Perhaps the reason is to be found in the far past.

Along with the pocket mice and pocket gophers, the spiny pocket mice seem to have originated in Central America. Possibly all three achieved their development when this part of the world was separated by geographical or climatic conditions from the north and south, and they were not subjected to the extremes of temperature they have to put up with today.

Though very different in appearance, the three groups have many strange features and habits in common, especially their hermit-like life, the urge to hoard food where it does not seem to be an absolute necessity, and cheek pouches in which to carry it to their storage rooms.

Spiny Pocket Mouse Babies. Mother spiny pocket mouse may bear her babies, up to five in number, at almost any season of the year. They are well furred when they come into the world, but their flat spines are soft. Two months later the now half-grown youngsters shed their baby fur and get a new, shining coat of stiff, sharp bristles, the trade mark of their breed.

There are two main kinds of spiny pocket mice. The Lesser Spiny Pocket Mouse, *Liomys,* the more northerly type, is mouse-gray above, white below and on its limbs. It is about five inches long, with a tail of equal length. The Greater Spiny Pocket Mouse, *Heteromys,* is a few inches longer, and more extensively black.

KANGAROO RATS—FRIENDLY JUMPERS
OF THE DESERT

The Kangaroo Rat, *Dipodomys,* looks like a pygmy kangaroo. One of the handsomest of the smaller rodents, it resembles the true rat only in its size. (It is about a foot long, but over seven inches of this is the tail.) In its large, oval head there are big, round, dark eyes; atop it, rather small ears.

Like a kangaroo, this quaint-looking creature sits up on its great hind legs and hops around in a series of continuous six-foot to eight-foot leaps. It uses its long tail, which is tipped with a large, feather-like brush, to maintain its balance while it is in the air.

IT NEVER TOUCHES WATER

The tiny kangaroo rat, with its powerful hind limbs, can cover more than six feet in a single leap. A creature of the American deserts and dry plains, it gets all the liquid it needs out of its food—even tame kangaroo rats are indifferent to water. This animal has large eyes, which correctly suggest that it is active by night; the kangaroo rat passes the daylight hours underground.

The kangaroo rat lives in the warm, dry parts of western North America, from Oregon and Colorado in the United States south into Mexico and as far as Veracruz. In particular it favors sandy plains thickly dotted with bushes and cacti. Here it dwells not far from others of its kind, lying up during the day in an underground burrow it has dug. Like the pocket mouse, it may keep the entrance to the passageway securely closed with dirt, except when it goes above ground in the dark, in search of seeds.

Picking the seeds from various plants, the kangaroo rat loads them into its pockets or cheek pouches with its forefeet. It fills the pockets with the hard grains so rapidly that there is a continuous rattling sound. When it has returned to its den, it ejects the loot equally fast, aiding itself with a forward squeezing motion of its forefeet. It is not unusual for one of these rats to accumulate fifty quarts of seeds in its underground storerooms.

——How It Gets Its Water. This desert creature never drinks a drop of liquid from the day it leaves its mother's lap until it dies. It may never have a chance to drink and doesn't want to. For water, it eats small juicy tubers that grow abundantly on the desert and can be found an inch or two below the surface of the ground.

——Fighting to the Death. Except during the breeding season, kangaroo rats live alone. Put two of them together and they will fight to kill. Apparently they do not use their teeth in battle but leap and spar, striking each other with all the force of their clawed hind feet. There is no quarter expected and none given. They fight silently until one is beaten to death.

——The Babies Come. Most kangaroo rats mate in March or April. The babies, from two to five in a litter, are born with their legs and tail quite short. Like other mothers, theirs is attentive and loving. If danger threatens—the burrow may be flooded or a badger may call—she will carry off her pink little nurslings in her arms.

About fifteen days after birth the young open their eyes, and a week later are weaned. Their life span is two years or so.

——Making Friends with Kangaroo Rats. Though these galloping ghosts of the desert, as Morley Cooper, the naturalist, calls them, are timid and shy, one can gain their confidence with patience.

Mr. Cooper's first acquaintance with the miniature kangaroos was nothing more than a strange flash of sand-colored animation he saw from his trailer parked far out on the Colorado desert. In time he had them not only eating out of his hand but responding to his call, when they would climb onto his knee for food. They loved to be stroked but resented being held or restricted in any way; they bit viciously when he tried to seize them.

If you wish to "tame" some kangaroo rats, says Mr. Cooper, take your time about it. Begin by leaving bits of dried bread or nuts near the entrance to their burrows in the evening.

After about a week of this, wait around until the animals come out. They will at first be half-scared out of their wits, but in a few days will accept food from your hand. From then on it will not be difficult to persuade them to hop on your lap and to come out when you call them by name.

———A PRETTY "RAT." There are some nine distinct groups of kangaroo rats. The giant of the breed, the Banner-tailed Kangaroo Rat, has a length of fourteen inches, tail and all, and will weigh six and one-half ounces. The smallest, the Dwarf Kangaroo Rat, is only six or seven inches long.

These animals are beautifully colored; the fur on the back is a soft shade of tan or gray, while the under parts are snowy white. There is a large dash of white behind each ear, and a clear white band cuts across the back below the hips right to the tail. This color pattern is pretty much the same throughout the eighty-two forms of kangaroo rats that have been named.

BEAVERS—NATURE'S FLOOD-CONTROL EXPERTS

The beaver, famed for its skill as a builder of dams, is also valued for the handsome, dark-brown coat of thick fur that covers it. The creature is not at all well known in the Old World, for it almost disappeared there centuries ago. In the New World it continues to prosper with man's protection.

This animal is a rodent, though it is hard to think of it that way. What is more, it is the largest member of its order that we meet in the Northern Hemisphere; in fact, the only rodent exceeding it in size is the capybara of South America.

A full-grown beaver weighs a good thirty to fifty pounds. If exceptionally large, it may come closer to one hundred. It continues to grow through life. From the tip of its nose to the end of its broad tail, this great animal measures some three or four feet. (The tail makes up about one-third of the length.)

The Beaver Loves Bark. Trees mean life to the beavers. Their favorite food is the bark of the poplar or quaking aspen, but they will seek their fare on most hardwood trees; some vegetation also finds its place in their diet. Primarily, however, they feed on the bark peeled from the top branches. To get at these, the animals have to chop the tree down.

With its powerful yellow chisel-teeth, a beaver can fell in fifteen minutes a tree four inches thick; in some instances a beaver has felled trees over five feet in diameter and over one hundred feet tall.

TALENTED WOODSMEN

The cutting is generally done by a pair of adults, helped by their grown-up children. They usually work in turns, while one keeps watch. When the tree begins to crack, they prudently desist for a while; if the tree does not come down, they continue until they see it start to fall. At that moment, all plunge into a nearby pond and seemingly wait to observe whether the noise has attracted unwelcome attention.

Occasionally a tree falls the wrong way and is prevented from coming to the ground by the branches of other trees; alas, the beavers' good labor is wasted. In rare instances they have been killed by falling timber.

Can Beavers Climb? If you were to ask the average wildlife expert: "Can beavers climb trees?" the answer would bring forth a resounding no.

Recently, however, there came from Nova Scotia an eyewitness account of a beaver that was seen cutting the bark of a birch tree twenty feet from the ground! The creature had not scrambled up a leaning trunk; it was actually at work on a tall straight tree. Having satisfied its hunger, it came down with a rush, leaped into a nearby pond, and spanked the water with its tail in typical beaver fashion.

The author does not mean to lead you to believe that beavers habitually climb trees—they do not—but rather that the behavior of wild animals is unpredictable.

A SPEEDY SWIMMER

This fascinating creature's talents as a woodchopper, great though they may be, are hardly second to its skill as a swimmer. The beaver's speed under water and its lung capacity are truly remarkable: it is able to cover a quarter of a mile in fifteen minutes without coming up for air.

On the surface, the burly beaver can swim at the rate of two miles an hour, propelling itself with its webbed feet. Its flat tail acts as a rudder, and the animal certainly needs one when it is hauling a load of timber to construct a dam. By turning the tail at an angle, the beaver can set its course direct for its objective instead of being forced to travel in a more or less circular route by the unbalanced load of freight it often carries.

HOW THE BEAVER BUILDS

The beaver, you see, is no wastrel. After it has peeled off all the bark it wants, it has uses for the rest of the fallen tree. Accordingly, it proceeds to chop it up. Some parts it uses to build its house, some to form the foundation of the dams it is always constructing.

Having transported the branches to the chosen site in a stream, the animal lays them down with the thick ends side by side facing the current, and weights them with mud and rocks. It piles on layer after layer, until the desired height has been reached. Then it completes the dam with a coating of mud.

MARVELS OF BEAVER CONSTRUCTION

Building a dam is hard work, even for the industrious and powerful beaver. It has a very serious purpose in undertaking its construction jobs.

The animal, by its body and habits, is meant for a life in the water and near it. That is why it builds the dams. It wants to make certain it will have plenty of water of adequate depth close to its home, and it will get that water even if it has to block shallow streams and brooks and turn them into ponds.

How the Dams Help. One fortunate result of the beaver's work is that water conservation is helped enormously. Its dams store water during the rains for periods of drought; there are many places in the western states where farmers are dependent on the beaver for their water supply in the irrigation of their crops. Likewise, these structures help in the control of floods.

Each family of beavers creates its own particular pond by means of its dams. The water they hold back amounts to thousands of tons. It provides drink for deer, moose, and other animals, besides supplying moisture for trees and vegetation (the dams keep a trickle of water running all year). Beaver ponds are valuable also as forest-fire guards, and make excellent breeding places for fish.

Built to Endure. Beaver dams will stand for many years. You will find them in many different sizes. There are beaver dams three hundred feet long that contain a hundred tons of material. The record dam is believed to be one that was built in Montana—it measured 2,140 feet. The highest dam will not exceed twelve feet, with a base fifteen to twenty feet thick.

THE BEAVER AT WORK

Beavers do most of their work at night, and their labors consist largely of gnawing and felling trees, cutting them into convenient lengths, and carrying these away to build dams and houses. With its strong rodent teeth, a beaver can bring down a tree in fifteen minutes. The bark of the tree serves the animal as food.

Most do not approach these dimensions, however; the average dam is not more than four or five feet high, though it may be several hundred feet long. The larger dams are the work of many beavers, each of which adds to the pile heaped up by its predecessor.

Beaver Canals. Beaver canals are still more remarkable, not only because they may extend over one thousand feet and are often branched or forked, but because of their locks. The lock is made by raising a low dam that causes the water level to rise; over the dam the logs must be dragged.

Beaver canals are made for much the same purpose as our canals —for the transportation of freight too heavy to drag overland to the place where the animal is preparing its lodge or pond. The beaver expends considerable effort in the construction of its canals and in keeping them in repair. They are about two or three feet wide, with about eighteen inches of water throughout.

THE LODGE OF THE BEAVERS

The beaver often makes its house, or lodge, out in its pond. The dwelling is roughly conical in shape, perhaps ten to twenty feet across and four or five feet high, with walls rising abruptly from the water.

The animal uses heavy poles and thick sticks and plasters the whole structure with mud. It leaves a small chimney, or air hole, in the top for ventilation, and builds its entrance tunnel beneath the surface. Inside, there is a one-room apartment, with the floor just above water level; on one side the animal makes itself a soft couch of shredded bark.

In the fall, the beaver works overtime caching green branches in the mud at the bottom of the pool below the frost line. This is its winter food supply. It cuts the branches into lengths that it can easily handle, and stores them beneath the frozen surface, where it can reach them in a quick swim from its lodge. This is a wise provision. During severe winter frosts, the sap in the standing trees freezes so hard that not even the chisel-teeth of a beaver could cut them down.

Not every beaver lives in a lodge. On swift rivers, the beaver may burrow a hole in the bank, and make its chamber at the end of it. The entrance tunnel is frequently very long and is slanted downward, with its entrance right in the water.

BEAVERS ARE LOVING PARENTS

Family ties are durable among the beavers; a male and female will live together until some tragedy separates them. They mate early in the year. Two to six young, or "kittens" as they are called, are born about four months later. They are less than a foot long and weigh under a pound each. Their eyes are open from the first, and they are covered with soft fur.

The kittens mature slowly. In spite of the fact that they are out learning to swim when a month old and are weaned after six months, they remain under their parents' care for about a year. Their father and mother are good parents and spend much time training and instructing the kittens.

When the young beavers are close to two years old, breeding time comes again. Last year's family, that have lived in the shelter of the parents' home until now, take their departure just before the arrival of the new family. It may be that the mother suddenly forces them to leave, or perhaps they get the wanderlust. But go they must. Even the dutiful protector and father must seek quarters elsewhere for the time being.

Alone now, the prospective mother gathers new materials for her children's crib—finely shredded bark and other soft materials. She heaps them all on the nursery floor, a raised platform in the lodge. Then she waits for her babies to come. Thus life is handed on in the world of the beavers. Ten or twelve years is as long as these animals live in the wild; nineteen years is the record under the easier circumstances of captivity.

BEAVERS AROUND THE WORLD

The beaver is active by night, more or less, and though it is common in some localities, we rarely see it between seven-thirty in the morning and sunset. The American Beaver, *Castor canadensis,* is found in the forests of North America, from Alaska and Labrador to the Rio Grande. Close to two hundred thousand skins of this species are taken every year, half of them in Canada.

The Eurasian Beaver, *Castor fiber,* used to dwell throughout the entire forested region of Europe and east in Asia to Mongolia. It is now restricted to eastern Europe, remote parts of Scandinavia, Finland, Siberia, and Mongolia. Though some authors report it to be a burrower, on the whole it behaves much like its American cousin, building lodges and dams and cutting trees. However, a large percentage of the Old World beavers are bank-dwellers.

Made for a Life in the Water. It would not be fair to leave the beavers without taking a quick look at the remarkable equipment they possess for their life in the water. We have already noted the broad, scaly tail, and how the animal uses it in swimming. The hind feet are large and webbed for propulsion in the water; the front feet are relatively small.

Nature has even provided the beaver with a comb for its superb coat; the second toe of its hind foot is cleft, and the beaver uses this to groom itself when it emerges dripping from a stream. Its small ears, like its nose, are equipped with valves that shut these organs securely when the animal goes on an underwater trip.

Keeping its mouth open underwater poses a serious problem for any animal. How does the beaver carry branches in its open mouth below the surface? The answer is that it has loose lips, and can draw them in behind its front teeth and seal them together, permitting it to use the teeth freely and hold objects with them when it is submerged. Because of its large lungs and liver, the beaver is able to carry a considerable amount of air and oxygen-rich blood for its extended stays under the water.

"DEVIL'S CORKSCREWS" AND GIANT BEAVERS

The beaver (family Castoridae) has been with us for a long time indeed. For a good many years, farmers in Wyoming, South Dakota, and Nebraska were puzzled by hard, lengthy, spiral-shaped formations they used to encounter when they dug into their land. Scientists were unable to offer a satisfactory explanation of these strange things. The name they gave them was "daimonelix," but the formations were popularly known as "devil's corkscrews." Ultimately, their riddle was solved.

From fossils that have been found, we now know that giant beavers, seven and one-half feet from nose to tip, once lived in North America. The time was many thousands of years ago, during the later glacial periods. Some of these primitive relatives of the beaver dwelt in underground burrows, which they excavated in the form of spirals. Later the burrows were filled with vegetable débris that became fossilized—much harder than the surrounding earth—resulting in the "devil's corkscrews."

Thus another of nature's mysteries, when explained, was not mysterious at all, but a reminder that life on this planet is infinitely varied and of great antiquity.

AFRICA'S SCALY-TAILED "SQUIRRELS"

The scaly-tailed "squirrels," at home in central and western Africa, are not squirrels at all. What is more, it is not obvious at first glance that these little creatures are scaly-tailed.

Look at a scaly-tailed squirrel closely, however, and you will see, on the underside of the tail, near the base, peculiar scaly outgrowths. The scales have sharp, protruding edges which conveniently project backward and serve the animal as anchors or climbing irons that help support it in the trees.

The scaly-tailed squirrels spend the day sleeping in hollow trees. They frequent the heavy forest, where the timber towers some forty-five yards skyward, and use holes that may be situated from ten to 120 feet above the ground. Often the natives of the Congo smoke the animals out by starting a fire at the base of the tree and then kill them and use them for food.

GLIDERS OF THE TROPICAL NIGHT

Most of the scaly-tailed squirrels are gliders. They leave their roosts soon after sunset. There is very little twilight in the tropical regions where they live, and once they are on the prowl it is hard to see them in the gloom.

In the dark, the scaly-tailed squirrel runs swiftly up tree trunks and along branches until it reaches the uppermost limbs. Here it pauses briefly before launching itself into the empty void. With a sudden spring, it sails outward and downward.

For an instant you may see the animal's almost square silhouette against the starlit sky. Then it has vanished from sight—to land on the trunk of a tree sometimes sixty or eighty feet away. Soon it repeats the performance. Caught in the glare of a flashlight, its big eyes shine with a dull yellow glow.

Gliding Equipment. Like other gliders, this one, you have observed, is a creature of the night. It has much the same sort of gliding equipment as other gliders, too.

In its short aerial voyages, the animal is supported by flight membranes—thin, furry folds of skin on its sides, stretching between its fore and hind limbs. On its elbow the scaly-tailed squirrel has a long, slender spur which it can extend outward to draw the membrane still tauter. For added support, it has an extension of the flying membrane spread between its hind feet and the base of its tail.

AT REST AND IN FLIGHT
The scaly-tailed squirrel makes its home in the trees of the African jungle. It can run nimbly from branch to branch but its greatest talent is for gliding—a sixty-foot flight is by no means a record for one of these animals. What is even more impressive, they make their glides in the dark.

Some Well-known Scaly-tails. These African gliders live either singly or in pairs, and feed on nuts, fruits, seeds, and the like. As a group, they have no close relatives; they form a distinct family of their own (Anomaluridae, which means "exceptional tails"). Best known, and one of the largest, is the Gray Scaly-tailed Glider, *Anomalurus*—it has a head and body length of twelve inches, with a tail a little shorter.

Oddity of the group is the Scaly-tailed Tree "Squirrel," *Zenkerella*, which lacks the flight membranes but otherwise resembles its gliding cousins quite closely.

SPRINGHAAS—JUMPING HARES OF AFRICA

The Springhaas, *Pedetes*, of East and South Africa, got its name from the Boers. Springhaas means "jumping hare," and we often call it that in English.

This sandy-colored creature is about a foot high sitting on its haunches. It has a lengthy, hairy tail with a thick black brush at the tip. Its large, rounded head bears prominent and widely separated ears, which tend to fall to one side. Although timid by nature, it is attracted to camps, and at night one occasionally sees its big, round eyes shining like balls of fire, flashing back a beam of light.

The springhaas has long hind limbs and feet and gets about much like the kangaroo, progressing by remarkable two-footed leaps and bounds. Searching for food, it often journeys six to twelve miles a night. In times of severe drought it may travel a distance of twenty miles in one night to parts where rain has recently fallen.

On its long jaunts it frequently follows highways and Kaffir paths; here its movements can be easily observed.

FARMER'S PEST AND BUSHMAN'S BLESSING

The natural fare of this little African consists of bulbs and roots, which it digs out of the ground with the strong, curved claws on its front feet. It is very destructive to grain crops. Systematically, it uproots the young plants to get at the seed below. It will also eat the ripened grain.

Home Life of the Springhaas. The springhaas lives in burrows or warrens scattered over an area of about a hundred yards. The warrens often have four to eight openings, and may be used jointly by a pair of animals, but there are no community dens. These creatures have a curious way of sleeping—sitting up on their haunches. They never come out before dark, and generally go underground before daylight, closing the "door" behind them with plugs of earth. If disturbed, they may erect two or three such barricades.

The springhaas is not a fast breeder. A single baby in a litter is normal; twins are rare. Still, the animal seems to maintain its numbers, even in populated districts.

When common, the springhaas forms one of the main sources of food for the natives. Bushmen catch it with the aid of several reeds tied together to form a single flexible rod, fifteen or twenty feet in length. There is a large wire hook fastened to one end, and they push this down the burrow, and twist it about until eventually the animal is hooked and dragged out.

The springhaas family (Pedetidae, a name meaning "leapers") is a "problem child" for naturalists. It has no living relatives, and even fossil forms are not found outside Africa. There are no giant or dwarf springhaas, the animals forming one general tribe.

Scurriers, Jumpers, Swimmers, and Burrowers—Mice, Rats, and Their Kin

GERMAN FOLKLORE has a legend about a talented piper who had a way with rodents. His tunes, we are told, charmed all the rats of Hamelin to such a degree that they cheerily drowned themselves in the river Weser. Well, it would take a legion of virtuosos like him to rid the world of the incredibly enormous and specialized armies of mice, rats, and their relatives that occupy it. Their realm stretches almost from pole to pole.

For most of us, the word "mouse" or the word "rat" conjures up an annoying picture of the common household variety of these animals. It is a false picture, however—the domestic mice and rats form only the tiniest fraction of the group of rodents to which this chapter is devoted: the "myomorphs" or "mouselike" rodents (suborder Myomorpha). Quite a number of the wild members of this group are handsome little creatures, beautifully furred, with ways and habits as fascinating as those of the tiger, the hippopotamus, the lion, and the elephant, on a small scale.

So, before we proceed any further, you would be wise to banish from your mind all traditional ideas you may have about rodents as such, and let the behavior of the creatures speak for itself. That there are pleasing wonders of animal life in store for you here, the author can safely guarantee.

The "mouselike" rodents are the most abundant of all. Why, just one family alone, which we shall immediately turn to, has over seventy imposing groups to it with generic names! Simply to call the roll of their species and subspecies would be a gigantic task.

We may, however, mention a few, to give you some idea of the variety we find in this family—Rice Rats, Water Rats, Harvest Mice, White-footed Mice, Wood Rats, Cotton Rats, Muskrats, Voles, Lemmings, Field Mice, Spiny Mice, Tree Rats, Vesper Rats, Grasshopper Mice, Pygmy Mice, Little Brown Mice, Leaf-eared Mice, Gerbils, Antelope Rats—but here we had better desist, before we succumb to the notion that they, and not we, are the masters of the earth. Indeed, they almost are, for their hordes include all the mice and rats of the New World, as well as many in Europe, Asia, Africa, and Madagascar; they have never reached Australia. Perhaps the most popular member of this family (Cricetidae) is a little Eurasian that has now been adopted in the United States, the Hamster, *Cricetus,* for which the family is named.

NEW WORLD RATS, MICE, VOLES, GERBILS— AND THEIR OLD WORLD RELATIVES

The Rice Rat, *Oryzomys,* is a little creature of a cleanly nature, and does not enter human dwellings. It is very much at home throughout South and Central America and Mexico; we find it from Patagonia north to Texas and, on the Atlantic seaboard, as far north as New Jersey. It is the common rodent of tropical America, just as the house rat is of Europe and Asia.

The name "rice rat" was given to this small animal because it was once extremely abundant in the rice fields of the southeastern United States, doing considerable damage to the crops when rice was extensively grown there. Actually, the rice rat is misnamed, for it does not favor rice so much as it does green grass stems. Every week it consumes almost twice its weight in food.

The rice rat is a good diver and swimmer. It prefers to live in meadows and marshy areas near water (this is true of the North American species), though some individuals are found at high altitudes, especially along watercourses. The animal spends the day in its nest of plant fibers, which it places in a shallow burrow or under masses of vegetation. In the tidewater marshes it elevates the nest in the reeds and bushes to be above high-water level.

——AN AGGRESSIVE FEMALE. In warm climates, the rice rat breeds the year round. The female does not stay at home waiting to be wooed, but goes out looking for a mate.

Courtship is short with this fickle lady—it never lasts more than a few hours. Then, unceremoniously, she turns on her mate and drives him out. Twenty-five days later, and ten hours after her family of four or five is born, Mrs. Rice Rat is out searching for a new mate.

When twelve days old, the babies are weaned and their mother drives them out into the world. She must get about her main business—she produces up to eight or ten litters a year—and she has to be prepared to care for her new family. Since the young are ready to breed when they are seven weeks old, you can judge for yourself how great are the numbers of these animals.

The rice rat is a fighter and a killer. It feels no qualms about devouring its own kind. Not only does its own belligerent nature help to keep its numbers in check; its natural enemies, the owls, snakes, and weasels, will often pounce upon it in the night, when it is active, or seek it in its nest.

——THE LONG AND SHORT OF IT. There are more than 180 different kinds of rice rat, and many vary greatly in size. On an average, they are a foot in length, or shorter, tail and all. The Pygmy Rice Rat, *Oligoryzomys,* of northeastern South America, is no bigger than a house mouse; at the other extreme there is a so-called "Muskrat," *Megalomys,* dwelling in the Lesser Antilles, with a total length up to thirty inches. Species found in the United States are about the size of an overgrown house mouse.

Rice rats vary in color, too. They range from pale shades of buff or gray to rich tawny or russet, more or less mixed with black. Their fur is often rather coarse and fairly long. They have a scantily haired tail, usually about three-quarters the length of the head and body.

Other Rats and Mice of Central and South America. The tropical regions of America support rats and mice in great numbers, but we must content ourselves with mentioning only one, the Vesper Rat, *Nyctomys* ("night mouse"). This, the most attractive and squirrel-like of all the Central American rats, is a tawny-colored tree-dweller with an almost bushy tail. The animal builds neat little nests of shredded bark high up in the tall trees, where it lives in colonies. It rarely comes down to the ground, for there is food aplenty for it in the trees; it is especially fond of the fruit of the avocado tree and wild figs.

The American Harvest Mouse, *Reithrodontomys,* is not really a harvester, as you might suppose it to be. This dainty creature comes by its name through being found in the fields when crops are gathered. But it is only there searching for seeds and grass. It looks very much like a house mouse. Seldom over three inches long, it has a slender, finely tapered tail five inches in length.

——A First-Rate Builder and Acrobat. The harvest mouse is a firm believer in fresh air, and builds its nest in tall grasses. It is fascinating to watch the skill with which this creature constructs its home. It goes to work weaving the grasses into the form of a cup, and tucks in the loose ends with great care. The tiny hands move busily until the cup takes the form of a ball. The little builder uses coarser grasses on the outside to anchor the house securely to the supports. Inside, the dwelling is lined with finely shredded dry grass.

When completed, the nest is a perfect sphere, weather and draft proof; only one little round hole is left open, and this is the door. Sometimes a woodpecker's hole in a tree is chosen as a building site.

Not all harvest mice make their homes off the ground—some prefer to build the dwelling in a depression on the surface or in an underground tunnel. The timid little creatures seldom leave their nests before dark, and are back home again before or soon after sunrise.

At home in its jungle of tall grasses, the harvest mouse is very active, climbing the tall stalks to get at the seeds on top as the stalks sway back and forth in the breeze. From this dizzy height it will swing itself like an acrobat to other swaying grasses. As it climbs, its long tail helps it to maintain its balance.

——Bugle Call of the Harvest Mouse. The harvest mouse usually breeds twice a year. The height of the mating season comes in April and September. During this time, the male gives voice to a shrill, buglelike song—it is very faint and in a key almost too high for the human ear.

From three to seven helpless babies are born about twenty-four days after mating time. These mites may weigh as little as one-twentieth of an ounce and are naked and blind. Their eyes open, and they get their first teeth, in about eight days. They are weaned when two weeks old and ten days later they are on their own. Full grown at about five weeks of age, they will weigh about a third of an ounce or more.

By the time the young mice have been running about their native fields or meadows three months or so, they must start raising their own families. Time is short in the harvest mouse's world; at the end of a year the animal is quite old.

The harvest mouse is a field mouse of the western United States, but has extended its range across the Mississippi into South Carolina, Virginia, and Florida; southward, it spreads through Mexico and Central America to Ecuador. There are about seventy different kinds, but their habits and general behavior are much the same. Their color varies on the back from dark brown to buff, with white or pinkish-white under parts.

The White-footed Mouse, *Peromyscus,* makes its home in many different parts of North America, and when an animal gets around as much as this one does, it acquires a good number of names. The white-footed mouse is called the "wood mouse" because it lives in the woods, the "deer mouse" because of the deerlike color of its fur, and the "vesper mouse" because it comes out in the evening. A Florida white-footed mouse even lives in the holes of the gopher turtle, and for that reason is known as the "gopher mouse." We will frequently find Mr. White-Foot climbing up a tall tree, but more often we see him scurrying across the ground.

The white-footed mouse will make its nest almost anywhere so long as the spot is warm and dry. A hollow tree is the place it likes best, but a vacated squirrel nest or bird nest will also serve its purpose. In the winter it has been discovered in a beehive along with the bees. On the prairies some of these creatures dig burrows. The author, on periodic short winter visits to his country place in Connecticut, has found white-footed mice snug and warm in a mattress and in bureau drawers, but when he makes a protracted stay in the spring, they usually move out.

No matter where these little creatures live, they have a keen homing instinct; individuals taken prisoner and later released two miles away have been known to return to the place where they were captured.

The white-footed mouse has other remarkable traits as well. It is a musician, and will on occasion indulge in a prolonged buzzing hum. It also makes a drumming sound by tapping its front feet rapidly on some object such as a dry hollow reed or a dead leaf.

IT HUNTS INSECTS IN THE DARK
Note the large ears and lengthy whiskers on the little white-footed mouse—the animal is active at night, and these help it find its way about in the dark. There are scores of different kinds of white-footed mice spread far and wide over North America.

Less appealing is the damage the animal does to crops in fields; it feeds on seeds and nuts. Still, it is not so destructive as its cousin the meadow mouse, and it favors man by eating insects in sizable numbers.

——MOTHER WHITE-FOOT AND HER BABIES. Mice are breeders, and the white-footed member of the family is no exception. The mother produces several litters of one to nine young each year. At birth her babies are blind and bare of fur; they open their eyes for the first time when about two weeks old. From this point on, they develop rather rapidly. They are weaned about a week later, and achieve full growth at ten to twelve weeks of age. They mate when they are eight weeks old.

The mother shows considerable solicitude for her babies. But for the few moments she is out looking for a mate, every moment of her summer is devoted to her children—one litter or the next. Her nest is made of the softest material she can find, and she keeps the entrance closed, so the dwelling is warm and comfortable. If anything seems to threaten the safety of her children, she carries them off one at a time, holding each at the back of its neck with her teeth, to a hastily constructed new retreat.

When the mother is about to have a new family, she does not drive her previous children away from home but moves out herself and builds another nest. This is not an act of unselfishness but a matter of necessity—the old nest is now too contaminated to house newborn babies. The white-footed mouse, though most fastidious about its personal toilet—it continually washes and grooms its fur, keeping its coat spotlessly clean—is not so meticulous in the matter of housekeeping.

——WHITE-FOOTED MICE—AND MORE WHITE-FOOTED MICE. We find some 178 kinds of white-footed mice on the North American continent, from Panama to the Arctic Circle. Most are medium sized, being a little larger than the common house mouse, and have a hairy tail about equal in length to the head and body. Their soft fur is brown or buff on the back and strikingly white below. Their eyes are prominent, round, and black. The ears are large and well developed and the whiskers long—both adaptations of great value to an animal that moves around in the dark.

Closely related to the white-footed mouse is the Lesser White-footed Mouse, *Baiomys*, which we find from southern Texas down to Nicaragua. This drab-colored creature is only about two inches long, with a tail half an inch shorter. It lives on the ground like the meadow mouse or vole and makes runways through the grass. It is not so likely as some rodents to fight with its own kind. Moreover, there is reason to believe that the male shows affection for his children and helps the mother to watch over them.

The Grasshopper Mouse, *Onychomys,* is also known as the scorpion mouse, but neither the grasshopper nor the scorpion could find any pleasure in having this fierce little rodent as a namesake. For it is out after them every evening, its mouth watering for such delicious morsels.

——A FEROCIOUS HUNTER. Leaving its hole in the ground when the sun has set, the grasshopper mouse stalks its prey on soft padded feet, nose to the ground. Like the rabbit hound, it gets excited when on a fresh trail, uttering a series of sharp squeaks or barks.

Nothing can deter the grasshopper mouse once it has scented a victim, and it follows the trail at a fast pace. Its beady black eyes sparkle as it comes within striking distance of its game. With a mighty rush, the sturdy little hunter is at its victim's throat; the long, sharp front teeth slash into the brain, and then all is quiet once more.

To all these talents as a hunter the grasshopper mouse adds a virtue—patience. Sometimes it attacks "big game"—for example, a pocket mouse carrying a load of grain—by leaping from an ambush where it has been lying in wait.

Like most creatures of prey, the grasshopper mouse lives a hand-to-mouth existence. When fortune smiles, it feasts royally, but on unlucky nights it starves. It will gorge itself with half its own weight in flesh and blood once a day and will keep this up for weeks when opportunity offers such bounty.

As fearsome as it is to its enemies, this mouse is useful to man. The insects and rodents it destroys are often serious pests, and the gory activity of the grasshopper mouse means considerable savings in DDT and arsenic. Only one-tenth of its food is vegetation, seeds and grasses.

——SHARP CLAWS, SHARP NOSE. The grasshopper mouse has many would-be enemies in nature, but as it lives in a hole underground and is never out hunting before dark, their ravages are cut to a minimum. It is an able digger. Not only does it sometimes excavate its own nest, but also, having located by its keen sense of smell the place where an insect is hibernating below the surface, it claws its way down rapidly and gives the sleeper a rude and final awakening.

In captivity, grasshopper mice show a different side of their character. Now they are gentle and quite friendly to each other. But they will protest when they are handled, showing their resentment with a bite from their sharp teeth.

——BABIES WEIGHING ONE-TENTH OF AN OUNCE. Life starts slowly for the new grasshopper mouse, but soon increases its tempo. The first young of the year come about April or May. There are four or five naked, sightless babies in the family, and they weigh only about one-tenth of an ounce each at birth. They do not open their eyes before they are two weeks old—still, they are out feeding themselves in another ten days. Now let all small things that creep and run and hop beware; there are more appetites abroad, and they are mighty ones!

——GRASSHOPPER MICE NORTH AND SOUTH. There are two major groups of these rodents. The typical Grasshopper Mouse, *Onychomys leucogaster,* is a sturdy, medium-sized mouse with a comparatively short tail. The back and the top of its head are buff; the rest of the soft, silky fur is snow-white. We find this mouse in western North America from British Columbia and Saskatchewan south to northern Mexico. The Scorpion Mouse, *Onychomys torridus,* is smaller and has a bright tawny coat and longer tail. It makes its home in the hot, arid deserts of the Southwest.

——WHEN WINTER COMES. The grasshopper mouse does not hibernate even in the coldest part of its territory. Its body and tail usually become especially fat and plump in the fall and it does make some efforts to store up food for winter use. When the weather is exceptionally cold, the animal may stay home for a week or more and draw sustenance and energy from its stored-up fat and the seeds it has laid up.

The Cotton Rat, *Sigmodon,* was so named in the southern United States because of the balls of cotton found along its runways after it had dined on cotton seeds. It is a medium-sized, robust rat with a tail usually shorter than its head and body length, and it has short, broad ears. Its hair is moderately long, coarse, and grizzled, or finely mixed buff and black.

The cotton rat is at home not only in the southern United States, but also in Mexico, and as far south as Venezuela to Peru. Active during the daytime, this creature may be seen in many different types of country. It frequents wet meadows, dry fields, cultivated land, salt marshes, and tidewater flats, and may even be encountered high in the mountains.

This rodent does not feed exclusively on cotton seeds. It will eat most kinds of edible vegetation but favors grass, sedges, and the roots of succulent plants, which it digs out of the wet earth. Unable to climb, it gets at fruit and seeds by cutting off the plants near the bottom; they will not fall in a dense meadow, and so the rat pulls them down within reach. It also devours quantities of insects, eggs, and crabs.

The cotton rat is a great quarreler, and its arguments often end in cannibalism. An injured or trapped animal will be promptly consumed by its fellows, and a female may even kill and devour an over-zealous suitor.

——A Prolific Female. The female, bloodthirsty as she is, is much more remarkable as a giver of life. She has an extreme reproductive capacity when there is an ample supply of attractive food. She breeds frequently in the warm southern states and each litter contains four or more babies; a few hours after their birth she will mate again. The next brood comes in twenty-seven days and, if there is plenty of food, more babies follow quickly.

Not only does the mother have large families, but she will permit several previous generations to stay in the home nest.

The retreat of the cotton rat may be in an underground tunnel or in a shallow depression in the ground. The nest is made from dry grass and root fibers, and in the cottonfields a cotton rat may collect a peck of cotton to line it.

Females often mate when only seven weeks old and there is much interbreeding between close relatives. The mating season extends from February to November; it may be continuous the year round under favorable conditions.

Five hundred cotton rats to an acre is not very unusual in cultivated areas. You can readily see that its great numbers make this rodent a serious menace to crops. The cotton-rat population suffers periodic setbacks every four or five years, when the animals are attacked by a fungus disease that sweeps through their hordes and eliminates whole colonies. In six months or a year, however, new stock moves in and the process of fast multiplication is on again.

The Wood Rat, Pack Rat, Trade Rat, or Cave Rat, *Neotoma,* is a rodent famed in tales of the North American West because of its unusual habits. It has a compelling desire to collect unusual objects, and keeps them in a little "museum." In its treasure house you may find such things as nails, coins (sometimes stolen from the pockets of sleeping people), bits of tin, colored glass, china, rags, bleached bones and skulls, eyeglasses, and false teeth.

——A RODENT TRADER. Closely associated with this acquisitive instinct is the wood rat's habit of "exchanging" articles. In rifling the pockets of a sleeping person, the wood rat will leave behind a few nuts or a pine cone. On one occasion, according to an oft-repeated tale, a wood rat left some gold nuggets on the table in a prospector's cabin in exchange for some trivial trinkets. By following the animal's trail, the prospector found his fortune in a rich gold-bearing vein.

——THE WOOD RAT'S "CASTLE." Although the wood rat is most numerous along the backbone of the continent in the Rocky Mountain region, its range extends from the Atlantic to the Pacific, from Nicaragua northward, though not so far as the Hudson Bay and Great Lakes regions. It inhabits cliffs, caves, open woodland, and arid regions.

The wood rat is a homebody and takes great pains with its "castle." On the Pacific coast the house may be five or six feet high and have one or two rooms. In general, it is a globular affair of sticks and grasses built in a cavity among the rocks, in a hollow tree, in the branches of a tall tree, or in a cactus growth. The inside is lined with soft shredded bark or grass. Since the nest is a permanent home, the animal enlarges and improves it from time to time.

Like the squirrel, the wood rat hoards large quantities of seeds, grain, and nuts in the fall for food during the winter, laying them up in a storeroom. A most fastidious housekeeper, the animal has a place for everything, including a regular garbage dump for refuse.

While the wood rats are sociable in the sense that they live in colonies, they do not visit one another's homes though there are well-worn community trails. Active mostly by night, these rodents feed on vegetable matter, which includes greens and all food of this nature. Some greens are put out on rocks to dry and cure before being taken home to the storehouse.

A number of the wood rats drink considerable water, but others that live out on the desert have little use for it; they get their liquid from the pulpy cactus flesh and succulent root tubers.

——A LONG JOURNEY, A HARSH GREETING. The wood rat breeds once or twice during the year. The male gets restless in January and makes nightly trips beyond the usual home territory, in search of a mate. Sometimes he travels half a mile or more. Having found a likely prospect, he proceeds with caution. Even though he may be acceptable to the female, she will not be won without considerable sparring. Her temper may break out at any moment and an overpersistent suitor may get a split ear or a wounded tail for his trouble.

However, a successfully mated couple of wood rats will remain together longer than most rodents during courtship. The male may be tolerated in the home even after the young are born. They come, two to six of them, about four weeks after the mating, and each weighs about one-half ounce. Weaned at three weeks of age, they begin to forage for themselves. The mother takes good care of them, and may allow them to stay with her when they can already find their own food.

——A DRUMMER AND A CHIRPER. While the wood rat is not credited with unusual vocal powers, it will thump on the ground with both hind feet when alarmed, or vibrate the tip of its tail rapidly up and down. When it taps on dry leaves, the noise will carry a considerable distance; it probably serves as a danger signal. Like any rat, when seized by an owl or other foe it will give out a desperate shriek. Occasionally, during the mating season, it has been heard to make low chirps.

The bushy-tailed rats of western North America are the most attractive of the wood rats; indeed, with their deep, soft fur, they are more like squirrels than rats. Large ones will weigh up to one pound or more and measure nine inches in head and body length, with a tail about an inch shorter. Such a rat will stand about three inches at the shoulder. All told, there are twenty-eight species, with some close relatives in Mexico.

The Fish-eating Rat, *Ichthyomys,* and several closely related smaller water mice dwell in the mountains of tropical America, from Honduras south to Peru. They are rodents that have to a good degree turned away from the tribe's traditional habit of feeding on seeds and vegetable matter and have gone a-fishing or a-hunting.

We know little about these strange creatures. The naturalist Stirton, however, has observed some in El Salvador. He found them in streams at the bottom of deep canyons, with heavy cloud-forest vegetation on both sides, and with only tiny spots of sunlight on the dripping fronds and moss-covered walls. Large oaks were laden with orchids, and other plants overhung the banks.

The fish-eating rats also frequent the countless crystal-clear streams that plunge down the mountain slopes through the damp forests at elevations between three thousand and eleven thousand feet. By night, the animals swim about in the rock-bound pools and scramble over partly submerged tree trunks in search of salamanders hiding behind stones, or water beetles concealed in dark corners.

These rodents often have a strong fishy smell when captured, and we assume that occasionally one will catch and eat small fish, but we have no direct evidence of this. Of seven animals examined by Stirton, three *Neusticomys,* or fish-eating mice, had fed bountifully on beetles, fresh-water snails, crustaceans, and mussels. Three of the fish-eating rats of Ecuador, *Anotomys,* had been eating some kind of mammal, and had considerable hair in their stomachs but no bones. This hair apparently came from one of their kind, suggesting cannibalism. Feathers of what was probably a wren, and the skin and bones of a salamander, were also found in a water mouse, *Rheomys,* in El Salvador.

The fish-eating rat, *Ichthyomys,* is the largest and handsomest of the five known kinds. It is about the size of a large house rat—seven inches long, with a hairy tail almost as long again—and has small ears. Especially adapted for life in the water, it possesses soft, dense fur and glossy overhair, which serves to keep the animal warm and dry as it moves along in a chilly stream or pool. Its hind feet are greatly enlarged for swimming, and are fringed with stiff hairs. It is glossy grayish black above and silvery gray below. Literally, its scientific name means "fish mouse."

HAMSTERS—BURROWERS OF THE OLD WORLD

Hamsters are fat, chubby, little animals with thick, soft fur. They have short limbs and a little bobbed tail. You cannot hear these creatures as they patter about at night, for the soles of their feet are well padded with hair. They possess large cheek pouches in which they transport grain.

The hamsters are great hoarders. Thus we are not surprised to learn that in Central Europe the word "hamster" is used to signify selfishness or a greedy person. The name, however, once had a different meaning. It came from an Old High German word, *hamastro,* meaning "weevil." Like that insect, the hamster is a borer, but mainly under the ground, where it lives in tunnels.

Although tame hamsters have achieved a great vogue in the United States in recent years, they are not native to the New World. The common hamster we see in pet shops today is the descendant of animals imported from southeastern Europe and southwestern Asia. In the wild, hamsters are better known in Europe than elsewhere, but they are also plentiful over most of northern Asia.

The European Hamster, *Cricetus,* is the largest of the hamsters—it is about a foot long. Its fur is very thick, with a typical color pattern: light brown on the back, with white and red markings on the sides. The animal's under parts are black.

This is odd, in a way, for it is the reverse of the usual natural color scheme. Other animals are nearly always dark above and light below. The light under colors tend to eliminate a perceptible shadow on the under side of the animal, and so help it to escape detection. In this hamster, however, the shadowed under parts are greatly emphasized by the black.

The European hamster frequents farm lands in eastern Europe and western Asia. It is common in grass fields and cultivated areas but shows a preference for dry, sandy soil in which to dig its labyrinth of subterranean runways. The entrance to the den, or "creeping-hole," as it is called, is marked by a large pile of excavated earth. The animal makes its runways about two inches in diameter and digs them on several levels. Conveniently, all lead to the central nest chamber, two or three feet below the surface.

——Food for a Rainy Day. Under cover of darkness the hamster sallies forth in search of plunder. It digs up potatoes and tears down stalks of wheat and oats to get at the grain on top. Food is not eaten on the spot but borne home to the underground storehouse. The hamster carries potatoes and other tubers between its front teeth; it stuffs wheat and other grain in its cheek pouches until they are filled to capacity. Home at last, and ready to unload, it empties the pouches partly by blowing and partly by pressing with its front feet on its cheeks.

No matter how well fed the hamster may be, its natural instinct urges it to collect food for a rainy day. One hamster storeroom may contain as much as a whole bushel of grain besides quantities of roots. The food is kept in good condition, and is not permitted to rot with dampness; the hamster stores the potatoes and root crops separately from the grain. There is a place for everything, and everything must be in its place, in the pantry of this surprisingly clean, methodical creature. In addition to the foods already mentioned, the European hamster will eat beets and fallen apples. However, it is not just a vegetarian, but kills and eats small animals and birds and their young.

——SLEEPY TIME. In the fall the hamster gets fat, and, with its storehouse now well filled, stays home in the nest most of the winter. It may reach a dormant state but apparently it does not go into complete hibernation. Early in the spring, the animal moves to a new location and digs a fresh burrow in which to live during the coming summer.

This hamster will breed four or five times during the year. Usually it bears families of from five to twelve young, but sometimes there are as many as eighteen babies in a litter. The infants make no great demands upon their parents' patience: two weeks after birth they have left home and each is setting up housekeeping in a burrow of its own.

——FIGHTING THE HAMSTER. Because of the damage it does to crops, the European hamster is hunted by the farmer. Sometimes he uses dogs to kill it, and sometimes he floods the burrows with gas. However, the cornered hamster is a courageous fighter and will not hesitate to spring at either dog or man; there is a record of one hamster that seized a horse by the nose when the animal stepped on its burrow.

In defending itself, the hamster will make use of its unusual food-unloading practice, already referred to. It will blow the food content of its cheek pouches in the face of an enemy; the points of some seeds strike the foe with such force that they can cause severe pain, making him take to his heels.

Trapped and killed, the hamster yields up a valuable pelt, used particularly to line coats.

Hamsters Around the World. Relatives of the big European hamster are an interesting lot. The Golden Hamster, *Mesocricetus*, is the best known, and one of the most popular pets of the day. It is a golden brown color and noted for its rapid rate of reproduction; it lives about two and one-half years. Much like it is the South African Hamster, *Mystromys*, the only one found south of the Equator.

Not all hamsters are alike in size. Some of those we find in Asia are no larger than a mouse, and one in Siberia (Miller's Hamster) turns white during the winter. There are hamster moles, with hardly any eyes or ears, and hamsters with manes, in this large group.

VOLES, LEMMINGS, AND MEADOW MICE

Under this popular heading comes a vast army of small, short-tailed rodents that far exceed in numbers any other group of mammals found in their particular domain, the cool and temperate regions of the Northern Hemisphere. Grass is the fastest-growing and most prolific vegetation on this planet, and the voles and their kin are grass-eaters. They are the mills that make the quickest turnover of vegetable matter into flesh and bone to feed a host of hungry meat-eaters.

The True Lemming, *Lemmus,* is a chubby, little bobtailed vole about six inches in length (only one inch of this is the tail) with long, soft fur completely concealing the ears. Its feet are padded with fur to protect them from the snow and ice. The general color is a golden yellow-brown or buff. On the back of some species we see a dark stripe, while the Scandinavian lemming is very ornate: from the top of the head to behind the shoulders it is glossy black, in sharp contrast with the golden color of the back.

——Strange Lemming Migrations. Lemming migrations are one of the wonders of the world. Every now and then the lemming population in a district builds up to enormous proportions. All the food in the region is consumed, and the lemmings must seek fresh pastures. As the little rodents scamper onward, their ranks are swollen by additional bands traveling in the same direction, until thousands of them are on the march.

——A March to Sure Death. Once the animals have started on their traditional pilgrimage, nothing deters them from their course. Not even swift rivers or the sea will halt the hurrying hordes, though death by drowning is certain. The inherited impulse to travel carries them on and on until the multitude dwindles and fades away. Only a few escape, or are left at the starting point, to carry on the race.

During the mass lemming migrations, all the flesh-eating birds and mammals—including gulls, hawks, owls, foxes, weasels, bears, cats, wolverines—close in, for here is food for the taking, without the usual hunt or chase. The fish get their share when the lemmings cross rivers and lakes. Even the caribou join in the feast, crushing the little animals between their teeth and swallowing them whole.

The peak of the cycle in lemming population is reached about every fourth year. The migration usually begins in the late winter or early spring and may last a few weeks. But some of the migrations in Norway may continue for a year, the females making short stopovers to raise a family before moving on again.

——WHY DO THEY DO IT? American Eskimos and peasants of northern Europe have a simple explanation for the sudden appearance of the lemming hordes in their midst. They claim that the animals spiral down from the heavens in a snowstorm. Some of the old Eskimos actually believe that they have seen the creatures falling with the swirling snowflakes.

An equally quaint notion—but this one was begotten by our early scientists—was that when the Scandinavian lemmings migrated, they were seeking their ancient home on the now submerged land of Atlantis. Others have suggested the theory that the lemmings' buildup in numbers is governed by sunspots, but no one really knows the cause.

——THE LEMMING'S HOME. The Brown Lemming, a common little animal of the colder regions of North America, usually constructs a globe-shaped nest on the surface of ground more or less covered with moss and vegetation, or burrows beneath a boulder. Soon the nest is filled with five or six babies, the average litter. Under favorable conditions, when the lemmings are building up their numbers before a migration, families may contain as many as eleven; at these times, there is a rapid succession of litters between April and September.

During the long, hard winter, the lemming's nest is covered by a deep blanket of snow. Under it the animal finds ample food and is safe from birds and beasts of prey as well as winter's icy blasts.

Beneath this blanket, too, the lemming is often placed in cold storage by its enemies. The Arctic fox is largely dependent on the little rodent for food, and caches it in large numbers in the icy cold ground as a supply of food for the winter.

The Water Vole, or Water Rat, *Arvicola*, is a familiar figure to every country boy in England, who often sees it sitting up on its haunches along the banks of rivers and ponds nibbling stalks of green vegetation. Sometimes this big brown field mouse (the animal's head and body length may be up to eight inches, the hairy tail another four) is found living at a considerable distance from water—too far away for convenient commuting.

The water vole is perfectly at home in the water, has hind feet somewhat adapted for that kind of life (they are not webbed) and is an accomplished swimmer and diver. It is easily tamed and makes a fine pet, but requires plenty of water to swim and bathe in.

——A RODENT SUNBATHER. The water vole is largely active during the hours of light, but may be seen about at any time of the day or night. It feeds almost exclusively on vegetable matter such as duckweed, roots, or water lilies and marigolds. On occasion, however, it will eat small fish, mussels, and fresh-water crustaceans. It has an interesting habit of building, among the reeds, little platforms of twigs and cut grasses on which it sits and suns itself.

The home of the water vole is a ball-shaped nest of dry grass either in the reeds two or three inches above water level or in a hole in the bank. There is usually an extensive burrow in the bank, with an emergency entrance under water. A family generally consists of from five to eight babies. (There are some two litters a year born between April and September.) The mother often carries her children about as a dog does its puppies, transferring them from one dwelling place to another while they are still naked and blind.

——MANY ENEMIES. Moving about on the surface of the water, this small rodent hardly qualifies for the title of a champion swimmer. Under the water it goes faster. Pursued by an enemy, it partly swims and partly runs along the bottom to its emergency hole. As it flees, it raises a cloud of mud that acts as a smoke screen covering its retreat.

The water vole has many foes: otters, stoats, weasels, hawks, owls, and herons are among them. Pike have often been seen taking a water vole, and a large eel was shot while it was swallowing a full-grown one.

——EUROPE'S "MUSKRAT." Though charged with few bad habits, this harmless and rather friendly creature may undermine embankments and dams when excavating its runways. Such offenses are never serious and are quite rare.

In many ways the water vole resembles the American muskrat and fills a similar position in Europe. It has a similar thick coat of fur. The flesh of the water vole is a popular dish in some parts of France just as the flesh of the muskrat is in some parts of America.

A native of Europe and most of Asia north of the Himalayas, the water vole is, as we have observed, common in England, but oddly enough it has never reached Ireland. We find a similar situation in Asia; the water vole is common in Siberia yet unknown in China.

The Muskrat or Musquash, *Ondatra,* is North America's most valuable fur-bearer in point of the total number of skins used. Trappers take between ten and twelve million muskrats every year and so their pelts have become among the cheapest on the wholesale market.

In the trade the processed fur reappears under elegant names. You

A VALUABLE FUR-BEARER
    The muskrat is highly esteemed for its fur, which, when dressed, looks somewhat like that of the fur seal. Muskrats are extensively trapped, but they are in no danger of being wiped out; the animals are prolific breeders, and it is not uncommon for a single female to bear over thirty babies a year.

will often meet it as Electric Seal, Near Seal, Bisam Mink, Hudson Seal, Hudsonia, Loutrine, River Sable, River Mink, and Water Mink. The muskrat, however, is none of these exotic creatures, but a humble rodent that dwells near swamps, lakes, and streams, over the greater part of the continent, from the northern tree limit south to the Mexican border.

———Why It Lives There (Indian Version). The American Indians have a colorful legend to explain how the muskrat came to occupy the haunts in which we find it today. They say that once it aided Nanabojou, their sun god, during a great flood. As a reward for this good deed, he gave the animal the choice of living in any part of the country it wished. The muskrat was so enchanted by the deep blue lakes that it chose to dwell there.

Alas, the muskrat, it seems, is a fickle creature—or this one was, at any rate. Soon it was back in the god's presence, asking to be given the grassy banks instead. Kindly Nanabojou complied with its wishes.

The following day, however, Nanabojou's patience was sorely tried when the muskrat reappeared, this time to complain that it had nowhere to swim in its new home; it wanted to be returned to the lakes.

Said Nanabojou: "One day you want land and the next you ask for water. Since you do not know your own mind, I shall decide for you. Henceforth your home will be in the marsh, the borderland that is neither dry land nor open water. Here you will have long green grass to eat and water deep enough to swim in."

This proved to be just what the muskrat wanted, and it has lived in such places until this day. There, to dwell in, it often digs a hole in the bank, with the entrance under water, or else it builds itself a house of reeds and grasses out in a pond or lake, but always in shallow water.

———A Dual-Purpose House. House-building with the muskrat is not an engineering achievement, as it is with the industrious beaver. In fact, the house is a shoddy piece of construction, although, as we shall see, it has a twofold purpose.

The muskrat first heaps up rushes and reeds until it has made a pile that reaches well above the water line. It then chews out a cavity in the middle for a nest chamber with an underwater entrance. Additional material is stacked on the pile from time to time. Although in other seasons it eats herbs, grain, and water animals, in winter, when everything is frozen hard and food is scarce the muskrat sits at home and feeds on the inner walls of its house.

Muskrats breed throughout the summer, from April to September. Two to six babies come about a month after the adults mate. In another month the youngsters are able to find food on their own, and their mother's sharp teeth show them they must be on their way; she has to get ready for another brood.

——A Big Meadow Mouse. Weighing two or three pounds, and about ten inches in head and body length (the scaly tail is half as long again), the muskrat is smaller than the beaver—actually, it is just an overgrown meadow mouse, made for a life in the water. Its hind feet are broad and partly webbed for swimming. Its thick, soft fur is waterproof, and is overlaid with long, oily, reddish-brown guard hairs which enable it to shed moisture. Its tail, vertically flattened, is an efficient rudder.

——How the Muskrat Got Its Name. The muskrat got its name from the musky secretion of the perineal glands. The odor is not unpleasant, and the secretion is sometimes used in the preparation of perfume.

These animals are in general inoffensive, so far as man is concerned. Sometimes, however, the muskrat does cause some trouble, as in Europe, where it has been introduced. In some places it undermines dikes and dams as it pursues the inclinations of a burrower. In North America its chief enemies are the minks, snapping turtles, hawks, and eagles.

——Florida's Muskrat. Florida has a muskrat all its own. This one, not over eight inches in head and body length, is even more like an overgrown field mouse than is the common muskrat. It has a round instead of a flat tail, and is known as the Round-tailed Muskrat, or Florida Water Rat, *Neofiber*. As the scientific name suggests, it belongs to a different genus.

The Pine Mouse, *Pitymys,* was so named because it was first discovered in the pine forests of Georgia, in the United States, probably on the LeConte plantation near Riceboro. Like so many other animals' names, this one's is misleading; pine trees are not necessarily a part of the pine mouse's homeland; open meadows and pastures provide

an equally suitable setting for the animal's activity. Nor is the creature found only in Georgia—we meet it in other eastern states, and
in Mexico as far south as Veracruz, as well as in continental Europe
and Asia.

The pine mouse is a small rodent, very similar in general appearance to a meadow mouse but more or less modified for a life under
the ground. The American pine mouse has very close soft brown fur,
small eyes, and reduced ears.

This rodent digs long, shallow tunnels and pushes up the dis-
placed soil into small mounds of earth. It feeds on tubers and will
clean out a field of potatoes, leaving no visible trace of its raids except the dead potato tops. Moles are often blamed for the damage
done to bulbs and roots by the pine mouse.

——GREAT DAMAGE DONE BY THE PINE MOUSE. Given a fast-grow
ing root crop, the pine mouse is capable of rapid mass reproduction.
Its numbers will multiply sufficiently to consume many acres of available potatoes in a short time. In a field of potatoes in Connecticut
completely destroyed by these mice, the author found every row honey-
combed with runways; when he started to dig, he could see many
of the mother mice running away over the surface, their babies dangling from their mouths as the parents carried them to safety.

Once the harvest was over, these hordes of Connecticut mice were
confronted with only a normal supply of food, not nearly enough for
such quick breeders. They turned to other fields for sustenance.
Some young orchard trees close by had their entire root systems
devoured by the hungry pine mice, and the first high wind blew the
trees clean out of the ground.

The Common Field or Meadow Mouse, or Vole, *Microtus,* one of the
most abundant of all rodents, is an inoffensive, drab-colored creature
only three or four inches long. It is not especially attractive—just a
ball of long, soft fur, two little sparkling black eyes, and a short tail.

Despite its small size and humble appearance, the common meadow
mouse plays an important role in the lives of many larger animals
and birds. An almost endless array of appetites depend on it for sat-
isfaction: the meadow mouse is food for cats, lynxes, skunks, weasels, martens, fishers, minks, opossums, dogs, foxes, coyotes, wolves,
badgers, black bears, grizzlies, and brown bears, as well as many

kinds of hawks, owls, eagles, crows, jays, magpies, sea gulls, snakes. This is not nearly the end of the list—even fish and snapping turtles get their share of meadow mice.

But for the industrious reproductive habits of the meadow mice, there would not be nearly enough of them to go around. Their breeding season is almost never closed; there are young in the nest from January to December. A single female may produce as many as seventeen litters of four to nine young (sometimes as many as thirteen) during one year. The babies are born naked, blind, and helpless, about three weeks after mating time; two weeks later they are weaned and on their own. The nest, a globelike shape of woven grasses, may be hidden in a depression in the ground or under an old log. Sometimes it is underground.

——THE SHORT-LIVED MEADOW MOUSE. The meadow mouse expends a tremendous amount of energy in an apparently endless round

THE MOUSE THAT LIVES A YEAR

The common field mouse is short-lived, indeed—only the hardiest will survive longer than a year. One reason is that it furnishes food for many larger animals and birds. Another is that this minute creature devours its own weight in grass and seeds every day, and it wears itself out in the never-ending hunt for food.

of day and night activities. It consumes its own weight in food every twenty-four hours and so it must always be searching for the leaves, seeds and grasses it needs to keep itself going. Plants make up most of its diet, though it will eat some insects and meat.

With its constant hunt for food, its constant breeding, small wonder that the life fires of the meadow mouse are burned out before its first birthday comes around. Some doddering old males may live eighteen months, but few ever reach that old age.

——MEADOW MICE GALORE. The nervous little meadow mouse has never been satisfied to stay just in meadows. We find it in all kinds of places, hot and cold, high and low—in swamps and woods, on plains and prairies, from sea level to mountain tops. From place to place, it has many different forms—there are 238 types of meadow mice named, including many subgenera. They have an enormous range in the Northern Hemisphere, including all of North America from Alaska south to Guatemala, all of Europe, and northern and central Asia, and Asia Minor.

——MOUSE PLAGUES. The ancients knew the meadow mouse well. If you have read Greek literature, you probably are familiar with the worship of the Mouse God Apollo. Apollo was looked upon as the instigator of the various mouse plagues from which Greece suffered. It is easy to understand the reverence in which the old Greeks held his powers, for food was scarcer then than now, and a mouse plague might destroy an entire year's crops, bringing hunger to whole countrysides.

Even in our own time a mouse plague is no laughing matter. Under favorable conditions, especially in Europe, the meadow mouse multiplies in an incredible manner. There are many instances where harvests over large tracts of land have been completely destroyed during what is known as a "vole year." Fortunately, when the meadow mouse or vole population has reached a high peak, they have a plague of their own and their numbers are quickly reduced below normal.

SOME OTHER CURIOUS MEADOW MICE AND VOLES

The Snow Mouse or Collared Lemming, *Dicrostonyx,* lives further north than any other rodents; it dwells in Asia and North America, and makes its home under the ground. With the exception of a small Asiatic hamster, it is the only rodent that changes from a brown summer coat to a snow-white one in winter.

Another curiosity of the snow mouse is that it is the only mammal that sheds its toe-nails annually. The third and fourth claws on the front feet grow excessively long and broad in winter and are replaced by normal claws in April or May. The animal may or may not have a tawny band across its throat.

THE MOUSE THAT IMITATES THE ERMINE

The snow mouse, which lives in the colder parts of Asia and North America, is the only mouse that wears a white coat in winter, a brown one in the summertime. This animal lives underground, and in the winter makes runways in the snow. It grows longer claws at this time, possibly for digging in the ice and snow.

Relic of the Ice Age? For a number of years the skulls of a strange mouse with broad, grooved front teeth kept turning up in owl pellets in populated districts like New Jersey, but no naturalist could find where the owls got them. Eventually one labeled "Hoboken, New Jersey," turned up in a museum collection.

This rare and elusive vole is now known as the Lemming Mouse, *Synaptomys*, and lives largely in cool, moist swamps and bogs in northeastern North America. It is not to be confused with the lemming, though it has much the same habits, including the urge to migrate. Some scientists consider it a hangover from the Ice Age; they believe it was left behind in cool sphagnum bogs and on shaded mountain slopes when the ice retreated north.

A Handsome Little Brownie. One of the comeliest little denizens of the North Woods is the Red-backed Mouse, *Clethrionomys*. It is a pretty, furry little creature with a broad splash of reddish-brown color down the middle of its back. Known as the Bank Vole in Europe, this tiny brownie favors the northern belt of evergreen forest that encircles the globe. It follows no beaten trail but trots along the forest floor scrambling over fallen logs, and even climbs trees.

A Vole That Lives in Trees. While practically all the voles make their living on the ground and rarely climb trees, the Red Lemming, *Phenacomys,* has reversed the order—it lives in the trees and rarely descends to the ground; for this reason it is often referred to as the Tree Lemming.

The red lemming feeds on the fleshy wood and needles of the Douglas and Grand firs in the Rocky Mountains. Its nest, sometimes thirty feet above the ground, consists of twigs and pine needles. Unlike all the other voles, this one has the long tail of a tree-dweller. (However, many of the species actually have short tails and never climb trees.) It also differs from other members of its tribe in having a slow rate of reproduction, usually two in a litter, which do not leave the nest until a month old.

It Digs With Its Teeth. The Mole Lemming, *Ellobius,* of Asia Minor and Central Asia is the subterranean member of the voles. The claws on the front feet are not especially large for a burrower, but the long, powerful front teeth projecting beyond the closed lips are a fair compensation. This novel specialization enables the animal to hack away at the earth with its teeth without getting its mouth full of soil, just as the beaver keeps its mouth dry when cutting wood under water.

GERBILS—RATS OF THE OLD WORLD DESERTS

Gerbils are the typical small mammals you will encounter if you travel across the desert regions and sandy wastes of Asia, Africa, and southern Russia. Here, in the hottest and driest parts of the world, these animals often live many miles from water.

A burrow, excavated in the sand, is the gerbil's home. The animal may be sociable and share community tunnels or else lead a solitary life; male and female usually do not nest together. In Russian Turkestan the author saw a dozen or more of them, the Sand Rats, *Meriones,* that appeared to be chasing one another around in sport. They kept it up until he came within twenty or thirty yards of them, whereupon all dived into their holes. These seemed to constitute a common network of underground burrows.

Most of the gerbils are about only during daylight hours. They feed on seeds, grasses, and roots, which for the most part contain a little moisture. There are quite a number of different kinds of gerbils, the majority about the size of a house rat. Largest of all is the Great Sand Rat, *Rhombomys;* at home in central Asia, the Caspian Sea region, and Mongolia, this creature has surprisingly thick fur for a hot-country animal. Usually gerbils are protectively colored like the desert sands in which they live, and have large ears so that they can hear sounds from afar.

——JUMPERS OF THE DESERT. Often the gerbils are called "antelope rats" because of the way they move about. Their hind legs are fairly long, and they hop rather than scamper or scurry in typical rat fashion. In this respect they remind us of the jerboas, or jumping rodents; indeed, "gerbil" is just another form of the name "jerboa."

OLD WORLD RATS AND MICE—AND THEIR NEW WORLD DESCENDANTS

Just as America owes its first white settlers to the Old World, so does it owe its population of house mice and rats. They were fairly early settlers, too—they arrived in the United States at the time of the American Revolution. The conflict they started, however, has long outlasted that one.

The scurrying legions of domestic mice and rats form only two small branches of a huge rodent family, the Muridae (the name comes from the Latin word *mus,* "mouse," and old Linnaeus, who pretty much set the style in the scientific naming of animals, applied it to all rats and mice). Although this group was originally limited by the shores of the Old World, some of its members have penetrated into almost every part of the globe, including many of the islands and even distant Australia, where they developed into true curiosities.

A number of these creatures are genuinely handsome, but most look rather like the familiar rat and mouse, and possess a fairly long,

naked tail. By and large they are land animals, with a marked tendency to take to the trees. Given an occasion to enter the water, they
generally show that they can swim well.

The Dwarf Mouse, or Old World Harvest Mouse, *Micromys minutus*,
is one of the great acrobats of the mouse world. It looks as though

TINY GATHERER OF THE HARVEST

The dwarf mouse or harvest mouse of the Old World searches for seeds and grass in
the fields at harvest time. A talented acrobatic performer, this small rodent has a long
tail (half of the over-all length of five inches) by which it may suspend itself while it
engages in its antics. The mouse shown above is resting on its ball-shaped nest.

it were built for its trade, too. Among the smallest of all rodents, it has a slim body that ends in a slender tail about as long as the rest of the animal. The tail is actually prehensile—it can hold onto things. We find this tawny or reddish-brown creature spread from Great Britain and continental Europe east to Japan.

The dwarf mouse loves to bask in the warm sunlight. It is a great performer and takes its exercise in the daytime, tumbling about on twigs and grass stems, holding on with its tail, which it sometimes wraps twice around a twig or grass for a firm hold.

To appreciate the acrobatical antics of this mouse, you should see it on top of a swaying wheatstalk, sitting on its haunches, grooming its tail with both hands. When the wind blows, the mouse rides its "bucking bronco" with great skill. In captivity four or five of these tiny animals will simultaneously perform in a space of six cubic inches, never hitting each other or missing their foothold.

——CRADLE OF THE BABY MICE. The summer nest of the dwarf mouse is a small round ball of cut grass and leaves, about the size of an orange, suspended among reeds or shrubbery about a foot above the ground. It shows no opening, and, when entering, the mouse has to remove a part of the covering. Inside, the dwelling is lined with finely shredded grass and leaves. The nest sways in the wind, and serves as a cradle for the young.

From five to eight babies are born, naked and sightless, about three weeks after mating time. They grow rapidly, and, when about a week old, completely fill the little ball, scarcely leaving room for the mother to crawl inside to feed them. They must soon leave the nest and learn to climb in search of their own food—seeds and insects. There may be two litters in a little more than a month during the height of the breeding season.

In winter, the harvest mouse has a snug, warm retreat in a hedgerow or a hillside, or buries its nest under dense vegetation. During frosty weather, it will stay home in its cozy nest but it does not hibernate.

The Yellow-necked Mouse, or Old World Wood Mouse, *Apodemus,* is one of the commonest small rodents of Europe; it takes much the same place in the Old World as the white-footed mouse does in the New World. You may find it in forests and wooded country or among rocks, but you will never see it abroad by day. It is strictly a creature of the night.

Although it occurs in a great variety of forms, the wood mouse can generally be recognized by its lengthy tail—this is as long as, or a little longer than, the three- or four-inch body—its large ears, and its big dark eyes. The soft fur is usually some shade of tan or brown with a dark broad band down the back.

——BROAD-MINDED MOTHERS. The wood mouse is a prolific breeder —one pair may raise six families of four or five young during the year. It may locate its nest in almost any place so long as it will be warm, dry, and reasonably safe from its enemies. Several families sometimes are raised in one burrow and in what seemingly is one nest. It is believed that under such circumstances the young do not remain with their respective parents but accept milk from any one of the mothers that happens to come along.

——A LESSON FROM THE WOOD MOUSE. Just as the captive lion of fable was aided by a mouse, so were Dutch hyacinth growers by this one. In fact, it gave them a lesson in horticulture.

The growers had noticed that certain hyacinths here and there, instead of blossoming in the usual way, made innumerable bulblets and that in a few years hundreds grew to perfection where there had been only one. Examination of the bulbs when they first failed to bloom revealed that they had been gnawed to the heart by mice. Dutch growers now increase the supply of valuable hyacinths by slashing the bulb to the heart with a knife and cutting numerous cross sections.

——WHERE WE FIND IT. This wood mouse lives in the northern temperate regions of Eurasia, from Ireland to Japan and south to northern India and Mediterranean Africa. Cold weather works no hardship on it—it is active all winter but avoids going out during rain and sleet storms.

THE TRUE RATS—A GREAT ARMY

The True Rat, *Rattus*, with its more than 550 recognized kinds, forms a great army which harries man throughout the world. The remorseless rat divisions are made up of creatures of all sizes—there are small ones, only five inches in head and body length, looking like overgrown mice; there are large ones, up to a foot in length, that are a fearful sight. The tail is scaly and may even be longer than the rest of the animal.

Rats vary also in their color and the texture of their hair, which is often gray or brown and sometimes mixed with spines. However, no matter what the variety, you will generally know a rat when you see one—the ratlike form is much the same throughout this huge group.

Man's Close Companion. To man, the house rat is the most objectionable of all living creatures, yet with the exception of the house mouse it is more closely associated with him than any other animal. Wherever man has gone, the rat has followed. It has boarded the ships and traveled to distant lands with him, it has climbed onto the trains and accompanied him inland, and stolen rides on the covered wagons along with the pioneers. It has followed man to war and grown fat on the spoils.

Throughout the years the rat has acquired a liberal education in combatting man's efforts to destroy it. To date, it has had the better part of the battle. There are more rats in North America than there are people. They do not accept any meager dole but annually exact a sizable tribute from the income of every man, woman, and child.

Rats not only thrive in the filth and squalor of city slums and garbage dumps but enter the best of homes and somehow find their way into "ratproofed" warehouses and granaries. Professional exterminators may destroy them by the hundreds, but there are thousands of others ready to move in and take over. They feed on anything edible, even each other if need be.

The Norway Rat, *Rattus norvegicus,* is the common rat found in most cities in the temperate regions, especially in Europe and in the northern United States and Canada. It is also known as the Surmulot, Gray Rat, Brown Rat, Wander Rat, House Rat, or Wharf Rat. Its scaly tail is about equal to the length of its head and body. The animal weighs some one and one-half pounds, but here and there we encounter giants of four pounds.

This rat breeds the year round. It takes roughly three weeks to bring a litter of babies into the world. Under favorable conditions one mother may bear twelve families in one year; six or seven babies come at a time but fourteen are hardly unusual, and there may even be more.

The infants grow rapidly—all too rapidly, one might say. Some rats are ready to breed eight weeks after birth but three months is the normal age that they start mating. One and one-half to two years is the limit of a rat's sexual activity and few ever live to the ripe old age of three.

Another important rat, and very much like the Norway species in its habits, is the Roof Rat, or Alexandrian Rat, *Rattus rattus*. This is the common house rat in the Mediterranean region, the southern United States, Central America, and South America. It is not quite so large as the Norway rat but has a longer tail. Its color may be grayish brown or black. In South America the black kind is commoner.

Originally the Norway and roof rats were confined to the Old World, but today they are found on every continent and most islands throughout the world. They reached America as stowaways about 1775.

Quarrelsome and Quick to Learn. Rats are usually quarrelsome. Large numbers are often brought together when food is plentiful; on one occasion the author has counted fifty of them in a small hay loft, but it is doubtful that this was a social gathering. Rats learn from the fortunes of their neighbors. A poisoned rat is a recognized warning of concealed danger.

Curious Tales About Rats. There are many curious tales told about rats. Perhaps the oddest is the one that credits them with carrying

UGLY IN ITS LOOKS AND ITS WAYS

The common rat is a city dweller, largely in the temperate parts of the earth. It has always lived close to man, feeding on his supplies and spreading disease among his numbers. The wild mice and rats are quite different from this creature, and often have charming habits, but all have suffered because of their city cousin's reputation.

away hen eggs whole. Eyewitness accounts claim that one rat clutches the egg with all four feet and rolls over on its back; one or two other rats seize hold of the first rat by the tail and drag it away, and even lower it down ladders.

Accounts of such rat egg-wagons have been popular since 1291; the latest is quite recent. All may well be true, as many eyewitnesses claim they are, but perhaps not in the sense they were intended. For one thing, these rat antics have always been observed in dim light, where the imagination works very powerfully. The rat holding the egg may have been trying to keep it from its mates.

The vulnerable part of a rat, we must remember, is its tail, and when one rat attacks another that is what it goes for. The rat holding the egg might permit the others to drag it across the floor by its tail, while it still clung tightly to the booty. Whether the rat would live to enjoy the egg is still another matter.

Great Mother of Rodents. A close relative of the common rat, and one of the most noteworthy members of its clan, is an animal that goes by the singular name of the Multimammate Mouse, *Mastomys.* Usually a female rodent has five pairs of mammae, or teats, but this creature possesses at least eight pairs—sometimes up to twelve pairs. That is more than any other rodent, and probably more than any other mammal except the domestic pig, which may have twenty-eight teats in all.

The multimammate mouse does not allow its exceptional gift to go to waste. On an average she may rear from a dozen babies to a score at a time. Where conditions favor the species, it increases enormously.

Africa is the home of this buffy-brown rat-sized rodent, and it is found in most parts of the continent. It prefers to dwell near cultivated land. Not only does it do great damage to grain crops, but it also carries bubonic plague into human dwellings when the disease is prevalent.

THE COMMON MOUSE—SOMETIMES IT "SINGS"

The Common Mouse, *Mus,* unlike its large relative the rat, is generally regarded by man with contempt rather than with fear. It is a hider and a scurrier, so that its name has come to mean the same as "coward." In older European traditions it was not always held in such low esteem. The mouse was regarded with some dread, and was believed to be the form taken by the soul when it escaped from the lips of a dead person.

Cowardly or not, the common mouse is mighty in its numbers. There are about 130 different kinds, and they vary in size, color, and length of tail. They originated in Eurasia long ago, but since then they have traveled far. Today we find them all over the world.

The House Mouse, *Mus musculus* (the second scientific name means "little mouse"), is the typical representative of the group. It is indeed a little mouse—only six inches in length, long tail and all. It has soft fur, and this may be brownish gray above and buff on the under parts. The animal was not known in the New World till about the time of the American Revolution, when, like the rat, it arrived as a stowaway aboard transatlantic ships, and came ashore with the cargo.

The house mouse likes warmth. Established in a heated house, it keeps up a steady increase the year round. There are four to six in normal litters but at times this is stepped up to nine or ten. They are born about twenty-one days after their parents mate, sometimes later if the mother is nursing a previous litter. The young themselves are ready to breed when two months old.

Snared by a Spider. House mice are active mostly at night. They have many enemies. It is surprising to find that spiders actually snare them. In one instance a black widow spider not only bound a house mouse in its web but administered a lethal bite to subdue its struggles, then ingeniously hoisted the mouse, completely suspending it in the air. There the mouse hung, till the spider was ready to eat it.

"Singing Mice." Reports have come from all parts of the world claiming that the house mouse actually sings. Its voice has been described as birdlike in quality but weak, and its song as consisting of a series of pleasing musical chirps and twitters.

When experts have examined the "singing mice" carefully, they have usually discovered traces of abnormal conditions in the nose and throat. They attribute the supposed singing to nothing more than bronchial disorders and asthmatic conditions.

Pests and—Lately—Helpers. All in all, there is little that can be said in favor of the house mouse. Fortunately, it is not suspicious and will walk or run into a trap that would not fool a rat for a minute. The greater destruction of food by the house mouse is not due to the amount it consumes, but to the quantity it renders unsuitable for human eating by contamination with droppings and excrement.

On the positive side, though, domestic house mice are used extensively for experimental medical purposes and in that way have made valuable contributions to human society. White mice are one of the breeds that man has produced from the parent stock of the house mouse.

BANDICOOT RATS—THE "PIG RATS" OF THE EAST

The Bandicoot Rats, *Bandicota* and *Nesokia,* are famous animals in their homeland of southern Asia, from Turkestan east to Burma and the Malabar coast. They are no more ratlike in appearance than they are in habits; their native name, *pandi-kokku,* in the Teluga language of India, means "pig rat," and was probably applied to them because, like the pigs, these rats dig in the wet soil for tuberous roots and bulbs, turning up piles of earth. They are in no way related to the true bandicoots of the Australian region.

These burrowing rodents are equipped with strong claws and broad feet for digging in the earth. They have a rather thick, full coat of fur, soft in some kind and rather coarse in others. The tail is naked and scaly, and about equal to the length of the head and body. Most of these "bandicoots" are about the size of a house rat but the Malabar Bandicoot (one of the *Bandicota* group) is a giant—it has a head and body length of fourteen inches.

Raiders of the Rice Fields. The bandicoot rats do much damage in the rice fields of India and Ceylon, besides rooting far and wide for tuberous roots; they may rob truck gardens of yams and potatoes, but they never enter human habitations.

Creatures of the night, the bandicoot rats visit their favorite feeding grounds only under cover of darkness. By day they stay in hiding. Some species live completely underground and, like the American pocket gopher, push up large mounds of soil.

Family Life Under the Ground. These creatures favor moist ground as a rule, though the author has found some high up, in the arid foothills of the Elburz Mountains of northern Iran. Underground, each animal lives separately, for the bandicoot rats are individualists.

Every one has an extensive set of burrows all its own, dug deep in soft, damp soil. Along one gallery there may be storerooms, which are kept packed with grain, roots, and other food. The nest or den is a circular chamber three or four feet below the surface, lined with leaves, straw, and soft roots or twigs.

It is in this nest that the babies are born. Families of *Nesokia,* it is said, are not large, but little is known about how the young are raised. The female of the greater *Bandicota* has twelve teats, three pair on the breast and three pair on the abdomen, to feed the ten or twelve infants she produces in a litter.

At the Mercy of the Tide. These animals are often good swimmers and can travel long distances either on the surface or below water. The author has found bandicoot rats, *Nesokia,* fairly common on the moist plains of Iran along the shores of the Caspian Sea. Their holes were at high-water mark and more or less flooded at times.

The animals seemed to be feeding partly on shellfish and partly on the roots of reeds that grew profusely there. The greatest activity was about the main entrance, where the rats hauled out fresh earth, representing a night's excavating for tuberous roots. Often the creatures walked into traps the author had set up.

These bandicoot rats always left their holes open. Possibly they wanted to be prepared for a quick getaway, should a high tide cover the burrows. That such events happen the writer saw for himself, for one wild, stormy night a high tide not only submerged the bandicoot burrows on the shores of the Caspian Sea with a foot of water but flooded his tent as well. Somehow, the bandicoot rats managed to survive.

The bandicoot rats are often referred to as "pest rats" and are supposed to be host for bubonic and other kinds of fever. Such a charge seems unreasonable in view of the isolated lives of the individuals.

EXTRAORDINARY RATS AND MICE
OF ASIA AND THE PACIFIC

Some Pretty Tree Mice. Even the rats have some attractive relatives. The Long-tailed Tree Mouse, *Vandeleuria,* is a handsome little mouse with a red or bright chestnut coat. It lives in the trees of eastern Asia from Ceylon and India to Indo-China, and feeds on fruits and buds of trees by night; by day it rests in a nest among branches, or in a hollow tree. It is an active little creature and the long tail is semi-prehensile, serving as an additional hand.

The Marmoset Tree Mouse, *Hapalomys,* of Indo-China has hands like a wee monkey, with an opposable thumb for taking a firm hold of tiny branches and picking up seeds and berries. Its soft, thick fur is brownish gray on the back and snow white below and the long tail is tufted at the tip.

Unusual Pests. A rat of economic importance to the people of India and Ceylon is the Coffee Rat, *Golunda.* The attention of Europeans was drawn to this rat when it became a serious menace to the coffee industry—whole plantations were destroyed. The number of these rats once became so great in Ceylon that a thousand were killed in one day on a single plantation.

In New Guinea there is a surprising number of rats. The Mosaic-tailed Rat, *Uromys,* is one of the largest, sometimes being over a foot long in body length. It gets its name from the mosaic pattern of the scales on its tail. Being a big and powerful rat, its booty is the biggest of all nuts; with its chisel-like front teeth this giant can cut through the shell of a coconut.

The natives consider the flesh of the mosaic-tailed rat a great delicacy and hunt it while it sleeps during the day in the fronds of palm trees.

AFRICA'S GIANTS AND PYGMIES

Africa has a fair share of the rats and mice. Some of them are quite attractively marked. One species, the Striped Grass Mouse, *Lemnisomys,* has eight or ten, sometimes fewer, light-colored lines down the back. The Grass Rat or Kusu, *Arvicanthis,* is represented in thirty-six different forms. It is much like the American Cotton Rat and has rather coarse hair.

Africa's Biggest Rat. The African Giant Rat, *Cricetomys,* a truly enormous creature, measures from twelve to eighteen inches in head and body length—with an over-all length of three feet! It frequents the dense thickets and forests of tropical Africa and moves along with measured tread, carrying its tail at an absurd angle in the air. Inoffensive and good natured, it leads a solitary life, feasting on fruits, seeds and berries.

Tree and Swamp Dwellers. The little African Tree Mouse, *Dendromys,* found south of the Sahara, is as tiny and dainty as the giant rat is great. There is a large group of these so-called tree mice; ornate little animals with one or more dark stripes down the back, they are more apt to be found in the thickets and tall grass than in lofty trees.

The Swamp Rat, *Otomys,* and its relatives are among the commonest rodents of Africa; we meet them from Ethiopia to the Cape. They are the grass-eaters of Africa and are referred to as the "groove-toothed rats." They are about the size of a small house rat.

RODENT ODDITIES OF AUSTRALIA

Rodents That Act Like Marsupials. Rats and mice are among the few placental mammals that reached Australia. Their ancestors probably found their way to this long-isolated land mass aboard floating trees, or possibly primitive man took them there—unwittingly, to be sure— in his dugout canoes or on his rafts.

The animals have changed greatly since their arrival. We are tempted to suppose that there must be something in the food or air of Australia that makes so many of its animals propel themselves along with a jumping action rather than by running. In any event, a good number of that country's rodents have developed long hind limbs and taken to hopping.

The Australian "Jerboa," *Notomys,* is one of the most interesting— it bounds along like an American kangaroo rat or a true jerboa. It has extremely lengthy ears (we have learned to associate these with the desert, and that is where the animal lives), and a long, bushy tail, which acts as a balancing arm in the jerboa's flying leaps.

Living in a land of marsupials, this rodent seems to have acquired yet another of their habits. Some newborn jerboas, as well as babies of other Australian rodents, have been seen firmly fixed to their mother's teats, clinging to her with mouth and claws as she hopped around in the open.

There are a host of tiny Australian mice, but *Pseudomys,* a delicately colored, soft-furred creature, is the most attractive. Like the "jerboas," these interesting rodents of the forests and deserts also show a tendency to stand up on their hind legs and hop along.

It Looks Like a Rabbit. Australia has an animal that closely resembles a rabbit—it has long ears and a blunt nose, and sits hunched up like the familiar bunny. Although the settlers called it the "native rabbit," it has long since been named the Nest-building Rabbit Rat, *Leporillus*. And what curious nests it builds!

This odd creature first achieved prominence in 1838, when Mitchell, the surveyor general, came upon its dwelling places. He found piles of brushwood, which he supposed had been built by the aborigines for signal fires. But, on close examination, Mitchell perceived that the sticks were securely woven together. Inside the pile he discovered a nest of soft grasses, and little animals with big ears and downy fur; they almost impressed him as being baby rabbits, except that the tail was too long.

Each stick house, we have learned, is a family dwelling. These dwellings are grouped together to form little towns, suggesting a social bond and some sort of community activity. The house is well constructed, too. Even Australia's wild dog, the dingo, cannot break in and devour the young.

Australia's Muskrat. The Australian Water Rat, *Hydromys*, a big, glossy, blackish-brown creature with interesting habits, takes the

WELL EQUIPPED FOR ITS TRADE

A relative of Australia's water rat is the New Guinea water rat, a large animal with webbed feet and a streamlined body. In the water it is almost as agile as an otter, and can overtake fish with ease.

place of the muskrat in the Australian region, where it is of considerable economic importance as a fur-bearer.

This animal's home is an elaborate, well-organized castle in the bank of a stream. The bedroom has a soft bunk of finely shredded bark or grass; a nearby compartment serves as a sort of larder or dining room and is usually littered with bones and shells left over from a feast. The front door is under water but there is an emergency exit in the bushes; the living quarters are ventilated by a perpendicular vent hidden in a thicket.

The Australian water rat, on close study, proves itself to be an ingenious fellow. It will roof over the abandoned nest of water fowl for a summer retreat and will use a flat stone surrounded by water as a dining table. It is a fast swimmer and an efficient diver.

DORMICE—FAMED AS SLEEPERS

Nearly everyone knows the dormouse by name. But who has ever seen one—outside *Alice in Wonderland*, at any rate? What are the facts about this popular but mysterious creature?

First of all, the dormouse is found only in the Old World. Second, it looks more like a squirrel than a mouse. It is covered with very fine, soft, silky fur and has a long, bushy tail. Its round eyes are large and bright.

The dormouse has the ways as well as the pleasing appearance of a squirrel: it spends most of its life in the trees, and is fond of nuts, acorns, and seeds, and, in addition, apples, and other fruits.

The Sleepy Dormouse. The "dor" in dormouse is supposed to come from the French word *dormir*—it means "to sleep"—or an English dialect word "dorm" meaning "to doze." Like many other rodents, the dormouse sleeps through the lean winter season. Often it hibernates as long as six months at a time, and so it has earned a place among the traditional "seven sleepers" of the animal world. (The other six distinguished by this title are the ground squirrel, marmot, hedgehog, badger, bat, and bear, but of course many other animals are winter sleepers, too.)

As fall draws near, the dormouse gets fatter and fatter. Finally, by October, it is ready to hole up in a hollow tree or an abandoned bird nest weatherproofed with moss. Crawling in, it covers over the nest securely, and closes its eyes till spring. Unfortunately, its foe the weasel does not feel tired at all while the dormouse slumbers, and often pulls it from its cozy dwelling.

Young Dormice—Not So Sleepy. The dormouse breeds twice a year—once in the spring, and again in the autumn. About three weeks after mating, the female bears two to four infants. Although they cannot do much for themselves at first—they are naked and blind at birth —they mature quickly. They are not fully adult until fifteen months old, or thereabouts. Like many other children the author knows, young dormice do not seem eager to go to sleep. They do not bed down for the winter the same time adults do, but stay active for a while afterward.

THE DORMOUSE—IT LOOKS LIKE A SQUIRREL

This squirrel-like mouse likes to pass its time in the trees, where it finds nuts, acorns, and fruit to satisfy its appetite. It is a deep sleeper—it spends the coldest months of the year slumbering in hollow trees and living off the fat it accumulated in the fall.

In its waking season, the dormouse is abroad only by night, and that is why it is so little known as a rule. It spends the day sleeping in a nest in the trees. Its life expectancy: six years.

"A Biting and Angry Beast." It is said that the Romans ate a certain species of the dormouse, which they caught in the fat period, before it retired for the winter. The dormouse, as might be expected, had a place in the folklore of Europe during the Middle Ages. In England it was sometimes considered to be as poisonous as a shrew. Topsell, an old chronicler of animal ways, explains why in his *Four-footed Beasts:*

"If the viper find their [i.e., the dormice's] nest, because she cannot eat all the young ones at one time, at the first she filleth with one or two, and putteth out the eyes of all the residue, and afterwards bringeth them meat and nourisheth them, being blind, until the time that the stomach serveth her to eat them everyone.

"But if it happen that in the meantime any man chance to light upon the viper-nourished blind dormice, and to kill and eat them, they poison themselves through the venom which the viper hath left in them. Dormice are bigger in quantity than a squirrel. It is a biting and angry beast."

Dormice Around the World. In different parts of Europe, Asia, and Africa we find quite a variety of dormice. While they are all medium or small in size, some show interesting adaptations to their surroundings.

The European Dormouse, *Glis,* is the largest, being about the size of a red squirrel. It is not uncommon on the Continent; in some localities large numbers are trapped for the fur trade. A smaller and more attractive species, the Hazel Dormouse, *Muscardinus,* is the reddish-brown little fellow that frequents the hedgerows and woods of England as well as of the Continent.

There are many other members of the dormouse family (Gliridae), but none is more curious to look upon than the Rock Dormouse, *Gliriscus,* which lives in the treeless mountain country of South Africa. This creature has an odd flattening of the skull and body—a specialization that enables it to crawl into narrow crevices in the rocks, where it can be followed by very few enemies.

JUMPING MICE

The Meadow Jumping Mouse, *Zapus,* is also known as the Kangaroo Mouse, and for good reason. It can clear twelve feet in a single leap. Since it weighs less than one ounce, this makes it, relatively speaking, the champion jumper of the mammal world.

Although the meadow jumping mouse has small forelegs, its hind limbs are greatly elongated for leaping. (The mouse's scientific name, *Zapus,* literally means "exaggerated foot.") Its tail, twice as long as its three-inch body, serves to maintain the little creature's balance while it is in the air. Oddly enough, it often appears to make its flying leaps at random, without any special landing point in view when it starts.

In other respects, this animal is not very spectacular. Tawny or yellowish brown in color, it has a broad dark band down the middle of its back. Its feet and under parts are white or yellowish and it has a spot of black at the tip of its tail.

LITTLE JUMPER OF THE NORTH AMERICAN MEADOWS

Like the kangaroo rat, the meadow jumping mouse has enlarged hind limbs on which it leaps about; the long, slender tail helps it to balance itself while off the ground. At the slightest sign of danger, the mouse goes bounding off in search of safety, often covering twelve feet in a single jump.

The meadow jumping mouse is about in the bright sunlight as well as at night. It does not follow a beaten highway in its search for food, but travels in any direction that appeals to it. A pond will not stop it, for it is a doughty little short-distance swimmer. It feeds on seeds and berries. When blackberries are ripe, its light-colored vest and feet are often stained purple with the juice of the berries.

The jumping mouse usually builds its nest aboveground, but if its homeland is a wet, marshy area it may establish its dwelling in grass or bushes, where it can stay dry. Winter brings feeding problems with it, and the jumping mouse meets them by spending about six months of the year in profound sleep.

——TIME FOR REST. In preparation for bedtime, the mouse puts on a layer of fat—its only cache of food for the winter. Then it enters an underground burrow below frost line, closes the door securely behind it, and crawls into a comfortable nest of dry grass. It now curls up in a tight little ball, its breathing slackens, and its body temperature declines. To all outward appearances it is dead. The animal remains rigid, cold, and lifeless until the warm breath of spring rouses it to action again.

——BABY JUMPING MICE. The active life of the meadow jumping mouse begins in April, when it comes out of its winter quarters. May is the mating season, and the young are born about thirty days later in a nest underground or on the surface.

There are four or five babies in an average litter, but on occasion we find up to nine nestlings. At birth, they weigh about one-thirtieth of an ounce and look quite unlike their elders. Besides being naked and without sight, they do not even have any whiskers, and their tails are relatively short. After three weeks they see and hear perfectly, and after three more they reach their adult weight of one ounce.

The Woodland Jumping Mouse. In North America the meadow jumping mouse ranges from the Arctic south to California and North Carolina. Its cousin, the Woodland Jumping Mouse, *Napaeozapus*, makes its home from southern Quebec and Ontario down to North Carolina and Tennessee. This creature has a white tip to its tail, and the fur is more yellowish on the sides of its body. As its name implies, it favors forests. Here, not far from water, it digs a burrow, in which it generally passes the daylight hours.

On moonlight nights during the mating season this mouse has been observed behaving in a most unusual manner. It will come out of its hole, bounce around in a sort of erratic dance, collect an armful of nesting material and retreat to its den. In a few minutes the performance is repeated.

These animals have a number of relatives in Europe and Asia (all make up the family Zapodidae), but none matches the Olympic jumping feats of the American branch of the family.

JERBOAS—"KANGAROOS" OF THE OLD WORLD'S DESERTS

The jerboa is another noted leaper of the rodent world, like the jumping mice of the meadows and woodlands, whose ways we have just looked into. In contrast to these animals, the jerboa has chosen as its homeland not only the hottest places on earth, but also the driest and most barren ones. It loves the arid deserts of the Old World, and appears able to get along completely without water.

Of all the rodents, this kangaroo-like creature is perhaps the most highly developed for getting around on two feet. (As a matter of fact, its family name, Dipodidae, means "two-footed.") Its hind limbs are large and very long. Its front limbs are correspondingly smaller, so that the animal could hardly walk on all fours if it had to.

The jerboa prefers to stand up on its hind legs and hop along, covering from two to six feet in a single jump. Its lengthy tail has a neat little brush at the tip; not only does the tail give the jerboa support when it is standing—it also helps the animal to maintain its balance as it leaps along. It has thick hair on its feet, which absorbs some of the landing shock and serves to give a grip on shifting sand.

AN ANIMAL WE SELDOM SEE

Few people ever see a jerboa, even in localities where it is common, because this mammal holes up in its den under the ground during the intense heat of the desert day; it comes out only after sunset and makes sure to retire before sunrise. Furthermore, it leaves no trace of its activities. Although the jerboa is a social animal, there are no telltale runways and, when it retires for the day, it closes up the entrance to its burrow to keep out the hot sunlight.

At night the jerboa is very fond of rolling in the cool sand and scratching itself. It will lie down on the ground, leisurely stretch out its long legs one at a time, and scratch and comb them from hip to toe with its front paws. It also uses its front paws to hold the grass seeds on which it feeds.

If you should ever meet the jerboa in its home territory, you would find it to be a medium-sized rodent, from two inches up to eight in head and body length. Its tail, usually about two inches longer than the head and body, is round for most of its length and broadly tufted at the tip with long black and white hairs.

The rest of the jerboa's appearance suggests its home and habits. Its ears are comparatively enormous in size—a trait we have found in other desert animals—and may equal half the length of the head and body, in some species. The eyes are large, as they often are in animals active by night. Its color varies more or less from locality to locality, but it is usually in shades of buff mixed with black or pale russet, and the under parts are white.

AN ANIMAL WE SELDOM SEE

The jerboa, which makes its home in the arid wastes of the Old World's deserts, is another remarkable rodent leaper. This small creature can travel by leaps and bounds considerably faster than a man can run.

SOME REMARKABLE JERBOAS

It is in Africa, Asia, and eastern Europe that we find the jerboas. The African Three-toed Jerboa, *Jaculus,* a typical member of the family, is the largest and best known of all, and has a head and body length of close to seven inches, and an eight-inch tail. It has been credited with a top speed of forty miles per hour but the author has easily overtaken the animal when he traveled at that speed in a car.

Besides the typical jerboa, we find a number of others that are curiously different. There is a Fat-tailed Jerboa, a Flat-tailed Jerboa, a Dwarf Jerboa; some have five toes on the enlarged hind feet while others have only three toes. On the Big-eared Jerboa, *Euchoreutes*, of Chinese Turkestan, we see "enormous" ears measuring one and one-half inches—well, they seem enormous when you compare them to the three-inch body.

Most, if not all, jerboas sleep through the cold winter months, especially in the northern part of the range. Life begins again in April, when these animals come out of hibernation. The males are the first to appear and expend great energy in their search for a prospective mate. Very little is known about the breeding habits of these animals, but the young are born some forty-two days after mating time.

OTHER CURIOUS RATS AND MICE

There are numerous other kinds of rats, mice, and their relatives in the world, but here we have time only to glance at a few of the most curious.

Blind Rats of Southeastern Europe. The Russian peasants say that the Mediterranean Mole Rat, *Spalax*, can give you such healing skills as no medical university can teach. All you have to do is catch this furtive rodent, hold it in your bare hands, and permit it to bite you. The next and indispensable step is to squeeze it to death. Forever afterward you will be able to cure illness simply by laying your hands on a sick person.

How such a tradition got started we can only guess, but the mole rat is without question an oddity, being one of the few mammals absolutely without sight. It does have traces of eyes, but they are quite functionless and sunk below the skin. There are only vestiges of ears, and there is no tail. All in all, this robust, yellowish-brown rodent is adapted for a life under the ground, resembling the mole in habits as well as appearance. We place it in the family Spalacidae. (The name means "moles," though of course this is a different group.)

Bamboo Rats—Tastier Than Pork. Another group of burrowing rodents are the Bamboo Rats, which live in Asia and Africa. Of these, many seem to spend a good deal of their time on the surface—notably the Asiatic Bamboo Rat, *Rhizomys*, which sometimes dwells in the bamboo belt in the mountains and feeds on the roots and shoots of bamboo. Some of the bamboo rats—they make up the family Rhizomyidae—are of a good size (well over a foot in head and body length); the Chinese dig them out of their dens and use them as food, preferring their flesh to pork, we are told.

Porcupines, Guinea Pigs, Chinchillas, and Their Relatives

OLD WORLD PORCUPINES— "SWORD-RATTLING WARRIORS"

T HE CRESTED or Old World Porcupine, *Hystrix,* found over most of Africa, all of southern Asia, and throughout southeast· ern Europe, is quite unlike its New World counterpart. So different are they, in body and habits, that we place them in separate families. Of course they both have quills, as their common name reminds us ("porcupine" originally meant "pig with spines"), but even the quills show important differences.

BIGGEST PORCUPINE ON EARTH

The crested porcupine is the largest living porcupine; it may be over three feet in length and weigh between forty and sixty pounds. Its tail is just a few inches long, quills and all.

Right here and now we should see why the animal is called a "crested porcupine." Extending from the nape of its neck and down its back it has a mass of quills (far longer than those in the New World species). These are real weapons—needle-pointed spines that are mixed with much longer and more slender flexible spines, or guards, measuring up to twenty-one inches in length. The guards protect the sharp points of the quills when they are not in use.

A WARNING, THEN A DEADLY BLOW

In spite of what we have often heard, the porcupine cannot shoot its quills into the flesh of an enemy. But, as already suggested, they are effective weapons nonetheless.

When a porcupine is disturbed, it rattles the quills on its tail. These produce a warning signal that resembles the noise created by a rattlesnake's tail.

If the sound does not make the would-be aggressor change his intentions, the "sword-rattling" warrior turns its back on him, erects its sharp rapier-like quills, and charges backward. The bristling armament, with its multitude of sturdy spikes backed by forty pounds of porcupine, will generally dampen the ardor of the most adventurous foe.

A Dead Panther. It seems, however, that many animals have more courage than sense—especially the big cats. E. C. Morris of Mysore has described how he "once came on the remains of a panther that had met its death through attacking a porcupine; the decomposed head was run through and through with no less than seventeen quills, two of which had penetrated the eyes into the brain. Its paws were also full of quills.

"The panther had evidently rushed the porcupine, which, seeing it in time, had quite obviously whirled around, presenting its back to the panther with quills erect, such being the method of defense."

GREAT DIGGERS AND HIKERS

In contrast with its tree-dwelling relatives in the New World, the crested porcupine is hardly a climber at all. It does not seem to be able to jump, either. It makes its nest in a burrow, and may live in almost any kind of country within its range, so long as it is undisturbed and there is suitable rock or brush cover. We find it in arid mountains, rocky outcrops, wooded hills, scrub-covered plains and thick forest.

The crested porcupine's nest may be one hundred feet from the entrance of the tunnel. The burrow is usually marked by the presence of well-gnawed bones and skulls strewn near the entrance (although the animal is not a killer, it likes to chew bones, much like our dogs). Often six or seven porcupines share a communal burrow or "earth," which they provide with six or seven entrances.

A seasoned hiker, the crested porcupine may travel as much as ten miles in search of food. It feeds on bulbs, the bark of trees, and fallen fruit, and is destructive to farm crops, including root tubers, pumpkins, sweet potatoes, Irish potatoes, and maize. It is commonly believed to be active only at night, but in Iran the author has seen crested porcupines about at noon and found, to his surprise, that they could gallop along a little faster than he could run.

THE BIGGEST PORCUPINE ON EARTH

The African crested porcupine, over three feet long, is the largest living porcupine. Its quills are very sharp and dangerous. When annoyed, this porcupine rattles the quills on its tail to alert the intruder, and follows the warning with a backward charge that may mean death to the enemy. Porcupines never shoot their quills.

DANGEROUS WHEN TEN DAYS OLD

This animal mates early in the year. Its babies, numbering from one to three—but usually two—are born between six and eight weeks later, in a nest of leaves, dry grass, and root fibers. They come into the world rather well developed—their eyes are wide open and they have soft, flexible spines. The babies remain in the den until the spines have grown and hardened; these are already quite dangerous at the end of ten days.

The crested porcupine has lived for a little over twenty years in captivity, but appears to average twelve to fifteen years in the wild. With its relatives, it forms the family Hystricidae. All the animals you will read about in this chapter are called "hystricomorphs," or "porcupine shaped," and make up a rodent suborder (Hystricomorpha), named in honor of the crested porcupine. Like it, most are fairly large, and many have spines.

OTHER CURIOUS OLD WORLD PORCUPINES

Asia and Africa have some other queer-looking porcupines. The Brush-tailed Porcupine, *Atherurus,* of southern Asia and Africa, is only twenty inches in length, not including the nine-inch tail. It is a forest dweller. The long, spiny tail terminates in a tuft of stiff bristles, for which the animal is named. The odd thing about this brush is that the bristles are composed of alternating thick and thin regions, giving a fantastic appearance suggestive of a string of beads.

The Long-tailed Porcupine, *Trichys,* of the Malay Archipelago, is a smaller and comparatively soft-spined species. The South Asiatic Porcupine, *Acanthion,* is much like the familiar crested porcupine but can be recognized by the absence of the very long, slender crest quills.

NEW WORLD TREE PORCUPINES

The North American Tree Porcupine, *Erethizon,* may not be bright or fleet of foot, but it is a formidable opponent all the same. It wears a coat of some thirty thousand spines loosely attached to its skin. True, they are small and insignificant—they average about one and one-half inches each—as compared with the long, rapier-like quills of the large African and Asiatic porcupines, but they are equally effective if not more so. In reality, they are barbed darts.

30,0000 QUILLS—AND HOW THEY CAN KILL

Unaggressive, good-natured creatures though they are, few porcupines meet a violent death, thanks to the protection afforded by their quills. Normally the great mass of the spines lies smoothly back as the animal ambles slowly along. Overtaken by a dangerous foe, it assumes an "on-guard" position. Its back arched and every spine bristling, the porcupine whirls about rapidly so that it is always presenting its rear to the foe.

THE CANADIAN PORCUPINE CRAVES SALT

This quill-covered animal has a remarkable liking for salt and, prowling around cabins in the North Woods, will gnaw almost any object with human perspiration on it because of the salty taste. Porcupines prefer not to fight, even though their quills are an excellent weapon, and will attempt to escape up a tree.

If the enemy is persistent, the porcupine backs up to him. Then it will suddenly lash out with its short, well-armed clubtail and drive a dozen or more quills deep into the flesh of the intruder. It strikes with lightning speed, perfect timing, and great accuracy, generally aiming for the face.

What the Quills Look Like. If you examine the quills of a porcupine closely, you will find they are slender shafts tapered at both ends with a highly polished horny surface. One end of the quill is blunt and loosely attached to muscles just under the skin. The business end of the shaft, however, is exceedingly sharp; about a thirty-second of an inch below the tip, microscopic barbs appear which increase in number back to the shoulder of the shaft. These barbs lie flat against the quill until they find their mark, usually the mouth, nose or paw of an aggressor.

"Bomb" With an Automatic Time Fuse. Each quill on the American porcupine is virtually a bomb with an automatic time fuse that explodes a few seconds after it enters the victim. The explosion is minute, but it raises the microscopic barbs on the tip of the quill. The quill cannot now be removed without literally tearing out flesh with it.

A quill can and does automatically work its way into the victim. Mountain lions, foxes, lynxes, and eagles have been killed by porcupine quills.

Pills and Quills. Canada porcupine quills are used by the American Indians, who weave them into their buckskin clothing in a decorative pattern. The author has a pair of moccasins with a handsome design of quills made by Indians on the Liard River, Northwest Territories.

The Indians there told him that a number of years ago a trader sold them pink cure-all pills; but, instead of taking the pills, they dissolved them in water and used them to dye some quills, which became a most attractive shade of purple. There is now quite a demand for this particular brand of doctor's pills in the area.

THE SHUFFLING PORCUPINE

The North American tree porcupine can walk, swim, and climb, but, no matter how much it tries to hurry, the fastest gait it can achieve is a clumsy shuffle. Its home is a hole in the ground or in a hollow tree. It feeds on green vegetation most of the summer and is very fond of clover and alfalfa.

This animal does not hibernate in winter. At this time its diet is completely changed to bark, which it peels from the upper branches of evergreen trees. It sometimes causes a certain degree of damage in forested areas in this way.

Still, some written laws and certainly the unwritten law of the wilderness have put the porcupine on the protected list. You just don't shoot a porcupine. It is a quaint animal, not a very bothersome one, and moreover a man lost in the woods and starving can readily catch and kill it with a club, which cannot be said of most forest mammals. Its flesh is surprisingly tasty.

BIG PORCUPINE BABIES

Porcupines increase at a slow rate. They mate in the fall and the young are born about seven months later. Most females have only one baby a year.

The newborn porcupine, with its eyes wide open from the very first, is fully clothed, including the spines, and is in possession of all its faculties. It weighs one pound—actually more than a newborn black bear cub—and measures a foot in length. Its nursing days are few, the Indians even claiming that the mother does not nurse her baby at all. Still, it does not reach complete maturity until the fall of the year.

Life expectancy for the porcupine in the wild is not more than about six years. Under exceptionally ideal conditions it may live to be nine or ten years of age. Its weight averages fifteen pounds, but in some cases has reached thirty-five pounds or higher.

WHERE WE FIND THEM

We find the North American tree porcupine over most of North America's forests north of the 40th parallel, and south in the Rocky Mountains to the Mexican border. The animal's entire body—limbs, head, tail, and sides of feet—is covered with thick blackish hair, which in winter completely conceals the spines. The claws are strong and curved, for climbing trees. The tail is short, broad, and well armed, as we have seen.

There are two species of North American porcupines, both large, measuring up to three feet. The Eastern Porcupine is black except for the white band on the quills, while the Western Porcupine, generally a little larger than its cousin, has greenish-yellow instead of black hairs on the head.

South of the Mexican border we meet the Prehensile-tailed Porcupine, *Coendou*. Like so many other South American animals, this
creature has a long tail with a naked tip, which it uses as a fifth
hand to grasp hold of branches with. In fact the creature is quite
capable of hanging by its tail. It is more streamlined than its North
American cousins and, while it has similar spines, they are shorter
and closer together.

PORCUPINE WITH A CURLING TAIL
The prehensile-tailed porcupine, at home in Latin America, can use its tail to get a firm
grip on boughs and twigs as it climbs about in the trees. Its quills, though barbed and
dangerous, are not nearly so long as those of its relatives to the north.

There are two other South American porcupines. One is the Short-
tailed Porcupine, *Echinoprocta*, of Colombia—it possesses a short,
hairy, non-prehensile tail and the spines are long and only bristly on

the back. The other variation on the porcupine theme dwells in Brazil: the Thin-spined Porcupine, *Chaetomys,* is covered with very wavy, bristly hairs, with sharp quills restricted to the head. We place all the New World porcupines in the family Erethizontidae—the name, appropriately enough, comes from a Greek word meaning "to irritate."

GUINEA PIGS, CAVIES, AND CUYS

The Typical Guinea Pig, Restless Cavy, or Cuy, *Cavia,* is not a pig at all, though it may grunt like one when it feels the pangs of hunger. Actually, it is a rodent of South America. Originally brought to Europe by Dutch and English slave traders, some of whom found it in Guiana, it soon became known by its present common name.

That name, of course, is nowadays synonymous with someone or something used in an experiment. Hundreds of years ago, the Incas of Peru domesticated the wild guinea pig and used it for food, but in the United States and Europe the animal is much more familiar for the services it renders in laboratories. Because it breeds rapidly, it is used in the study of heredity, but it is also valuable for the isolation and breeding of bacteria as well as the production of serums.

——WILD AND TAME GUINEA PIGS. There is an old story that if you pick up a guinea pig by its tail, its eyes will drop out. Unfortunately, we cannot test the truth of this for ourselves, since the guinea pig has no tail. The animal is a small one—it may grow up to a foot in length—and has a rather fat body and short limbs. Its ears are short and round. Like other cavies, of which group it is typical, it lives in burrows in the ground, and favors broken brush country rather than open plains or forests. Vegetation is what it likes to eat.

The guinea pig is a fertile rodent. Although the female has only two teats, she will bear two or three young or more in a litter, twice a year in the wild. When she is domesticated, the number goes up: three or four babies are the average, and the litters come five or six times a year.

Each family is born about two months after mating time; the babies are well-developed, active little creatures, and are out feeding themselves when just a day old. At two months of age they are ready to take their turn on the guinea-pig production line. The life span is eight years, on the whole.

Guinea pigs are easily raised. They require about the same kind of accommodations as rabbits, and can be fed the same diet. Although they are much less subject to disease than rabbits, they cannot adjust themselves so well to changes in temperature. A sudden drop downward, particularly to freezing, may prove quite injurious to them.

The guinea pig makes a friendly pet. Perhaps the most objectionable feature about it is its unpleasant odor. There is a popular belief that rats will not enter a guinea pig pen, but experience shows this to be untrue. The rats will not only come in; they will devour their fellow rodents' food and their babies as well.

——GUINEA PIGS AS FOOD. While guinea pigs are seldom eaten in the United States, all wild cavies as well as domesticated forms are accounted good food in South America. The Moco, *Kerodon,* and especially the Rock Cuy, *Galea,* are much hunted in parts of Brazil. The Peruvian method of dressing a guinea pig for the table is much like that used for a sucking pig. The rodent is scalded in hot water, the hair is removed, and the skin is scraped with a knife. The animal is then cleaned and roasted.

These interesting little creatures come in different colors and kinds of fur. In some the fur is rather long and stiff, in others it is soft. The fur is reddish or grayish brown in the wild state. The majority of domestic animals are spotted; the common colors are fawn, light gray, reddish-brown, white, or black. We find the animals from Peru, Bolivia, and Argentina, to Brazil, the Guianas, Venezuela, and Colombia.

The Patagonian Cavy. Of all the strange and curious animals of South America the Patagonian Cavy, *Dolichotis,* known locally as the Mara, is one of the most amazing. It is almost harelike in appearance, with big eyes, large ears, and long legs, but the hind feet are armed with sharp, hooflike claws. The Greater Patagonian Cavy, the larger of the two species, stands about one foot at the shoulder and may attain a length of three feet.

A sociable creature, the big Patagonian cavy loves company. A dozen or more may live together in holes in the ground or bask or feed in the sun. At the first sign of danger they make off at a high speed, with a most peculiar galloping, hopping run, pausing every hundred yards or so to turn around and satisfy their curiosity. Natives hunt the big cavy for food but it is much too fast to be caught by any of the native dogs.

A FAST RUNNER

The Patagonian cavy is a long-limbed creature, and can run with great speed when pursued, as it often is, by the South American natives, who esteem it as food (it tastes much like rabbit). Like the rabbit, this odd animal has an underground retreat.

CAPYBARAS—GIANTS OF THE RODENT WORLD

The Capybara, *Hydrochoerus,* is hardly known outside its native continent of South America, yet it is the largest rodent on earth. A full-grown male capybara may stand twenty-one inches at the shoulder and measure all of four feet in length; he may weigh over one hundred pounds.

You need not let the thought of such a great relative of the rat dismay you—the capybara looks much more like a giant edition of its closer kinsman the guinea pig. Indeed, one of its names is the

Giant Water Guinea Pig; others are Chigwire, Warpincho, and Water Hog (this last is an accurate translation of the animal's scientific name).

If you should someday come face to face with a capybara in eastern South America, where it lives, you may safely assume there will be water near by. The animal is at home among the tall grasses that grow along the banks of such rivers as the Orinoco, and we find it as far north as Panama. Grass and water plants are the favorite foods of this inoffensive, peace-loving creature. Having eaten its fill, it likes to lie quietly and bask in the sunshine on a river bank. When pleased, it often produces a low, clicking sound.

BIG BUT PEACEABLE
The capybara, which may grow as large as a pig, is a very able swimmer. It lives along the banks of South America's mighty rivers, and is a harmless vegetarian, feeding on weeds, grass, and other plants.

——THE CAPYBARA'S ENEMIES. The shy capybara would rather run than fight. It must always be on the alert for its deadly enemies, the jaguar and the cougar. At the slightest sign of one of these, the capybara leaps to safety in the water. Though the three toes on its hind feet are only poorly webbed, it is a first-rate swimmer. It can travel long distances below the surface, too. But even in the water it dare not let down its guard, for the stream may be alligator-infested.

In a zoo, you will find that the capybara, giant of the rodent world, is a friendly animal, not so likely to flee as it is in the wild.

——Baby Capybaras. Capybaras are more or less social creatures and often travel about in troops. Their families are large: four to eight babies are born at a time, about four months after mating has occurred. They are well developed and can soon take care of themselves. Apparently they enjoy each other's company, for the family does not break up quickly.

——Hunting the Capybara. Ten years is an old age for the capybaras; few ever reach it. They are too gentle or else they have too many enemies. One of these enemies is man. South American natives hunt the capybara in canoes and kill it when it comes up for air. They eat its flesh and make ornaments of its large teeth.

——Capybaras of Yesterday and Today. Although fossil remains tell us that long, long ago there were other forms of capybaras, some of them even larger than the animal we know today, there is only one species surviving in the family (Hydrochoeridae): about the size of a pig, it has a broad head, a blunt nose, and eyes that are disproportionately small. Stiff yellowish-brown fur forms a rather sparse covering for its body. The limbs of this oversized guinea pig are short, and it has only a trace of a tail.

PACAS AND AGOUTIS—RABBIT-LIKE RODENTS OF THE AMERICAN TROPICS

Anyone living in tropical America knows the agoutis—tail-less rodents about the size of a rabbit, with a golden brown or reddish coat of sleek hair. They are much sought after for their flesh, which is highly esteemed by the natives.

So favored is the agouti as a dish, that it would not survive at all in populated districts but for the fact that it hides in its underground burrow by day, coming out to feed mostly at night. It dines on leaves, roots, and fallen fruit. The natives are well aware of its eating habits, and have learned to fool the animal by throwing stones into leafy branches. The agouti, fancying it hears fruit falling, emerges from its hole to investigate, whereupon the hunters attempt to shoot it.

The best known of the agoutis, the Common Agouti, *Dasyprocta,* stands high on its slender legs, and is a swift runner, with hooflike feet developed for speed. It travels in a series of hops and springs that take it over considerable ground in a surprisingly short time. Pursued by dogs, it will make for its underground den if possible. It takes readily to water and swims well, but does not seem to have learned the trick of diving for safety.

This creature with the rabbit-like head, short ears, and shiny hair is just as popular with flesh-eating animals as it is with man. In its native brush country, ocelots and a host of other beasts are ever on the alert to catch the elusive agouti off guard.

HUNTED FOR ITS FLESH
The paca is a sturdy animal, attractively decorated with spots. It makes its home in a hole in the bank of a river, or digs a burrow in the ground. It is a favorite food animal in South America. The skin is of value, too, being used for leather.

Their prey, however, is equipped for survival almost at birth. Agoutis are born with their eyes wide open, are fully furred, and can move about under their own power from the very first. They weigh about seven ounces at birth; the mother bears two of them at a time, some forty days after mating.

We find the common agouti on the mainland of the tropical Americas and in the West Indies. Often we observe, dwelling close by, a somewhat smaller species, the Acushi, or Short-tailed Agouti, *Myo-*

procta. Their relative, the Paca, *Cuniculus,* is in reality a large, spotted, heavy-bodied agouti with much the same habits. It will measure about thirty inches in length (a big agouti reaches only twenty) and ranges from Mexico to Paraguay.

The pacas and agoutis make up the family Dasyproctidae. This name means "shaggy rump" and is applied to them because of the thick, long hair on the back, which falls over the hindquarters, concealing the fact that they have no tail.

THE FALSE PACA

Something of a contrast is provided by a rare animal known as the False Paca, or Pacarana, *Dinomys*—it has fully six inches of tail and rather short limbs, although this large and robust creature otherwise much resembles the spotted paca, being about the size of a marmot (thirty inches, not including the tail).

A RODENT ODDITY

This strange, long-whiskered fellow—he dwells high up in the Andes—goes by the name of "false paca." The animal is a rarity, and was quite unknown to science a hundred years ago. Except for the hairy tail, the false paca looks rather like the "true" one.

The false paca is at home in the eastern Andes, where it lives in burrows in the ground or among the rocks. This great rodent was almost unknown to the outside world until fairly recent years. It was first discovered in 1873 but nothing much was heard about it until 1925, when specimens began to appear in zoological parks. Now the powerful false paca (family Dinomyidae—"fearful mice") with its massive head and striped back, is an important drawing card at our zoos.

VISCACHAS AND CHINCHILLAS— STRANGE SOUTH AMERICAN RODENTS

In the foregoing pages we have had an opportunity to make the acquaintance of many strange creatures that haunt the pampas and mountains of South America, but the viscachas are as noteworthy as any we have encountered. The Plains Viscacha, *Lagostomus*, of Argentina, a most unconventional-looking animal, appears to be a collection of mismatched parts and must be seen to be appreciated.

To begin with, the creature's face is a sight to behold. Below each smallish eye there is a large patch of long, bushy black hairs. Two white bands run across the middle of the face. The ears are fairly big and erect. The animal's massive head looks too large for its sturdy twenty-inch body.

The front legs are surprisingly short and heavy, but then, again, the hind legs seem much too long. The seven-inch tail is crested with lengthy stiff hairs. In general color, this rodent oddity is a mixture of gray, black, and brown.

A GREAT NATURALIST REPORTS ON THE PLAINS VISCACHA

The strange-looking plains viscacha attracted the attention of Charles Darwin when he visited its homeland. He wrote of the rodent in his journal: "The viscacha is well known to form a prominent feature in the zoology of the Pampas. The gauchos affirm that it lives on roots, which, from the great strength of its gnawing teeth, and the kind of localities frequented by it, seems probable.

"As in the case of rabbits, a few holes are commonly placed together. In the evening the viscachas come out in numbers, and there quietly sit on their haunches. They are at times very tame and a man on horseback passing by seems only to present an object for their grave contemplation.

"They do not wander far from their burrows. They run very awk-wardly, and when hurrying out of danger, from their elevated tails and short front legs much resemble house rats. Their flesh, when cooked, is white and good, but is seldom used."

VISCACHAS AT HOME

The plains viscacha, or viscachón, as it is commonly called, is about only at night, as Darwin suggested. During the day it lies up in community burrows called *viscacheras*. It appears to have a strange desire to collect "objects of art"—an assortment of stones, bones, and other odd things is piled about the entrances to its warrens. As is the case with many other animals, a sentry seems to be posted during the hours of activity to warn the colony of approaching danger. (In any event, one animal warns the rest when an intruder draws near.)

The Mountain Viscacha, *Lagidium*, unlike its cousin on the plains, gets up at sunrise and retires to its rocky den before dark. It resembles a large chinchilla, having big ears and thick, soft, buffy-brown fur. (Together with the chinchillas, the viscachas form the family Chinchillidae.)

MOST VALUABLE FUR-BEARER ON EARTH

The Chinchilla, or Royal Chinchilla, *Chinchilla,* is the most valuable fur-bearer on earth. People have been known to pay as high as one hundred thousand dollars for a coat of pelts.

It takes more than one hundred pelts to make a chinchilla coat. The animal itself is not a big one, being about ten inches in length, with a bushy tail half as long again. The creature looks something like a squirrel, with a rabbit-like head and large, round ears, about two inches long.

The fur of this beautiful little rodent is an exquisite pale blue-gray or silver-gray, deep and full. The most luxurious and delicate of all furs, it is so fine that an individual strand is not visible to the naked eye: it is finer than a spider web. Because of the quality and dense texture of the fur, the animal is said to be immune to para-sites. It has no perceptible body odor.

——WHERE WE FIND IT. Once the chinchilla existed in great num-bers in nature. Its original home seems to have been the mountains of Peru, Bolivia, northern Argentina, and Chile. Today it is rarely seen—wild—outside Chile.

The chinchilla dwells high in the Andes, scrambling over the rocks with amazing speed in the dark, when it is most active. At the end of each toe it has a large, soft pad which protects its feet; it possesses only vestiges of claws, so it cannot climb trees or dig in the earth. Many chinchillas lived together in holes in the rocks before the fur hunters whittled down their numbers long years ago. Stern conservation laws protect the animals today.

MANY HAVE ENVIED THE CHINCHILLA ITS BEAUTIFUL COAT
The chinchilla is highly prized for its fur. This small animal was once common in the high Andes, but constant hunting brought it close to extinction. Domestic breeding began in the United States in 1923, and today there are numerous chinchilla farms.

——Breeding the Chinchilla. Even if a plague were to wipe out the wild chinchilla, the animal would not become extinct. Its great value encouraged domestic breeding, which began in the United States in 1923, when eighteen animals were brought in by

M. F. Chapman. There are many chinchilla farms today, and breeders have produced a number of domestic hybrids.

The chinchilla is old enough to mate when seven months old but its rate of reproduction is extremely low. Under natural conditions there is only one litter a year, but in captivity there may be two. The young—there may be one to four in a litter—are born 124 days after mating takes place. They are well developed at birth: their eyes are wide open and they have a full set of teeth. Fully clothed, they are able to move about almost from the very first. The babies are weaned and able to look after themselves when sixty days old. Until then, both parents watch over them. Length of a chinchilla's life is about nine years.

HUTIAS AND COYPU RATS— VALUABLE FOR FOOD AND FUR

Early in this book we talked about a group of rare animals known as the solenodons—animals found only in the West Indies and believed to be the survivors of the ancient mammal life of a sunken continent. This also appears to be the story of the hutias, for with but one exception all are restricted to the West Indies.

The islands on which the hutias now dwell are the mountain peaks of what was once a great land mass. From the caves and limestone cliffs on these islands we can learn much about the animals of ages past. Here, preserved for all time, are the fossilized remains of big ground sloths, tiny insectivorous animals, and many rodents—including one the size of a bear. The author has discovered some of these prehistoric animal remains in the rocks under the water along the coast line of Anguilla, and others embedded in stalactites hanging from the roofs of dark caves.

It is in the earth's rock diary that we can read the past of the hutias, and here there is evidence that makes us suppose these animals were once much more common than they are today. Not before 1822 was the first of the living hutias reported; in 1836 Baron Cuvier, the French naturalist, described another. Later decades turned up more genera in the rocks than in the flesh.

HUTIAS ALIVE

Today we know of only a few living species of hutias, all told. They are heavy, thickset rodents; the largest of the group is the Cuban

Hutia, or Jutia, *Capromys pilorides,* almost two feet in length, with a tail a third as long again. Its hair is harsh, close, and grayish brown in color. Although, like other hutias, it makes its den underground or among rocks, it spends a considerable part of its waking hours in the trees, and has broad feet of the climbing type. It is often referred to as the "tree rat." A smaller Cuban species possesses a grasping tail[1].

Much like a small, dark reddish-gray woodchuck is the Short-tailed Hutia, *Geocapromys,* of Jamaica, the Bahamas, and Swan Islands. In Jamaica it frequents only the roughest hill country and is sometimes called the "cony"; the natives also name it the "grazee," because it feeds on grasses and the leaves of low shrubs. The flesh of the hutia is quite palatable, and the natives hunt it with dogs and dig the animal out when it has been run to the ground. The Jamaica species has only a two-inch tail on its seventeen-inch body.

COYPUS—EXTRAORDINARY BEAVER RATS
OF ARGENTINA

The Coypu, *Myocastor* ("mouse beaver"), is a big, strong rodent swimmer of the water courses of southern South America. It is also known as the Nutria, which is Spanish for "otter"—and an otter is just what the animal looks like. Its underfur, which is light brown or black, is highly durable, and is valued in the fur trade, being blended to imitate beaver.

The coypu is nowadays found a long way from home. Because of the excellence of its fur, it has been introduced into the United States and Europe; colonies of coypus established in such places as the swamps of Louisiana and the marshy meadows of New Jersey yield thousands of furs annually.

Normally, the coypu feeds on green vegetation. In the United States it does little damage, since the land turned over to it is of little worth. Not so in England and other parts of Europe. There the coypu has on occasion escaped from the domain turned over to it, and proceeded to wreak havoc amid growing things.

We cannot blame the animal for such misbehavior—it is only following its normal instincts, but in abnormal surroundings. Nor can we blame it for the fact that it used to startle thousands of Englishmen when it was shown to them by enterprising showmen as an example of what could be produced from London's sewers.

——THE BIG COYPU. The coypu is fairly sizable for a rodent—it sometimes grows to two feet in head and body length, with a thick, round tail half as long again; a male may weigh nine pounds or more. Its head is large, with small ears, and four of the toes on each hind foot are webbed for swimming. The fur is heavy and thick, and consists of deep, dense, waterproof underfur overlaid with long, coarse guard hairs.

——MOTHER COYPU. Mother coypu is the most interesting member of the family. Her teats are not situated on her abdomen but high up, on her sides. This arrangement is most convenient for her babies—they can suckle while they are in the water with her.

OTHER INTERESTING DWELLERS IN THE "LAND OF RODENTS"

Have you observed how many of the animals described in this chapter are natives of South America? Just as that continent is noted for its lack of big game, so it is famous for its hordes of small gnawing mammals. Indeed, it has been called the "Land of Rodents."

Perhaps the absence of large numbers of flesh-eating animals is the reason South America has such a great abundance and variety of rodents; it would also explain why so many of them can manage to survive with their low rate of reproduction.

In tropical South America there is a big standing army—eleven genera and scores of species—of spiny and semi-spiny rodents (family Echimyidae), including several forms that have spread northward into Central America. They are medium to large in size and some are covered with sharp, spiny bristles; a number are very showy, with white markings, especially the Crested Spiny Rat, *Echimys*. We find these animals in the trees as well as on the ground—the only places they have not penetrated to are the upper slopes of the higher mountains.

The Rat That Loses Its Tail. The Spiny Rat, *Proëchimys,* is of special interest because we often encounter it without a tail—that is to say, somewhere along the line many of these large, tawny creatures actually lose their tails through accidents. There is a weak link near the base of the tail, and with the least strain it will separate at the fifth vertebra. Since the entire tail comes off, including the bony structure, the animal cannot grow a new one. Fortunately for this rat it lives practically wholly on the ground—it would be handicapped in the trees without a tail.

Just how or why this seeming deformity was developed is a matter for conjecture. We do observe that it acts as a safety device for the rat, just as the same "weakness" does for the lizard. Caught by the tail, the animal merely parts company with this appendage and continues on its way.

RODENT MAKERS OF THE SOIL

Another group of rodent curiosities are the Andean Eight-toothed Rodents. The little creatures of this family have played a big role in making their native South America the fruitful, habitable place it is today.

How could they, in view of their size? They are burrowers, as a rule, and there are a great many of them. They serve in the capacity of soil makers, much the way the pocket gophers do in North America. By burrowing in the ground and turning up the subsoil, they plow leaves and vegetation under. In the course of time this turnover of the soil transforms barren wastes into fertile valley and plains.

The best known of these rodents is the Degu, *Octodon,* of Peru —its name has been given to the whole family (Octodontidae). A large-eared, somewhat ratlike animal, it has soft, reddish brown fur. Roughly seven inches in length, it has a tail about half as long again, which is furred and bushy at the tip.

Perhaps you are wondering why these creatures are called "eight-toothed rodents." Other rats and mice have only three molar teeth, more or less, on each side of the upper and lower jaws; the eight-toothed rodents, or octodonts, possess eight in each jaw (this figure does not, of course, include the gnawing teeth at the front of the mouth).

TUCO TUCOS—BOLD ENOUGH TO ATTACK SHEEP

Common throughout the tropical lowland pampas and upland plateaus of South America is a fairly large and extremely pugnacious rodent, the Tuco Tuco, *Ctenomys*—we find more than sixty differ-ent forms from Brazil south to Tierra del Fuego. The Guarani In-dians made up the animal's common name in imitation of the sound this burrower utters underground.

Practically the whole of southern Patagonia, east of the mountains, is fenced and devoted to sheep farming. During the summer, the sheep are rounded up and driven from one region to another; some-times as many as fifty thousand closely packed animals pass over long stretches of grassland. You might suppose that all ground-dwelling rodents would retreat before the advance of such a horde, but not if you knew the ferocious nature of the tuco tucos. According to re-ports, these angry creatures come out of their burrows and actually attempt to attack the sheep, and we are told it is not uncommon to see a sheep with a furious tuco at the end of its nose.

The tuco tuco also has been given the name of Mole Rat because of its habits. It looks rather like the pocket gopher of North Amer-ica, except that it has no cheek pouches. A soft coat of dark brown to pale buffy-brown covers its cylinder-shaped nine-inch body (the tail adds another third to this length), and it has short limbs. We can recognize the animal for the burrower it is by the large digging claws and the tiny eyes and ears. It makes up the family Cten-omyidae.

AFRICAN CANE RATS

In the large swamps and cane fields of Africa—especially where there are many square miles of reeds partly submerged the year round—we find the cane rats (family Thrynomyidae). These are big, heavy-bodied creatures, that actually hardly look like rats at all; as a mat-ter of fact, the people of West and South Africa often call them "ground pigs," and they form an important part of the natives' meat supply.

The largest of the group, the Greater Cane Rat, or Bamboo Rat, *Thrynomys* (the scientific name means "reed mouse") may be a good two feet long, with a thick, hairy tail that tapers to a length of six or seven inches. Small ears are hidden in the dense, almost spiny brown-gray hair that covers its body. Just like it in appear-ance, only smaller, is the Lesser Cane Rat, *Choeromys,* whose scien-tific name means "pig mouse."

Although the cane rats are not gregarious, they live close together. They feed on shoots and roots of reeds, water grass, other green vegetation, and the bark of certain trees. They do not habitually dig burrows in the ground, but sometimes take refuge in the burrows of the aardvark and the porcupine. They may be active by day or by night.

Spring and early summer are the breeding season of the cane rats. Two to four young are born in nests or forms in dense reed beds. The mother keeps her babies more or less covered with a thin layer of dry grass or shredded reeds, but they do not need this blanket for long. At birth they are well covered with hair; their eyes are wide open and frequently they are able to run about the moment they come into the world.

HUNTING THE CANE RAT

In many parts of Africa, the natives conduct organized hunts for cane rats. During the dry season the hunts take place almost daily: at this time the reeds can be fired easily, and the rats forced out into the open.

There is considerable sport derived from the cane-rat drives, which are carried on much like pig-sticking, only on foot. The natives wait with spears and clubs ready, while the dogs are sent ahead to round up the rats and drive them to where they can be butchered conveniently.

Once on the alert, the burly rodent is not easily captured by dogs, however. It has an effective method of eluding them: it rushes swiftly forward under cover; then it stops suddenly and remains motionless under its pursuer's nose. The dog, taken aback, may turn and run. The rat may repeat this prank whenever the dog gets too close for comfort.

The cane rat is a strong swimmer and usually manages to make good its escape if it can reach water. Here it remains submerged with only the tip of its nose above the surface until the danger is over. Its principal natural enemy is the leopard.

LAST OF THE GREAT ORDER OF RODENTS

It took a world war and the terrific conflict between the Allies and Rommel's troops in North Africa to make the world even realize

that there was such an animal as the gundi. When the soldiers con-
tracted a rare malady known as toxoplasmosis, it was found that the
gundis were the hosts. The disease is communicable to man, brings
out a rash on the skin, and affects the lungs like pneumonia.

The gundis live among the rocks in the desert regions of North
Africa from Senegal and Morocco to Somaliland. There are four
genera of these small, short-tailed guinea-pig-like rodents that vary
from seven to twelve inches in length. The ears are short and rounded,
the fur soft, and in one species there is practically no tail.

Their ancestry obscured by their peculiar ways of life and unique
characteristics, the gundis (family Ctenodactylidae) might well be
referred to as "the forgotten rodents." In fact, even their origin is
uncertain. All that scientists seem to be sure of is that they are not
related to the squirrels.

We find many other rodents in Africa and South America, but
they are not too strikingly different from those we have already
looked at. The African Mole Rat or Bles Mole (family Bathyer-
gidae) in general resembles the pocket gopher or the tuco tuco, but
has on its head or muzzle a white spot or "bles," as the Dutch call
it. The animal lives underground and feeds on roots and tubers.

Most interesting member of the African mole rat group is the
Naked Bles Mole, which has only a few hairs scattered over its body.
Hardly more than four inches in length (plus a fairly long tail), it is
the only small mammal that goes about literally naked. Since it lives
beneath the sands of tropical Somaliland, it does not have to worry
about the cold.

Whales, Dolphins, and Porpoises —
Mammals That Live in the Water

D ID YOU KNOW that the whale is not only the biggest creature alive today—it is the biggest that ever lived? The giant of all whales, the blue or sulphur-bottom whale, may reach a length of one hundred feet, weigh over one hundred tons. That is larger than the dinosaurs, the great reptiles that dominated the earth in prehistoric times. The biggest dinosaur weighed a mere fifty tons, according to careful estimates.

There are much smaller whales, of course. Moreover, some of the whales' relatives, the dolphins and the porpoises, are only six feet long. A number of these creatures are of such a size and shape that scientists have never quite decided whether they are whales, dolphins, or porpoises.

Some kinds of dolphins and porpoises are commonly confused. The most marked difference between the two is that the dolphin has a snout—a well-defined beak—and the porpoise hasn't. As you might expect in nature, there are also a few intermediate forms. But all belong in the same order of fishlike mammals (Cetacea, from the Greek word for "whale") that spend their entire lives in the water and are completely independent of dry land.

It was not always so. Many millions of years ago, even long before the Eocene period, the ancestors of the whales, dolphins, and porpoises were landlubbers. We have not found the fossil remains of these ancestors, but they must have existed on land at one time; it was on terra firma that the mammals had their beginning. For some unknown reason the forerunners of the whales left their old home and went to sea.

This was not a poor move on their part. The seas, after all, provide an immense field for the development of living things. Sea water covers more than three-fifths of the earth's surface, and the room available for marine life is actually three hundred times greater than that for life on land. Water provides support for an animal's body, permitting it to grow larger than it could on land.

While the whales, dolphins, and porpoises look like fishes, the resemblance is only superficial. The cetaceans are just as much mammals as are lions or deer. Like other mammals, they are warm-blooded. They breathe air. They bring forth their young alive, and they suckle them. Fishes, on the contrary, are cold-blooded. They get their oxygen from the water by way of their gills. They do not possess mammary glands, and usually their young develop from eggs.

OFTEN GLIMPSED OFF THE SHORES OF THE ATLANTIC
A gray- or greenish-skinned creature, the bottle-nosed dolphin prowls the waters of the Atlantic coast from Florida to Maine, and is also seen in the Gulf of Mexico. Note that, like many of its relatives, it is lighter on the bottom; its enemies find difficulty in detecting it from below, viewing it against the brighter or sunlit waters at the top of the sea.

You may never get a chance to observe a whale close up, but, if you did, you would see that its round body is streamlined, tapering to a broad, flat tail. Interestingly enough, the tail is not vertical, like a fish's, but horizontal. A notch in the center divides it into a pair of flukes. These have no bony support, like a fish's tail, but are made up of cartilage. Because its tail is horizontal, the cetacean can move forward in an even, undulating manner at the surface of the water. Also, it can come up fast for air.

A whale actually has limbs, not fins, toward the front of its body. These limbs are paddle-like in form and we call them flippers. They aid the animal to balance and steer itself. It relies on its powerful tail for moving about. There are no hind limbs, for these were lost long ago, leaving only internal traces behind. There is a dorsal or back fin as a rule, well to the rear.

A whale's skin is hairless and smooth—qualities that make for speedy progress through the water. It may or may not have a few bristles on its snout, relics of its hairy ancestry. Below the skin it has a thick layer of fatty tissue. This is the blubber. It serves to protect the warm-blooded whale against the extremes of temperature and pressure it encounters in the depths of the oceans, and prevents the loss of body fluids. The eyes are small and better adapted to seeing under water than above. A special substance produced by the tear glands protects the eyes against the irritation of salt water.

Although the whale lacks external ears, it has a hearing canal that leads to the internal ear from a tiny opening in the skin, and we believe the whale hears sounds in the water quite well. So far as we know, it has no sense of smell.

HOW SMART IS A WHALE?

Whales are far more intelligent than the fishes, and more so than many kinds of mammals. They have a mentality superior to that of an ox and probably close, if not equal, to that of a dog or a horse. Dolphins have been taught many tricks and will learn to come when called. They soon learn that if they do what is expected of them they will be rewarded with a choice morsel of food.

It is almost certain that an animal with such a highly organized brain must sleep. Humpback whales have been seen "dozing" with their heads in the air but it was impossible to say whether or not they were actually asleep. Many whales have been struck by large ships, chiefly at night, and it is believed that in such instances the animals were asleep.

TWO KINDS OF WHALES

You may have heard there are many different kinds of whales, but you will probably be surprised to learn that they fall into two main groups: the toothed whales and the whalebone whales. The toothed whales have in the lower jaw, or in both jaws, simple, cone-shaped teeth. These serve to catch and hold the food—marine animals ranging from shellfish, squids, and fish to seals and other whales and occasionally birds. The food is swallowed whole. In this toothed group belong porpoises, dolphins, killer whales, and sperm whales.

THE WHALEBONE WHALES

The second group, the whalebone whales, get their name from the whalebone, or baleen, which they have in place of teeth. Whalebone is not bone, as many people believe; it is a horny substance. Hundreds of long, thin, tapering whalebone blades hang in two rows along the roof of the mouth, one row on each side. These blades completely fill the space on either side when the mouth is open.

The whalebone whale feeds on plankton—tiny plants and animals as well as jellyfishes and other weak swimmers that live near the surface of the sea. When it opens its huge mouth, it takes in great numbers of them, water and all. Then it closes its jaws, catching the plankton inside the whalebone blades, which automatically fold backward as the mouth is closed. The inner edge of each blade is frayed into loose bristles; these fringes of the closely placed blades make an effective strainer to trap the plankton when the whale's muscular tongue forces the water out.

Whalebone isn't important only to whales; man has put it to a variety of uses for a long time. It boomed in value in the days when crinoline was in style, and was employed to make bustles. We still occasionally use it as a stiffener in collars, corsets, whips, fans, and similar objects. Good kinds of whalebone are obtained from the bowhead whale and the southern right whale in particular. The whalebone is first softened by boiling, and it is often dyed black or bleached white.

GREAT EATERS AND DIVERS

Large whales consume about a ton of food a day during the summer but the daily ration is much less in the winter, when food is scarcer. Most whales feed on or near the surface of the sea; others descend to great depths in pursuit of food. The larger ones "sound" or go down and stay under for fifteen or twenty minutes and on occasion nearly an hour.

Such feats of deep-sea diving require special equipment, and the whale possesses it. Near the crown of its head the whale has one nostril or a pair of them, depending on the species. These are the famous blowholes, and connect directly to the lungs, which are extremely elastic and can hold great quantities of air. Valves in the blowholes provide a means of closing the nostrils against the entry of water.

You will often hear people say that a whale takes water into its mouth and spouts it out through the blowhole. This is untrue. A whale cannot breathe through its mouth; as we have seen, there is no connection between the mouth and the lungs and nose, as there is in land mammals. Before diving, the whale fills its lungs with air. The air becomes heated and saturated with moisture during the animal's long stay in the depths. On rising to the surface, the whale opens the valves of its nostril and expels the air through the blowhole. When the heated breath discharged from the lungs comes in contact with the colder sea air, it forms a visible column of vapor. This is the spout.

Odd to relate, you can tell the name of a whale by its spout. The shape and height of the spout hold true for the species. For example, all rorquals spout in a single column; the sulphur-bottom whale has a thick, tall spout; the finback a thin, tall spout; the humpback emits a long, rounded cloud. The right whale's spout divides at the summit and falls on either side, while the sperm whale has a low, rounded puff directed forward and upward.

LOVE AMONG THE WHALES

Most whales and porpoises are sociable. They have been seen in groups of a few individuals and in herds of hundreds or even thousands. Many species are affectionate by nature, especially during courtship, and toward their young.

So far as we may judge, the whales are polygamous. The male, or bull, will often keep a harem of cows. Dr. Roy Chapman Andrews, one of the few naturalists to observe the mating antics of whales, makes this interesting report on the courtship behavior of humpback whales in his book *Under a Lucky Star:*

"An amorous bull whale may be very amusing to us but to his lady friend he is doubtless as exciting as a matinee idol is to a debutante. In this particular case the gentleman whale executed a series of acrobatic performances evidently with the object of impressing the female. He stood on his head with the tail and fifteen feet of body out of water. The great flukes were waved slowly at first; then faster until the water was pounded into spray and the terrific slaps on the surface could be heard a mile away. This performance ended, he slid up close to the female, rolling about and stroking her with his right flipper. She lay on her side apparently enjoying his caresses. Then he backed off and dived. I thought he had left her for good but she lay quietly at the surface; she knew full well that he would not desert her—yet. He was gone for, perhaps, four minutes, then with a terrific rush he burst from the water, throwing his entire fifty-foot body straight up into the air. It was a magnificent effort and I was proud of him. Falling back in a cloud of spray, he rolled over and over on to his mate, clasping her with both flippers. Both whales lay at the surface, blowing slowly, exhausted with emotion."

THE BIRTH OF A WHALE

There is no fixed breeding season for most whales. A female gives birth to a single calf, as the baby is called, at a time; twins are rare. The young cetacean is bigger than any other mammal infant: sometimes it is twenty feet long.

Just as the giant California redwoods that tower 350 or 400 feet skywards, dwarfing all other trees, sprang from tiny seeds no bigger than a grain of wheat, so the great whales, largest of all past and present animal life, grow from minute eggs. A "large" egg—from an adult finback whale—can just about be picked out against a dark background, with the naked eye. Such an egg measures about 0.00065 inches in diameter.

From the moment of its birth, the calf can swim—as indeed it must —and is able to keep up with the school it belongs to. The mother nurses her baby for about six months. She has two teats toward the rear of her under side, and the milk collects in reservoirs; when the calf is ready to nurse, a muscle goes into action, emptying the milk rapidly into the baby's mouth. This is fortunate, for prolonged suckling under water has its problems.

The average life span of the large whales is remarkably short. Few of the baleen or whalebone whales live more than twenty years, and the life of a sperm whale is even briefer.

HUNTING THE WHALE

Whales frequent not only the high seas but inland waters as well; some ascend large rivers above the pull of the tide. Some migrate with the seasons from ocean to ocean. Other whales are restricted in their range by forces such as climate and food, and the problem of safety.

Wherever the whales have gone, men have followed after and wrested a living from these giant mammals of the deep. When whaling first began we cannot say, but England's King Alfred wrote, over a thousand years ago, that the Norwegians were expert whalers, as indeed they still are today. Basque, French, and Spanish ports were the center of a thriving whaling industry during the Middle Ages; they supplied whalebone and oil to much of Europe. With time, this trade grew. We are told that in 1697 close to two thousand whales were taken off Spitzbergen alone by 188 ships.

Americans began to engage in sperm whale fishing late in the seventeenth century. At the time of the outbreak of the American Revolution 360 colonial vessels were hunting the whale for its oil, ambergris, and spermaceti—the latter being an oily substance found in the head of the sperm whale and used to make ointments, clear-burning candles, and the like. At the peak of the American trade, in 1846, the ships were 735 in number, most of them from New Bedford, Massachusetts, and its vicinity.

In the days of the New England whaling ships a catch on a three-years' cruise would average about forty whales per ship and rarely more than one hundred. We do things bigger and better today; the modern whaling ship is a power-driven factory and with its auxiliary cruisers will take as many as seventy-three whales in one day.

Although in earlier years much whaling was carried on in coastal waters and the Arctic, activity has now shifted to the Antarctic, where more whales may be found.

MOST IMPORTANT PRODUCT FROM THE WHALE

Oil, obtained from blubber, is the most important commercial product derived from the whale. One recent whaling season in the Antarctic produced 2,158,173 barrels of oil. We use it in the manufacture of soaps, cosmetics, ointments, and edible fats such as margarine. Whale oil is now also in great demand for making glycerin, used in the manufacture of munitions; a special kind of whale oil is excellent for lubricating the moving parts of delicate machinery, chronometers, etc.

In the past, people lit their lamps and street lights with whale oil and employed it in the manufacture of paints and varnishes as well as for finishing leather and tempering steel.

AMBERGRIS—TREASURE-TROVE OF THE SEAS

Ambergris, pound for pound, is the most valuable product of the whale. An opaque waxy substance, it has an odor suggesting musk, which is pleasing to most people.

Ambergris does not bring a high price because of the odor, however, but because it is a good fixative for perfume. Four hundred pounds of it, in a mass, on one occasion was purchased for more than one hundred thousand dollars.

Now, in case you have decided to go off in search of ambergris, you should know where to look for it and how to test it when you find it. While ambergris may be discovered almost anywhere along ocean beaches, it is most likely to turn up in Australia and New Zealand waters and on the shores of the Indian Ocean. It is ash colored or darker—some ambergris is black—and can be softened in the palm of the hand and melts below the boiling point of water. At higher temperatures it evaporates into a white vapor.

The Chinese test ambergris by scraping a trifle in hot tea, in which it will dissolve, leaving no fatty film. (In the Orient ambergris is used for spicing rare wines.) There is, however, no single or simple chemical test that will identify ambergris.

Some people find ambergris without even looking for it. In a classic story that may well relate a genuine incident, a woman on some unnamed island sat down on a rock and after a while discovered the rock had melted a little and stained her dress. The shopkeeper to whom she went to get her dress cleaned recognized the ambergris on it and together they made a fortune out of the sale of the "rock."

Despite the golden reward it brings, ambergris has a lowly origin, like the pearl. It is a secretion produced in the alimentary canal of a sick sperm whale. The sperm whale is fond of feeding on squid; it is believed that squid beaks frequently become imbedded in the walls of the whale's alimentary canal and set up an irritation, which causes the ambergris to form.

We do not yet know whether the whale manages to pass the ambergris during life or whether this precious substance is released after death, when the body disintegrates.

WHALE MEAT

The whale yields up other things to us. Not the least important of these is meat. Whale meat is now sold as food in numerous stores in the larger cities of North America; the Japanese and Chinese have been eating it for many years.

The meat of the whale neither tastes nor looks like fish. A whale steak may be dark in color, like liver, and some have said it reminded them of sirloin steak.

THE WHALE IN DANGER

Reports show that whalers took 6,158 blue whales, 17,989 finback whales, 2,108 humpback whales, and 2,566 sperm whales in a single season in the Antarctic, recently. This does not include 2,459 whales taken by the Russians. At such a rate, the modern whaling industry will soon wipe out the whale population. Leading whalers and their governments, deeply concerned about the situation, are trying to develop rules and fishing laws that will help the animals to survive.

Still, we cannot hope for much success until we know more about these deep-sea mammals. We are seriously endeavoring to get this information. A practice of marking whales, now in effect, should in the future shed a good deal of light on such major questions as how fast each kind grows, how long it lives, and the places it visits in its migrations.

How are whales marked? The method is to fire a numbered dart which lodges in the blubber of the living whale; a reward is offered for the return of the marker with information about its finding. Markers have already been discovered up to twenty-five hundred miles from the position of marking, and up to ten years from the time of marking. There are considerably over five thousand marked whales at large in the southern seas, which will bring valuable new evidence in the future.

JONAH AND THE WHALE

The author is frequently asked: What kind of a whale swallowed Jonah?

According to Scripture, Jonah had been called by the Lord to Nineveh to preach to the people about their wickedness. But, fearing to do so, he embarked at Joppa on a ship for Spain. On the voyage he was caught in a storm. The ship's crew believed Jonah to be the cause of it; at his bidding they cast him into the sea in order to calm its rage.

An accurate translation of the Hebrew text reads: "Now the Lord had prepared a great fish to swallow up Jonah. And Jonah was in the belly of the fish three days and three nights." Note that there is nothing to show that a whale was intended. That it was a whale is supposed to be indicated by a passage in the Gospel of Matthew: "For as Jonah was three days and three nights in the whale's belly; so shall the Son of Man be three days and three nights in the heart of the earth." But the word here translated as "whale" is Greek and properly means "sea monster."

The story may actually have referred to a small boat which, in the rough sea, was likened to the bowels of a sea monster; perhaps, after three days of bad weather, the boat brought Jonah to land. Some scholars have conjectured, also, that the idea of a sea monster was given to the author of the book of Jonah by the local legends connected with Joppa, the port from which Jonah embarked; for it was here that Andromeda (of Greek mythology) was rescued from a sea monster by Perseus.

If a whale actually did swallow Jonah, it certainly was not one of the whalebone whales. The throat in all whalebone whales is far too small to swallow a human being, especially a grown man. Even the largest of these whales do not have a gullet bigger than a man's fist. The sperm whale is the only whale existing that is capable of such a feat, and it is interesting to recall, in connection with the story of Jonah, that sperm whales have been observed in the Mediterranean a number of times.

SAILOR INSIDE A WHALE

Jonah's adventure has—or appears to have—a modern parallel. Sir Francis Fox, an English engineer, relates that in 1891 James Bartley, a sailor on a whaling vessel, was swallowed by a sperm whale and remained alive though unconscious in the animal's belly for twenty-four hours. He was rescued by his shipmates when they cut up the whale.

For two weeks Bartley's mind was unbalanced but eventually he recovered his senses and was able to resume his duties, we are told. Where his skin had been exposed to the gastric juices, it was blanched to a deathly whiteness.

This story is a provocative one. There is, of course, some oxygen in the belly of a whale, and it seems possible that a man could stay alive under such conditions for twenty-four hours or longer. On the other hand, Sir Francis's facts were second hand, obtained from the captain and others on the whaling ship. If the story is true, then Bartley was the only man in history to repeat Jonah's experience.

The whale, in any event, has made a great impression on mankind because of the role it plays in the Bible as well as because of its size. It has even earned immortality: according to the Islamic faith, only ten animals will enter Paradise, and one of these is the whale that swallowed Jonah.

Toothed Whales, Dolphins, and Porpoises

Although whales and porpoises look alike, they are vastly different in their size and habits and the way they behave. Most of the larger whales are mild, inoffensive creatures. One member of this group, however—the killer whale—is probably the most savage and ferocious of all wild animals. Schools of killer whales hunt on the high seas like wolves in a pack, ready to gang up on a defenseless creature and tear it to ribbons.

The group name of these animals (suborder Odontoceti) means "toothed whales" and the adult whales have teeth that are usually numerous and cone-shaped. They feed on squids, octopuses, and fish. The blowhole is a single opening. The males are larger than the females.

Although dolphins are sometimes called porpoises, and porpoises are sometimes called dolphins, as suggested earlier we apply the name "dolphin" to those cetaceans whose muzzle is drawn out in the shape of a beak, while the porpoise has a rounded muzzle; there are some in-between forms which could be classed under either name.

SPERM WHALES—THEY CAN CRUSH A WHALEBOAT

The Sperm Whale, or Cachalot, *Physeter,* to whose clan Moby-Dick belonged, is perhaps the most famous of all whales. A sixty-foot monster, it ranges all the seas and migrates north and south with the seasons. Although normally peace-loving, the animal will, when wounded, crush a whaleboat as if it were matchwood; its mighty, blunt head, used as a battering ram, has staved in the hull of more than one wooden whaling ship.

The sperm whale's head makes up one-third of the animal's enormous length. The head contains a huge reservoir filled with the whitish oily substance known as spermaceti. We believe that this oil pocket acts as a cushion that somehow protects some of the animal's vital organs from the excessive pressure it must sustain when it descends to great depths. The sperm whale will go as far down as 3,200 feet, where the pressure is 1,400 pounds to the square inch, and will stay there an hour or more.

The sperm whale feeds on giant squid and cuttlefish, which it hunts on the ocean floor: it consumes about a ton a day. On one occasion a ten-foot shark was found in the stomach of a sperm whale, and we can safely assume it could swallow a human being. Normally its lower jaw is armed with about two dozen teeth in each side for grasping its elusive prey (once in a while we find a sperm whale with teeth on the upper jaw). The sperm whale is the one that produces ambergris when its intestine is irritated.

FAMILY LIFE OF THE SPERM WHALES

A full-grown bull sperm whale is a massive creature. A forty-three-foot specimen weighed 86,000 pounds, the liver 925 pounds, and the heart 277 pounds. Some males grow to eighty feet or longer. There is a marked difference in the size of the sexes, the cow often being scarcely more than half as big as a large bull.

Sperm whales appear to be polygamous, the bull whale keeping a harem. There is no fixed breeding season. The baby whale is not born until a year after the mating. Newborn, it will measure about fourteen feet in length. Its mother nurses it for the first six months; by the time it is fully weaned it may reach a length of twenty feet or more.

In nursing her baby, the cow rolls on her side; by doing this she enables the calf to breathe freely while it is sucking at her breast. The calf reaches full maturity at about eight years of age. The mother will protect it until weaned, but not the father, who looks after his own interests when danger threatens.

A GREAT WHITE WHALE

The sperm whale is dark in color, sometimes black. It may produce an albino offspring, but this is a great rarity. Apparently not since the legendary Moby-Dick in Herman Melville's classic book on whaling has one been chronicled. Or, rather, such seemed to be the case until the winter of 1951-1952.

In that season the Norwegian whaling cruise took some 3,066 sperm whales in the Antarctic. Among the catch was a milky-white sperm whale, killed off the coast of Peru. Except for a slight bluish coloring about its flukes, the animal was completely white. This was the first albino ever caught, to the recollection of the whalers on the fleet, some of whom were veterans with more than thirty years' experience hunting the great ocean mammals.

TOO VALUABLE FOR ITS OWN GOOD

A sixty-foot sperm whale may produce eighty barrels of oil (there are fifty gallons to the barrel, and most of it comes from the blubber). Sperm whale oil differs from that obtained from the whalebone whales in that it is not suitable for conversion into edible fat. It has other important uses, however: women will be interested to learn it goes into the making of their cosmetics.

All this makes the sperm whale valuable to the whalers—too valuable for its own good. Considering its short life expectancy—fifteen to twenty years—and its slow rate of reproduction (the female usually bears one calf every second year), the present pace at which it is being destroyed may spell complete extermination of the sperm whale within a very few years.

PRODUCER OF AMBERGRIS
The sperm whale, a powerful creature that may grow to a length of eighty-five feet, has a square, blunt head that can easily shatter the side of a wooden vessel. The animal is highly valued, for it yields a great quantity of oil and, on occasion, ambergris. Note that the tail is horizontal—not vertical, as in the fishes.

A rapid swimmer, the sperm whale cruises along at about four knots but it can triple this speed if it has to. It is the commonest large whale on the high seas. Formerly schools or "pods" of one thousand individuals were recorded on the migration routes. However, groups of two or three are all one can hope to see today on a transatlantic voyage.

STRANGE MASS SUICIDE OF WHALES

Years ago, when sperm whales were plentiful in the waters of the earth, a curious thing sometimes happened: they appeared to commit what seems to have been mass suicide. In any event, sizable numbers used to be stranded and die. On one occasion—this happened in 1723—thirteen whales were found dead on the shores of the Elbe.

But an even more remarkable stranding of these giants occurred on the coast of France. We are told that at six o'clock on the morning of March 14, 1784, extraordinary loud bellowings were heard toward Cape Estain; the sound was so great it carried more than two miles. Two men coasting along the shore were terrified when they saw some enormous animals struggling in the foaming waves and rolling in the shallows toward the shore. The men's amazement was redoubled when they perceived thirty-two of these sea monsters piled up on the beach. It is a curious fact that most of them were female sperm whales.

Whales, though they breathe air, will die of suffocation on land. This phenomenon is easily explained. A whale stranded on the beach and left by the receding tide loses the support of the water. The weight of its body now presses on the lungs so that the animal cannot breathe.

Not so easily explained is how or why whales get stranded. Whales have lived in the sea for well over sixty million years and it is out of the question to suppose that they would accidentally get caught by seasonal high tides or be driven ashore in stormy weather. This might account for the stranding of a wounded or aged individual but not for whole schools of whales.

No, there is some far more deadly cause, some urge within the whales themselves—not only in an individual but the school—to give up life. Where they have been rescued and towed out to sea, whales have come right back and beached themselves again.

A VICTIM OF BARNACLES

The sperm whale's generic name, *Physeter*, means "blower." Its blowhole is situated well forward for a whale and bears a resemblance to an *S*. Its flippers or pectoral fins are relatively small and it has no dorsal fin.

A life in the water does not keep this huge mammal from being afflicted by a number of parasites, which infest its skin in large numbers. Most common among them are the amphipod and the barnacle.

THE PYGMY SPERM WHALE

Much like the sperm whale in ways and appearance is its little cousin, the Pygmy Sperm Whale, *Kogia*. The pygmy reaches a length of about thirteen feet, weighs about nine hundred pounds. It is blackish in color, has a dorsal fin, and feeds on squid and cuttlefish, which it hunts at great depths on the ocean floor.

Although it has been reported in many different waters, the pygmy whale is not very common anywhere. With the big sperm whale, it makes up a distinct family (Physeteridae).

BEAKED WHALES

COWFISH—WHALES THAT LOW LIKE COWS

The "toothless" whale of Le Havre was one of the first of the beaked whales to gain recognition by science. It was captured at Le Havre in August, 1828, and attracted considerable popular interest at that time. It lived for two days out of water and was offered soaked bread to eat.

Reports tell us that this creature emitted a deep sound like the lowing of a cow. Such, no doubt, is the origin of the name Cowfish, now used for the Beaked Whale, *Mesoplodon.*

There are ten different kinds of cowfish, but none of them is over twenty feet in length. They can be recognized by the long, rounded snout (or "beak") and the pair of converging furrows or "pleats" on the throat. These creatures, like other beaked whales, feed on squid and cuttlefish, and are native to all the warmer seas.

So far as we know the cowfish are the survivors of a once numerous race of cetaceans. (With the other beaked whales, they form the family Ziphiidae.) They have only one or two pairs of functional teeth at the tip of the lower jaw. (Probably these were worn down in the whale captured at Le Havre, and that is why it was called "toothless.") Strangely, there are often a number of small teeth in both jaws hidden in the gums and not attached to either of the jaws.

GOOSE-BEAKED WHALES—SCHOOLS OF DIVERS

Another beaked whale worthy of mention here is the Goose-beaked Whale, *Ziphius,* often called Cuvier's Whale because Cuvier was the first to recognize it (he named it in 1823). This animal's habits are much like those of the cowfish but it is a somewhat larger whale and travels in schools instead of singly or in pairs.

Schools of these beaked nomads of the deep cruise all open oceans. A group will roll along the surface for a while, in perfect unison; then, as if at the command of a leader, the whole school goes down simultaneously in a deep dive, and may stay under thirty minutes or more.

We have observed that among land animals there is competition among males for possession of the female. The situation is no different among whales, and the bulls fight terrific battles during the mating season. In their frenzy they may even attack an innocent cow or calf that gets in their way.

BIGGEST OF THE BEAKED WHALES

The largest of the beaked whales, Baird's Whale, *Berardius,* a creature that may grow close to forty feet in length, is at home in the Pacific Ocean. It has two pairs of extraordinary teeth in the lower jaw—they can be depressed or elevated at will, and are particularly serviceable when the animal is defending itself or attacking its prey. The teeth are embedded in a cartilaginous sac in the sockets of the lower jaw and are moved up or down by a muscular action. The animal has been described as bellowing like a bull.

BOTTLE-NOSED WHALES—DANGEROUS TO HUNT

This brings us to the Bottle-nosed Whale, or Bottlehead, *Hyperoodon,* the most commercially valuable of the beaked whales. It is one of the few cetaceans that show a marked difference between the sexes, other than in point of size.

A male bottle-nosed whale has a head that very roughly suggests a bottle. A very high forehead rises abruptly behind the rather short beak. This raised crown encases a reservoir of high-grade oil or spermaceti. The male also has a distinctive white patch on the forehead and a white dorsal fin. The plainer female displays none of these characteristics.

Sudden Dives. Though mild tempered and seemingly unafraid, the bottle-nose is one of the most dangerous whales to hunt on the high seas, not on account of any attack that it might make on a whaling boat but because of the suddenness and rapidity with which it will sound when harpooned. A slight twist in the harpoon line may result in capsizing the boat, or else the line may loop around a seaman and whip him down to his death with unbelievable rapidity.

Norwegian whalers choose single men to man their whaleboats. They consider the task too hazardous for married men with families.

Hunting the Bottle-nosed Whale. When a school of bottle-nosed whales is sighted, one or two boats are launched and speed toward the animals. It is the habit of these whales to rise from the depths at several successive intervals of from one-half to one minute each; then they plunge down in a deep dive and remain under from thirty minutes to two hours, searching for cuttlefish, the favorite food of the beaked whales. They rise again in the immediate vicinity where they sounded. The whalers make use of this fact, the steersman in one of the boats maneuvering his craft in position for the harpooner to take aim.

If he makes a hit, the harpooner twists the line several times around the "puller," and henceforth it is the enormously important job of the steersman to keep that line clear. If a snag should form in the line, he immediately shouts "Clear!" and the line is cut with an axe. Should there be a delay of even a fraction of a second, the boat and its crew would be dragged under and probably all would be killed.

The "Death Fish." The stricken whale goes straight down. It plunges so fast and furiously that it will run out five hundred fathoms (three thousand feet) of line in two minutes. The friction of the line is almost unbelievable. The line would burst into flame if water were not poured on it constantly.

After about one hour, the harpooned whale or "death fish," as it is called, weakened from loss of blood, comes to the surface. The second boat now moves in and kills the animal with a long lance or spear which is thrust into the heart.

Despite the strong points of this whale, one habit has often proved its undoing. The herd—it sometimes has several hundred members—will never leave a wounded comrade, and so they are "sitting ducks" for the whalers. However, as soon as the injured animal is dead, the rest move away and are safe for the time being.

Bottle-noses Change Color with Age. Bottle-nosed whales spend the summer in the Arctic seas; later they migrate south in the Atlantic to the latitudes of the Mediterranean Sea. Although some herds are large, occasionally groups of only three or four whales are reported. The animals mate in April or May, and it is a full year later that the single calf is born.

Baby Bottle-nose is a relatively large black creature, a mere ten feet in length. As it gets older its color changes; yellowish spots begin to appear on its skin. These gradually increase in size, until, in old age, the whale may be completely white or yellowish white. A full-grown bottle-nose will yield about one ton of oil; the male animal may be some thirty feet long, the female about six feet shorter.

WHITE WHALES AND NARWHALS

THE BELUGA, OR WHITE WHALE

The Beluga or White Whale, *Delphinapterus,* has another name that you might hardly expect to find applied to a whale. This animal is sometimes called the "sea canary" because it actually makes trilling sounds when it is under the water!

The sounds produced by the beluga, or white whale, have actually been recorded over a hydrophone (a machine that detects underwater noises) by William E. Schevill and Barbara Lawrence, of the Museum of Comparative Zoology, Cambridge, Massachusetts. The animal's "utterances" may be described as resonant whistles, squeals, and bell-like tones, varied with tickings and clickings, which sound like an orchestra tuning up. Occasionally they remind one of a crowd of school children shouting at a distance.

Counting a Whale's Heartbeats. The hydrophone is not the only modern scientific instrument that has been used to find out things about the white whale. Believe it or not, this animal's heartbeats have been recorded on an electrocardiogram! The researchers discovered that the pulsations—those of a fifteen-foot, two-thousand-pound white whale—were similar to the heartbeats of a human being or an elephant, but closer to the latter's when the whale is diving.

How did they get the whale to sit for its electrocardiogram? The researchers prepared a harpoon which contained in its point the metallic contact normally placed on the skin in human diagnoses; this harpoon the researchers connected to their apparatus. Then they sailed until they found a whale and skillfully shot the harpoon into it. It can hardly be said that the animal was benefited by such a diagnosis.

They Enter Rivers. At home in the coastal waters of the Arctic and Subarctic seas, the white whale also travels up rivers far above the pull of the tide. It has been observed a number of times in the lower St. Lawrence River, and can be readily recognized by its white skin and the absence of a dorsal fin. Full-grown males average twelve or fourteen feet in length. These animals are fast in the water and can speed up to six miles an hour. They feed on squid and prawns and will take salmon when the fish enter the rivers in the spring.

An Eskimo Field Day. The white whale is fond of company and gathers together in herds or schools numbering from a few individuals to probably a thousand. In 1898 an enormous herd was reported trapped in a "hole" in the ice 150 yards long by 50 yards wide at Point Barrow, Alaska. The water here was thirty fathoms in depth, and the animals were too far from open water to attempt to swim under the ice and escape.

When the incident was investigated, 150 whales killed by Eskimos were found lying on the ice, half as many more were tied to the edge of the ice, and hundreds more were still alive.

The Eskimos literally had a field day. In all, by actual count, three hundred whales were taken out of the school, which originally numbered more than nine hundred, according to the estimate of the natives. (Of the survivors, we are not told; perhaps the strongest and boldest made the hazardous trip to safety under the ice.) The whales came up to breathe every twelve or eighteen minutes, took ten or fifteen blows (breaths) of one to two seconds each, and dived again, if they had been lucky enough to escape the harpoons. The majority rose to breathe simultaneously and were so crowded in the small space that some were actually heaved out of the water.

Eskimo Magic. The white whale, you can see, plays no small role in the lives of Eskimos. The Koryak Eskimos of the Sea of Okhotsk even have an annual feast in honor of the white whale: they call it the Festival of the Whale Guest. A ritual accompanies the feast, which consists of paying homage to the severed head of a white whale. Canny folk, the Eskimos have a very "practical" purpose in conducting these rites.

The ceremony is carried on in a native hut, where the whale head is exhibited on an altar. The Eskimo leader, wearing a collar of plaited grass, takes a piece of whale fat, throws it into the fire, and exclaims: "We are burning it in the fire for thee." After this, he places pieces of the fat before the head and also smears the mouth of the whale with fat. This is the sign for the feast to begin. Two priestesses hidden in grass masks now do homage to the whale.

As a finale to the festival, the whale's head is lifted through the roof. The Eskimos launch the head on the sea with two bags of provisions and a farewell message: "Goodbye, dear friend, when the next high tide comes in, bring all your relatives with you."

The name "beluga," which the Russians give to the white whale, comes from their word for "white." This species is one of the few whales that have a distinct neck, and it is capable of turning its head to some extent. It has ten teeth on each side of the upper jaw and eight on each side of the lower. The animal is placed in the family Monodontidae, with the narwhal, since it has many of the same characteristics as that curious creature.

NARWHALS—WHALES WITH TUSKS

The Narwhal, *Monodon*, a native of the waters of the Arctic and North Atlantic, is especially noteworthy for the great tusk of ivory that projects from its upper jaw. The animal itself may reach a length of twenty feet; the tusk may be as long as nine feet.

Usually only the male sports the tusk. So far as we can determine, the narwhal does not use this projection as a weapon of attack, though perhaps it serves that purpose in battles between males for the possession of cows.

Like many other water-dwelling mammals, the narwhal keeps places in the ice open for obtaining air. In these holes it has been observed in company with its cousin the white whale. The narwhal is not a fast swimmer. But under the water it is quick enough to catch the creatures it feeds on—cuttlefish, turbot, cod, salmon, skate, halibut, flounder, sea scorpions, shrimp, and other marine animal life. It may crush fish between its jaws but it usually swallows them whole.

Just as the narwhal surfaces, it emits a shrill whistle; this may be the air being expelled from its lungs through the blowhole. Often a deep roar and a low-pitched bellow are heard from a narwhal—it could be the female calling her calf.

When full grown, the narwhal is grayish in color with numerous darker mottlings along its sides and back. This is supposed to account for its name; it meant "corpse whale" in Old Norse. Eskimos eat the narwhal's flesh and burn the oil, which is of fine quality, in their moss lamps. They make the intestines into lines or clothing.

The Tusk Is a Tooth. Sometimes a narwhal is found with two tusks, but normally there is only one. It is actually the animal's left upper canine (the creature's scientific name, *Monodon*, means "one tooth"), and projects from the left side of the upper jaw. Because of the tusk, some seamen used to call the narwhal the "sea unicorn."

ANCESTOR OF THE UNICORN
The narwhal, a whale with a long, twisting tusk of ivory, is quite at home amid icebergs, in the coldest of waters. The tusks of dead narwhals, washed ashore, are said to have played a part in the creation of the old legend of the unicorn, a fabulous beast with magical powers that is pictured in the British royal coat of arms.

The Narwhal and the Unicorn. Very likely, narwhal tusks, picked up by Scandinavian fishermen long ago, helped develop our picture of the fabulous unicorn. Even as late as Shakespeare's day many people took that beast of fable for a real animal.

The starting point of modern zoology is a book called *Historia Animalium,* or "Story of Animals," by Konrad von Gesner (1516-1565). Although this old Swiss naturalist made a serious attempt to sift facts from fiction, he could not altogether free himself of the fancies of his time; like the Roman naturalist Pliny, fifteen hundred years before him, Gesner described the unicorn as an actual member of the animal kingdom. In his illustration of this mythical beast, he figures it with a straight, spirally twisted horn in the middle of the forehead—a perfect example of a narwhal tusk—the body of a horse, cloven hoofs, the tail of a lion and the beard of a goat.

Although a narwhal tusk is an object of some value today, it was an exceedingly precious find in the past. The people of the Middle Ages, considering it the unicorn's horn, looked upon it with great awe. They thought it was capable of rendering all poisons harmless and of changing the deadliest draught into a wholesome beverage. The unicorn, they believed, had need of such a weapon because it lived in the desert among all kinds of loathsome beasts and poisonous reptiles whose look was contamination and whose touch was death. The tusk of the narwhal—the doughty weapon of the unicorn—they supposed had been torn from the animal's forehead despite its supernatural strength and superhuman intellect.

Actually, the unicorn legend goes back further than the Middle Ages—even further than Pliny. A unicorn is mentioned in the Bible several times. The Psalmist, for one, says: "But my horn shalt thou exalt like the horn of an unicorn: I shall be anointed with fresh oil" (Psalms 92:10). Later fables about the animal may have gotten confused with stories reaching Europe of the one-horned rhinoceros of India.

DOLPHINS—NOT ALL OF GOOD OMEN

Ever since ships went to sea it seems the appearance of dolphins coursing alongside a vessel's bows has been regarded by seamen as a good omen and a promise of fair weather and steady winds.

Most of the dolphins are harmless to man, and some are even friendly. One ranks among the fiercest creatures of the deep. This is the so-called killer whale.

Compared to their big relatives the whales proper, the dolphins must be considered medium to small in size. Generally, as mentioned earlier, the snout is narrowed to a beak, and often there are numerous teeth in both jaws. We find the members of this family (Delphinidae) in all open seas; they often ascend large rivers, and some of them live in fresh water.

The dolphin, with its antics and friendliness, probably attracted the fascinated attention of the first men that sailed in boats. It has been a famous animal ever since, and is even associated with Scriptural events. According to one interpretation in folklore, the animals owe their origin to Pharaoh's forces that perished in the Red Sea pursuing the Israelites.

This horrible death of so many people was not enough to satisfy the wrath of God; the Egyptians were turned into dolphins and, we are told, must wander to the end of time through all the seas. The legend carries this proof for the unbeliever: Fishes do not come to the surface to breathe but the dolphins must come up for air every so often.

THE DOLPHIN AND THE SCHOOLBOY

Tales about dolphins abound in ancient literature. Pliny, the old Roman writer, tells one of the most appealing ones—of a dolphin which had great affection for the child of a poor man and carried him to school each day.

Pliny's story is dated as in the reign of Emperor Augustus. It relates that at whatever hour of the day the dolphin might be called by the boy—and even though it might be at the bottom of the water—it would hear the summons and instantly fly to the surface. After feeding from the boy's hand, the dolphin would present its back for him to mount, carefully concealing the spiny projections of its fins in their sheath. Sportingly taking the boy up on its back, the dolphin would carry him over a wide expanse of sea to the school at Puteoli, and in a similar manner bring him back again.

This tale may have been derived from the ancient Greek coins that figured the son of Poseidon (Neptune) seated on a dolphin. Dolphins, according to many of the classical writers, were harnessed to chariots and it was believed that the dolphin acted as a carrier to gods, as well as children and maidens in distress. To the early Christians the animal was a symbol of love and diligence, or speed.

DOLPHINS CAN BE TRAINED

Perhaps the legends of ancient folklore were not quite so groundless as we are apt to believe. Recent experiments at Marineland, Florida, show that some cetaceans can be trained. A bottle-nosed dolphin has been taught to retrieve a stick and a ball thrown by its trainer.

This particular animal works willingly in harness. It actually pulls a surfboard in a lagoon, giving free rides to a girl and a dog. On a signal of the voice or hand, the dolphin will leap through a three-foot hoop suspended three feet above the water. It even does this jump through a sheet of paper pasted to the hoop and thoroughly enjoys the fun for a reward in the form of a fish.

Marineland has also confirmed the fact that dolphins make a wide variety of audible sounds, such as a drawn-out grunting noise, jaw clapping, chirping, and squeaking. One young dolphin, temporarily separated from its mother, whistled persistently and was frequently answered by its mother.

The Common Dolphin, *Delphinus,* one of the handsomest of its tribe, is found in all seas but is most plentiful in warm and temperate regions. It is the sportive, happy-looking creature usually seen from the decks of transatlantic steamers. In graceful and seemingly effortless leaps, the common dolphin breaks water as it overtakes and passes ships traveling at sixteen or eighteen knots; a speed of thirty knots has been reported for this well-named "Arrow of the Sea."

A slender creature, the common dolphin has a sharp-pointed beak, six inches long, set off from its forehead by a groove. There is an air of scholarliness about the animal; a black ring circles each eye, making the dolphin look as though it were wearing glasses. Its greenish-gray or brown flanks are marked with stripes of a darker shade.

This speedy swimmer is only about seven feet long and has a single blowhole. Like its larger relatives, it has a thick padding of blubber to keep it warm. It possesses numerous teeth, sometimes as many as one hundred in each jaw, and they interlock to form a perfect vise for catching and holding the fish the dolphin feeds on. A sociable animal, it communicates with its fellows by whistling.

From afar, the common dolphin might easily be mistaken for a whale; bigger dolphins are, as a matter of fact, often called whales.

This attractive animal, however, is much too small to be worthwhile prey for professional whalers.

——BIRTH OF A DOLPHIN. Like most of the other dolphins, the common species bears a single baby at a time. The infant is born about eleven or twelve months after mating time. It takes some thirty-five minutes for a baby dolphin to be born, but its actual entrance into the world is exceedingly fast.

Born in deep water, the baby must reach the surface almost instantly to breathe. Immediately after the birth, the mother dives under to assist in bringing her baby up. Normally, however, it can break the surface of the water under its own power.

FROLICKING IN THE WATER
The common dolphin, in a playful mood, will leap high out of the water and sport about the sides of ships, to the delight of the passengers. This black- or gray-skinned creature has a long beak armed with many teeth which it puts to good use when it goes fishing.

Thirty minutes after birth the baby is ready for its first meal. It is nursed under water at intervals of about one hour at first. During the early period of nursing the baby dolphin comes up for air every five seconds. The milk is injected rather than sucked into its mouth.

KILLER WHALES—FIERCEST OF THEIR CLAN

The Killer Whale, *Grampus* (*Orcinus*), the most bloodthirsty of marine mammals, is actually a dolphin. Found in all seas including those of the Arctic and Antarctic, it is readily recognized by the tall black dorsal fin that cuts the surface of the water as the animal cruises along.

A huge, powerful beast, the killer whale may reach a length of thirty feet. The white patch above and to the rear of each eye (in the Atlantic species) and the snowy white of the under parts extending up on the sides are in sharp contrast with the jet-black color of the animal. Its head is bluntly rounded; its frightful jaws are armed with forty stout teeth or more. There is no beak.

The Savage Killer Whale. No animal is more aptly named than the killer whale. It travels in schools of from a few individuals to forty or more. They move along rapidly in close formation, rising and diving at a uniform pace. Seals, whales, and dolphins frantically seek safety at the approach of a pack of killers. The hair seals make for shore and some of the whales head toward the beaches and slide into shallow water.

It is hardly likely that a pack of killers would attack the great sperm whale, but we know they do attack and kill the California gray whale and probably some of the other great whalebone whales. A pack of killers will encircle a large whale, leap at it from all sides, tear at the lips, and rip out the tongue, until the animal is exhausted and cut to pieces.

The killer whale is the only cetacean that feeds on its own kind and on other warm-blooded mammals. One old writer, speaking of its rapacious habits, claims that a killer whale was seen with a seal under each flipper, a third tucked away under the dorsal fin and a fourth in its mouth. Of course this is physically impossible. But Scammon, a modern scientist and authority on marine mammals, relates how killer whales may sometimes "be seen peering above the surface with a seal in their bristling jaws, shaking and crushing their victims."

In northern waters the killer pursues the walrus. The killer is no match for the adult, whose massive tusks afford adequate protection; it is the young the whale hunts. A walrus cub will climb on its mother's back for protection and cling to her tightly while she carries it to safety.

A killer whale can swallow a porpoise or a seal whole. Some conception of its gluttonous ferocity can be gathered from the fact that fourteen seals and thirteen porpoises were found in the stomach of one individual that measured twenty-one feet.

The Swordfish and Whale Story. The swordfish and whale story—to the effect that a bloody feud exists between these two giants of the sea—has been generally accepted as true from time immemorial. It is very colorful, and has been related by writers both ancient and modern. Other stories of battling sea monsters echo it with some variations. Let's look at one of the older accounts first.

Bartholomew Anglicus, a Franciscan of the middle of the thirteenth century, wrote a treatise explaining the allusions to natural subjects in the Scriptures. His principal sources of information on natural history were the ones you might expect for a writer of his day—Aristotle and Pliny. Anglicus' version of the whale and swordfish story reads:

MORE DREADFUL THAN THE SHARK
The killer whale is the terror of the deep. It travels in a pack, and few creatures that live in the ocean are safe from the relentless attack of these swift, ferocious marauders. Killers will make short work of some of the largest of whales; they also take a fearful toll among seals, porpoises, and dolphins.

"Also Jorath saith, that against the whale fighteth a fish or serpent's kind, and is venomous as a crocodile. And then other fish come to the whale's tail, and if the whale be overcome the other fish die. And if the venomous fish may not overcome the whale, then he throweth out of his jaws into the water a fumous smell most stinking. And the whale throweth out of his mouth a sweet smelling smoke, and putteth off the stinking smell, and defendeth and saveth himself and his in that manner wise." (The sweet-smelling smoke probably referred to the spout of the whale; the other facts we shall consider in a moment.)

Coming up to modern days, from time to time we find vivid reports of terrific battles between sea monsters in newspapers, such as this account from the Nantucket *Inquirer and Mirror* (June 26, 1909):

"A remarkable fight between monsters of the sea was witnessed by the passengers and crew of the steamer *Esparta*, which arrived at Boston from Port Limon, Costa Rica, on Monday.

"The thrilling battle occurred south of Nantucket South Shoale Lightship, between a whale and another great fish believed to be a swordfish. The whale was vanquished.

"The whale was the only one of the two fighters visible to the passengers and crew. The great mammal lashed its tail violently, churning the waters into a mass of foam, while it was believed to be attacking the swordfish with its teeth. Several irregular plunges appeared to indicate a successful plunge by the fish beneath, and finally the great whale was seen to throw its massive bulk clear of the water and then sink from sight. The water for a considerable distance about was dyed red with the blood, and it was believed the whale had received a mortal wound."

Some years later the Boston *Transcript* printed a like report of a "sea battle" witnessed by passengers on the steamship *Cymric* when about a day's run from Boston. In this instance the two combatants were "an enormous whale and a thresher" (the latter is a large shark with a long tail). "The whale could be seen to dive in the attempt to escape his tormentor," declared the *Transcript*, "but the thresher was on him with agile leaps at every reappearance, and the water for yards around was stained with blood."

From what we can judge by the behavior recorded, the whales in both these incidents were humpbacks and the attackers, if there actually were any, probably were killer whales. Norwegian fishermen often refer to the killer whale as the swordfish or "sverdfisk." On the other hand, the humpback is noted for its playful activities in the water, such as beaching and lobtailing, as described under this species. To the inexperienced observer such antics might seem to indicate a terrific conflict with an unseen foe.

Would a true swordfish attack a whale? Not very likely. A swordfish would have little reason to do so, and could inflict only slight damage if it were foolhardy enough to try.

There are two species of killer whale: the Atlantic Killer Whale, and the Pacific Killer Whale. They are much alike in appearance and habits, except that the Pacific form lacks the white patch over the eye.

The False Killer Whale, or Little Killer Whale, *Pseudorca,* found in all seas, is a gentleman compared to the true killer whale. Although smaller than the true killer, this species is still large when compared with other dolphins. Its usual length is twelve feet or so; extra-large individuals will measure eighteen feet in length and weigh one and one-half tons.

The false killer is completely black and has a short dorsal fin. There are from eight to twelve strong teeth on each side of the upper jaw and on each side of the lower. Despite its massive form and formidable appearance, the animal is not credited with any bad habits. It feeds for the most part on squids and cuttlefish.

As with some of the other cetaceans, great schools of false killer whales invade shallow water, where they are left to die by the receding tide. Hundreds of individuals have beached themselves in mass in northern Scotland and in South Africa. So far, no one has offered a plausible explanation of this strange sporadic behavior. It certainly is not accidental, since no seafaring mammal is stupid enough to involve itself in such a predicament unless driven by some overwhelming urge.

BLACKFISH—THEY FOLLOW THEIR LEADERS TO DEATH

The Blackfish, Pilot Whale, or Caaing Whale, *Globicephala,* is not a fish but a member of the dolphin clan; all that the name "blackfish" tells us about this big mammal is its color.

The other popular names of the blackfish do reveal something of its habits, however. People call it a "pilot whale" because it will follow a leader blindly, even to certain death. The name the Scotch have for it is "caaing" or "ca'ing whale." They are no longer sure why they gave the animal this name. "Caaing" means both "driving" and "calling"; some say the word comes from the practice of driving schools of blackfish into fjords, others that it alludes to the bellowing noise the whale makes when it is beached.

We find the blackfish in all seas except those of the polar regions. It measures up to twenty-eight feet in length and has a beak, like other dolphins, but a short one. *Globicephala* means "ball head," the blackfish's head is rounded; the forehead bulges. The animal has glosssy black skin, the only markings on it being a white line on the chest that broadens into a heart-shaped patch on the throat.

Blackfish travel in schools of many hundreds of individuals that migrate north in the spring and south in the fall. They swim at a good fast pace, groups rising and diving together in perfect unison. Squids and cuttlefish form a large part of their diet, which they vary with shoal fish in season.

Bent on Self-Destruction. Whole schools of blackfish have been known to beach themselves. On March 7, 1944, sixty-five blackfish came ashore at Bull's Island, South Carolina; on March 15 of the same year, thirty-five more, apparently the rest of the school, were stranded at Atlantic Beach, North Carolina, and had to be buried in the sand by the United States Coast Guard. It would appear that the entire herd was bent on self-destruction for reasons unknown.

Blackfish, like other sizable whales, have considerable economic value. In 1936, a large school of blackfish that was stranded on a sandbar at Cape Cod, Massachusetts, yielded several hundred barrels of oil; this netted local fishermen some thousands of dollars. In northern Scotland the local fishermen draw a good income from blackfish that they capture in the bays and voes, or inlets.

Blackfish Drives in Scotland. Catching the blackfish is exciting sport as well as profitable, and all the men in a Scottish village will take part in the hunt. When a school of blackfish is sighted close to shore by a fisherman, he raises a garment on the mast of his boat as a signal. The villagers join in a mad scramble to reach their vessels and get them into the water.

Once they are close to the whales, the villagers draw the boats together in a semicircle around the school. Now they begin to pitch stones into the water and chase the animals until they have entered a shallow voe. In the whale voe, as it is called, the boats are arranged in three lines; if the whales break through one line, they are stopped by the second or third. At this point the fishermen proceed to kill the blackfish with spears. They dry or pickle the meat and convert the stomachs into buoys.

Millais, the famous British naturalist, tells a most amusing story about the ethics among the Scots when a school of blackfish is sighted:

"The minister of Dunrossness was in the middle of his sermon one Sunday afternoon when he noticed that several of the congregation were feeling for their hats. When some of them stole out of the church he understood and closed the service hurriedly with these words: 'I have only one final word to say, my brethren, and that is: Let us all have a fair start—just a fair start.' Then he opened his pulpit door and ran out as fast as his legs could carry him."

A HIGHLY SOCIABLE ANIMAL
This dark fellow is appropriately known as the blackfish, but it is of course a dolphin. The blackfish craves company, and is seen in schools of hundreds of individuals.

OTHER INTERESTING DOLPHINS

The White Dolphin. The dolphins, like the whales, feed on living animal life. There is, however, a unique exception, the White Dolphin, *Sotalia.* One species that frequents the Cameroon River in Africa is a vegetarian. A small amount of vegetable matter has been found in the stomach of other whales but in this species no other food was present.

Folklore relating to this ghostlike whale is prevalent in its tropical homeland, and some legends are surprisingly contradictory. In China the animal is looked upon as a creature of ill omen and even its name is taboo, while to the natives of South America the white dolphin is a sacred animal that will bring ashore a dead or drowning person.

The Spotted Dolphin, *Stenella,* is often seen from coastwise steamers traveling along the Atlantic shores of the United States. Its spots are not discernible except at close range. The animal has been known to keep ahead of steamers traveling at fifteen knots.

Risso's Dolphin. Perhaps the most famous single dolphin in history was the one named Pelorus Jack. This friendly fellow belonged to a group known to science as Risso's Dolphin, *Gramphidelphis*—another warm-sea dolphin, more or less solitary in its habits.

Pelorus Jack was a tradition to all who traveled the Nelson-Wellington passage of New Zealand about half a century ago. No ship entered or left Pelorus Sound without being escorted for about five miles by this famous dolphin, leaping and gamboling about its bows.

Occasionally Pelorus Jack would disappear for a few weeks—even a month or more—but eventually he would reappear in his old haunts. For more than ten years the dolphin enjoyed absolute protection, granted by the New Zealand legislature.

Finally, in April, 1912, Pelorus Jack disappeared for the last time. What his fate was, nobody knows, but his memory still lives on in New Zealand.

The Bottle-nosed Dolphin, *Tursiops,* should not be confused with the bottle-nosed whale, an entirely different animal. This dolphin is the one most frequently seen just beyond the breakwaters by visitors to bathing beaches in temperate and warm climates. It is a sturdy creature, ten or twelve feet in length, and travels in schools sometimes numbering several hundreds. (Incidentally, it is one of the few cetaceans whose heartbeats we have a definite record of: 110 when breathing and fifty in a dive.)

THE DOLPHIN FEEDS ON FISH

Shown taking its food from a diver at the famed Marine Studios Oceanarium at Marineland, Florida, is the bottle-nosed dolphin, a creature common along the Atlantic coast of the United States. Although rather like a fish in appearance, the dolphin is a mammal; it is warm-blooded, bears its young alive, and must regularly rise to the surface of the water to breathe. Dolphins belong to the same order of animal life as the whales and porpoises. They are fast swimmers, traveling at a speed of up to thirty knots. Sometimes schools of several hundred are seen.

The White-beaked and the White-sided Dolphins, *Lagenorhynchus,* are large deep-sea animals. They are perhaps the most gregarious of all the cetaceans, schools of fifteen hundred not being unusual. They are common in the North Atlantic, and feed on fish, squid, and crustaceans; quantities of hermit crabs and the snail known as the common whelk (the kind used for purple dyes) have been found in their stomachs.

The Skunk Dolphin. In the southern seas the Black and White or Skunk Dolphin, *Cephalorhynchus,* is the common species. There are several kinds, recognized by the pattern of black and white markings. Commerson's Dolphin is the best known of this group; it is frequently seen by passengers on ships passing through the Straits of Magellan.

A Water-squirting Dolphin. Either in sport or for a definite purpose the Irrawaddy Dolphin, *Orcella,* squirts water from its mouth in an upward and forward direction; it is definitely water and not moisture-laden breath that is expelled from the lungs.

A slate-blue beakless creature with a curiously rounded bulging forehead, the Irrawaddy Dolphin will measure seven or eight feet. Native fishermen in Burma believe that it intentionally leads or drives schools of fish into their nets.

The Right Whale Dolphin. The superficial resemblance of the Right Whale Dolphin, *Lissodelphis,* to its big cousin the right whale suggested its name. This dolphin is the trimmest of the marine cetaceans. It is streamlined from the short beak to the flukes; even the dorsal fin is absent. The entire animal is velvety black, except for a white "waistcoat." The right whale dolphin is six or eight feet long and cruises only on the high seas.

RIVER DOLPHINS—NOT MANY LEFT

River dolphins are members of a waning group (family Platanistidae) found today only in the fresh or brackish water of southern Asia and tropical South America. They differ from the true dolphins in having each of the bones in the neck separate as in land mammals, instead of all seven being joined together in one piece. These animals possess a very long, narrow beak and jaws studded with numerous teeth.

PROBERS IN THE MUD

Most famous of the group is the Ganges River Dolphin, *Platanista*.
Natives, in naming an animal, often will imitate the sound it makes.
The Indians call this dolphin the Susu, which is a fairly accurate
rendering of the noise it produces when it spouts. Poor susu is almost
blind, and probes for prawns and sluggish fish in the mud at the
bottom of the Ganges and Indus.

A DOLPHIN THAT LIKES THE BOTTOM
Best known of the river dolphins is the dark-skinned Ganges River dolphin. This animal
has a long snout or beak—a common feature of the dolphins—and with it stabs into the
muddy bottom of the Ganges and Indus Rivers, searching for food.

Another curious species, the White-flag Dolphin, *Lipotes*, is also
blind, or nearly so. This animal, blue gray in color, may reach a
length of eight feet. Its dorsal fin, when it appears above water, is
supposed to resemble a flag.

We find this dolphin only in the fresh-water lake Tung Ting in
Hunan Province, China, six hundred miles up the Yangtze. Presumably it was "stranded" in the lake a long time ago, but the natives have their own way of explaining how it got there. They believe that it is a descendant of a princess who perished in the lake
many years ago.

Because of this tradition the Chinese are reluctant to kill the animal. When a dolphin is accidentally killed, they use the blubber as a
treatment, both internally and externally, for colds and other ail-
ments.

STRANGE DOLPHINS OF THE AMAZON AND LA PLATA

None of the fresh-water dolphins grows over nine feet in length, and some are quite a bit shorter, like the La Plata Dolphin, *Stenodelphis*, which does not reach seven feet. This creature travels and breeds in small schools in the estuaries of large rivers along the Atlantic coast of South America. It feeds on the shoals of silvery mullet and the so-called "croaker" fish, which has the ability of making a drumming sound.

The Amazon Fresh-water Dolphin, *Inia*, is often flesh colored, and occupies in the folklore of the Amazon natives much the same place that the Lorelei does in Europe. They will tell you that on occasion this dolphin takes on the shape of an attractive young lady and perambulates the river banks. Meeting with an impressionable young man, she—the lady-dolphin—entices him by the aspect of the long hair hanging loose to her heels. Thus she draws him nearer and nearer the bank, until he is close enough to touch her. Then she disappears with him beneath the waters.

The natives also believe that the Bouto, as this dolphin is called, will attack a man in the water. They dread the creature greatly, and will not dare to spear it. On the other hand, they assert that another Amazon River dolphin (*Sotalia*) will endeavor to protect people. The friendly dolphin, we saw earlier, was a familiar figure in European folklore long ago.

TRUE PORPOISES—FAMED AS LIFESAVERS

The porpoise differs from the dolphin in having a blunt, rounded head and no beak. Otherwise, it is much the same kind of animal. It frequents coastal waters and goes far up large rivers.

Like the stormy petrel, the porpoise has had the reputation of foretelling foul weather. To quote Sir Francis Bacon: "Porpoises, or Sea Hogs, when observed to sport and chase one another about ships, expect then some stormy weather."

How such traditions begin, one can readily guess. Some sailor must have seen porpoises playing as Bacon relates, and then a storm followed. Since one event came before the other, it was mistaken for the cause. As we have seen, the presence of dolphins meant fair weather to old seafaring men.

The porpoise (the name means "sea hog"—from the French *porc-*

poisson) was once considered a great delicacy, and was a dish fit for kings as late as the reign of Henry VIII. As it was considered to be a fish, it could be eaten on fast days and was served with a sauce made from bread crumbs, vinegar, and sugar.

SAVED BY A PORPOISE

As we have already observed, folklore has handed down through the ages many strange and mysterious tales about things that happen at sea. Some of the superstitions, interestingly enough, are based on fact although the interpretations are often misleading. The belief on the part of sailors that porpoises (like dolphins) will befriend a drowning person and attempt to save his life has been reported from many parts of the world. (It is usually the porpoise involved, as dolphins do not come close enough inshore to aid the average bather that gets into trouble.)

The legend does seem to be almost too fantastic to be considered seriously but now we have some tangible evidence from Florida that will speak for itself; it was written by the lady involved. She reports:

"The waves were not over two feet high and I waded out just waist deep before I realized that there was a terrific undertow. Just as I started to turn back the undertow swept my feet from under me and knocked me flat in the water. I swallowed a lot of water and in spite of repeated tries, could not get my footing. I tried to call. . . . and I kept thinking as I gradually lost consciousness, please, God, can't someone push me ashore?

"With that, someone gave me a tremendous shove and I landed on the beach, face down, too exhausted to turn over. . . . It was several minutes before I could do so, and, when I did, no one was near, but, in the water, about eighteen feet out, a porpoise was leaping around and a few feet beyond him 'another' large fish was also leaping.

"When I got enough energy to get back up the steps [on our beach], a man who had been standing on the other side of the fence . . . said that he had seen only the last part. It was the second time, he asserted, that he had seen such a thing happen. . . . I looked like a dead body and the porpoise shoved me ashore. It was his belief that the porpoise was trying to protect me from the 'other' fish which he described as a fishtail shark." (*Natural History,* November. 1949.)

THE HARBOR PORPOISE AND ITS RELATIVES

The Harbor Porpoise, *Phocaena,* is one of the best known of the cetaceans. It measures from four to six feet in length, and possesses a rounded head and a small triangular dorsal fin. Its home is in the coastal waters of the temperate northern seas.

Harbor porpoises are sociable and travel in small schools varying from a few individuals to seventy-five or one hundred. The newborn calf, from thirty to thirty-four inches in length, is nursed by the mother as she swims tilted over on one side. These animals feed on crustaceans and squids as well as on various kinds of fishes, such as whiting and rock cod, that are found in the shore waters of the Atlantic and Pacific.

Dall's Porpoise, *Phocaenoides,* is the black and white porpoise that frequents the inland waters near Kodiak and the Aleutian Islands in the North Pacific. Another species, the Black Finless Porpoise, *Neophocaena,* dwells in the coastal waters of Asia from western India to Borneo and southern Japan. As much at home in fresh water as in salt water, it ascends rivers for a distance of one thousand miles from the coast. Its name describes it well—it is lead black on the back (paler below) and lacks a dorsal fin. The porpoises make up the family Phocaenidae.

Whalebone or Baleen Whales

Although this group is not so impressive as the toothed whales in number of species, in it we do find some of the most remarkable of all whales: the blue whale—the greatest creature that ever lived— and the humpback whale, the weirdest-looking animal of its kind. The females, if not deadlier than the males, are at least larger.

The whalebone whales are the giants of the sea, varying in length from under fifty feet to over one hundred. It seems odd that these leviathans should feed upon tiny organisms, for the most part. The whalebone whales, we saw earlier, have, projecting downward from the upper jaw, instead of teeth, hundreds of whalebone or baleen plates, to which the animals owe their common name (also the scientific name of their suborder, Mysticeti). These plates serve as a food strainer.

As explained at the start of this chapter, the whalebone whale

takes into its mouth water that is alive with minute plants and animals, called plankton, found at the upper levels of the sea. The water
spills out but the catch is kept inside the mouth by the whalebone
filter, through which it cannot escape. A quick upward movement of
the tongue and the water is forced through the strainer. The whale's
dinner, now dry, is flung down its throat and swallowed. Not all the
baleen whales are plankton feeders exclusively. Some of them, like
the least rorqual, also feed on cod, herring, and many other kinds of
fish.

The Biggest Mouth of All. The great yawning mouth of a bowhead
whale could easily accommodate a man standing on its huge tongue.
The monstrous lips are seventeen feet long or more, from the corner
of the mouth to the front of the horrible face. The width of the
mouth, straight across from corner to corner, is nine feet.

The whalebone or baleen of this species may number 360 closely
packed blades on each side of the mouth—the lengthiest, near the
middle of the row, may be twelve feet long and a foot wide, and have
a hairy fringe two feet long. The whalebone itself is imbedded ten
inches in the gum.

Other whales have much shorter baleen and fewer plates than the
bowhead.

We may suppose that in the dim past the whalebone whales actually had teeth. They show traces of teeth when they are in embryo,
but at birth these have disappeared completely.

GRAY WHALES—VANISHING GIANTS OF THE NORTH PACIFIC

The Gray Whale, *Rhachianectes,* a great slate-gray or black animal,
has had some tall tales related about it; one such yarn would have us
believe that a gray whale actually pursued a boat's crew on land and
"treed them all."

The plain fact of the matter is that the gray whale does come close
to terra firma, being a prowler of inshore waters. Its scientific name
means "surf swimmer." The animal has been seen to lie and play
among the breakers in water not more than thirteen feet deep. When
the tide goes out, it may lie and bask in the sun in no more than two
feet of water.

Paralyzed with Fright. Sometimes a pack of killer whales will attack the gray whale. Then it makes for shore, sliding into water too shallow for the killers to approach. At other times, however, it seems to become paralyzed with fright: it turns on its back and floats belly up. This maneuver does not make for a long life.

Big in Size, Few in Numbers. Once the gray whale haunted the inlets and bays of the North American coast and the Sea of Japan in large schools. Today this single member of the family Rhachianectidae has almost vanished from the earth. If found anywhere, it will be in the North Pacific.

The dark body of this whale may grow to a length of fifty feet. Usually it is marked by light circular scars, which we suppose are caused by parasites such as barnacles. The animal has a rather small head for a whale; there is a slight protuberance in place of the dorsal fin, and two or four furrows run lengthwise on the throat. The whalebone with which it traps its food is yellowish, thick, and heavy, measuring fourteen inches or longer. As with other whales, you may tell the gray whale by its spout—it rises vertically to a height of ten or twelve feet in the air.

Late in January, the mother gray whale bears a bouncing baby, a mere sixteen feet long or thereabouts. She nurses the calf for a half-year, sometimes more. By the end of this time it has reached a length of twenty-five feet and is ready to go off mother's milk and on a diet of plankton and small fish. Until the calf can take care of itself, the mother keeps a watchful eye out for it. She will attack a passing boat if her calf has been injured and will overturn the vessel and stave it in with a stroke of her mighty flukes if she can.

RORQUALS, FINBACKS, AND HUMPBACK WHALES
RORQUALS—FASTEST OF THE WHALES

The Common Finback Whale or Rorqual, *Balaenoptera physalus,* is the fastest swimmer of all the whales: it can race along at a speed of thirty miles an hour. A mighty creature that may grow to a length of eighty feet (sixty is more common), it can pull a ship when harpooned. One finback, or finner, as this species is familiarly known, towed a whaling vessel for three hours at a rate of twelve miles an hour. What makes this all the more remarkable is the fact that the ship's engine was running three-fourths speed astern!

Speed and strength are not the only traits for which the finback is outstanding. This whale has pluck. The whaling vessel *Gracia*, in 1894, was attempting to take a finner when the sea giant turned on her and charged. There was a shattering impact; the *Gracia* began to fill with water and went down. The crew escaped in boats.

"Whale with a Wing." The finback is the largest whale commonly seen on the North Atlantic coast of the United States though it frequents all the seas. In general, it is grayish above and white below; it has a long, slender, wedge-shaped body and its head is rather small. Strangely, the right side of the head is always whiter than the left side. On its throat the finback has numerous furrows, running lengthwise. Its family name, Balaenoptera, means "whales with a wing"; like other members of this group (including the humpback and the blue whale) it has a dorsal fin, in this case short and placed far back on the body.

We have observed that the finback is not afraid of ships. Sometimes it will sport about close to them. When it rises to the surface, it sends its spout up fifteen or twenty feet in the air in a narrow column that expands as it rises.

Migrating with the Seasons. The huge finner migrates with the seasons Mating takes place in the warmer seas during the winter. The fin-back then moves north or south to the polar regions for the summer months. Ten or twelve months later, in the fall, it returns to tropical waters. Here the calf is born. Usually there is only one young at birth, but occasionally there are twins. At birth, the calf's baleen is already coming into place and shows clearly in the gums. The calf is about twenty-two feet in length when born; it is not weaned until six months of age or older. Its life expectancy is about twenty years on an average.

It is hard for us to picture for ourselves the bulk and proportions of this gigantic creature. Still, these figures will offer some concrete idea of how large it really is: it weighs as much as 150 oxen—or twenty-five elephants! In a seventy-one-foot finback of 131,000 pounds total weight, the bony skeleton weighed 18,500 pounds; the head and jaws, 6,000 pounds; the whalebone, 1,050 pounds; the tongue, 2,700 pounds; and the heart, 840 pounds. The largest finback on record was eighty-two feet long.

Smaller Rorquals. The common finback whale has some smaller relatives. The Lesser Rorqual, or the Sei Whale, *Balaenoptera borealis,* is found in all seas from the Arctic to the Antarctic. Bryde's whale, a related species, is common along the coast of the Cape Colony, South Africa. Both are quite similar to the finback but rarely exceed fifty-six feet in length. Norwegian fishermen named this rorqual the "sei whale" because it arrived on their fishing grounds at the same time as the sei, or coalfish.

The Least Rorqual, or the Little Pike Whale, *Balaenoptera, acutorostrata,* no more than thirty feet in length, is the smallest of the whales with grooves on the throat. A distinctive white band crosses the upper side of its flippers. It favors coastal and inshore waters, where it is reasonably safe from attack by the killer whale. It was named "little pike" by the Scottish fishermen because of its tall dorsal fin.

HUMPBACK WHALES—THEY LEAP INTO THE AIR

The Humpback Whale, *Megaptera,* is a truly grotesque sea monster. This big black whale has a huge head, disfigured with rows of odd-looking protuberances. Knoblike growths form an edging on its long flippers; the rear border of its flukes is ornately scalloped. Whalers named it "humpback" because it arches its back when rolling over to dive.

Antics of the Humpback Whale. The humpback has a habit of breaching—that is, springing into the air either in play or to rid itself of barnacles. When it strikes the water again, its fifty tons of flesh and bone come down with a mighty splash that you can hear far off. It also indulges in lobtailing: it splashes the water with its powerful flukes again and again. It has two blowholes and sends up two jets of vapor that become one as they rise higher and higher and spread out. The spout is sometimes twenty feet high or more.

This whale has no fixed breeding season. The calf, born close to a year after the mating, is sizable. It measures fifteen feet or more at birth, and weighs up to two tons. The mother's affection for her baby is very strong. She will not leave it even in the face of danger and whalers used to take advantage of this habit by killing the calf first. Fortunately international law now protects baby whales.

In the Northern Hemisphere most of the young are born about

March in the warmer seas, but these whales have moved north by May, probably following warm currents like the Gulf Stream. The humpback visits all the seas while following its regular migration routes. It spends the winter in the tropics. It may travel in schools or alone.

Creatures of Regular Habits. The humpback appears to be a creature of regular habits. Fishermen of the Bay of Fundy, on the Canadian coast, used to tell of one humpback that visited the bay regularly for upwards of twenty summers. They could be sure it was the same whale because it always made a peculiar whistling sound as it spouted.

How could this whale whistle although other humpbacks cannot? It had a large barnacle growing at the edge of its blowhole. The barnacle acted much like a pea in a small boy's whistle, when the whale spouted.

Strange Death of a Humpback. Twenty years is a fair estimate of the humpback's life. But not all humpbacks round out their normal span of years. Besides the whaler's harpoon, the humpback must face the deadly teeth of the assassin of the seas, the killer whale.

Perhaps the most curious case of a humpback's death was mentioned in the *Transactions of the Natural History Society of Northumberland* in 1831. This publication reports a dead humpback that came ashore near Berwick, England, in September, 1829, and states that "on opening the mouth six cormorants were found in it and another in the throat, so that it was presumed this whale had been choked in an attempt to swallow the birds." We may suppose that the cormorants were feeding on fish and the whale engulfed birds and fish together.

No Pygmy, This. Like the finback or rorqual, the humpback has a dorsal fin, but the grooves on its throat are less numerous. From front to back, four hundred plates of whalebone, sometimes two feet long, hang from the roof of its mouth, and its lower jaw juts out far beyond its upper.

The maximum length for this thickset whale is about fifty feet. A forty-five-foot humpback that was captured weighed 91,000 pounds; its heart, 425 pounds; and the whalebone, 425 pounds. It yielded thirty-three barrels of oil. The humpback's whalebone and oil are not of the best grade, however.

BLUE WHALES—BIGGEST ANIMALS THAT EVER LIVED

The Blue Whale, or Sulphur-bottom Whale, *Sibbaldus*, is the largest creature that ever lived on this earth, either on land or in the sea. The biggest blue whale weighed on shipboard registered over three hundred thousand pounds, and was almost ninety feet long. No single ship-borne scales could be used for so vast a bulk; the whale had to be dismembered and placed on the scales piece by piece.

Capturing the Blue Whale. The taking of this huge monster makes a fascinating story that shows us how whalers work. The whale was caught in January, 1948, by a Japanese whaling expedition in the Balleny Islands in the Antarctic.

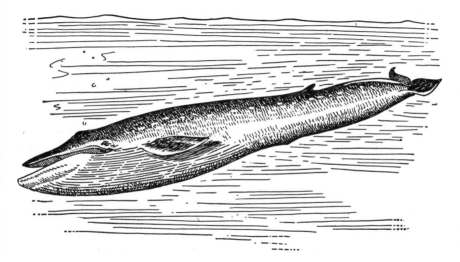

KING OF THE DEEP

The blue whale is not only the largest of the whales today—no animal ever lived that approached it in size. At home in both the Atlantic and the Pacific, the blue whale is faster and stronger than any of its relatives.

But for the fact that it sailed under the authorization of General Douglas MacArthur (Japan was still occupied by the Allied Powers) this expedition was a typical one. In it, carrying thirteen hundred Japanese, were twelve ships: six catcher boats, a ten-thousand-ton factory ship—the *Hashidate Maru*—two processing ships for salting and refrigerating the catch, an oil tanker, and two vessels for cold storage. They traveled six thousand miles from Japan to the whaling grounds. Here the ships had to sail far apart to avoid collisions with each other and with icebergs. In modern style, they carried radar, a great help in the dense fogs that prevail in that part of the world.

When the great blue whale was sighted, a catcher boat gave chase and harpooned it. The gunner found it hard to fire the last and fatal harpoon because whenever the catcher boat had the animal in range it dived under the water. The contest between boat and whale lasted two hours before the gunner could reel the whale in and give it the finishing blow. Then the catcher boat towed the monster tail-first to the factory ship.

Dismembering the Great Blue Whale. At the stern, the *Hashidate Maru* had an opening close to the water, leading to a skidway or incline. The whale was hauled up this skidway and deposited on the flensing deck. Eighty men labored close to four hours taking off the skin and blubber, cutting the whale apart systematically, and weighing the pieces. The tongue alone tipped the scales at three tons.

"Workmen laughed and leaped aboard loins that were skidding toward the loading chute," relates Lieutenant Colonel Waldon C. Winston, the American observer who accompanied the fleet. (He records its achievement in the November, 1950, issue of *Natural History,* published by the American Museum of Natural History, New York.) "Others there started a chanty. Over and over, they filled the box on the small platform scales, then emptied the contents down the loading chute."

Below decks was the processing section. Here the factory ship had special boilers; in these oil was processed from blubber, bones, and meat. There were also tanks in which to store the oil. There was even equipment that drew vitamin oil from the whale's liver.

From this blue giant the Japanese drew 133 barrels of whale oil, over sixty metric tons of red meat. The products, all together, were valued at $28,000, Mr. Winston declares.

Most Powerful Animal on Earth. The blue whale is not just the biggest—it is also the most powerful animal in existence. Its top speed compares favorably with that of our most up-to-date freighters. Although it normally cruises along at twelve knots, it can race along at twenty-seven knots. It is reported that one harpooned blue whale towed a whaling vessel—engines going full speed astern—at a rate of eight knots for a period of seven hours. Experts have estimated its greatest pull at four hundred horsepower.

A Ton of Food. For all this display of speed and power, the blue whale, like most other large whalebone whales, feeds on small fare— but lots of it. More than a ton of plankton has been found in the stomach of a single blue whale. When it comes up from hunting in the water, the animal breathes out a tall, thick column of vapor, perhaps twenty feet high.

Where plankton is, there you may look for the blue whale. The periodic abundance of these small creatures governs its activities. The blue whale spends the summer near the polar ice pack of either the Arctic or the Antarctic. Like the finback whale, it prefers the southern to the northern seas. In winter it is likely to move toward the Equator.

A Twenty-Five-Foot Baby. Mating takes place in temperate waters, about July. Weighing four short tons and measuring about twenty-five feet long at birth, the calf is nursed by its mother for fully seven months, depending upon her for food until it has attained a length of about fifty feet. It is ready to reproduce at three years of age, but may not be full grown for another ten years.

No one knows for sure how long a blue whale lives—certainly not more than fifty-four years or so, and probably much less. With the whalers in the picture, twenty years might be a good average.

Less social than the finback, the blue whale travels alone or with another of its kind. It appears to be monogamous, but the case would be difficult to prove. The female is larger, and may grow to a length of one hundred feet or more.

Although we also call the blue whale the "sulphur-bottom whale," the sulphur color on its underside is not a part of the animal. The color is due to a coating of diatoms—microscopic plants picked up on the ocean surface. Superficially the blue whale looks rather like the finback. Its general color, above, is bluish, as its common name suggests.

RIGHT WHALES AND BOWHEADS

The Right Whale, *Eubalaena,* was to the whalers of long ago exactly the right or ideal prey for them, and that is how it got its name, we are told. It possesses an excellent supply of oil—anywhere from forty to one hundred barrels. It is rich in whalebone—it has about 250 plates on each side of its mouth, the longest about seven feet. Best of all, from the whalers' viewpoint, the animal is a slow swimmer and often does not put up too rough a fight.

Thus, although this whale was once the commonest of all in the seas of the earth, it is now a rarity. Whalers still would like to haul the right whale up their skidways, but they must pay the penalty for the large-scale looting of the seas by those who went before them. Whaling, we know, was a major enterprise over two hundred years ago, and the plunder taken in oil and whalebone even then was gigantic.

——How the Indians Hunted Whales. There is good reason for thinking that the American Indians used to attack whales of this species, harpooning them with lances made of bone. Accounts of how the Indians captured a whale have been given in some of the old works on natural history.

These books tell us that the Indian, in his canoe, approached the sleeping whale and drove a wooden stake into each of its nostrils. After this he stood astride his quarry till its struggles ceased and then towed it ashore. An engraving illustrating this strange story was published in a book by Theodore de Brie in 1590, and here the right whale appears to be represented. A fairly similar technique is used by the Polynesians in killing the dugong.

The right whale has an extremely large head and a smooth, un-furrowed throat; the dorsal fin is lacking. (With the pygmy right whales and the bowhead, this animal forms the family Balaenidae, all being smooth-throated or finless whales.) Its chunky body is al-most entirely velvety black and rarely exceeds fifty feet in length. Near the end of its muzzle it has a horny growth or "bonnet"; this is usually infested with whale lice—actually small shellfish.

The right whale mates in July or some time during the summer in the Arctic seas, and the young are born in January or February further south. Like other whales, the female bears a single calf which she nurses for a half-year or longer. She displays considerable affection for her baby.

——Devotion of a Whale Mother. This trait is well illustrated by an incident that took place off Cape Cod in 1888. A calf was har-pooned and the cow, refusing to leave her offspring, circled round and round. Only death could make her give up—she finally suc-cumbed to bomb-lances shot at her.

A similar case is reported to have occurred off the Spanish coast in 1854. On this occasion the calf was harpooned and towed into a bay. Its mother followed. In her distress, she attempted to rescue her offspring by clasping it with her flippers and hugging it, in an effort to drag it away. Eventually, with a blow of her flukes, she broke the tow lines and succeeded in carrying her calf off. Next day it was picked up by a passing vessel and brought back to the harbor, still followed by the mother.

——THREE KINDS OF RIGHT WHALES. The right whale's spout is double, and the animal directs it forward and upward about fifteen feet in the air. There are three species of right whales, all similar in general external appearance: the North Atlantic Right Whale, the North Pacific Right Whale, and the Antarctic Right Whale.

The Pygmy Right Whale, *Neobalaena,* is smaller than the right whale proper, being only about twenty feet long. A very rare mammal, it is found solely in Australian and New Zealand waters and off South America; we know little of its habits. It has fourteen pairs of ribs instead of the usual seventeen and, unlike other right whales, possesses a dorsal fin. Some pygmies have been stranded on the eastern shores of the Great Australian Bight, usually during a time of high spring gales.

BIGGEST MOUTH ON EARTH

The bowhead, or Greenland whale, has a gigantic head, and its mouth is the largest of any animal. Lengthy, finely fringed whalebone lines the sides of its upper jaw; this great whale feeds only on the smallest of sea creatures.

The Bowhead Whale—Its Mouth Could Hold an Ox. Another member of this family is the Bowhead, or Greenland Whale, *Balaena,* a smooth-throated species, from fifty to sixty feet long, found in the Arctic, the North Atlantic, and the North Pacific. Its enormous head is more than one-third the animal's total length. The mouth could easily hold an ox—but the throat is not big enough to swallow anything larger than small fish like the herring!

The bowhead is almost extinct, so extensively has it been hunted for the 1,700 pounds of whalebone and ninety barrels of high-grade oil the average individual may yield. The fact that it cannot swim over eight miles an hour has not favored its survival.

The Wild Dogs—Wolves, Coyotes, Jackals, and Foxes

RUNNERS—that is the word for the wild dogs and their relatives. In past ages, however, they were not the speedy creatures we are familiar with; they once walked flat-footed upon the earth. But a swift animal is likely to be a longer-lived one. In time a change took place in the dog family: they came to walk about and run about on their toes. Nature favored them, and they replaced their slower ancestors.

Although the wild dogs, as we may call this group, can swim, and some are actually able to climb trees, they are built for a life on the ground. By and large, they have a long, narrow muzzle, large, erect ears, slender limbs, and a lengthy, bushy tail. When overheated, the dogs sweat through the pores or glands on the tongue. On warm days and after exercising, a member of the dog family will open its mouth, and the perspiration will drip from its tongue.

The wild dogs have good eyesight and a keen sense of hearing—

much better than man's. But they are even more remarkable for their exceptionally well-developed sense of smell. They can follow a trail through the forest on a dark night as easily as a man can follow a well-posted highway in broad daylight.

The domestic dog was tamed by man before the dawn of history. Many believe it was the first animal brought under human domination, and we possess evidence that the man of the New Stone Age had his own dog in 6,000 B.C.

In a general way, the dog was derived from the wolf stock of Europe and Asia (though not from the true wolf). By selective breeding, man has produced different types to serve him in diverse ways: as sheep and herd dogs, racing dogs and watch dogs, sled dogs and hunting dogs, to name only a few. Today there are some 145 popular breeds of dogs—more than we have of any other domestic animal, and in North America alone there are about twenty million domestic dogs.

Dogs will interbreed readily with wolves and jackals, but they do not breed with foxes, from which they differ significantly. Dogs, too, bear more young on an average than any of their kind. It is not unusual for a domestic dog to have sixteen puppies; the record birth, that of a fox terrier, was a litter of twenty-three young. The highest number of cubs in the wild is fourteen (for the wolf), but the average is six or seven.

THE GREAT ORDER OF CARNIVORES

The wild dogs form only one family (Canidae) of the great order of the Carnivora, or flesh-eating mammals, to which the following chapters are devoted. We find the carnivores in all kinds of places except the high seas. The wolf patrols the plains and prairies, and the cat keeps watch in the forests. The otter and the mink police the freshwater rivers. The badger goes underground, while the marten climbs trees. The raccoon haunts the swamps and marshes, the polar bear plies the Arctic coastal waters, and in the tall grass and brushlands the weasel is forever alert.

Not all carnivorous animals are carnivores. Some of the marsupials such as the Tasmanian wolf feed on flesh; opossums, hedgehogs, certain bats, and even some rodents do the same; on the high seas the killer whale also takes a large toll of warm-blooded animal life. All of these mammals belong in different orders.

On the other hand, not all members of the order Carnivora are strictly carnivorous. Many of them, such as the bears, feed to a large extent on fruits, berries, and even grass; some are exclusively insect-eaters, while others, like the giant panda, feed on nothing but vegetation.

WHAT IS A CARNIVORE?

Now, what, you may ask, makes an animal a carnivore? The answer is: structure, not habit. The Carnivora have sharp teeth and powerful jaws. The canine teeth are especially long and dagger-like, to hold the prey, and most carnivores have sharp shearing teeth, known as carnassial teeth, for cutting flesh and sinews. Nor is this all; in many

FAMILIAR TRACKS CAN RESEMBLE THOSE IN THE WILDS
At the left are the tracks of a house cat, next to them are the tracks of a lynx—with the same form, but more than twice as large. At the far right are the tracks of a dog; next to them are the footprints of a wolf. Both are exactly the same except for size; the wolf's tracks are larger than those of the average dog. The claws of the dog and the wolf are always unsheathed, and so you can see the marks they make.

carnivores the grinding teeth, or molars, are strong and thick—natural bone-grinders.

You see, then, that these animals are well equipped with the tools for capturing and devouring other animals, whether they use these tools or not. The carnivores have sharp claws, too, and at least four toes on each foot. In the cats, the claws may be drawn in or thrust out at will; the dogs' claws are always extended.

Most carnivores do feed on flesh, and it is for this habit that they were named. Although they prey on other creatures, they should not be looked upon as wicked, or a menace. Man is himself a meat-eater, like the lion and the tiger, though, like the bear, he varies his diet with vegetables.

The carnivores, as a rule, will not attack or bother a human being unless they have been sorely provoked. Moreover, they have their uses. Without the carnivores, wave after wave of rodents would swarm over the earth, spread disease, and pollute and devour all manner of edible food. Nor need we fear any excess of carnivores. They do at times increase their numbers, as their food becomes more plentiful, but the balance of nature is soon restored when other beasts of prey as well as plagues take their toll of the carnivore ranks.

WOLVES—NOT SO FIERCE AS REPUTED

The Gray Wolf, or Timber Wolf, *Canis lupus,* has never, to the best of our knowledge, made an unprovoked attack on man in North America. It has been the author's experience to sleep out alone of a winter's night in northern Alberta, without a fire, alongside a fresh kill. The wolves closed in when it got dark. Some stood and watched him from less than ten feet away. But not one made an unfriendly gesture, nor did they attempt to steal the kill.

Yet you will hear stories of American wolves attacking men without provocation. In number, such reports are few, and we have not had reliable proof of a single one of them.

On the other hand, there are so many stories of wolves falling upon and killing people in the Old World, especially in Russia, that we cannot discount such tales altogether. We may suppose that these wolves were on the verge of starvation and were attracted by the horse the man was riding or driving. It is quite possible, too, that the wolves of Europe have lost some of their fear and respect for man by interbreeding with domestic dogs. But, in general, wolves seem to know that human beings are their deadliest and most implacable foes.

WOLVES YESTERDAY AND TODAY

A long time ago the gray wolf was much commoner than it is today. It ranged over the entire Northern Hemisphere, from the plateau of middle Mexico to the Arctic regions, excluding the extreme desert areas. In Asia, we believe it prowled as far south as the northern regions of the Indian peninsula. But now we find the gray wolf only in the unsettled parts of its former range.

Throughout the ages human beings have waged unceasing war on the gray wolf. As civilized man has spread over the world, bringing his domestic stock with him, he has driven the wolf off. So it has retreated into the barren wilderness, far from human habitation. In a few states of the American West, in the wilderness of Alaska, Canada, and Mexico, it still survives. A hunted animal with a price on its head, it is well on the way to extinction.

The gray wolf disappeared from England and most of Europe hundreds of years ago. It seems hard to believe that once it wandered over those lands in sizable numbers. Wolves were so common and dangerous in England at about the time of Alfred the Great that the month of January was set apart for hunting them. It was called *Wolfmonat,* or Wolf Month. An interesting sign of the status of the wolf then is the fact that an outlaw of the period was known as a "wolf-head," a man with a price set on his head. We are told that wolves were exterminated in England in 1509 but they lingered on in the mountains of Scotland until the middle of the seventeenth century, and in Ireland until the beginning of the eighteenth century.

SMART AS WELL AS STRONG

It is easy to understand why people have feared wolves since first they encountered them. For man or beast, the wolf is not an opponent to be underestimated. It shows a high degree of intelligence —in this respect it compares favorably with the elephant, horse, or gorilla. The gray wolf is a mighty fellow, big and strong. Some Canadian wolves weigh up to 175 pounds; the largest one on record (shot in the foothills of Mount McKinley, Alaska, in the fall of 1950) weighed 197 pounds. A large gray wolf will measure four feet long without its twenty-inch tail. It stands three feet at the shoulder.

Although we call the common wolf the "gray wolf," that is not al- ways its color. Its long, thick coat—it is much like that of the Ger- man shepherd dog—varies in shade from almost black to white. Some wolves may be brindled brown or yellow. In the northern country the light shades are predominant, in keeping with the long, white winters.

The wolf has comparatively short ears. This is advantageous in a cold climate, for it helps to prevent frostbite at subzero tempera- tures. Its long, bushy tail serves a special and useful purpose. When the wolf sleeps out, it curls up and wraps the tail snugly around its naked nose and its feet, protecting them from the frost.

WOLVES AND THEIR YOUNG

From our viewpoint, the wolves offer a model picture of family life. They mate in the early spring. Usually the male will stay with one mate for life, unless he is forcibly separated from her. He helps her dig the underground den and the tunnel which leads to it—this last may be thirty feet long. (Sometimes the pair will use a rocky cave or the abandoned burrow of another animal.) For their home they gen- erally select the more remote parts of the wilderness, near a hilltop with an unobstructed view of the surrounding country.

Two months or so after the mating, the babies come into the world. Six is about the average number of whelps, but from four to fourteen cubs may be produced in a single litter. Most pups are born in May, or a month before or after. The newborn pup has a sooty- brown or light gray-blue coat of close hair. The animal cannot see at birth; its slanting, deep-blue eyes open between the fifth and ninth day afterward. Two months later the eyes take on a yellow-gray color, which is typical of the adult.

At the beginning, the babies' sole food is the milk provided by their mother. But in a few weeks she starts to wean them. Now she regurgitates for them meat which she has partly digested in her stomach. The whelps move more and more from a milk diet to one of flesh. In the early nursing stage the mother does not leave her babies at all, relying for her own food upon her mate or a close relative who brings meat to her den.

It is common practice for the male to hunt in faraway fields and bring back the kill in his stomach, to be disgorged and fed to the whelps. When not hunting, he dozes on a hilltop close by the den and keeps watch. If he detects any threat of danger, he first warns the family, then slowly retreats, drawing the enemy away from the den as best he can, yelping if necessary to attract attention to himself. If some misfortune ends the life of the mother, her mate will take over, feeding the pups on disgorged food and looking out for them.

In their early weeks the pups appear to be all head and legs. But they grow rapidly. After three weeks the parents remove them from the den to live aboveground. From this time on they accompany the parents in their daily activities and thus learn to hunt and to take care of themselves. Family ties are strong, and there is considerable display of affection until the whelps are fully grown. When one member of a family is caught in a trap, the others will make every effort to release it.

The young wolf is well grown when a year and one-half old. It is interesting to note that females mature faster than males. Males are not fully adult until they are three years old, but females are ready to breed at two. A wolf is approaching old age at ten or twelve years. At fourteen its teeth are worn down; then it is known as a "gummer" to the trappers. Twenty years is about as long as a wolf lives in the wild.

THE WOLF AS A HUNTER

Many fanciful things have been said and written about the feeding habits of the gray wolf. You may have heard that a hungry wolf will fill its belly with mud; that wolves are fattest at the time of the full moon and grow thinner with the waning moon; that they sustain life by sucking their forepaws; and that they drink only the blood of their victims. None of these things is true. Still, the reality of how a wolf gets its food is very impressive.

Usually, the gray wolf hunts in packs. Such a pack is not the great, fierce crowd of a hundred or more sharp-fanged beasts you may have read about in fiction. The wolf pack generally has in it no more than a dozen animals, all members of one family. Besides the parent wolves and their young, there may be several adult relatives.

Often these animals have a favorite hunting runway, perhaps a hundred miles long, and they seek their prey along its byways with marked regularity, killing deer, mountain sheep, caribou, and moose. They have been known to pursue herds of bison and to slaughter sick and aged adults, as well as tender calves, when they lagged behind. They will chase healthy animals as well, keeping up a pace of twenty miles an hour for a long time. It is reported that four hundred thousand caribou have been destroyed by wolves in a single year in the Canadian Barren Grounds. The number of wolves in this remote region has been estimated at close to thirty-five thousand.

ONE OF MAN'S OLDEST ENEMIES

The gray or timber wolf has a forbidding reputation—all of man's history is studded with accounts of its ferocity. Yet there is no verified report of a wolf's ever having made an unprovoked attack on man, anywhere in North America. In their family life, the wolves are far from savage. Wherever possible, both male and female remain together for life, and the father will give his cubs the same loving care as the mother.

In settled districts a gray wolf will prey on domestic stock: sheep, cattle, and horses. Smaller game, such as rabbits and rodents, and even carrion, finds its place in the wolf's varied diet. In fact, a wolf will eat almost anything edible, including berries and ripe watermelon. It frequently happens that wolves have only a single meal a week, but it must be a substantial one to keep their big bodies going. They can eat one-fifth their own weight at a time. Occasionally they bury left-over meat.

CALL OF THE WOLF

The first cry of the wolf in the evening—the evensong, or assembly call—cannot be compared with that of any other living creature; it is a long-drawn-out, deep, tremulous sound that will never be forgotten by anyone who has ever heard it. Stimulating every nerve in the listener's body, the call sends a shivering sensation down his back like a breath of chilly air. Horses have been seen to quiver and twitch at the howl of a wolf.

The wolf's cry is not limited to this sound only. The animal has six different calls, each with a special meaning. The high but soft and plaintive call that breaks the stillness of the night in the solitary northern forests seems to offer solicitude. The lusty, throaty howl that speaks of loneliness is the mating call, while the loud, deep guttural roar is the call of the chase. The howl of a wolf is ventriloqual and will confuse the hearer as to the number in the pack and the direction of the call.

CROSSBREEDING DOGS WITH WOLVES

The Eskimos sometimes cross their sled dogs with wolves to improve the strain. They may tether the female dogs in the open in wolf-infested regions. They have even used purebred wolves as sled dogs. One hunter has told of trapping a wolf, hitching it to a sled, and having it pull a load back to camp, although the animal had no prior training whatever.

Wolves raised in captivity grow up remarkably tame. On occasion, when some have been released, they seemed quite at a loss. For their own protection they had to be taken back into human custody.

THE WEREWOLF

Many children today have never seen a wolf but they still dread the animal, thanks to the story of Little Red Riding Hood. This tale offers only the smallest reminder of how sinisterly the wolf has loomed in man's consciousness. Long after the animal has disappeared from our earth, we shall still remember it; our folklore and literature have immortalized the wolf.

In many lands there have been legends of people who could transform themselves into wolves to satisfy an intense craving for human flesh—or else they were forced to assume this shape through malign magic. The ancient Greeks gave us a word for these people: "lycanthropes." The Anglo-Saxons called them "werewolves" (man-wolves).

Such legends may seem merely entertaining to us today, since most of us hardly know what a wolf looks like, but in other times, particularly during the sixteenth century in France, they were regarded as a fact. People were tried on charges of lycanthropy—of turning into wolves and devouring their neighbors. They were found guilty and executed. Fantastically enough, some readily confessed their "guilt." With our present knowledge of the human mind, we can see that these persons were mentally ill, the victims of delusions. Nowadays the term "lycanthropy" is used in psychiatry to describe the condition of insanity in which a person imagines he is a wolf.

Still, in far-off places, belief in werewolves lingers on. Generally, these are regions where wolves still exist. In the Orient, where the tiger and the leopard are better known, similar stories are told about these animals. In South America, the natives tell of men who turn into jaguars and prey upon other men. These beliefs need not surprise us. Animals are often remarkably "human" in the way they look or behave.

HUMAN CHILDREN REARED BY WOLVES

To balance tales of the wolf's ferocity and the werewolf, we sometimes encounter others that tell of good, humane wolves. Commonest, perhaps, are the recurring reports, from distant places, about wolves that have cared for human children. The most famous story of this kind concerns the wolf that suckled Romulus and Remus. In relatively recent times a number of accounts have come to us from Asia about the Indian Wolf, *Canis pallipes*, which is somewhat smaller than the gray wolf and dwells south of the Himalayas. W. H. Sleeman, a British Army colonel in India, reported a century ago five instances of children allegedly reared by wolves. Here is one of the most curious of them.

It seems that wolves were once very numerous about Cawnpore and Lucknow and that children were constantly being carried off by them. On one occasion, two horsemen in the service of the local king were riding along the banks of the Goomptje when they saw three animals come down to drink. Two were young wolves but the third was evidently some other animal. The horsemen captured all three, and to their great surprise found that one was a small naked boy. He moved about on all fours like his companions and bit and scratched violently in resisting capture.

The boy was brought up in Lucknow, where he lived for some time. He was quite unable to articulate words but was said to have a doglike intellect, being quick at understanding signs. It is believed that he ended in the insane asylum at Lucknow. The unfortunate aspect of most reports like this one is that the events they relate occurred long ago, and the information we have is second- or third-hand at best.

One such account is more up to date. In 1920, an Anglican minister, the Reverend J. A. L. Singh, told of rescuing two girl "wolf-children" from a den in India. According to him, there had been three wolves in the den with the children. Dr. Singh kept the girls in an orphanage.

This story received wide acceptance in the press of the western world. Unfortunately, when investigators tried to verify the details on the spot, the children had died—and so had Dr. Singh. All that remained was his diary and some vague photographs.

We are left, thus, with tantalizing possibilities but few facts to base a final conclusion on. Were these children really raised by wolves? Were they children who merely happened to be found near wolves and so were supposed to have been raised by them?

In India, a number of small children are carried off by wolves each year. The likelihood is that the children do not survive for very long. Still, it is not totally inconceivable that a female nursing pups would befriend a helpless child. Cats that have lost their kittens have gone out and found and raised baby rabbits, and a wolf might do the like. If only once in a thousand times, the circumstances might be favorable—the right wolf might meet the right child, one that happened to show no fear.

But, to prove any actual case, the facts are wanting. Besides "wolf-children," there have been reports of "baboon-children" and at least one "gazelle-child." When experts studied these children, the odd sounds and movements they made tended to prove that they were feebleminded rather than the products of animal upbringing. Nor was there unassailable evidence that the children's association with the animals was real rather than supposed. Someday an actual instance of a child that has been reared by a wild beast may present itself, but until that time we must regard accounts like that of Romulus and Remus and Dr. Singh's "wolf-children" as more provocative than factual.

There are a large number of gray or timber wolves, but all are geographical variations of the typical species, *Canis lupus*. Smaller than the gray wolf and more like a coyote is the Red Wolf, *Canis niger*. Once found in the Mississippi valley, the Gulf states, and Georgia, it is restricted nowadays to the Ozark Mountains and a few localities in Louisiana and Texas. It has a coat of rather coarse hair colored in shades of tawny mixed with gray.

COYOTES—WILD SINGERS

The Coyote, Prairie Wolf, or Brush Wolf, *Canis latrans* ("barking dog"), sings the evening song of the American West. After sundown, it leaves its lair and finds a nearby knoll. Here it sits down, alone or in company, to give voice to its serenade. One lone animal will sound like a whole pack as it runs through its entire gamut of cries: from short yaps, barks, and whines, to a prolonged lamenting howl that carries for a remarkable distance on the still night air. This evening performance is a regular ritual with the coyote.

The coyote is widely hunted, not because of its singing but because many sheepherders consider it a wholesale destroyer of their stock. But this is a case of "give a coyote a bad name and hang him." Wildlife experts have shown that the coyote kills only a fraction of the number of domestic animals it is thought to. It does more good as a destroyer of rodents than harm as a killer of livestock. Sheep, after all, need grass, and rodents consume it; the coyote, which can travel at a speed of forty-five miles an hour, is the only mammal fast enough to catch a jack rabbit, and the slower rodents easily fall prey to it.

Aside from rabbits and rodents, the coyote devours birds, reptiles, carrion, and insects. It stores food like other dogs. The coyote even goes fishing! Another surprising thing about its diet—it will feed on fruit and vegetables.

With a companion—the animal often hunts in pairs—the coyote may attack deer and elk and bring them down; but sometimes luck and the quarry's sharp hoofs and antlers bring defeat and death to the coyote. And it must look out for its big cousin, the wolf. The wolf is fond of the coyote—but only as food.

Coyotes never harm people. In the United States National Parks these animals are often quite tame, and will take food from your hand.

HOW THE COYOTES RAISE THEIR FAMILY

Like the wolves, coyotes usually mate for life—but should misfortune overtake one, the other will usually mate again. Breeding time is in February, as a rule, but earlier in the warm regions.

Shortly before the day comes for the female to have her pups—about two months after mating—she selects a den for the nursery with the aid of her mate. It may be in a cave, a natural shelter among the rocks, a hollow tree or a burrow dug in the ground. The nursery is quite bare, without any leaves or grass for a bed. If the pair make a burrow, they usually dig branching tunnels that may extend twenty-five or thirty feet underground to the chamber, and dig a ventilator through the roof. The two coyotes now take up residence inside the chamber.

A few days before the family arrives, the male coyote must leave the den and find himself a home close by. His mate stays behind and bears her litter, six babies as a rule but sometimes as many as nineteen.

While the babies are small the mother has no time to get about. The male is responsible for keeping his family supplied with food. He does not enter the den, but brings his daily offering of rabbits, rats, and mice and lays them at the entrance. Sometimes he disgorges partly digested food, and sometimes the mother does so as the infants are weaned and prepared for the hearty meals of meat they will consume later on. As the pups grow older, it takes all the time of both parents to keep them in food.

When six weeks old, the pups begin to romp and play outside but are not ready to join the chase until two months old. At about this time the father is permitted free use of the den and with the mother begins the serious duty of teaching the pups to hunt. The parents take their young on longer and longer trips away from the nursery and show them tried and true coyote ways of capturing their own mice, gophers, ground squirrels, and other prey.

By the fall of the year, the young coyotes are ready to leave the comfort of their parents' home to seek their own fortune in distant lands. Sometimes they must travel a hundred miles or more to find an untenanted range of their own. Inexperienced as they are, the adolescent pups fall an easy prey to their enemies. Many die of hunger and exhaustion before they can get located in new territory. Thirteen years is a long life for a coyote.

Coyotes sometimes mate with domestic dogs. The hybrid offspring of such a match lack the even disposition of the domestic dog and are not so easy to train.

Normally a creature of the open plains, prairies, and desert regions, the coyote has occasionally entered the forests. We find it in western and central North America, from Costa Rica north to Alaska and from the Pacific coast east to Ohio and Michigan.

Scarcely half the size of the gray wolf, this wild dog is an attractive slender animal, with thick, long fur, erect ears, and a lengthy, bushy tail tipped with black. Its coat is grayish or tawny in color, nearly white on the under parts. A full-grown coyote stands twenty-one inches at the shoulders and weighs between twenty and thirty pounds (not so much, compared to the male wolf's sixty to one hundred pounds). It is about four feet long; one-third of this is tail.

DINGOS—AUSTRALIA'S WILD DOGS

The Dingo, or Warrigal, *Canis dingo,* presents a fascinating puzzle to us. This wolflike dog is the only wild carnivore living today in Australia. We do not find it elsewhere in the world.

Why should the dingo be Australia's only carnivore? We do not know; we can only guess. Once, long ages ago, Australia was connected with other continents. As we have seen, at that time a more primitive form of mammal life, the marsupial (of which the kangaroo is a well-known species) flourished in many parts of the earth.

Geological changes took place. Australia became separated from the other great land masses, and the marsupials survived only inside her water-guarded borders, with minor exceptions. In other places they gave way before more advanced kinds of mammals, among them the carnivores. The kangaroo and its kind continued to reign supreme in Australia. It was impossible for carnivores to come in.

How, then, did the dingo travel across the ocean to Australia? We suppose it came there in boats with the first men, perhaps from the Malayan region. It must have been very long ago, probably during the Ice Age or Pleistocene era, at least forty thousand years back; we find the dingo's fossil remains with relics of that period, but not with older ones. We believe it was a tame dog in those days, and that after a while it ran wild. The dingo even in the most remote places in Australia has still a curious hankering after man and his fleshpots—and this despite the fact that it has been outlawed as a ferocious killer of sheep, and is always killed on sight for the price set on its scalp.

The dingo prowls the open plains of Australia as well as the open forests. A handsome, medium-sized wolf, it stands two feet at the shoulder. It is four feet long; about one-quarter of this is bushy tail like the wolf's. A dingo's soft fur is usually rusty red or tawny with the toes and the tip of the tail white, but the coats of some dingos vary from red to black.

The dingo's habits are much the same as the coyote's. It hunts singly or in family parties and preys upon kangaroos and other game, which cannot long withstand its wolflike fangs. The pups—there may be four to eight of them—are born in an underground burrow, a cave in the rocks, or a hollow tree. A purebred dingo does not bark like a dog but utters a series of yelps and a plaintive howl.

Australia has become the greatest sheep-raising country in the world. Since a large percentage of the game has been eliminated, and sheep are easy prey, the dingo has naturally turned to them for food. As a result, it is an object of national hatred. Yet, though to say anything in favor of the hated wild dog is tantamount to treason in Australia, a dingo wild pup—reared as a dog—is in fact a gentle, affectionate, and faithful creature. Despite public opinion, this, too, is certain: The dingo is the only local animal capable of dealing hard-hitting blows against the great plagues of rabbits that perpetually nibble the plains of Australia bare.

JACKALS—SCAVENGERS OF THE OLD WORLD TROPICS

The Jackal, *Thos* (*Canis*), suffers from a sorry reputation that it does not altogether deserve. Most of us think of the jackal solely as a skulker and a scavenger—how much of this picture is really true to life?

The jackal is the common wild dog of the warmer parts of the Old World. In the villages and towns of Asia and Africa we sometimes see small bands of jackals or single individuals skulking at night through the streets of outlying districts and scavenging among garbage heaps in search of food.

In the wilder parts of its range the jackal is always on hand to partake of the larger game killed by a lion or tiger. On several occasions the author has seen a lion with its kill and, a few feet away, a jackal waiting patiently, and a dozen or more vultures sitting in a nearby tree. Neither the vultures nor the jackal would go closer until the lion had had its fill and left. Then there was a free-for-all and the jackal moved in to get its share with the vultures.

THE "LION'S PROVIDER"

In Africa the jackal is sometimes known as the "lion's provider." Folklore has it that the jackal acts as a scout for these large cats, and, having found suitable prey, summons the hungry lion to the kill; for its services the jackal receives a share of the prey. As a result of these old traditions, we sometimes apply the word "jackal" to a human being if we want to say that he engages in low or sordid work for someone else's benefit.

Yet the jackal hardly merits our scorn for any of this. Quite the contrary; the animal serves a very useful purpose. As a scavenger, the jackal removes carrion, which might otherwise provide a breeding place for the germs of disease. It is a first-rate mouser and ratter —qualities that make it a boon in the rodent-infested areas of the Old World. (True, it has an unfortunate penchant for varying its diet with domestic fowl and an occasional lamb or kid, and this habit has not served to endear it to mankind.) It also eats other small mammals, lizards, and insects—even grapes, sugar cane, and coffee berries. In fact, it feeds on almost anything edible.

THE STEALTHY JACKAL

Rarely does the jackal make its home in deep forests; it prefers open or lightly wooded country. Its habits are stealthy and secretive, and we seldom see the animal, although it is by no means strictly a night prowler. Near more populated areas, it does not venture abroad much before dark. The jackal spends the nights hunting, usually in family groups or packs of three to six individuals. No mean runner, it is credited with a speed of thirty-five miles an hour.

Like the coyote, the jackal sings an evening song. At sundown it leaves its retreat, proceeds to the center of a small clearing or to a little knoll, sits up on its haunches, and howls.

THE JACKAL IS A USEFUL ANIMAL

Often belittled as a coward and scavenger, the jackal actually performs a great service to man. As an eater of carrion, it helps to eliminate breeding places of germs and disease. As an expert ratter and mouser, it is of great value in the rodent-overrun areas of the Old World. However, the beast also kills smaller domestic animals and poultry.

Those who have heard the jackal's cry do not soon forget it. A long wail, it is repeated three or four times in succession, each repetition being pitched slightly higher than the preceding one; the wail ends in a series of short yelps. The people of India interpret

dekens

A BERRY-LADEN HILLSIDE OFFERS GOOD FORAGE FOR BEARS

This cinnamon bear feeding on a hillside with three cubs is a female — the male's interest in family life does not extend beyond mating time. The baby bears are born while the mother is in her lonely winter den, and generally remain with her until the following fall or longer.

this cry into the words: "Dead Hindu, where, where, where." Most wild dogs have songs they sing at evening, and this trait still survives in some domestic dogs.

In parts of India there is an old belief that the leader of a pack of jackals has a horn in the middle of its forehead. The natives call this the "jackal's horn," and say it will confer great benefits upon any human being who acquires it. This tradition is much like the one about the unicorn's horn, which we spoke of earlier in connection with the narwhal. But the jackal has played an even more imposing role in the human past—an ancient Egyptian god, Anubis, who presided over the mummy tombs as Lord of the Dead, had the head of a jackal.

NOT FOND OF COMPANY

In its breeding habits the jackal is much like other wild dogs. The female gives birth in a burrow or cave, about two months after mating. Usually her litter contains four pups, but she may have as many as nine. Both parents are active in foraging for food for the cubs. Only when jackals are about to produce a family or have to care for an already existing one, are they really sociable. At other times, they lead a solitary life. When they travel together, it is food and not love of company that attracts them.

Jackals seem to survive fairly well in captivity. In the London Zoo one lived for over thirteen years, while nineteen others had an average life span of more than eight years. In the wild, though, few jackals—or other animals—ever die of old age.

There are a number of different kinds of jackal. The Gray or Yellow Jackal, *Thos aureus,* a typical species, looks like a wolf, but is smaller and more slender, with larger ears and a sharp-pointed face. Its head and body length is about two and one-half feet, its tail about eight inches; it may weigh about twenty-one pounds. We find this species from eastern Europe and northern Africa through southern Asia to Burma, India, and Ceylon.

In the mountains of Thailand and Burma dwells the Himalayan Jackal, which is slightly larger and brighter in color than the typical gray jackal. A black saddle, which contrasts sharply with reddish-brown flanks and legs, distinguishes the Black-backed Jackal of eastern and southern Africa.

In this part of the world, too, is found the largest of the group, the Side-striped Jackal. Full grown, it may weigh up to thirty pounds and stand seventeen inches at the shoulder. The general color of its fur is buff gray, but the hairs on the sides of the body have light tips that give the effect of a stripe on each side.

FOXES—ONLY SOME ARE CUNNING

ARCTIC FOXES—HUNTERS OF THE FROZEN TUNDRA

The Arctic Fox, *Alopex lagopus,* is one of the few animals that spend the winter in the frozen reaches of the Arctic. When the temperature drops below freezing and the icy air carries a warning of still colder weather to come, the hardy caribou and the wolf begin to shiver, and move south to the shelter of timber. But the Arctic fox stays on, spending its whole life on the tundra, so far north that trees will not grow there.

Feeding as it does on ground squirrels and other small rodents, you might suppose the Arctic fox would be hard pressed to find a living when summer's green has vanished and the tundra has become one vast expanse of driven snow. The ground squirrels have holed up for the winter, and the lemmings are protected by the snow blanket. There are Arctic hares to be had, but they are fast and not overabundant.

However, the resourceful little Arctic fox has its own special method of procuring a winter supply of food. During the fall, when squirrels and other rodents are filling their storehouses with seeds and nuts, the Arctic fox gathers a harvest, too—but this is a live one, of lemmings, ground squirrels, and mice, which it kills and caches in Nature's "ice-box" just below the surface of the ground.

Along the Arctic coast the foxes fare better. A whale stranded on the shore will feed a thousand foxes all winter. Polar bears are followed by these little foxes for a share in their plunder, since the great white bear is out hunting all winter and rarely eats more than a small portion of each kill.

Fighting Off the Arctic Fox. It was a great disaster for Commander Vitus Bering, the noted Danish explorer, when his ship the *St. Peter* was wrecked in 1741 during a storm in the North Pacific, and beached. But it was our good fortune that he had with him a trained naturalist, G. W. Steller, who kept a journal of the things he saw on the island where they found themselves—now called Bering Island. To Steller we owe some of the most interesting first-hand observations ever made of the Arctic fox.

Steller concluded that the foxes, which were very numerous, had been brought to the island on drift ice, and fed on what was cast up by the sea. They showed little fear of the newcomers.

"They crowded into our dwellings by day and by night," Steller wrote, "stole everything they could carry away, including articles that were of no use to them, like knives, sticks, bags, shoes, sacks, caps, etc. They knew in such an unbelievably cunning way how to roll off a weight of several poods [a pood is 36.113 pounds] from our provision caches and to steal the meat from thence that at first we could hardly ascribe it to them. While skinning [sea] animals, it often happened that we stabbed two or three foxes with our knives, because they wanted to tear the meat from our hands. . . . They observed all that we did and accompanied us on whatever project we undertook.

"If any animal was cast up by the sea, they devoured it even before one of us could reach it, to our great detriment; and if they could not eat it all up at once, they dragged it piecemeal to the mountains, hid it from us under stones."

The Arctic fox, for all its fearlessness, is not a large animal. It is not more than twenty inches long, with a tail half as long again. In summer its coat is gray brown, but light hairs begin to come in later, and in winter it is snow white, without any markings whatsoever; only its dark eyes and the black tip of its nose break the Arctic background of pure white. Its ears are rather short and rounded, an advantage in the land of ice and snow, since large ears are more easily frostbitten. We find it in the Arctic regions of both the Old World and the New.

In February the Arctic fox begins to lose its winter coat but the change is slow and the gray-brown hairs may not all grow in until late spring.

Furry Babies of the Northland. It is in the spring that pairing takes place. We have reason to believe that the Arctic fox mates for life. The males fight fiercely for the lady fox of their choice, but once the courtship is over they settle down to regular family life.

In May, about fifty-two days after mating time, the cubs are born. The normal number is six, but there may be up to twelve in a litter. At birth they are little dark-brown balls of fur, weighing about two ounces each. The den-nursery, typical among foxes, is a safe retreat in Mother Earth.

Each Arctic fox has its own special hunting territory on which other foxes are not permitted to settle. When the year's crop of young foxes leave their parents' home, they—like the young coyotes—have a hard time finding an untenanted location. Every three or four years a roving band of young foxes takes on the proportions of a migration, when thousands move together searching for the "promised land," where lemmings and other rodents abound. Some favored few eventually find a homestead, but the majority perish in the attempt.

Sleeping in the Snow. The short summer is over in August; and by September the Arctic fox has donned its warm winter coat, and even the soles of its feet are padded. When the icy winds blow and the temperature drops down to 60° or 75° below zero, the fox can find comfort curled up in a snowdrift, breathing into the long hair of its tail, which acts as a sort of radiator of self-generated heat.

The typical Arctic fox lives on the mainland of both Asia and North America. Other species include the Greenland Fox, the Pribilof Fox, the Hall Island Fox, and the Bering Island Fox. The blue fox is merely the typical Arctic fox with a coat of a different color, and occasionally occurs in an average litter. It commands a high price in the fur trade.

RED FOXES—MORE SINNED AGAINST . . .

The Red Fox, *Vulpes vulpes* and *Vulpes fulva,* is one of the most hunted animals in the Northern Hemisphere. It is pursued for sport, for its golden-red coat, and because of the raids it makes on poultry. Through the years the very existence of the fox has been challenged, yet wily Reynard has not given up any of its boldness. The animal stays on, close to civilization, dwelling right in the suburbs of big cities.

Listen to some farmers, and you would think all the fox eats is poultry! They would be well advised to try to understand the fox and its eating habits better. Then they would realize that the red fox does more to help than to hurt them.

The red fox is a prodigious eater of insects in the summertime, when they are abundant. The animal is even more notable for its skill as a mouse-catcher, and wherever there is a field or broken woods there are enough mice to support a normal fox population, with an occasional feast on a cottontail. Red foxes eat all sorts of rodents, as well as carrion, grass, and fruit. One may object, but no one can blame a fox for taking a nice fat hen put almost under its nose—especially when there is a family of hungry little mouths to feed.

The author's advice to poultrymen is: Mend your barnyard fences. Kept outside them, the red fox will do your work as well as its own.

The Fox Family. Like other members of the wild dog family, the fox is a good father. Foxes mate and live together for an entire breeding season; the family does not break up until the young are old enough to forage for themselves.

The den is often a hole underground, in loose soil, for foxes are not good diggers. Sometimes they choose the abandoned shelter of some other animal, and renovate it. The cubs—there are four to ten in a litter—are born in March or April, fifty-one days after the mating period. They cannot see until a week has passed. Five weeks later they are out in the sunshine, playing together like kittens.

To the den the father brings food to his family. When he is not hunting, he loiters nearby, on the alert for a marauding wolf, mountain lion, coyote, or lynx. Should one appear, he will do his best to attract its attention, then draw it away from the den. He will lay down his life in defense of his young.

The red fox uses the den only as a nursery. Once the cubs have come of age and can forage for themselves, nothing short of certain imminent death would drive a red fox underground—and that only after it had exhausted every effort to elude its pursuer on the surface. The red fox sleeps out even during the bitter-cold winter nights in the north country of Canada.

Eluding the Hunters. In Europe and in the United States, hunting the fox has been a favorite sport for hundreds of years. When pursued by a pack of hounds, a fox will lope along at about six miles an hour. If the hounds get too close, it can speed up to forty-five miles an hour, but it cannot hold this pace for more than a mile or so.

For its survival the fox depends not so much on speed as on artful maneuvers. Foxes have hidden in chimneys and even kitchen stoves as a last resort. On one occasion a hard-pressed Reynard sought refuge in a woman's arms; another retreated to the sanctuary of a church during the mid-morning service.

MASTER REYNARD—FAVORITE GAME OF MANY HUNTERS
The red fox is forever being hunted both for the fun of the chase and because the animal preys on domestic fowl. Master Reynard is not quite the poultry-stealer people suppose him to be—he is also very fond of insects, mice, carrion, grass, and fruit.

Nor should you think that these resources are all that this cunning animal has in its bag of tricks. One of its wiles for evading the hounds is to backtrack its own footsteps for some distance, then leap away to one side and make off in a new direction. Other ruses are: running along the top of a rail fence or a stone wall; running through a shallow brook to make the hounds lose the scent; crossing ice—so we are told—just thick enough to hold it but not strong enough to bear the weight of the pack. No wonder the fox has been admired through the ages for its cunning! The fox is a past master at eluding its human or animal enemies, and it is usually only the young and inexperienced foxes that get caught.

There are other situations, too, in which foxes seem to display a considerable amount of forethought or reasoning. A fox will never raid chicken pens close to its home. It will pass and leave untouched a nearby roost and travel a distance of two or three miles before robbing a poultry farm. Apparently it believes in keeping on good terms with its immediate neighbors.

Red Foxes in Varying Hues. With its large, erect ears, pointed face, and red coat, the typical red fox is familiar to all of us at least in picture form; it is by far the most colorful and jaunty of the foxes. Its long, bushy tail is by far the finest "brush" in the whole mammal world—it helps keep the animal warm when sleeping—and has a handsome white tip. The coat is not just red but more like burnished gold, and its legs and feet are almost black.

The red fox is much smaller than the wolf, with which it does not interbreed. A large fox stands sixteen inches at the shoulder and weighs between five and ten pounds. Its head and body length is about thirty inches, and the tail seventeen inches or more.

The red fox is not always red; sometimes it is a black fox, a silver fox, or a cross fox (this last has a dark cross on its back). But all three are color variations of the red fox, and may turn up in one litter of cubs. The platinum fox is a domesticated strain recently developed from the silver fox.

The general range of the red fox covers most of the United States, Canada, Alaska (except the extreme north), Europe, Asia (from southern China to Siberia), and the arid regions of North Africa.

Foxes Tame and Wild. There are about nine different kinds of American red foxes, five European and Asiatic species, and four that live in North Africa. Ten years is the life span of the average red fox, and we estimate fifteen years to be the extreme limit; one fox lived twelve years in captivity.

Even after several generations in captivity foxes are not really tamed or domesticated. Wild-caught foxes soon learn to respect their keeper, but he cannot afford to relax his vigilance; his charges will snap and bite with little or no provocation.

Fox Farming. Of all the members of the dog family, only the silver fox and platinum fox are worth raising as fur-bearing animals. Silver-fox farming is now a well-established business.

It was back in 1894, on Prince Edward Island in the Gulf of St. Lawrence, that silver foxes were first domesticated for their fur. Since then the industry has grown steadily. In 1913 a pair of high-grade ranch-bred cubs sold for anywhere from eleven thousand to fifteen thousand dollars. Nowadays the cost of stock for breeding is far more reasonable—fifteen hundred dollars a pair.

Fox farming is now successfully carried on in suitable localities throughout North America and in Europe. Climate is of prime importance: the best furs are raised in cool, naturally humid regions. If an area furnishes natural furs of high quality, then we know that area is suitable for fox farming.

Whale meat is used a great deal for feeding the foxes. However, the experts do not consider a steady flesh diet satisfactory. The ideal arrangement is to feed the foxes twice a day—meat in the morning, mush at night. Females are able to reproduce for about ten years, and roughly half of them breed each year.

So—provided with a favorable market, a good location, and a love for animals, almost anyone with ordinary prudence may engage in fox farming with prospects of satisfactory returns.

GRAY FOXES—THE ONLY ONES THAT CLIMB TREES

The Gray Fox, *Urocyon*, is the only fox that can actually climb trees. If the branches are low enough, it will go up by leaps from one branch to another. If the tree is tall and straight, with no low branches, the gray fox will grab hold of the trunk with its limbs and clamber up with the aid of its claws.

Sometimes the fox's reason for climbing is to get away from enemies such as dogs. At other times the animal may simply indulge a whim to crawl into the crotch of a tree and sleep in the warm sunshine. You may be sure the fox would not scorn eggs in a bird's nest if it found one in a tree.

The gray fox's tree-climbing ability often saves its life, for it is not a fast runner. Its top speed scarcely exceeds twenty-five miles an hour—and this for only the first hundred yards or so. Thereafter twenty miles an hour is the best it can do. Chased by hounds, it will quickly seek shelter in a nearby rocky den, or, failing this, will go up a tree.

A hunter as well as hunted, the gray fox feeds on much the same kind of fare as the red fox: moles, rabbits, mice, birds, lizards, shell-fish, and insects—as well as fruit. If it finds an opportunity to make off with a chicken, that chicken's doom is sealed.

Young livestock tempts the gray fox, too. It is reported to have a special taste for the liver of a lamb; it sometimes opens up the lamb, breaks off the liver, and departs with it.

The gray fox is sometimes heard at nightfall. Its bark is short, harsh, and deep. The animal is most active after sundown. The rest of its time it passes in a permanent den it has made in a hollow tree or in a hole in sandy ground; it may also dwell in a cavern among rocks. Occasionally it happens that there are many dens in an area, and the foxes haunt them year after year. The den is lined with shredded bark or leaves for warmth and comfort.

The gray fox mates in early spring in northern localities, in January or February further south. The male shows a keen interest in domestic affairs. When the blind and helpless young are born about two months after mating has taken place, he forages for food while the mother stays home to nurse the children.

The fox family may consist of four or five pups, rarely more, and occasionally fewer. The parents take care of them until they reach the age of five months, when a young fox generally considers itself ready to go out and get its own living.

Enemies of the Gray Fox. The foxes must keep a sharp eye peeled for their enemies—wolves, bobcats, lynxes, coyotes, and man. Like the red fox, this gray fellow is inclined to make things easy for himself by haunting the same runway in searching for food. Trappers take advantage of this custom.

The first move in the trapper's campaign is to look for scent posts—places where foxes (like dogs) habitually void water. Here traps are carefully concealed so that there is no sign or scent to show that a human being has been about. The animal has a sharp sense of smell and remarkable eyesight, so that no small pains are required to deceive it. If caught, its fur is not so valuable as the red fox's, but this creature seems to be more easily trapped.

An American Animal. A native of North America, the gray fox has no close relatives in the Old World, South America, or Canada. It ranges from the Canadian border south to the Canal Zone. Though more plentiful in the sunny South than in the cooler regions near

Canada, the gray fox sticks to timber; where there are no trees, there are no gray foxes.

Typically foxlike in appearance, this wild dog has a fairly long muzzle, erect ears, and a long, bushy tail. The "pepper-and-salt" gray fur, however, is rather coarse, and a mane of stiff hairs is concealed on the tail. The pupil of the eye is elliptical—a departure from the slitlike pupil of other foxes. An adult may weigh between seven and eleven pounds. The head and body length is about thirty-one inches, and the tail eleven inches.

OTHER FOXES AND FOXLIKE WILD DOGS

The Kit Fox and the Swift Fox. Though, as we have seen, the fox has been considered the symbol of cunning through the ages, not all of its kind live up to this reputation. Desert foxes of western North America, the Kit Fox, *Vulpes velox,* and the Swift Fox, *Vulpes macrotus,* are surprisingly trusting creatures. Unsuspicious by nature, they are easily caught in traps that would not fool a red fox for one minute.

Both these little foxes excel other desert animals in their power of great speed, and in making an escape will certainly practice deception. Alarmed, the kit fox makes off across the sandy waste with a remarkably sudden burst of speed. After darting off in one direction, it instantly—without checking its speed—shoots off at a sharp angle, completely bewildering any would-be pursuer.

The name "kit" hints at this animal's small size; but its ears are enormous, and so it is also known as the "big-eared fox." Smaller ears distinguish the swift fox from the kit, but both are gray and either will weigh about four or five pounds and have an over-all length of two or three feet.

These little foxes hunt at night, and are mouse- and rat-catchers. They make their home in holes in the ground and live too far away from human habitations to molest chicken farms.

The Chama, *Vulpes chama,* the desert fox of South Africa, is also known to the Boers as the Oraai and as the Silver Jackal. Because of its gray back, the fur trade calls it the Silver-backed Fox. In a superficial way it resembles the African Long-eared Fox, *Otocyon,* which belongs to an entirely different species.

It Doubles Back on Its Tracks. The African long-eared fox, an attractive little creature with a blackish glossy coat, is a familiar figure to hunters and travelers who cross the plains of Africa from the Cape of Good Hope to Ethiopia. It is a sociable animal, and travels in pairs, or parties of three or four, in quest of termites and other insects as well as any small rodents it can catch.

This animal has a most extraordinary habit of doubling back on its tracks. Even when released by a hunter, it does not directly make off for safety—as if controlled by some secret command, it doubles back on its own tracks quite frequently as it runs away.

A Fox with Enormous Ears. We know that most foxes have big ears but those of the Fennec Fox, *Fennecus*, are enormous. This little sandy-colored fox has a length of only sixteen inches from the tip of its pointed nose to the root of its bushy tail—yet its ears are more

THE BETTER TO HEAR YOU WITH

Foxes are noted for their large ears, but the fennec fox holds the record over all others Its ears are one-quarter the length of its whole body. We often find that animals that make their home in the desert have big ears, and the fennec fox, dwelling in the sandy wastes of the Sahara, certainly bears this out.

than four inches long. Big ears, we have observed, are associated with a hot, dry climate, and appropriately enough the fennec fox is at home on the Sahara, the greatest and driest of all deserts.

The Fox That Migrates. On the steppes of central Asia there is another little desert fox—the Corsac Fox, *Cynalopex*, a catcher of rats and mice. This reddish-brown creature migrates with the seasons, often traveling in considerable numbers.

An Eater of Locusts. An Ethiopian red dog better known as the Simenian Fox, *Simenia*, is neither fox nor wolf but combines some features of both, being almost as large as a wolf and having the pointed face and large ears of a fox. This golden, russet-colored fox feeds on locusts and small rodents that it finds on the high plateau regions of Ethiopia.

The Raccoon Dog, *Nyctereutes*, of northeastern Asia, is not only raccoon-like in appearance but in its habits, too. It frequents the brushland along watercourses and feeds on fresh-water crustaceans, frogs, and small rodents. The Chinese name for it is *t'u kow*, meaning "ground dog"—the Chinese dig it out of holes in the ground. Large numbers of pelts are sold for fur in the Chinese markets.

The Antarctic "Wolf." Perhaps due to inexperience, the South American foxlike wild dogs show little fear of man. When the first settlers arrived on the Falkland Islands, the so-called Antarctic "Wolf," *Dusicyon australis*, was so tame and unsuspicious that in a few years it was exterminated in the islands.

Charles Darwin, in his diary of his voyage around the world in the *Beagle*, tells of seeing one of these dogs sitting on some rocks near the southern end of Chiloé Island. The animal was so absorbed in watching the work of two surveying officers that Darwin was able to walk quietly up and knock the animal on the head with his geology hammer. "This fox," said the famous scholar, "more curious or more scientific, but less wise than the generality of his brethren, is now mounted in the museum of the Zoological Society."

Another Easy Target. The largest of the South American dog foxes, the Andean Wolf or Culpeo, *Pseudalopex*, is a grayish foxlike animal. It has some bright tawny color on the legs and pelt. The name "culpeo" is a Chilean word signifying "madness" or "folly," and is aptly applied to the conduct of this animal, which constantly offers itself as an easy target to hunters.

Foxes of the Pampas and Savannas. Some of the old sheepherders of Argentina and Chile still recall the days when the Pampas Fox or Chilla, *Cerdocyon griseus,* a small gray dog fox, was seen by dozens at a time. Large numbers of these animals would surround the sheepherders' camp at night, pilfering and marauding at every opportunity. It was not unusual for a thousand of the skins of these foxes to be brought to market. Relatively speaking, not many of the creatures are left today. The Savanna Fox, *Cerdocyon thous,* is larger and darker than the pampas fox and frequents the upland grassy plains of northwestern South America.

The Fox That Walks on "Stilts." Strange in appearance—it looks like an oversized stilt-legged toy dog—is the Red or Maned "Wolf," *Chrysocyon,* which ranges in the open brushlands of Brazil, Paraguay, and

WOLF OR FOX—OR WHAT?
The unusual-looking red or maned wolf has its home in Brazil, Paraguay and neighboring countries. With its slender head and long neck, it seems more like a fox. But the oddest and most unwolflike feature it has are its long, spindly legs, surmounted by the short, thick body; the animal is splendidly adapted for moving about in tall grass.

neighboring countries. It is almost as large as a timber wolf but in other respects suggests a fox. The slender head and long neck make the short body seem curiously dwarfed. Its large erect ears seem out of proportion with the comparatively short tail and only add to its odd appearance.

The Guara or Aguará-guazú, as this red wolf is locally known, feeds on rodents, birds, and some fruits. It is large enough to kill sheep, and hunts them alone, not in packs.

The Bush Dog, *Speothos,* is another interesting tropical American species. We can scarcely recognize it as a member of the dog family—it is rather like a badger but not quite so heavily built. The longish body with its short legs and short tail is black, while the large head, shoulders, and small ears are yellowish white or buff colored.

This little bush dog is not over twenty-five inches long and lives in holes on river banks in Venezuela, Brazil, and Colombia. It feeds on anything it can catch and kill. It is a favorite with the natives, who take the pups and raise them as household pets.

DHOLES—POWERFUL WILD DOGS OF INDIA

A very distinctive red coat flashes through the underbrush deep in one of India's great forests. Another and still another appears and fades silently until a whole pack of colorful red hunting dogs known as dholes (*Cuon alpinus*) have passed on the heels of a fleeing sambar deer. They have been trailing their quarry by scent—now they are pursuing it by sight. There is no violent outburst of speed, but with a steady, tireless trot the wild pack gradually close in on their quarry.

In an endeavor to shake its pursuers off the trail, the stag heads for heavy cover. The veteran lead dhole follows close behind and keeps the pack together by giving short directive yaps.

Brought to bay with its back against a big tree or a rock, the stag sells its life dearly. The dogs, now in a circle, attack from all sides and many an overbold dhole meets a horrible death impaled on the slashing horns of the stag and flung in a lifeless heap among its fellows. The more experienced are cautious and wait for the unguarded fraction of a second when the lead dog springs at the quarry's throat. Then, as if at a given signal, the whole pack leap in and finish the stag.

The speedy dhole is much like a red-coated wolf. Weighing about forty pounds, it has a head and body length of some thirty inches plus a fourteen-inch tail. Yet it is not a true dog—unlike other dogs, it lacks the last molar tooth in the lower jaw.

THE SOCIABLE DHOLES

Soon after or even before day breaks, the pack of dholes leave their rocky caverns, where they have lain up during the night. Some may have curled up in thick brush or a hole in the ground, but they soon make contact with each other by uttering a peculiar "whistling" cry best imitated by blowing across the open end of an empty cartridge shell. Hunters often call them out in the open and shoot them by doing just that.

The sociability of the dhole originates in the prolonged association between parent and young and the union of one or more families. Daylight seems to be the favorite time for activity, but the dhole does hunt at night and on occasion will lie up during the day.

With the coming of the breeding season the packs dissolve and pairs settle down to the serious responsibility of raising a family. A number of females may select a particular ledge or rock cavern and set up a community maternity ward. The mother dhole has from four to six young in January or February—nine weeks after mating. The pups are born naked, blind, and helpless. When weaned, they are fed regurgitated food by the mother until they are ready for a straight meat diet.

Dhole pups persistently fight each other until seven or eight months old; by that time one of them has emerged as the largest and strongest, and the wrangling suddenly ceases. He is the recognized lead and the others submit to his authority. The pups are full grown and ready to breed in one year.

HUNTERS OF BIG GAME

In India the dhole keeps close to timber, but in the bleak uplands of Tibet and Ladak it frequents the open country, as there are no forests in those regions. The dhole preys on deer, wild pigs, and goats; a large pack will hunt grown buffaloes and are credited with attacking bears and leopards.

Throughout India there is a general belief that these wild dogs hunt and kill tigers. However, we have no really reliable evidence to bolster speculation along such lines. In one instance, the remains of a tiger that had been devoured were said to have been found with three dead wild dogs. There is no doubt that wild dogs have at times fought with tigers or leopards over possession of a kill—but such an encounter is more likely to wind up in the death of the dogs rather than the tiger's or leopard's.

CAPE HUNTING DOGS—OUTLAWS OF THE AFRICAN BRUSH

The African or Cape Hunting Dog, *Lycaon,* is the terror of the brush country south of the Sahara Desert. It has been outlawed for its depredations. Hunting in packs of fifteen to sixty or more individuals, the wolf-like Cape hunting dogs usually prey on the smaller varieties of antelope but will run down and kill such big game as hartebeest and sable antelope.

The appearance of a pack of hunting dogs in the distance is a signal for all game to move out. Any animal that lags behind because of old age or sickness is devoured by the pack in short order. The hungry packs themselves travel great distances and are continually on the move. They pass from one region to another with few stopovers of more than a day's duration. After a while they come back to the same region, to ravage it again.

Cape hunting dogs are expert swimmers. Still, they decline to cross deep water, perhaps because they are afraid of crocodiles. The antelope seem to be aware of this foible on the part of their swift-footed enemies and take advantage of it when chased. Choosing to run the risk of getting caught by a lurking reptile rather than to be torn to pieces by the ferocious packs, they plunge into the safety of the waters.

Often the timid antelope can hear the pack before they see them, for the hunting dogs communicate with each other as they move along, uttering a soft "ho-ho." This clear, musical call is particularly noticeable at sunrise, when scattered members of a troop call to their comrades. The hunting dog has two other cries: a sharp angry bark of surprise and a chattering noise something like that of a monkey, usually uttered at night.

AN AFRICAN DOG TOWN

When breeding time comes—about March—the packs break up and their members retire briefly to devote themselves to the business of carrying on the race. They select a number of abandoned aardvark dens, safely surrounded by brush and conveniently close to water. They clean out the underground nests, enlarge them, and line them with dry grass for the expected family.

In this dog town, the babies are born about two months after the time of mating. There may be two to six of them in a litter, and a number of females will bear their young in the same den. Partly digested food is regurgitated by the mother when the pups are old enough to eat it. They join the hunt early, setting up a shrill, piping cry as they dash along.

OUTLAW DOG OF THE WILD

The African or Cape hunting dog is a dreaded beast of prey in the African brush country. It travels long distances in ferocious packs that ceaselessly search for kill. Wherever the pack appears, death follows for many kinds of game, especially antelopes. These wild dogs are fatally curious about man and thus they often present an easy target.

DOGS WITH THE WAYS OF THE WOLF

Why is the Cape hunting dog known to naturalists as *Lycaon?* In the mythology of the Greeks, there was a king with this name. The god

Zeus visited him in human form, and Lycaon, wishing to test his visitor's divinity, placed before him a dish of human flesh. To punish Lycaon for this misdeed, Zeus transformed him into a wolf.

The Cape hunting dog has many of the ways of the wolf. It is a strong, husky animal about the size of a small wolf (four feet overall), with long legs, a big head, powerful jaws, and a fairly long, bushy tail. Its close, coarse hair is tortoise-shell in color, and more or less irregularly blotched with patches of yellow, black, and white. Sometimes the animal is completely black. The ears, large and oval, remind us of the hyena's, and this wild dog is indeed sometimes called the "hyena dog."

Lions are the greatest natural enemies of these dogs. A whole pack will flee in mortal terror before a pride of lions. They should have learned to dread man, but they are more curious than fearful when he is near. Their curiosity is their undoing, and they present an easy target for a rifle shot. They are not known to attack people, however.

Hunting dogs may live for nine or ten years. Like the wolves, they have disappeared from populated areas, being found nowadays only in the more remote, unsettled parts of Africa.

The Bears—Shaggy Giants of the Forest

IT IS ONE OF NATURE'S oddities that the bear—the biggest of the carnivores—eats less flesh than its smaller relatives, the wolf and the fox. Even the great Kodiak bear, a rough brown giant that is nine feet long from tip to tail and weighs upwards of sixteen hundred pounds, will graze like a cow!

Bears will eat meat when opportunity offers, but most of them are not habitual hunters. Except for the polar bear, they feed on almost anything that happens to be available—grasses, roots, insects, ants, eggs, mice, nuts, and fruits, as well as fish and game. These massive carnivores simply have moved away from a total flesh diet. They could win it back if they had to—heavily built and powerful, bears are for their size among the strongest of animals. So mighty are they that they can hold their own against any natural foe. Rarely do they feel the need to seek safety in flight.

The American Indians of the North Country respect the bear, looking upon it as a fellow citizen of the woods. Many, when they kill a bear, are careful to apologize and to speed its spirit onward to the Happy Hunting Ground with prayers and sacrifices. In their belief, the animal's spirit is too powerful to be appeased by simple rituals—so they clean the skull and put it on top of a pole, where they hold it taboo.

This practice is common not only in the Canadian woods but also among the Tungus tribes of Siberia. There, in little clearings in the forest, the author has seen numerous shrines where half a dozen bear skulls, black with smoke, were exhibited. He would have liked to take some back to his museum, but it would have been as much as his life was worth to touch them. The Tungus will not eat the meat of a bear—nor will they feed it to their sled dogs.

The attitude of these natives is a matter of religion rather than fear. Bears never have been a menace to mankind. You may have read of conflicts between man and bear—Davy Crockett's account is a classic of its kind. But first-hand evidence shows that any attack made by a bear was accidental or, more often than not, was provoked by man. Bears, for the most part, are easygoing and self-sufficient.

You may well discount the story about the "bear hug"—that bears, when attacking, hug their opponent and squeeze him to death. It is questionable whether a bear could do such a thing. In an attack it strikes around with its paws; the terrific strength of its weighty arms drives the claws deep into the body of its victim. To an observer this might look like hugging, but in fact is far from it.

A CLOSE LOOK AT THE BEARS

Even at a good distance you can readily recognize a bear by its lumbering gait. Bears are flat-footed and put the whole sole of the foot on the ground when they walk. Though normally slow-moving, they can bustle along in a lumbering gallop if need be. But the bears are walkers rather than runners. Most can climb, but some are too big and heavy to go up a tree. All are good swimmers; the polar bear is particularly well equipped for long periods in the water.

There are a surprising number of different kinds of bears. We place these animals in the family Ursidae. They all have a thick, warm coat of hair, rounded ears, strong claws that cannot be drawn back, and a mere stump of a tail. Most bears are black, but brownish shades are quite common. The white fur of the polar bear is the exception. Bears have poor eyesight and only fair hearing, but a remarkably good sense of smell. Their nose tells them where food is to be had and when the weather is going to change.

Bears are creatures of the Northern Hemisphere; we find only one, the Andean black bear, south of the Equator today, and none

FOOTPRINTS OF CARNIVORES

    After a light snowfall, animal tracks are often seen in fields and near streams. These three sets of footprints are all made by flat-footed members of the great order of carnivores. At the left are those of a black bear. In the center are prints of a running raccoon, while at the right we see the tracks of a running skunk. Note that all of these animals have five toes.

in Africa or Australia. Most dwell in northwestern North America and northeastern Asia. In these two parts of the world live the biggest bears. Up the rivers in these regions millions of salmon come every year to spawn. Their life cycle complete, they die and are devoured by the great bears. There is no doubt but that the bears gather to eat the dead and dying salmon; and their large size may be due, at least in part, to this rich diet.

With their shuffling walk, bears travel many miles in search of food. Often they will cross snow-capped mountain peaks. Perhaps you have heard the strange legend of the "abominable snowman." Periodically, huge footprints are discovered in the Himalayas; the natives say they are made by this sinister creature, who they believe is a great, apelike man. This is a good story, but the fact is that bears are excellent mountain climbers, and their tracks in the snow are remarkably like a man's!

FAMILY LIFE AMONG THE BEARS

Wintertime sleepers, the bears go into their dens in the fall, when they are quite fat, and do not emerge until early spring. As a rule they go without food for several days before turning in for the winter; and when they come out in the spring they first have a long drink of cool water and then feed sparingly.

Although a bear may sleep soundly through the winter, it does not hibernate in the strict scientific sense of the word. Its body temperature remains nearly normal, and the animal occasionally rouses and comes out of the den on mild days in midwinter. With true hibernators, like the woodchuck, the sleep is a profound lethargy; the body temperature is only a few degrees higher than that of the air.

It is during the winter sleep that the cubs are born. Twins are usual in the bear world, but the rule is not a hard-and-fast one. At birth the young are very small; a two-hundred-pound she-bear may have twins that weigh no more than six to twelve ounces each. The cubs grow fast. Their mother lavishes care and affection on them during their baby period, providing for their needs and looking out for their safety. When they are tired they may even ride on her back. The author knows of a case of four little cubs that were playing about their mother when she took it into her mind to start off and climb a steep hillside. One of the cubs, more tired from playing than the rest, scrambled up to a point of vantage on some rocks and then hopped onto her back. The little fellow rode off in style, hanging on with his paws embedded in his mother's fur. The others in the family trailed along behind.

Unlike the kindly mother bear, the father shows no interest in his family whatsoever—the Story of the Three Bears notwithstanding. He seems a changed fellow from the bear he was earlier, in the courting season. During courtship, bears show great affection for their mates. They often stand up and fondly hug and paw each other. All this is most pleasant while it lasts—but the period is short lived. In one month, the prospective parents have lost all interest in each other.

For the next two years the female is quite indifferent to the opposite sex and concentrates on making a living for herself and her family. As for the male, he goes off by himself or seeks the companionship of his cronies. He enjoys his winter sleep alone.

TAME BEARS

Fifty years ago, except for an occasional Punch and Judy show, people in small towns had little in the way of amusement until the trained bear and its keeper came to pay a visit. Making the rounds of street corners and taverns, they would always draw a sizable crowd. Most often the animal was a Russian brown bear—it seems to be more tractable and trustworthy than others of its kind. Nowadays the strolling bear has almost vanished, but bears continue to be popular entertainers in carnivals and circuses.

Trainers have found that bears in general are playful and enterprising creatures, with a strong streak of mischief in them. Unlike lions and tigers, they are poker-faced; pleased or angry, they do not reveal their feelings, so that their trainers must always be watchful. Brown bears are easy to train, willing to learn, and anxious to maintain the good will of their keepers. They are said to have a poor memory for faces, but for that we cannot reproach them—most of us are the same way, at least when it comes to bears. Brown bears can be taught to wrestle and box, and in their acts often appear to show as much intelligence as a man. The dancing bears once famous in Europe were brown bears, mostly from the Pyrenees.

The Asiatic black bear or moon bear is one of the outstanding comedians of the bear family. It seems to love applause—or, to be more exact, the rewards that applause brings from its keeper. It learns early to draw the plaudits of an audience by acting awkwardly and falling off its performing stool. Often—so we are told—it is purposely late getting to its place on the stage because this brings a burst of laughter from the spectators.

From the trainer's viewpoint, other bears present serious problems. The tame American black bear, while playful and amusing when young, often turns out to be the most dangerous of all. When only two years old it becomes irritable and irresponsible. Without the least warning it may turn on its keeper and try to kill him.

Trained polar bears sometimes put on a delightful show in circuses. But they can never really be trained to the point of being trustworthy.

BEARS OF YESTERDAY

To most of us it comes as a surprise to learn that the bears are the dogs' closest relatives. In habits and appearance, the lumbering bear and the lithe, swift-footed dog seem poles apart. Today they are— but in the yesterday of millions of years ago they were one animal.

Paleontologists, the experts who study the fossil remains of ancient life, have discovered the missing link between the dogs and the bears. It is a strange fossil dog-bear—they call it *Hemicyon,* or "half-dog"—and it shows the physical characteristics of both kinds of animals. Its remains were found in rocks of the Miocene epoch.

In ancient times, before men learned how to write and record what they saw and did, different races of bears stalked the earth. The great cave bears of Europe were the largest that ever lived, larger by far than the Kodiak or the polar bear, today's giants. They were quite common in prehistoric days, but disappeared with primitive man. We have found arrows, spears, and hatchets of stone closely associated with the remains of the great bears.

Bears were well-known in England in historic times, and once there was even a British grizzly. "They transported bears," Plutarch tells us, "from Britain to Rome, where they held them in great admiration." The animals survived in England until the eleventh century, dying out several hundred years before the wolves did.

AMERICAN BLACK BEARS

The American Black Bear, *Euarctos,* may seem a friendly fellow to you in a zoo, but it is usually shy in the wild; there it moves off when man moves in. For example, once, while shooting at small game in northern British Columbia, the author chanced to flush a black bear that was browsing unseen in some bushes close by. Startled and bewildered by the noise, the poor beast charged out excitedly and, in its panic, tumbled over itself, scrambled up, and bolted off, galloping as fast as its clumsy fat legs would carry it. A guide met the bear five miles away, still streaking along at full speed, crashing through the bushes and making enough noise for a dozen animals its size. No fearful ogre this!

Although the black bear is afraid of people, it has an overwhelming interest in their belongings, particularly edible ones. It is a habitual camp robber. The animal is apt to make its first raid late at night. If the raid is profitable, more forays are sure to follow. With each visit the bear takes heart and advances the hour of its call. If you are camping out in bear country, you must not be surprised to see your erstwhile nightly marauder finally come marching boldly into camp in broad daylight!

THE BLACK BEAR IN THE TREES

The black bear is a good climber. Hugging a tree with its strong arms, it goes up paw over paw and backs down the same way. Just why this animal spends so much of its time climbing is a puzzle. There is little up in the tree to attract it, and it has no natural enemies to fear on the ground. Perhaps it is fondly hoping to find a nest of bees. If you hide a canoe, or any bundle for that matter, in the trees of the North Woods of Canada, some inquisitive black bear is likely to tear it apart. Maybe it imagines that the object must contain something to eat or it would not be hidden. Leave your pack on the ground, and oddly enough the gear remains unmolested.

Once the author wanted to cache a hind quarter of a sheep while he was out of camp for a few days, so he strung it high up on a fifty-foot rope suspended between the tops of two fir trees. Although we say a bear has poor eyesight, three days later the rope was cut down and the meat gone. Presently a black bear came along, stopped impudently and looked up between the two tall trees to see if there was any more "easy" meat up there.

Black bears mate only once in two years. The courtship takes place during the warm summer days, and there is a considerable display of affection between the sexes. But bearish endearments, we have seen, have all too short a limit. In a month or less, the lovers have turned into strangers. Still, they have served nature's purpose—that the species should survive. These bears are not sociable, although you would not call them quarrelsome either. Several bears may be attracted to a hillside where there is a bountiful crop of wild berries, and they will feed peaceably side by side.

CAMP ROBBER OF THE WILD
The American black bear is shy, but it loves to investigate people's belongings. It is a habitual camp robber; nothing is safe from its prying paws. It begins by raiding camps at night, but eventually carries on its thievery in the daytime. This animal is small by comparison to its cousin the grizzly.

WINTER BABIES

Having feasted through the harvest season and become extremely fat, the black bear turns drowsy when the weather gets cold. Now it is time to hunt up the winter den and prepare for the long sleep. A careful, tidy bear will clean out a cavity in a pile of rocks, or dig a hole in the ground if need be. Others less enterprising will curl up behind a windfall or in dense foliage and spend an unpleasant winter trying to keep warm.

In January or February, while the female is still in the sleepy stage, the den is suddenly transformed into a nursery. A good seven months have elapsed since mating time. One baby generally makes up the first litter, but later twins are the rule, with occasional triplets and, rarely, quadruplets. However, we know of the case of a female that was seen with five cubs. Perhaps she had adopted one or more into her family—it is not unusual for a mother bear to accept stray or lost baby bears.

The newborn cubs are a far cry from the two- or three-hundred-pounders they will be some day. Only about nine inches long, they weigh between six and ten or twelve ounces each. They could not long survive on their own: They are unfurred, blind, without teeth. For forty days and nights the young do nothing but sleep, feed, and snuggle up to their slumbering mother.

When the cubs weigh about four pounds apiece, they are big enough to take a look at the outside world. Rather unsteady on their legs at first, they soon learn to walk and scamper about. At the first sign of danger the mother sends her cubs scurrying up the nearest tree.

Like all other bears, the black bear is fond of honey. An experienced old bear will get the honey out of a tree with only a few stings; the youngsters, more greedy than wise, get badly stung and bawl with pain—but they do not stop until they have eaten all the honey.

By fall, the cubs of the year weigh about forty pounds. They spend their first winter in a den with their mother or nearby in individual huts of their own. Our young bears are much better climbers in the adolescent stage than when they are full grown.

The cubs grow rapidly. Still, they are not mature until two years old. A female takes even longer to come of age. She is usually three years old when she has her first cub. Once it has left its den in the spring, a bear does not return to it, at least not until the fall, but lives and sleeps in the open.

Day or night matters little to the black bear. Very irregular in its habits, it prowls about at all hours. It can swim well and will cross swift, broad rivers or a lake five miles wide. On land the black bear can move at a good, steady pace. In fact, it can race along at twenty-five miles an hour, if need be. But such bursts of speed do not last long.

NOT ALL BLACK BEARS ARE BLACK

By no means among the largest of the bear clan, the black bear reaches a top length of six and one-half feet. A female is generally a good deal smaller; she may be four and one-half feet long. When full grown, the black bear has a shoulder height of two or three feet and usually weighs between two hundred and three hundred pounds. If exceptionally large, it may weigh up to five hundred pounds. The animal has a rather long, thick coat, usually black but sometimes rusty brown. As a rule, the muzzle is brownish, and a white spot of variable size marks the chest.

Twenty-five years is a good life span for the black bear.

We find the Common Black Bear, *Euarctos americanus,* and ten related species in many of the wooded areas of North America including the plateau region of Mexico. All the variously colored members of the *Euarctos* group—the name means "typical bear"—are merely local variants of the black bear. For example, the Cinnamon Bear is cinnamon colored but in other respects resembles the common black bear.

There is even a white black bear! It lives on Gribble Island and the larger coastal islands of western British Columbia. Called the Island White Bear or Kermode's Bear, *Euarctos kermodei,* it sometimes has clear, creamy white fur, with no traces of any dark color. Even the claws are white. Its eyes are brown, and so it does not appear to be a true case of albinism.

Legend of the Blue Bear. Equally curious is the Blue or Glacier Bear, *Euarctos emmonsii,* of the St. Elias Alps, in southern Alaska. This small bear is bluish black in color. Gray hairs mixed with the black produce the blue effect. It is interesting to note, by the way, that the Indians avoid this animal. They believe it is possessed with the spirit of the shaman, and they consider it a medicine man among the animals.

The Indians explain that the hair down the back of the blue bear is very thick and matted like that of an Indian medicine man. To justify their belief still further, they will add the following story: A native hunter, more daring than his fellows, once killed a blue bear. Punishment for his sin was not long in coming. After skinning the bear, he packed it on his back to the river, where his canoe was waiting. As he walked in the shallow water that lay between him and his canoe, he went down in a pothole. He could not save himself, the Indians say, because the spirit of the bear took away his strength.

GRIZZLY BEARS—GRIZZLED RATHER THAN GRISLY

The Grizzly Bear, or Silvertip, *Ursus horribilis,* was in the early pioneer days the undisputed master of the American Northwest. Every creature knew better than to dispute its claim to the right of way: One stroke of the grizzly's great paw will break the neck of an ox or the back of an elk. The grizzly, however, soon learned that its might was no match for the slug from a high-powered rifle; today it takes the back road when man comes along.

Once, like the bison, the grizzly was strong in numbers. At least seven different species are said to have dwelled in California alone. Although Californians continue to call the grizzly their official state mammal, today we cannot even find it in their state at all. Its great range, which formerly stretched from northern Alaska to central Mexico, and eastward across the plains as far as Kansas, has shrunken sadly. The grizzly still exists in fair numbers from British Columbia to Alaska, but in the United States it has practically disappeared. About five hundred grizzlies linger on in the security of the national parks.

The grizzly got its name for an obvious reason—its fur is grizzled. Generally its color is dark brown, and the long hair of the back is heavily tipped with white. Thus it looks streaked or mixed with gray. Some grizzlies are yellowish, however.

Although the grizzly runs smaller than the Alaska brown bear, it is still a large, powerful animal. An average grizzly weighs five hundred pounds—exceptional ones weigh up to 750 pounds. It is from six to eight feet long, with its tail a mere two inches or so. At the shoulder the animal stands from three feet to nearly four. The grizzly has, over the shoulders, a distinct hump; its form is massive and robust. It has a sharply elevated forehead, and its claws are long and curved. All of these special features help us to distinguish the grizzly from its smaller cousin, the black bear. The black bear recognizes these differences more quickly than we do; it moves off to another area, or up into the trees, when the grizzly lumbers into view.

THE GREAT GRIZZLY IN ACTION

So strong is the grizzly that it can crush the skull of a bull with a single blow of its ponderous paw. The Spanish-speaking peoples, who are famous for their love of the bullfight, developed an exciting variation of that sport in Old California: they used to stage it with the grizzly in the place of the matador. In the bull rings of those early days, one bear might succeed in killing six bulls in a single afternoon. The maddened bear would rise up on its hind legs as the bellowing bull charged, horns aimed at the grizzly's exposed chest; then, with split-second timing, the bear would strike the bull dead with a blow between the eyes. A grizzly can not only kill a steer—it has been known to drag the carcass half a mile or more.

EX-RULER OF THE NORTHWEST
Like the bison, the grizzly bear or silvertip has all but vanished from the United States; there, only about five hundred of its kind survive, within the safe confines of national parks. However, it is still fairly plentiful in British Columbia and Alaska. Famed above most other animals for its strength, the mighty grizzly can, with one blow of its enormous paw, crush the skull of a bull.

There are many thrilling but probably exaggerated stories of grizzly bear fights with a mountain lion or a black bear. Enos A. Mills, an American naturalist, gives us a clear picture of what usually happens when two of the great carnivores meet on the trail:

"Before me, just at sunrise, a grizzly and a mountain lion met. The grizzly—the dignified master of the wilds—was shuffling along, going somewhere. He saw the lion afar, but shuffled along indifferently on. Within fifty feet, the lion bristled, and, growling, edged unwillingly from the trail. At the point of passing, he was thirty feet from his trail-treading foe. With spitting, threatening demonstrations he dashed by, while the unmoved, interested grizzly saw everything as he shuffled on, except that he did not look back at the lion, which turned to show teeth and to watch him disappear."

HOW THE GRIZZLY GETS ITS FOOD

In most of its habits, the grizzly often reminds us of the big brown bear. It never misses an opportunity to supplement its diet with good red meat. Ground squirrels are a favorite dish, though it takes some digging to get them. In the national parks, such as Yellowstone, you may come upon small craters that tell you a grizzly has been excavating for its dinner. Cattle, deer, and sheep, if they stray into grizzly country, must move fast when the great bear comes upon the scene—or else it will be after them in a quick run, surprising in such a heavy creature. It is not uncommon for a grizzly to hide the remains of a carcass under leaves and to watch zealously over the cache.

Snakes and birds often find their way into this bear's maw. For a good part of the time, if not most of it, however, the grizzly has to content itself with fruits, grass, and roots.

A WATCHFUL MOTHER

The grizzly breeds and brings up its young much as the other bears do. The mother is a staunch protector of her babies. Joseph S. Dixon, a wildlife expert who has studied the bear at close range, tells us of an experience in which "an old mother grizzly with her two cubs came and fed peacefully within fifty feet of me. This mother kept her eyes fixed intently upon me, and although she could not talk, she said as plainly as any animal could, 'Keep your distance.' I believe it would have been suicide not to have obeyed her warning. Persons should never get between a mother grizzly and her cubs, or go too close to any mother bear when she is accompanied by her cubs."

Young grizzlies are good climbers: They can go up a tree like a black bear. However, they lose this ability as they get older, and most full-grown grizzlies are too big and heavy to climb. Large grizzlies have been seen in trees, but they are exceptions. This is one of the major differences between the black bear and the grizzly.

Twenty-five to thirty years is a good life span for the grizzly.

"THE UNEXPECTED OLD BEAR"

The typical grizzly, or silvertip, has quite a number of relatives. A few are known only from the reports of Eskimos or the Hudson's Bay Company; the animals' skins have never been collected by a museum expedition, and they may be extinct—like the Patriarchal Bear, of which we have seen just a single specimen.

This great yellow bear, killed nearly a hundred years ago in the neighborhood of Fort Anderson, Mackenzie, Canada, appears to have been the last member of a rugged wilderness race that survived long enough to furnish us a record of the bears of bygone days. It had full, soft fur varying from grayish brown to buff. Its head was yellowish, the muzzle a golden brown that changed to tawny around the eyes.

Acquired by an Arctic explorer, the specimen remained unnoticed for more than fifty years at the Smithsonian Institution. Dr. C. Hart Merriam, dean of American naturalists, rediscovered this treasure in the vaults of the museum and named it *Vetularctos inopinatus,* the "unexpected old bear."

BLACK BEARS OF OTHER LANDS

The Moon Bear, *Selenarctos,* gets its curious name from a broad, crescent-shaped white mark on the chest. The rest of the animal is uniformly jet black except for the brown muzzle. This Asiatic black bear is smaller than the American species—it has larger ears, and the hair on neck and shoulders is longer than on the rest of its body.

The moon bear's range spreads out from Iran to Indo-China and north to Manchuria. In Japan it is held sacred by the aboriginal natives known as Ainus. When they celebrate their annual fall festival, they kill a cub moon bear raised in the house of the chieftain; then portions of its body are distributed to the guests at the gathering.

The natives of Hainan have many curious beliefs about this bear: They say that it sucks its paws when hungry, that it eats children, and that its gall bladder migrates to different parts of the body with the changing seasons. The Chinese call it by such names as "pig bear," "dog bear," and "man bear."

The Andean Black Bear or Spectacled Bear, *Tremarctos,* is the only bear found in South America. It owes its name to the fawn-colored ring that encircles each eye, giving a rather fanciful resemblance to eyeglasses. The jet-black coat is also varied to some extent by some brown or white about the muzzle and on the throat. This is a small bear—about two feet high at the shoulder and between three and four feet long. Close to a vegetarian in diet and a good climber, the spectacled bear goes up lofty trees for fruit and nuts. It roams the wooded foothills and forested mountain ranges from Colombia to Chile.

BROWN BEARS—INCLUDING THE BIGGEST

The world's largest bears dwell along the narrow margin of coastal land that stretches from Alaska to British Columbia and the neighboring islands. It is strange that these big brown bears, close kin to the grizzly, never wander inland very far beyond the influence of the salt-laden breezes that drift in from the sea.

The Kodiak Bear, *Ursus middendorffi,* is famous for its huge size. One of these yellowish-brown giants had a recorded weight of 1,656 pounds and measured nine feet in length. An animal this size would stand four and one-half feet at the shoulder, and when erect on its hind legs could reach twelve feet in the air. Such a Goliath is of course exceptional in the wild, but some fat zoo animals weigh considerably more.

Second only in size to the Kodiak is the Peninsula Giant Bear, *Ursus gyas;* the more typical Alaskan Brown Bear, *Ursus dalli,* is still smaller.

UNAGGRESSIVE GIANTS

Despite their enormous size and great strength, the big brownies are not aggressive and rarely kill large game. However, a brown bear with her cubs is best given a wide berth; when wounded, this animal can be as treacherous as the most ferocious wild creature. The brown bears feed mostly on vegetable matter, especially in the spring, when they come out of their dens. At this time they graze like cattle in the northern meadows. Later on, they add roots, insects, and mice to their diet.

In June, when the salmon ascend the rivers to spawn, the brown bears are on hand to take their share of the annual feast. This is good timing all round, as the salmon die by the thousands after spawning, and the bears help keep the rivers free of pollution. This rich diet, as has been suggested earlier, may be the clue to the mystery of how the bears grow to their enormous size.

Perhaps you have heard the wonderful story of how the brown bear does its fishing. Standing ankle deep on a sandbar or perched on a log, a brown bear will—or so the tale runs—with a lightning-quick stroke of a paw unerringly send a silvery twisting salmon up in the air to land high and dry on the bank. In a flash—almost before the fish comes to earth—the great hairy brute is there to devour its catch. This is a good yarn, but observation does not support it. The bear catches the fish and eats it in the water.

Except for family groups, the big brownie travels alone. Since there is no night during the summer in its northern home, the bear is necessarily abroad by day. Active as the animal must be during the short summer to support its huge frame, it still takes time out to rest between nine at night and six in the morning. Sleeping, it usually lies concealed among the alders or stunted pines found above the timber line. (It is here that the hunter looks for these animals, rather than among the tall trees.)

As you might expect, the family life of the big brownies pretty much follows the general pattern for bears. Family ties are strong and not easily broken among these huge bears. Cubs stay with their mother all the first year, and the whole family—except the father, of course—enters the winter den together. The second summer finds the cubs and mother still united, though the "babies" are now almost as big as she is. The young are on their own, but they continue to enjoy each other's company—until the brotherly bond is broken by the urge to seek a mate. The big brownies reach full maturity about the seventh year and probably live to the grand old age of twenty-five years.

OTHER INTERESTING BROWN BEARS

The Eurasian Brown Bear, *Ursus arctos,* was once common throughout Europe and most of northern Asia. At one time, as we have seen, bears roamed over Great Britain; Crowther's Bear, native to the Atlas Mountains, was the only bear ever found in Africa. There are at least a dozen kinds of Eurasian brown bears, ranging in color from pale fawn to cinnamon and from blue to jet black. The Siberian Brown Bear is by far the largest—in fact, the largest flesh-eating animal of the Old World. It may weigh up to eight hundred pounds or more, almost equaling the great Alaskan brown bears in size. Like them, it feeds on the salmon that come up the rivers to spawn.

The Manchurian Grizzly, *Ursus lasiotus,* is jet black and weighs up to six hundred pounds. Fierce and unreliable in disposition, it is one of the few species of bears that will make unprovoked attacks on man.

The Syrian Brown Bear, *Ursus syriacus,* is the bear of the Old Testament. It is the bear which was represented as coming out of the woods and avenging the insults hurled at Elisha—the bear which David fought and killed in defense of his flock. It is a rather light-brown bear averaging about three hundred pounds in weight.

The Sun Bear, or Bruang, *Helarctos malayanus,* is the smallest of the bears; some four feet long, it weighs about one hundred pounds. Its short close hair is glossy black with splashes of white or orange on the chest, and the muzzle is a grayish tan.

This bandy-legged tree-climbing little bear lives in southeastern Asia —the Malay Peninsula, Sumatra, Burma, and Borneo. It dines on almost anything edible. At home in the dense, damp jungles, the sun bear spends most of the day in the tops of tall trees, feeding on fruit and hunting for birds' nests. The creature's mobile lips and the long, extendible tongue are well suited for picking up termites and grubs. Like all bears, it is fond of honey—hence the nickname "honey bear" is often applied to it. The animal pays no attention to the swarm of bees buzzing about its head; its close fur is sufficient protection against their stings.

A sun bear is easily tamed and makes an amusing household pet. However, with age it is likely to grow bad tempered and become dangerous. The peculiar name of this strange little animal seems to have come from the yellow crescent on its breast—it is supposed to represent the rising sun.

POLAR BEARS—WHITE GIANTS

The Polar Bear, *Thalarctos*, is the swimmer of the bear family. Its scientific name means "sea bear," and sea bear it is—whether diving into the water and paddling, sometimes with its front legs, sometimes with all four, or else sailing out into deep waters on an ice floe.

This great white giant has been seen on ice floes more than two hundred miles from land, and has voyaged to Iceland and Greenland. On occasion it may travel as far south as the Gulf of St. Lawrence.

HUNTER AND HUNTED

Food is what summons the polar bear from its Arctic homeland, where it lives on the fringe of the northern seas. The most carnivorous of all the bears, it prefers to feed on seals and walrus cubs. (Not adult walruses—their tusks are effective protection.) Though a good swimmer, the polar bear has not attained the speed, grace, or agility of the seal in the water. However, the bear can and consistently does catch seals by stalking them on the ice. Its diet also includes caribou, foxes, birds, shellfish, and any other available forms of animal life. It will not disdain seaweed. Often, on a great ice island, the Arctic fox will trail behind its huge northern neighbor, watching for a chance to gulp down the bear's leavings. In spring the bear goes inland to forage for grass and vegetable matter.

A dweller in frigid, snowstorm-wrapped regions, the polar bear is not too well known to us in the wild. And, likewise, the bear sees man as a stranger; it has not learned to fear him. Good-natured in the summer, when food is plentiful, the polar bear will not bother the passer-by. But come winter, the animal feels hunger gnawing at its bowels, and it will track a human being across the icy wastes the way it will any other game.

Man hunts the polar bear, too. The Eskimos have a use for every part of the animal. Its flesh and its bones give them food and utensils, its hide becomes their clothing. But first they must subdue it, no mean test for people not armed with rifles. The Eskimo who brings down a polar bear is respected by his folk as a master hunter.

A GOLIATH AMONG THE CARNIVORES

The polar bear is one of the largest carnivorous animals in the world, narrowly surpassed by the gigantic Alaskan brown bear. (In a sense it has a claim to the title of largest carnivore, since the brown bear is carnivorous in theory and not in practice.) Large male polar bears may reach a length of nine feet, stand five feet at the shoulder and weigh about sixteen hundred pounds. But the average male is more likely to weigh nine hundred pounds, and the average female seven hundred; this difference is the only marked one in the appearance of the sexes.

Although the polar bear is a massive, powerful animal, it is comparatively long and slender. Its head and neck are especially lengthy for a bear; its ears are short and rounded. Its coat of dense, long white fur is tinged with yellow from the bite of the brine. The polar bear's feet are heavily haired—one of nature's wise provisions for an animal that must walk on ice. It has better vision than most other bears and a sharp sense of smell—valuable traits for finding food in a lean season.

POLAR BEAR BABIES

Surprising as it may seem to us, the polar bear does not retreat to a sheltered den in winter, though its home is in one of the coldest regions of the world. Only the pregnant female reverts to the typical bear habit of sleeping through the coldest months of the year. In the late fall or early winter she finds a sheltered bank, digs down under the drifted snow, and curls up to sleep; soon she is covered by wind-heaped snow. She does not so much hibernate as provide a safe receiving place for the babies that are to come. The sun, which for the last week has barely peeped above the horizon, now makes its final appearance, and the long, seemingly endless night hides the North in darkness.

With January—nine months after mating time—come the baby bears. Their eyes are closed, they are practically hairless and altogether helpless. They have a lot of growing to do, for at birth they weigh no more than two pounds, and are a scant ten inches long. But soon soft, downy fur creeps over the little bodies, and at six weeks the babies finally open their eyes. When day breaks once more and the sunlight reaches long, bright fingers into the den in March, the cubs are ready to answer its beckoning. Now they begin to investigate the outside world, clumsily scrambling after their fond mother.

All through the first year the young stay with her, and she teaches them to hunt and care for themselves. When they are sixteen or seventeen months old—now they weigh a stalwart two hundred pounds or so—they are sent about their business, henceforth to be entirely on their own. The mother is ready to seek another mate and think about raising another family; she soon will have more little mouths to feed, and her first brood's are big enough to offer a menace. At the age of thirty, the polar bear is well on in years.

WHITE GIANT OF THE NORTH
The polar bear's scientific name means "sea bear." The animal swims and dives in the icy waters of the Far North, its homeland, stalking seals and walrus cubs, and sometimes travels as far south as the St. Lawrence River, on an ice floe. The polar bear is sought by the Eskimos, who eat its flesh, make utensils from its bones, and clothes from the hide.

Visitors to a zoo often comment on how hot the polar bear must be, with its heavy coat of fur, in a warm climate. But the bear never appears to suffer from the heat. So long as it has a pool of fresh water in which it may cool off, from time to time, it is ready to make the best of circumstances.

SLOTH BEARS—SWIFT WHEN THE NEED ARISES

The Sloth Bear, *Melursus,* moves along with a rather slow shuffle most of the time—no need to wonder how it came by its name! But let it come against a foe that is more than a match for it, and you will see how deceptive a name can be. The sloth bear will take to its heels and dash away across rough country faster than a man can race. It is a hard-hitting fighter, too, when occasion requires, and possesses a powerful armament of claws.

Ceylon and India are the home of the sloth bear. A rather rangy animal, about five feet long, it weighs two hundred pounds or so, stands over two feet at the shoulder. We may say it has a longer tail than most bears, but three inches is still not very long. Extremely lengthy black hair covers this bear, making it a shaggy oddity. On its chest there is a whitish crescent; its muzzle is whitish, too.

The sloth bear is a first-rate climber. It likes fruit and honey (*Melursus* means "honey bear"), and it will go up tall trees in search of these sweets of the woodland. Coming down takes caution; the bear moves tail first toward the earth. On the ground, it finds a great variety of food. It will eat small rodents, grubs, beetles, sugar cane, or whatever else it can find to fill an empty stomach.

Termites are a dainty dish for the sloth bear; it has special equipment for capturing them. First it finds their nest, and digs them out. Then, with the help of its long, mobile lips, it sucks the scurrying victims into its mouth by means of deep intakes of breath. Any fugitives must beware of its long tongue.

The sloth bear makes its den in a cave in the rocks. It generally keeps to itself, though sometimes there are small family groups, especially at breeding time. The young are born blind and remain so about three weeks. Once they can see, they accompany their mother in her travels, often riding on her back and holding on to the thick tuft of hair on her shoulders. The cubs stay with their mother for two or three years, until they are almost full grown.

During babyhood the sloth bear makes an amusing pet, but it grows irritable and bad tempered with age. One sloth bear lived twenty-one years in a zoo; another, eighteen years.

Raccoons, Pandas, and Their Family

Most people will feel their curiosity aroused by the title of this chapter. Can the little raccoons of the New World and the great six-foot panda of Asia actually be relatives? Separated by the wide Pacific, these animals seem to be both geographically and physically remote from each other.

For a long time even the naturalists were fooled by the differences between these two creatures. The experts used to consider the giant panda a bear. But careful study showed them that the panda shares so many basic features with the raccoon that it belongs to the same family. It has only one other relative in Asia, and this one is an oddity, too. It is called the lesser panda, and it is a small, catlike creature.

The rest of the raccoon family is strictly American, ranging from the southern border of Canada all the way down to Paraguay. Many of us have never seen these animals or perhaps even heard of them. But although the names of the cacomistle, the coati, and the kinkajou may have a strange ring for our ears, people who dwell south of the Rio Grande know these alert and agile creatures well, often keeping them as house pets.

Although the raccoon's southern relatives differ in many ways, one thing they have in common—long, bushy tails, which remind us of the cats'. Sometimes, too, the tails are marked with alternate rings of dark and pale colors, like the raccoons'. These animals walk on the soles of their five-toed feet, but they are not completely flat-footed. Unlike the cats, they cannot draw in their claws. The family name, *Procyonidae*, borrowed from the raccoon, means "before the dog," suggesting that this group is more primitive than the full-fledged canines.

479

RACCOONS—INTELLIGENT AND NEAT

The Raccoon, *Procyon,* is at home about watercourses, lakes, and marshes. Here it hunts at night for other creatures that frequent water and its vicinity. A stout swimmer, the slender-fingered raccoon will reach out and catch fish, freshwater crayfish, frogs, salamanders, and mussels as it breasts a moonlit river or lake.

But the animal will pounce just as gladly upon eggs, birds, insects, mice, and every sort of creeping thing. It will dine upon nuts, fruits, and berries in season. When the corn on the cob is fat and juicy, the raccoon will make nightly raids until an alarmed and indignant farmer rounds it up with the aid of his coon dogs.

Quite singular is the coon's habit of soaking its meat in water be-

THE RACCOON'S DAINTY TABLE MANNERS

With delicate, bare-skinned fingers, the finicky raccoon always washes its meat and fish in water before eating it. This odd habit often has no hygienic value; the raccoon will repeatedly wash food that is already quite clean. Catlike in size, the raccoon can always be identified by its black facial mask and its large bushy tail, banded with rings of black and light buff. From earliest pioneer days, "coon" hunting has been a popular sport in the United States—the animal is esteemed for both its flavorful meat and its useful fur.

fore eating it—an eccentricity that has earned the typical species the name of *lotor,* or "washer." No matter how clean a piece of flesh may be, if there is water nearby, the raccoon dunks and thoroughly washes the meat.

The raccoon's fingers are long and extremely sensitive. In the process of dunking, the animal never so much as glances at its busy hands, but looks around in an inquiring, detached manner as if it were capable of two separate thoughts at one time.

The raccoon's dwelling place may be a hollow tree or a warm cavern among the rocks. Although this carnivore is a talented climber, often saving its life by taking refuge in the trees, it spends most of its waking hours on the ground. After a long summer's season of resting idly by day and prowling for food in the dark, the raccoon tucks itself comfortably away in its den and sleeps until spring. It awakens to mate and sometimes to feed.

Like the bear, the male coon solves his family problems by simply refusing to assume any responsibility. After a brief midwinter courtship, he returns to his solitary bachelor life.

LIFE OF A YOUNG RACCOON

In April or May, nine weeks after mating time, the baby coons arrive in their fluffy warm coats, marked just like the parents, with rings on their tails and a black facial mask. Three weeks later, their eyes open for the first time, but it is two months before they are big enough for their mother to take them on their first jaunt through the forest.

Their walks in the woods are an exciting experience for the young raccoons. The four or five little fellows follow their mother in single file. Here and there some of them stop to investigate matters of interest. Then they remember they are lagging behind in a very strange world, and they catch up with those ahead.

Like the female of the black bear, the mother raccoon shoves her tiny tots up the nearest tree when danger threatens. That precaution taken, she leads the would-be attacker an exhausting and unsuccessful chase through marsh, mud, and swamp. If she gets cornered, she will put up a furious fight. Only when she knows there is no one behind her does she return to recover her family.

A raccoon is fully grown when twelve months old, but females may mate at ten months. Nine or ten years is the natural life span for a raccoon; some have lived for thirteen years or a little longer in captivity. Raccoons are easy to tame if they are captured young. Because they are intelligent and playful by nature, they make delightful pets.

ESTEEMED FOR FLESH AND FUR

The "black mask" previously mentioned is one of the notable features by which you can recognize the raccoon. The mask runs across the eyes; below it, the muzzle is sharply pointed; above, the raccoon's long ears stand erect. The animal's brush of a tail may be ten inches long and on it rings of black and light buff alternate. Most of its body is covered with brownish gray fur, but it may be more yellowish or even almost black. The fur is long and thick, giving the raccoon a sturdy appearance. About the size of a large house cat, it weighs fifteen pounds on an average. Still, there are "big" animals in almost every kind, and a large raccoon will come closer to fifty pounds.

The early American settlers valued the raccoon for its meat, which has a good taste, and its fur was famous in the coonskin caps of frontier days. Raccoon fur continues to bring a worth-while price in the fur trade, often being sold under the more attractive name of "Alaska sable" or "Alaska bear."

While you are more likely to find the raccoon between the southern border of Canada and the Rio Grande, it ranges south through Mexico and Central America. A close relative, the Crab-eating Raccoon, dwells in South America. Although it resembles its northern cousin in a general way, it has shorter, coarser fur and a less bushy tail. It also spends less time in the trees. Some animals have a way of not living up to their names, and the diet of the crab-eating raccoon is by no means limited to crabs.

CACOMISTLES—"MINER'S CATS"

The Cacomistle, or Ring-tailed Cat, *Bassariscus,* is an attractive, furry little animal, like a cat in its build, like a marten in its looks. It has a sharp-pointed face, large ears, and great big eyes that seem full of feeling to us. A long, showy tail, marked with broad alternate rings of black and white, arches out gracefully behind the cacomistle, adding to the charm of its appearance.

This appealing small carnivore is extremely shy. Living among rocks and caves on hillsides—from southwestern Oregon to Colorado and south to Mexico—it comes out of hiding only at night. Thus, even though it is fairly common in the southwestern United States, the people there rarely get an opportunity to see it. However, there are times when it sheds its timidity and takes up residence in a prospector's cabin or an old Indian hut. Now it earns the name Southwesterners give it—"miner's cat"—and tracks down mice and rats with relentless single-mindedness. It is one of the best of the ratters; it can keep a house free of rodents as few other mammals can.

Ratting takes alertness—a quality the ringtail possesses in good measure. It is an intelligent creature in the bargain, and makes a fine pet. But you must catch it young if you want to raise it tame, a rule that applies to almost all animals.

CREATURES OF ROCKY PLACES

In the wild, the ringtail haunts places where there are broken rocky outcrops, rock slides, and rimrock, a supply of clear running water and scattered pine trees. Here it hunts down woodrats, ground squir-

IT COULD MAKE A PLEASANT, USEFUL PET

A ratter, second to none, the ring-tailed cat or cacomistle has been nicknamed "miner's cat" in the southwestern part of the United States. It will often move in with prospectors and completely exterminate the rodents in their cabins. If the ring-tailed cat is taken young and tamed, it will make a likable and bright pet as well.

rels, mice, lizards, and chipmunks, racing after them across the rocks with remarkable agility. Hair on the soles of its feet makes the going easier. Just as the ringtail must be fast to bring down its food, so it must be ready to dash off lest it end up in another animal's stomach. Owls and snakes appear to be its special enemies.

In many ways the ringtail's habits parallel those of the raccoon. The ringtail is at home in the trees as well as among the rocks and it is an adept climber. To some extent it feeds on fruit. Sometimes the young are born in a hollow tree, sometimes in a cave. In May or early June, the female brings forth her litter of three or four "kittens." They are blind, toothless, and have a scant covering of down. At the end of the fourth week their eyes open.

Now and then the father takes a hand in bringing food for the family, but such paternal interest seems to be an individual peculiarity rather than the general practice. Raising the young is a mother's job in the world of ringtailed cats, and she does it well, looking out for their safety until they are ready to take on the responsibilities of adulthood.

An adult ringtail wears a handsome coat of fur. It is soft, pale yellowish-gray tipped with black. The animal's glory—its tail—is even longer than its body, which may be about fifteen inches. The ringtail stands only six inches at the shoulder—we said it is catlike—and a full-grown adult weighs close to two and one-half pounds.

In Central America and Mexico, the ringtail has a cousin, the Middle American Cacomistle, *Jentinkia,* that lives in the trees of dense tropical forests and has darker-hued gray fur. ("Cacomistle," by the way, is the name the Aztecs gave the animals long ago.)

COATIS—FRIENDLY BUT LONG-FANGED

The Coati, *Nasua,* an odd-looking creature, is extremely rare north of the Rio Grande, and Americans know little about it. When they meet it—as they may, once in a long while in the forests of New Mexico and southern Arizona—they are likely to shoot first and ask questions afterward. From Mexico south to Paraguay, the people know it better; some of them even have pet coatis in their homes.

What kind of creature is the coati? It belongs in the raccoon family and looks like a raccoon—only it is longer and has a projecting piglike snout which is rather flexible. That is why naturalists call it *Nasua* (from the Latin word for "nose"). The Tupi Indians of South America gave the coati its common name. They seem to have put together their words for "belt" and "nose" to christen it. We suppose they were referring to its comfortable habit of sleeping away the hot midday hours all curled up, its snout snug against its belly, in the shade of the forest trees.

There are red coatis and there are brown coatis, and many are grayish brown; some are more yellow or black. On the chin and throat, the fur fades to white. A mask of light brown proclaims the coati's membership in the robber band of the raccoons.

Another mark of kinship to the raccoon is the coati's long tail: It is striped with indistinct brown rings and is thinly furred. When the coati struts through the woodland, it carries the tail proudly behind it, pointing upward in a sharp curve. The larger species of coati may reach two feet in length, and the tail is almost as long. We find coatis that weigh as much as twenty pounds, but the run-of-the-woods member of the group is more likely to average ten.

Not so exclusively a night worker as the raccoon and the cacomistle, the coati picks its hunting hours for comfort. It likes morning and early evening best; the remaining hours it will laze away or sleep through.

GOOD CLIMBERS, STAUNCH FIGHTERS

This little fellow is fond of companionship and often travels in parties numbering from five to a dozen or more. Each member of the troop carries its tail aloft and pokes its long nose into every nook and corner in search of some lurking insect or reptile. Whenever the group reaches a fruit-laden tree, they scramble up like a band of monkeys and climb out on the branches to devour the fruit.

The coati feeds on almost anything edible—mice, rats, insects, worms, fruits, and seeds. With coatis about, even a bird isn't safe in the trees—the animal may pounce on it or loot its nest. The coati is a staunch fighter, for it is well armed; it has long fangs with razor-sharp edges capable of inflicting fearful slashing cuts.

We know surprisingly little about the breeding habits of the coati in the wild. One observer reports seeing a female that was carrying five young, quite hairless, early in September; and another female with four young in October. So we may assume that this is pretty much the time when baby coatis come into the world. We do know they are born about seventy-seven days after mating time.

AN EVER-SEARCHING SNOUT

Native to Latin America only, is the ring-tailed or red coati. It exhibits two sure signs of raccoon brotherhood—a facial mask (rather light in shade) and a striped tail. No raccoon, however, can lay claim to such a long, flexible snout; the coati is forever poking it into corners and the holes of trees, looking for birds and insects. True to South American custom, the coati likes to take a siesta in the hot afternoon.

"A HARUM-SCARUM LOT"

Frank M. Chapman, who was Curator of Birds at the American Museum of Natural History, spent some time watching the activities of the coati on the island of Barro Colorado, off Panama. Dr. Chapman tells us some more about this animal: "During the greater part of the year male coatis live alone while the female is accompanied by her five or six young, probably until the summer, when another family appears. Several times I was visited by a female and her well-grown young (December or January); a harum-scarum lot scampering through the edge of the forest and coming out cautiously for bananas."

The coati has a number of aliases. One of them is "coatimundi." In Mexico the people call it *chaluga* or *challa*; further south they call it *pisote,* and the male *pisote solo,* for he is more or less solitary. Females usually travel in bands with their offspring, except during the mating season, and are noticeably smaller than the males.

KINKAJOUS—"HONEY BEARS" WITH REMARKABLE TAILS

The Kinkajou, or "Honey Bear," *Potos,* is both a cousin and a neighbor of the coati. We find it in the tropics from southern Mexico to Mato Grosso in southern Brazil. The great oddity of this brown-furred little creature is the long, powerful tail. It is prehensile ("grasping"), like the tails of the tropical monkeys that share the forests with this southern kinsman of the raccoon. The animal can curl it to hold on to things and indeed uses it as a fifth hand.

So strong is this tail that the kinkajou can even swing suspended by it from the limb of a tree. It takes special delight in this stunt, performing it often. To its ground-prowling enemies it almost seems to say: Look at me way up here—get me if you can!

Nothing can shake a kinkajou out of a tree. Not even a tornado can break its stranglehold with its tail aided by the firm grip of all four feet. The kinkajou is one of the few animals that can climb up its own tail as you hold the end of that appendage, and then onto your hand.

This lithe creature travels monkey fashion through the trees of its forest home. Rarely does it descend to the ground. To get to its destination, it simply swings from tree to tree.

CURIOUS FEEDING HABITS

During the daylight hours, the kinkajou sleeps curled up in a ball, with its tail wrapped around its body, in thick foliage or inside a hollow tree. With the evening comes waking time and feeding time. Fruit seems to be the kinkajou's favorite food—especially wild figs, which are abundant in tropical America. It uses its long, extendible tongue to extract the pulpy meat.

When hungry and in a hurry, the kinkajou will grasp food with its hind feet as well as the fore feet, just as monkeys often do. With the amazing tail it can stretch out and clutch fruit beyond its normal reach, and bring the food to its hands or mouth. Occasionally, when feeding in the treetops, it utters a soft hiss or a short, low bark, but it is silent most of the time.

In Mexico, the natives often refer to the kinkajou as *mico león* or "monkey lion." One may well doubt, however, that the kinkajou would attack a monkey. It is rather a case where a carnivorous animal has deserted its flesh-eating habits and climbed into the trees to live like the monkeys on fruits. The kinkajou is a gentle animal and, when tamed, makes a lovable pet.

A TAIL LIKE A STEEL CABLE
"Raccoon" of the tropics, the kinkajou or "honey bear" is more likely to bring to mind a monkey than any other animal. With its powerful, prehensile tail it swings from tree to tree in the South American forests, or takes hold of food impossible to reach with its hands. Once the kinkajou fastens its tail on a tree branch and decides to hang there, few forces short of death can dislodge it. An ex-flesh-eater, it has a long, flexible tongue with which it scoops out the soft pulp of fruit.

KINKAJOUS LIVE LONG

We do not know much about the life history of the kinkajou in its natural state. One, in the London Zoo, was alive and healthy after nineteen years of captivity. This was no doubt a record. Kinkajous frequently live ten years or more in zoos. A pair at the Milwaukee zoo lived together for nine years and had their first litter—twins—when actually twelve and one-half years of age.

Two to four young are the rule. At birth they are about the size of newborn kittens and covered with short black fluffy fur. They open their eyes for the first time when they are about ten days old. Their tails do not show any prehensile strength for about a month. At the age of seven weeks, however, the little kinkajous are able to hang by their tails.

A grown-up kinkajou's tail is about twenty-two inches long—somewhat longer than its head and body together. Large eyes sparkle in its rounded catlike head; its face is short and pointed, its ears small and round. It has short legs and its fur is soft and thick, and uniformly tawny or golden brown.

The Tupi Indians of South America appear to have given the kinkajou its name. Some tribes call it *potto,* from which naturalists derived the name for the genus. Strangely, the potto of Africa has the identical native name but is a lemur, much resembling the kinkajou except that it lacks a tail.

More like the kinkajou in its looks and habits is the Olingo, *Bassaricyon* ("fox-dog"), another member of the raccoon family that has sometimes been found feeding on fruit in the same tree with the kinkajou or traveling in its company. The olingo ranges from Ecuador to Nicaragua. It is a slightly smaller animal, but its golden-brown fur is longer and thicker. The tail is bushy and not prehensile.

GIANT PANDAS—FOREST-DWELLERS OF CHINA AND TIBET

The Giant Panda, *Ailuropoda,* did not make its appearance in an American zoo until 1937. This uncommonly appealing animal lives high up in the mountains of southwestern China and eastern Tibet. Here it haunts the almost impenetrable forests of bamboo. So dense and compact is this woodland that the trails the panda must follow are actually tunnels through the green. Along them stalk the black bear, the leopard, the takin, and the wild boar.

When you consider how remote and inaccessible the mountain fastnesses of China are, it does not seem odd that the western world never heard of the giant panda before 1869. Perhaps the first European to see the animal alive was J. H. Edgar, in 1916. In the wild country of the upper Yangtze, not far from Kinsha, Edgar beheld a large white animal curled up in a great ball, asleep in the forks of a high oak tree. It was the *beishung,* as the Chinese call it—the "white bear." Today, having studied it closely, we know the giant panda is not a bear but rather the biggest member of the raccoon family.

BEARLIKE, BUT NOT A BEAR

The giant panda certainly is bearlike in its size and its shape, right down to its stumpy little tail. About six feet long, the animal may weigh two hundred pounds or more. A handsome and amusingly colored creature, it almost seems designed for a child's delight. The giant panda is creamy white, but it wears black stockings on its legs, and a yoke of black runs over the shoulders. The great white head has small black ears perched atop it and a black patch covers each eye, making this a funny-looking fellow indeed.

Perhaps these colors serve a serious purpose, however. As the white-and-black animal moves across the snow where rocks crop out and the trees cast dark shadows, it is often lost against the background.

Like the bear, the big panda is flat-footed (naturalists say "plantigrade") and moves overland with a similar lumbering gait. Still, it is a good climber and agile in the trees. Its food seems to be almost exclusively bamboo shoots. In its homeland the young shoots continue to grow from June to September and are white within and excellent eating. In the winter there are bamboo leaves and stalks to chew. Because the animal is so big, naturalists estimate it must eat for ten hours a night to keep itself going.

HOW THE GREAT PANDA EATS

For feeding on the fibrous bamboo, the panda has developed exceedingly large and broad molar teeth, with tremendous grinding and crushing power. Strong jaw muscles also help out. But the teeth still show us this animal is a carnivore, and suggest that the pandas of ages past were substantial eaters of flesh. Those of today may now and then dine on the smaller animals in the forests of China. In a zoo, when bamboo is not available, the panda will feed on vegetables, cereals, cod-liver oil, and milk, and seem none the worse for the change to a civilized diet.

On each of its front paws the panda has a pad—the animal's scientific title, *Ailuropoda,* means "cat feet." The panda can use these pads like thumbs in bringing food to its mouth. Such equipment is an oddity among the carnivores. Interesting indeed is the way the animal eats. Sometimes it uses both hands like a squirrel, or lies on its back, heaping a pile of food on its belly before starting a meal. It will hold a stalk of celery in its fist and bite off a mouthful at a time. It is much handier with its paws than a bear.

DELIGHTFUL CLOWN OF THE ZOO

In the zoo, the giant panda is always a star attraction. Its amusing white face with the blackeye patches and its shaggy, rotund body give it great appeal; the animal is familiar to thousands of children because it has so often been copied by toy makers. In the wild state, the giant panda lives a secluded life in the remote forests of Tibet. The creature is a relative of the raccoon, and its ancestors once dwelt in the New World.

There are too many animals whose life history is almost a closed book to us, and the rare giant panda is one of them. We have every reason to believe it does not hibernate or sleep through the colder months of the year. Its cubs number one or two, and are born in the winter. They weigh only a few pounds at birth, but by the end of their first year may reach sixty pounds or more. Because the pandas keep to themselves and are shy, quiet creatures in the wild, seldom wandering far from their chosen haunts, it is hard to find out much about them.

Since its introduction to the western world in 1937, the giant panda has been an overwhelming favorite with zoo visitors. To the delight of countless spectators—and its own delight, too—this engaging buffoon never fails to indulge its insatiable desire to perform in the broadest comedy, even of the slapstick variety. It is a pity that the panda, like many bears, tends to grow sullen and bad-tempered with age.

LESSER PANDAS—THEY LIVE HIGH UP

The Lesser Panda, or "Cat Bear," *Ailurus,* sits up on its hind legs and strikes out with its forepaws like a bear. It climbs the way a bear does and, when irritated, it makes the same sudden rush as the bear. It even emits the same kind of cry. But how different this little Oriental is from a bear!

The lesser panda (we must call it that to distinguish it from its big relative, the giant panda) is only about two feet long—roughly the size of a large house cat. Long, luxuriant fur, ruby red or deep chestnut in color, covers its lithe body. The watchful face, in which two lustrous little eyes shine, is white, but a narrow dark stripe runs from the eyes to the corners of the mouth, adding to the animal's wistful charm.

Nearly straight out behind it the lesser panda carries a handsome bushy tail, about sixteen inches long and ringed with bands, alternately dark and light, that put us in mind of the raccoon. There are short claws at the end of its rather stubby legs. The animal can partly draw these claws in, so they are known as "semi-retractile." With its good looks and friendly manner, the lesser panda is one of the most attractive and appealing members of the animal kingdom, especially when it has gotten settled in a zoo and become accustomed to people.

We find the lesser panda in the forest-clad Himalayas of northern India and in western China, at elevations of seven thousand to twelve thousand feet. Slow and awkward on the ground, the animal is a first-class climber and spends much of its time in the trees. Although it may eat some insects, mice, and other small animals, its food consists mostly of vegetable matter like bamboo shoots, leaves, and fruits. The lesser panda prefers to make its den in a hollow tree, where it bears one or two young in a litter.

The Weasel and Its Family—Minks, Martens, Polecats, Sables, Badgers, Skunks, and Otters

FEW ANIMAL FAMILIES are more important to us than this colorful group. It contains some of our most valuable fur-bearers—the marten, the sable, the mink, and the otter. All are beasts of prey that render man great service by keeping in check the rodents, his rivals for possession of the earth.

The mustelids, as we call the members of this family (Mustelidae), include the smallest of all flesh-eaters, the weasel. Symbol of furtiveness, this little animal is nonetheless one of the most ferocious mammals on the face of the earth. It will attack creatures many times its size, including people, and will fight to the death. For centuries, too, the lowly weasel has been associated with royalty. The fur of the white weasel, known as ermine, or miniver, is as much a part of British coronations as the royal crown; it provided the trimming on the train of the gown Elizabeth II wore on the day she became queen.

Members of the weasel family are found all over the world, except in New Guinea and the Australian region. Many, like the weasel, stay on the ground. But some, such as the marten, have climbed into the trees, while others—the badger is an example—burrow in the earth. A number are good swimmers: the mink and the otter hunt in and along the watercourses. All these carnivores are medium or small in size and the female is not so large as the male. They have scent-producing glands, though not always so effective as the skunk's.

WEASELS—SMALL BUT STRONG

The Ermine, *Mustela erminea,* is the most sought after of all the weasels because of the soft and luxurious white coat it wears in win-

493

ter. In the summer, however, it looks like a different animal. Then its garb varies from yellowish brown to chocolate brown. But warm season or cold, it always wears a black tip to its tail.

The ermine seldom changes from its brown summer coat to its white winter coat before the first snow. But a long fall without snow may retard the change, and early snows hasten it. Although the transformation is a rapid one, it is no overnight affair: it may take from ten days to three weeks. The ermine does not merely alter in the pigment or color of its hair, but gradually sheds, or molts, the old coat, whereupon new, denser fur comes in. (This white phase, we shall see, is typical of the northern weasels in general, which are then loosely called "ermine" in both the Old World and the New.)

Once the change is made, the ermine remains white until the spring molt; then it changes back to the brown coat. When a spell of warm weather in midwinter melts the snow and leaves the ground bare, the white weasel's camouflage is no longer a help, but a dangerous handicap. The animal continues to move about on top of the ground as if it were quite confident that its white body did not stand out in sharp contrast to the brown background. The ermine's enemies cannot fail to see such a public invitation to dinner.

——THE ERMINE'S ENEMIES. Ermine are killed by most hawks and owls, as well as house cats. In Connecticut the author chased a Cooper's hawk that was carrying something in its claws; it soon dropped the excess weight, which turned out to be a freshly killed ermine. At Hamilton Bay in Ontario, Canada, Ernest Thompson Seton knew a youth who shot a bald eagle which had the bleached skull of a weasel attached to its throat.

These are not the only animals the ermine must seek to elude, summer or winter. All the larger flesh-eaters, including the snakes, hunt it down.

——RELENTLESS KILLERS. In their turn the weasels (of which the ermine is typical) take an almost unbelievable toll of animal life. They are without exception the most bloodthirsty, relentless slayers among the smaller mammals. A weasel kills not only to eat, but it literally kills for the sake of killing. It destroys not just littler animals and animals its own size, but also some that are many times larger. Normally it eats only red meat soaked in hot blood.

So fierce a creature must inevitably play a major part in controlling the great hordes of rodents in its homeland, the Northern Hemisphere. The ever-multiplying ranks of the despoilers and disease carriers, the rats and mice, would quickly overrun the earth were it not for the insatiable, tireless weasel.

This courageous little carnivore enters the dens of rats to fight and kill whole colonies, destroying them to the last individual before it will eat its hard-earned repast. It also preys upon rabbits, another serious pest.

Now and then it will raid a chicken coop, and this behavior has given the animal a bad name. But let there be no "Weasel words" about it—to man the weasel is more friend than foe.

Although the ermine, like other weasels, spends most of its time on the ground, it can swim; often, too, it climbs trees in search of bird nests to rob. Sometimes it may have another purpose in going aloft. The nest of a female ermine has been found in a hole of a tree trunk, fourteen feet above the ground. In typical weasel fashion, the nest was lined with rabbit fur. In it lay the head of a rabbit. The ermine must have had a difficult job hauling the head up the steep side of the tree. But the prospect of work or war seldom daunts a member of the weasel tribe.

——ERMINE AT PLAY. Ermine have their playful moods, too. At times, several will perform in a most amazing manner. They roll over each other, twist, turn, and spar with each other. Often they will spring four feet in the air and turn as perfect a somersault as any boy at play. In this gay mood the ermine utters a chuckling, happy sound in a high or a low key. (When it is angry, you will hear a loud, chattering noise from it.)

——HUNGRY BABIES. The ermine and other northern weasels usually mate in July or August, but the babies do not come until the following March or April. The den, or nursery, is a hole in the ground or under a rock (the former rat or rabbit occupant having been slain by the new tenants). There are from six to twelve young in a litter (seven or eight is average). Since each baby consumes more than half its weight in food every day, it would hardly be possible for the mother to supply the family needs without the aid of the father. Not only do both parents take an active part in caring for the young; we sometimes find a year-round association of the male and female.

The baby ermine, like so many other carnivores, is blind at birth. It weighs under two grams, is flesh colored, and has a fine, downy covering of white hair. It does not open its eyes until about thirty-five days have passed. In another week it goes on a meat diet, but remains under parental care until August. High-strung animals, continually on the move, and apparently indefatigable, the ermine reach old age in seven or eight years.

——WHERE WE FIND THEM. In adulthood, American ermine average about eight inches in head and body length, with a three-inch tail; they do not weigh much more than 3 or 4 ounces. Their range extends from the Arctic to northern Connecticut and the Great Lakes in the eastern states and about five degrees farther south in the Rocky Mountains. We find a number of different-named varieties in Europe and northern Asia, and these are about twice as large as their American cousins and belong in the same genus. (In its brown summer coat, the European ermine is popularly known as the stoat.)

All in all, we may observe that the ermine's range covers pretty much the region of heavy snowfall in the Northern Hemisphere, a fact that has been extremely significant in the animal's development.

Why Some Weasels Are White in Winter. We have suggested that the underlying reason for the remarkable whitening of the winter coat of the ermine (or, for that matter, of the weasels that we generally find in the northern part of the world) is protective coloration. These weasels are always white where snow lies deep on the ground all winter and every winter.

Where there is never, or rarely, any snow, weasels are brown in winter. The color change, where there is one, is effected by a molt in the autumn and one in the spring, we have seen. But even the weasels that are brown in winter undergo the same two annual molts. These animals change coats, although not colors.

The change from a brown summer to a white winter coat is hereditary. A brown weasel—from an area where no seasonal changes in color take place—if kept in the north where there is deep snow, would still be brown, winter after winter. If a white weasel (one born and raised in the north) is transferred to the south where there is no snow, it will continue to turn white every winter. The change, we perceive, is a calendar routine; neither snow nor temperature is the direct cause.

Until recently, the mechanism of the color changes was a mystery. Now we know they are actually determined by the amount of light. As the days get shorter in the fall, the weasel receives less light through its eyes. This causes the pituitary gland to stop producing a substance known as gonadotropic hormones. The lack of these hormones deprives the hair cells of pigment, and the new hair growing under such conditions is of course white.

In the spring, the story is exactly the opposite. The nights get shorter. The increasing amount of light coming through the eyes of the weasel now stimulates the pituitary gland and increases the pigment in the hair cells, which gives color to the hair in the spring molt.

EXCEEDINGLY ALERT AND WARY

The weasel is the smallest of the flesh-eaters, but what it lacks in size it makes up in ferocity. This short-legged beast hunts by scent and is a relentless killer of mice, rats, moles, rabbits, and poultry. Northern weasels wear a snow-white coat in winter, a brown one in other seasons.

A white weasel kept in a dark place would have a tendency to stay white through lack of light, but because of heredity would change to brown with the spring molt or white with the fall molt.

Color changes in other animals like the snowshoe rabbit are effected in a similar manner. It is interesting to note that cave-dwelling animals that live in near total darkness, such as fish and salamanders, are often white. These same creatures would have color if they lived in the light. Some late-flying bats that roost in dark caves are also white. Most of the animals we find in the Arctic regions, where the light is never strong, are white: examples are the Arctic fox, the polar bear, the snowy owl, and the white gyrfalcons.

The Long-tailed Weasel, *Mustela frenata,* is the common species of the weasel and the one we usually see in most parts of the United States, where it takes the place of the ermine; its range extends from the Great Lakes in Canada to Ecuador and Peru in South America.

This animal's typical color is deep reddish-brown, grading to almost black. The tropical American weasel has on its face a white marking in the form of a bridle—"bridled weasel" is actually the meaning of its scientific name. Only in the northern part of its range does the long-tailed weasel turn white in winter. Then people often refer to it as an ermine, though it is really another species.

The long-tailed weasel seems to prefer more open country than its shorter-tailed, more northern cousin. We find it in regions where there is an abundance of small animal life upon which it can feed. In search of food it may cover several miles in a single day, but usually it moves about in an area of not more than fifteen acres.

Little Bridle-Face's home life is like that of the other weasels. It lives in a shallow burrow in the ground. The den is usually some six inches or so below the surface and the nest chamber about ten or twelve inches in diameter. It provides a fine warm lining for the nest —chiefly the fur of its victims.

June or July is the mating season for the long-tailed weasels, as a rule. There is a period of delayed development of the embryos as with all weasels, and babies are born from 220 to 337 days after mating time. The weasel mother finds from four to eight young in her litter. They will average about three grams each when a day old —no substantial weight when you consider that a cigarette weighs about a gram. In two weeks they are clothed in a silky white coat.

By the time the young weasels open their eyes (on the thirty-sixth or thirty-seventh day) they are well on the road to maturity: these "babies" are weaned when five or six weeks old and full grown at ten weeks. Naturalists who have studied the long-tailed weasel closely, claim that both parents work together in caring for the young, and this would indicate pairing for life.

The weight of full-grown males may reach six ounces, while the head and body generally span about ten inches. The tail may measure close to half a foot in length. Is that really long? Only in comparison with other weasels' tails, and so we call this one the long-tailed weasel.

There are many forms of long-tailed weasels, including the well-known New York Weasel, but all are subspecies of *Mustela frenata*. The bridled weasel is the one you are most likely to encounter in South and Central America.

The Short-tailed Weasel, or Snow Weasel, *Mustela nivalis,* a common animal in the Old World, is a creature for which the author has a special affection. As a boy, in England, he made a pet of one. When he found it, it was only a baby, having been dropped by its fleeing mother. He fed the tiny weasel on warm milk until it was able to eat raw meat. Gentle and friendly, it never lost its amiable disposition and loved to hide inside the author's shirt for warmth.

However, a full-grown male that the author caught in a mole runway had an entirely different temperament. This weasel lived on in captivity for six months, but never did it change its ferocious nature. The animal remained savage and intractable, permitting no one to pet it, and would attempt to sink its teeth into any moving object that came near. Such behavior is typical of its kind.

——AN ANIMAL OF GREAT RAPACITY. The short-tailed weasel feeds primarily on mice; it may also climb low shrubbery to stalk birds. It has larders in crevices and holes in trees in which it stores food. What a good supply of meat this hungry little butcher keeps! One such storehouse was found to contain three wrens, one goldcrest, one chaffinch, one mouse, two pigeon heads, one pigeon leg, and other remains unidentifiable.

Those who know this beast well, have many anecdotes to relate concerning its tenaciousness, courage, and rapacity. For example, more than one dog has retrieved a rabbit to which a short-tailed weasel was still clinging, unwilling to loosen its hold on the prey's throat. On one occasion an English kestrel was seen to rise a good thirty feet in the air and let something drop; it turned out to be a dead rat with a weasel grimly hanging to it. Few records of dauntlessness can equal these.

Call a person a weasel, to suggest that he is cowardly or a sneak? That would hardly be doing justice to the fearless weasel.

——"DANDY DOGS." According to tradition, the short-tailed weasel travels and hunts in company after dark. This may well tie in with a superstition that still lingers in the west of England to the effect that hares are hunted at night by packs of little fairy hounds known as "dandy dogs." The local country folk will assure you that they have watched them with awe.

The author has found sufficient evidence to prove that the weasel often travels and hunts in packs of up to eight individuals. However, it is generally one family that is involved.

——SMALL ENOUGH TO ENTER MOLE RUNWAYS. No need to guess where the short-tailed weasel gets its name. The tail (which lacks the black tip characteristic of many other species) is only two and one-half inches long; the rest of the animal may be eight inches. This weasel is small enough to enter underground burrows; it has turned up in the author's mole traps, caught as it traveled along the runways of the garden mole in search of prey.

The short-tailed weasel makes its home in Great Britain (where it is called a weasel, as opposed to a stoat or ermine), Europe, and Asia; we encounter related forms in Egypt and on the islands of the Mediterranean. The short-tail has brown fur, but, like its long-tailed relatives in the New World, it will wear a white winter coat in the northern part of its range.

The Least or Pygmy Weasel, *Mustela rixosa,* is the smallest of the weasel tribe. It is only about six inches long, and has a one-inch tail with hardly a trace of the usual black tip. In summer this little fellow is a uniform reddish brown on the upper parts, and white below; in winter it is an unbroken white.

No wide-roaming hunter is the pygmy weasel. It has a maximum home range of about two acres and seldom travels far from its burrow in the ground. However, having cleared one area of mice, it moves on to another.

When the pygmy settles in a new locality, it selects a mouse's nest in some concealed place either on the surface or, more often, underground. It immediately starts to line the nest with hair plucked from its victims. The pygmy will carry mice into the den and consume them there. Sometimes it will store them in connecting galleries.

The pygmy differs from its relatives in that it has no fixed breeding season. Its young may be born in any month of the year, but spring and winter seem to be the commonest times. The average litter contains four or five babies; however, there may be up to ten.

The homeland of the pygmy is the northern regions of the earth. We find the animal spread across Europe and east as far as Siberia. In North America it is present from Alaska south to Nebraska and, in the eastern United States, in the Allegheny Mountains of Pennsylvania. In Alaska it is highly regarded by the Indians, who view the capture of the least weasel as a piece of good fortune. One old Indian claimed that his brother, who had caught one when he was a child, had in consequence become a "big chief."

The Kolinsky, *Mustela siberica,* the large yellow weasel of northeastern Asia, is perhaps better known dyed and made up into a fur coat than as a wild animal. It got its name from Kola, a district in northeastern Russia, where the best pelts come from. Kolinsky also goes under such names as Shantung, China mink, Japanese mink, and yellow mink. For the living animal the natives of northern China have the most picturesque name of all—they call it *huang shu lang,* meaning "yellow rat wolf."

The author caught a number of the big yellow weasels along the banks of frozen rivers in Siberia. He found them still active at temperatures 60 degrees below zero, and was surprised at their resemblance to mink in all respects except color—even their habits were like the mink's. Although the fur lacks the luxuriant luster of our true mink, still kolinsky is an important item in the trade.

A related species, the Alpine Weasel, lives in the high mountains of Tibet. The Java Weasel is even more minklike than the kolinsky, but, as you have probably guessed, the fur of tropical weasels is a poor grade. In northern Burma and Indo-China we find the only weasel with a striped back.

MINKS—FISHERS AND HUNTERS

The Mink, *Mustela (Lutreola) vison,* looks like a weasel, only one grown large and robust. It has the same long, supple body and short limbs. It has the same murderous habits, too, with even greater power and skill to exercise them.

This weasel-like creature can and does hunt fish. With a normal swimming rate of some two miles an hour, it catches the wily trout in fast-running streams. It can swim faster under water than a muskrat but not so far or so deep. No matter—it catches the muskrat often enough.

The mink wreaks terrific havoc among marsh birds, and young snapping turtles also fall prey to it. Like the weasel, the mink is fond of rats, mice, and rabbits, which it hunts in the woods and bushes. Unlike the weasel, it does not seem to practice killing so much for the sheer joy of it.

THE MINK'S LAIR

The mink is chiefly active at night, but you may see it about at any hour of the day. It makes its home near watercourses, on the margin between the dry land and deep water. Here an individual's territory covers an area about five miles in diameter, over which the animal ranges for its food supply. Its lair is a hollow tree, a crevice in the rocks, or a burrow dug in a river bank.

Often this carnivorous creature will carry its kill home and eat it. A mink's lair is always littered with the bones and scales of its victims. Where there is good hunting and fishing, a whole week's supply of dead fish and animals may be cached in the mink's storehouse. In one mink's den, for example, thirteen muskrats and three waterfowl were found.

RUNNING AND PLAYING

On land, the mink is not so swift as the weasel. It may gallop along with arched back or walk at a rapid, nervous pace. In a lighter frame of mind, it has been known to slide down hillsides in simple, playful fun. On one occasion a mink was seen to make eight slides, one after another, down a snowbank.

ENEMIES OF THE MINK

A mink's life is not all hunting and playing, however. The large owls sometimes swoop down upon it from the air; sometimes the lynx and the fox eat it. The stench the mink produces from its musk glands, although more potent than the weasel's, and extremely annoying to human beings, is not effective enough to drive larger enemies away. The mink will put up a good fight, however, before it is taken.

FAMILY LIFE AMONG THE MINKS

The mink mates in February and March. About a month and a half later, the litter comes, with four to eight sightless, almost naked kittens in it. They open their eyes when five weeks old, and at about this time they begin to eat solid food. The father pitches in and helps the mother to find it for them.

During their adolescent age the young are very playful—in a sav-

THE MINK PATROLS LAKES AND STREAMS
The lustrous fur of the mink has such great value that the animal is now raised in large numbers on farms in the Scandinavian countries, Canada, and the United States. Hundreds of thousands of the animals are also taken in the wild. A fierce and active creature, the mink feeds on much the same fare as the weasel, plus fish, frogs, and crayfish.

age sort of way. Their games are mostly of the rough-house type: they spring and jump at each other, lose their tempers and squeal, hiss, or growl angrily. As they grow older, they begin to fight and quarrel in earnest. Now, too, they are getting big and strong enough to earn their own keep, and they follow their mother and father on hunting trips.

For most of the summer, the family remains together, hunting or frolicking. With fall comes an end and a beginning. Each of the minks goes its own way to find a new territory in which to settle. At this time of the year they often travel a considerable distance from water, cutting across from one watershed to another.

MINK FUR AND FARMS

Mink fur is a staple item in the fur trade. It is fine and beautiful, with great durability and an attractive natural dark brown color. It is perhaps the most popular fur in the market and always commands a high price.

Throughout the world, about a million mink are taken each year. So great has been the demand, that it laid the basis for a new industry, mink farming, which began almost a hundred years ago. Mink farming has released some of the pressure on the wild mink, and today over two hundred thousand ranch-raised animals are harvested annually in the United States, most of them in Louisiana.

MALE AND FEMALE

An adult mink (male) weighs about two pounds. It is about two feet long, and its rather bushy tail is roughly a third as long again. The soft, thick underfur is overlaid with long black glistening guard hairs, which protect the animal's coat when there is swimming to be done. It may have white spots on its chin and throat. The female is smaller, but has the same coloring.

Where We Find Them. The mink is found over nearly all of North America from the Gulf of Mexico to the Arctic, and in the Old World from northeastern Asia to Finland and from southwestern France to eastern Rumania. There are a number of different geographical forms but only two living species: the American Mink, *Mustela vison,* and the European Mink, *Mustela lutreola.*

MOTHER AND YOUNG SKUNKS INSPECT AN OLD TRESTLE
When the skunk appears, human beings are likely to depart, yet this striped, cat-sized creature is more a force for good than evil. Not only does the common skunk consume insect pests in large number; it is also a destroyer of rodents. Occasionally, though, it preys on poultry.

A larger species, the Sea Mink, *Mustela macrodon,* used to be found along the coast of Maine and the adjoining Canadian seashore, but it died out about one hundred years ago. Today the only relics of this animal are fragments of skulls from the Indian shell heaps at Brookline, Hancock County, Maine.

POLECATS AND FERRETS

The Common Polecat or Fitch, *Mustela putorius,* is the only member of the weasel family that has been truly domesticated. This legendary animal is about the size of an alley cat, with a bushy tail. The beautiful soft fur is uniformly buffy gray in color, overshadowed with black-tipped hairs.

There seems to be some question as to where the polecat got its name. It could be just plain "Polish cat" but more likely it was derived from the Gaelic for "pool cat," signifying a cat that lives in a hole in the ground. The French word *poule*—it means "fowl" or "hen"—is another possibility, as the polecat is noted for robbing chicken pens.

The popular word "polecat," signifying an evil-smelling animal, originated with this animal, but formerly the name had no such meaning. The American skunk is sometimes called a polecat because of its odor.

The polecat is a homebody and a good housekeeper. Its den is usually a hole in a well-drained dry bank or among the rocks. There is an outside toilet, a warm nest chamber (the polecat loves comfort) and a connecting runway that leads to the larder, which is kept well stocked with good things to eat. Here one may find birds, rats, rabbits, and reptiles. In one polecat's pantry were found fifty frogs and toads; all were alive, but each had been bitten through the brain and thus rendered helpless.

March and April is the time for courting, and both parents take an active interest in the family that comes forty days later. The kittens are born like so many other young animals—naked, without sight, and quite dependent. They open their eyes for the first time twenty-one days later.

Baby polecats make their first appearance in the outside world when six weeks old. They love to sport and play and in the warm sunshine they dance around each other in a most amusing manner.

At the first sign of danger, however, the little playfellows dive for home after colliding with, and falling over, each other in their terrified scramble to get safely underground. The life span of these animals is nine or ten years.

We have seen that in earlier days the polecat did not possess the reputation of being an evil-smelling creature. Attacked by dogs, or badly scared, it can, like the skunk, eject a nauseating liquid secretion from the musk glands situated at the base of the tail. But normally it makes every attempt to escape before resorting to chemical warfare. When it is kept in captivity there is no indication of an offensive odor.

——Polecat Hunting. Fifty years ago polecat hunting was a popular sport in the north of England. The chase, generally conducted on moonlit nights with a pack of hounds (a cross between otter hounds and fox terriers), would cover a distance of six or seven miles. In the sporting field the polecat was known as the foumart ("foul marten") to distinguish it from the sweet marten and on account of the objectionable odor it emitted when captured by the hounds.

——Where We Find It. The polecat is at home in semiwooded and open country in Europe, from Great Britain east to Siberia and Mongolia and south to the Himalayas. In North Africa it makes its home in the mountains of the western Rif, in Morocco. There are three species.

HUNTING WITH FERRETS

The Domesticated Polecat, *Mustela furo* ("weasel thief"), is the common ferret. It is well known in Europe but has scarcely been heard of in America. Because they possess long, slender bodies and a keen desire to kill, ferrets are used to drive rabbits and rats out of their holes so that they can be shot, or killed by dogs.

Ferreting has been a popular sport in Europe for several centuries, but it was practiced in Asia as early as the first century before Christ. The ancient tribes of that continent selected the smaller wild species, *Mustela eversmanni,* for their purpose. It has since been crossed with the larger European polecat, but in the selective breeding of ferrets the smaller polecats are used. Ferreting was also a common sport with the Romans. Strabo states that ferrets were originally brought from Africa to Spain; Pliny was familiar with the sport in his day and refers to it as being practiced in hunting rabbits.

——CATCHING RABBITS AND RATS. There are three methods used in ferreting—one for catching rats and two for rabbits. In rabbit hunting the ferret is muzzled with a "cope," made by looping a piece of twine around the muzzle and over the back of the ferret's head (to keep the mouth closed so that the animal cannot kill rabbits it corners in a dead-end warren). The ferret is then turned loose in the rabbit hole. The escaping rabbit is shot by a gunner or netted in a bag placed over the hole.

The second practice is to hold the ferret on a line and let it down into a dead-end rabbit hole. When the hunters have determined that the ferret has come upon the rabbits, they sink holes in the ground a yard or so apart to locate the line, and trace it in this way until the rabbits are located.

Hunting for rats is a far commoner sport. Favorite places are cornfields and the vicinity of farm buildings. After finding the ratholes, the hunter unleashes his ferret without a muzzle, and then stands ready with the terriers. It is not long before the ferret drives its prey into the open. There may be a whole pack of rats—three or more—and exciting moments follow as the terriers dash after them and bring them to earth.

The male ferret is called a "hob" and the female a "jill." These animals have been dependent on man for a livelihood for so many years that they cannot survive without human care. A lost ferret will die if it is not recovered in a few days.

——HEALING POWERS OF THE FERRET. The ferret enjoys great esteem in the folklore of the superstitious peasantry of Europe, especially for its supposed power to heal the sick. Particularly efficacious, we are told, is milk that the ferret has instilled with a curative quality merely by tasting it. To quote an old Irishman: "Doctors give 'er up and she comin' to directly by a drop o' milk the blessed little craythur had been a-lappin' at; and it's the only rale remedy ye can put ye're intire faith in."

OTHER INTERESTING FERRETS AND POLECATS

While the Black-footed Ferret, *Mustela nigripes,* resembles the ferret and the polecat in size and general appearance, it in reality is an entirely different animal. This big, yellowish-buff weasel with the black feet is at home on the Great Plains and prairies of the United States, from North Dakota and Montana south to Texas, the region originally covered by the prairie dog towns. Since the dogs, its chief source of food, have all but disappeared on the western plains, the black-footed ferret is on the road to extinction.

In the Gobi Desert and the steppe country west to Rumania and Hungary dwells a very ornate little polecat, the Tiger Weasel, *Vormela.* The Afghans' name for it is "gorkhus" or "grave-digger," because they believe it frequents burial grounds. It is about thirteen inches long, plus a seven-inch tail, and is capable of emitting a disagreeable odor.

This animal's color pattern is most unusual for a member of the weasel family. It is a deep reddish-brown, almost black, broken by numerous dots and dashes of reddish-brown color.

Though a creature of the open desert, where there are a few trees the tiger weasel climbs them freely.

MARTENS AND SABLES—PRECIOUS FUR-BEARERS

The True Martens and Sables, *Martes,* have the finest and most beautiful fur of all the carnivores—it is even more durable than that of the chinchillas. It is deep, soft, full, and generally rich golden brown in color.

Indeed, these lords of the treetops have a most comely appearance. The head is well formed, and the ears are rather large and evenly rounded. A throat patch of creamy buff sets off the golden brown of the long body. The tail, about half the length of the cat-sized body, is bushy as a fox's.

The marten (or sable—the names are often interchanged) dwells among the thick forests of the Northern Hemisphere. An active and agile climber, it can chase up a tree like lightning. It easily outstrips the speedy squirrels, which then must pay with their lives. So many squirrels does the marten eat, that we may almost call it one of nature's checks upon the tribe of nut hoarders.

A SAVAGE FIGHTER

Possessed of the typical ferocity of the weasel family, the marten will sometimes fight animals many times its size. There is a remarkable instance where a marten attacked a cheviot sheep in Scotland. The sheep was found dead with its neck jammed against a rock; underneath its neck lay the marten, killed, apparently, by the impact when the sheep, in the final struggle, had dashed against the rock. The sheep had died from loss of blood through a wound in its throat.

Normally, the little marten feeds on smaller animals. Prominent on its menu are grouse, mice, and rabbits. In the fall, when the berries are ripe on the mountain ash, the marten grows fat on this fruit.

So sharp are the marten's claws and wits, that few other creatures, outside man, can kill it. The great horned owl and the lynx are said to have occasional success. Unless its days are shortened by these animals or by trappers, the marten has a life span of seventeen years or so.

A LIFE OF COMFORT

A worshiper of warmth and comfort, the marten loves to lounge on the limb of a large tree and bask in the sunshine. Inside a hollow tree (but sometimes in a burrow) the marten builds its moss-lined den, at some distance above ground level. The animal's pet aversion is water, and on a wet day it will stay home and go hungry rather than get its dainty feet wet. It does not hibernate in the winter.

FOUR BLIND LITTLE BABIES

The mating of martens takes place in July and August. It is a long time before the young—usually four per litter—are born. Not until April or May do they come into the world. Still, the kittens are naked, and without sight at birth. When they are five weeks old, their eyes open. Father isn't interested in the babies; their mother has complete charge until the fall. At this time the young martens, with their long, sinuous bodies, look much like their parents and are ready to set up housekeeping on their own in the trees.

Except in the breeding season, the martens live alone and hunt alone. Squirrel-like, these animals bury excess food. Leaping from one branch to another, sometimes descending to the ground, they will hunt mile after mile, pursuing the hapless squirrels high and low, not giving up the chase until the prey has found safety in some hole too small for a marten to enter—or, more likely, has died from a sharp bite through the neck.

FATAL CURIOSITY

Although the marten has a distaste for human companionship and moves back as civilization advances, it has not learned to avoid man-made traps; in fact, it is one of the easiest animals to catch in the North Woods of Canada. The more obvious a trap, the better are its chances of catching a marten—due, no doubt, to the unrestrained curiosity of the animal.

HUNTING THE MARTEN

The high price set on the pelt of the marten—a good one is worth its weight in gold, ounce for ounce—leaves little chance of the animal's survival. It is not a fast breeder and probably mates only every second year.

Trappers have been whittling down the marten's numbers for a long time. The Hudson's Bay Company's take in 1743 was already as high as fifteen thousand pelts. Still, the animal could find comparative safety by retreating further into more remote, snow-shrouded forests. Not so today. Using planes, trappers penetrate deeper and deeper into the marten's last strongholds. Some twenty thousand martens continue to be trapped annually in Canada, but the present stock cannot stand such a drain on its number much longer.

THE FABULOUS RUSSIAN SABLE AND OTHERS

There are a number of different species and subspecies of martens and sables. Perhaps the most famous is the Russian Sable, *Martes zibellina,* which ranges from European Russia across through Siberia to Japan. Its fur is exceedingly precious—so much so that the search for it lured men into the frozen wastes of Siberia long ago, and to no small degree laid the basis for the early development of that land, just as the hunt for the furs of other animals helped to open up Canada and the western United States.

Anyone who has ever seen Russian sable can appreciate why it is so highly valued. It is exquisitely soft, delicately textured fur; each hair is evenly tapered to a fine point. The general color of the coat is gray-brown, with underfur varying from soft gray to light yellowish-brown (though some sable pelts are almost black, beautifully and evenly flecked with white hairs). The most esteemed grade of sable skins generally comes from the smaller animals.

Artists' "Sable" Brushes. Although artists will tell you that the best brushes they use—brushes that come to a fine point when wet—are made from the hairs of the sable's tail, this is an instance of mislabeling; the so-called "sable" brushes are actually made from the hairs of the kolinsky (and that animal, we have seen, is more a weasel than a true mink).

Tassels of the Tungus. The sable is a tradition not only with those who can afford it, but also with the people in its home territory. The Tungus tribes of Siberia admire it greatly, and it plays an important part in the culture of this Mongoloid people. Elaborate decorative patterns in native clothing represent two sables fighting. The tribesmen's coats of scarlet and blue are worked in these patterns; so, too, are their gloves and shoes. Nearly every native tribesman has a tassel to his cap that is supposed to be the tail of a sable—but in most instances it turns out to be a squirrel tail!

Stone Marten and Sweet Marten. The Stone Marten or Beech Marten, *Martes foina,* has fur which is not so fine as that of the more northern species. We find this animal in continental Europe and east to Mongolia and China. It is the common marten of central Eurasia but it never did occur in England. There, the European Pine Marten, *Martes martes,* is the usual species, though it is rare today. Its range covers the wooded regions of Europe from Britain across to Asia.

The European pine marten is dark brown with a cream-buff throat patch; it has a head and body length of nineteen inches and a tail half as long again. Hundreds of years ago, when the creature was more abundant in England, hunting it was a favorite sport. To distinguish this animal from its evil-smelling relative the European polecat, or foumart ("foul marten"), it is sometimes called the "sweet marten."

The American Pine Marten. About the same size is the American Pine Marten, or Hudson Bay Sable, *Martes americana,* which lives chiefly in Canada from the Great Lakes north to the timber line and west to Alaska. This marten possesses a handsomer fur; it is rather pale buff-brown in color, and shadowed with the dark tips of the long guard hairs.

The "Honey Dog." In the wooded mountainous country of eastern Asia dwells the Yellow-throated Marten, *Charronia*. It is larger than the pine marten, growing up to two feet in length, and has a longer tail (about seventeen inches). Its general body color is dark brown, almost black; the chin and throat are white, and the under parts are yellow or bright orange.

The Manchurians call the yellow-throated marten a *mi-kow,* or "honey dog," because it has a sweet tooth. This large, robust marten has been seen in China, now and again, sitting outside a beehive snapping at the honey bees going in and out; apparently it is attracted there by the smell of the honey.

The yellow-throated marten is also fond of fruit, berries, and nectar from flowers, and sometimes it will hang by its hind feet from one branch while reaching for fruit on another. But otherwise this animal is close to the pine marten in its ways.

THE FISHER—MOST FEROCIOUS OF THE MARTENS

The Fisher, *Martes pennanti,* is the terror of the American North Woods. When angry, it is the embodiment of unrestrained fury. Its eyes blazing with a green glow, it hisses, snarls, and screams its hatred at an aggressor. With its back arched and fur bristling, it presents a front that few animals would dare approach. It can whip any dog or coyote, or even a black bear in single combat, and send them scurrying off to lick their wounds.

The Fearless Fisher. Though streamlined like its relative the weasel, the fisher has tremendous power. Every living thing it can master (and that includes all but the largest carnivores in its home range) is food for the fisher—fox, lynx, raccoon, as well as rabbits, mice, rats, squirrels, grouse, amphibians, and reptiles are preyed on by the whirlwind spitfire. According to reports, it will kill deer, and probably mountain sheep are hard put to defend themselves against it.

Killing the Porcupine. The fisher is the only carnivorous animal that habitually assaults the porcupine and suffers no ill effects from the spines: it swallows the barbed quills like a carnival glass-chewer.

The fisher knows just how to get past the porcupine's guard without being clubbed by the needle-spiked tail. It speedily sinks its sharp teeth into the unprotected throat or the under side, and the porcupine is no more.

For the fisher, killing the porcupine in the snow is a much-relished pastime. Sometimes the porcupine hides its vulnerable head under a rock or a log and rattles its deadly tail, daring the fisher to come closer. The wily fisher has an answer for that one; it burrows under the snow and gets the porcupine from below.

Fishers Are Big Martens. What manner of savage beast is the fisher? In reality, the animal is a large marten. It looks a good deal like the pine marten, only its fur is dark and not so fine, and the ears are shorter and more rounded. From the tip of its nose to the end of its foot-long tail it may measure four feet (females are smaller). It weighs up to eighteen pounds.

Sometimes the fisher is known as the Pekan, Pennant's Marten, or the Black "Cat." Fisher seems to be the most popular name, though oddly enough the animal does not fish.

A Great Climber, Leaper, and Swimmer. The fisher, if it is found at all, will be seen near watercourses in forested lowlands. It can swim across swift rivers and broad lakes. In the trees it is one of the swiftest of climbers, and even races down tree trunks head first (many other animals back down cautiously). Traveling on the ground, it bounds along, covering four feet at each leap.

This carnivore is a night prowler, and is active the year round. It may stay in its den during a severe storm, but ordinary snow and rain will not keep the fisher home.

The Fisher Family. The fisher's breeding habits remind us of the marten's. Its favorite den is a hollow tree. It mates in April, and the young are not born until eleven months later.

The fisher family consists of about four babies. They see the light of day seven weeks after birth and do not venture outside the den until they are fully three months old. Throughout, they are exclusively under their mother's care.

In the fall, the young are ready to investigate distant fields and find a home for themselves. They reach full maturity when two years old, but females will breed within a year from birth.

A Scarce Animal. The fisher may be encountered from northern New England northwest to the lower Mackenzie River, Canada, south in the Rocky Mountains to Wyoming, and almost to San Francisco Bay on the Pacific coast. Though it has lingered longer than the marten in many parts of its range—a clever beast, it readily recognizes traps and is adept at robbing them—it never was very common anywhere, and is now quite rare, even in remote parts of Canada.

Today there is on an average not more than one fisher to a hundred square miles in its present range. Most of the pelts that come into the market are from Quebec, Ontario, and British Columbia.

TAYRAS, GRISONS, AND ZORILLAS

"WEASEL BADGERS" OF SOUTH AMERICA

South America has its own particular group of "weasel badgers." Largest of all is the Tayra, *Eira,* which haunts the tropical forests and brush country from southern Mexico to Bolivia and Paraguay. The tayra measures two feet in length without the seventeen-inch tail, and is a long-bodied, short-legged animal, coal-black in color except for the head and neck, which vary from almost black to nearly white.

Being a good climber, the tayra spends much of its time in the trees hunting for fruit, berries and birds' eggs, but almost anything edible is food for it. It is socially inclined and travels in family groups. This animal's bold and curious nature is often its undoing; it will fearlessly approach an armed man and learn too late he is no one to take lightly.

A much smaller animal, the Grison, *Grison,* is a neighbor of the tayra. It resembles a tiny gray badger and lives in the ground. We can distinguish it from yet another interesting "weasel badger," the Quiqui or Huron, *Grisonella,* of Argentina and Chile, by the broad white line that extends across the face and back along the outside of the grison's neck. The quiqui is trained by the natives to drive the chinchillas out of their dens in the rocks.

ZORILLAS AND STRIPED "WEASELS"

On the other side of the world there are a number of other small carnivores that also combine characteristics of both the weasels and badgers. The Zorilla, *Ictonyx,* known locally as the Striped Muishond ("mouse hound"), is the most familiar species in Africa. It ranges from the Cape north to the Isthmus of Suez and into Asia Minor. Its long, loose fur is marked with black and white lines that extend from the head to the lengthy white tail. This creature is not more than fifteen inches in head and body length.

In general the zorilla and its close relatives (among them there is a Striped "Weasel") are useful animals as they destroy large numbers of snakes, small rodents, and injurious insects (they will also kill birds up to the size of a guinea fowl). When attacked by dogs, the zorilla ejects a nauseating musky fluid in the face of the attacker and then feigns death until the coast is clear. Thus it combines in its defense the pacifist characteristic of the American opossum with the positive action of the skunk.

WOLVERINES—RUTHLESS DESTROYERS

The Wolverine, *Gulo,* is one of the most thievish, daring, and powerful animals in the world. It is the biggest member of the weasel family, and none exceeds it in ferocity and cunning.

NOT MUCH LIKE A WOLF

The wolverine got its name because it was supposed to resemble the wolf. It possesses that animal's savage nature, but in general it is built more like a badger. The fearless wolverine will slay almost any animal in its range, including the deer.

Not many people know this shaggy, four-foot-long creature that prowls the northlands. But as it stalks along, the animals that glimpse the dark-brown bearlike form, with the telltale broad ribbon of pale brown fur on each side, start up and look for refuge. Even the massive bear, the wolf, and the mountain lion, gorging themselves on their kill, will move off rather than contest its possession against the sharp claws and teeth of the wolverine.

NO QUARTER ASKED OR GIVEN

The wolverine is a killer. When it fights, it fights to win; it neither asks nor gives quarter, and it does not know the meaning of fear.

Not fast on foot when compared to the caribou and mountain sheep, the wolverine captures both of these large animals by stalking them stealthily and craftily. It will climb into a tree or up on a high rock and leap upon them, sinking its teeth into their neck. Almost no four-footed mammal, including the bear and possibly the puma, is secure against its attack.

Trappers hate the wolverine. Their traps, to it, are like so many free-lunch counters. It will remove the bait and eat it, then, more likely than not, damage the traps or carry them off.

Woe betide the trapper whose cabin the wolverine enters! Later he will find everything in confusion: tea, flour, pots, and pans are scattered hither and yon, his meat supply is gone, and the foul odor of the animal's scent glands is everywhere. What the wolverine cannot eat, it befouls. This is the way it protects its own caches, too, from other prowlers.

"THE GLUTTON"

The wolverine got its name because of its supposed resemblance to the wolf, either in its looks or its habits or both. It is also known as the Carcajou or Skunk-Bear. Another common name, and well deserved at that, is "glutton." This animal indeed possesses a ravenous appetite. It appears always to be hungry. No other carnivore, we are sometimes told, can devour so much in a single meal.

Occasionally the wolverine will clean up a whole deer or a caribou in what may seem to be a continuous feast, but what is really a number of successive meals. Accordingly, there is a tradition that the wolverine consumes more than its own weight in food at one time. This is simply not true. An average wolverine weighs thirty or thirty-five pounds; a big one, fifty. It never eats such a poundage in one repast. To understand this ferocious beast's hunger, you must realize that there are long gaps between its meals; sometimes its fasts may last a week or two.

The famous old scientists Linnaeus and Pallas showed they were well acquainted with the wolverine's habits when they named one common species *Gulo luscus.* The first half of the name means "glutton"; the second half refers to the animal's poor eyesight, and could be translated as "half-blind." The wolverine gives marked evidence that it cannot see well. It will sit up on its haunches and shade its eyes with a fore paw in a most human manner. This curious habit has been witnessed on several occasions, and one of the animals frequently repeated the performance. Since the wolverine is subject to snow-blindness, we may suppose it shields its eyes to protect them from bright sunlight when peering into the distance.

THE SOLITARY WOLVERINE

The wolverine is solitary in its habits. After a brief courtship in February or early March, the male and female split up, each going its own way.

The female's den may be a hollow tree, a cavern among rocks, or any hideaway that is comfortable and sheltered. Here, during the warm days of June, when the sun never sets in the northland for four long weeks, the young—they rarely number more than two or three —are born. The babies are clad in thick woolly fur. Their mother takes good care of them, and by fall they are half-grown. When the first snow flies, they must forage for themselves.

A FUR THAT DOES NOT FREEZE

Wolverine fur is not outstandingly valuable in the fur market, but it does have a unique use. It is the only type of fur that does not mat and freeze when the temperature drops to sixty or seventy degrees below zero. The Eskimos are well aware of this: they trim their parkas with wolverine fur around the hood and sleeves, where body moisture escapes. Any ordinary fur will freeze to the face and wrists under conditions of extreme cold, but wolverine fur remains unchanged. Nowadays the makers of aviators' clothing are borrowing a leaf from the Eskimos' book.

The range of the wolverine in North America extends from the southern islands of the Arctic Ocean across the Barren Lands to southern Quebec in the east, and to Colorado and southeastern California in the west. It is now practically gone from the United States; the last individual had disappeared from Michigan, the Wolverine State, long before any official record was made that the species had been exterminated there.

There are three species found in North America: the American Wolverine, the Mt. McKinley Wolverine, and the Southern Wolverine. In Europe and Asia, the animal is found in the Arctic and sub-Arctic regions, but it is fast vanishing everywhere.

BADGERS—FAMED AS DIGGERS

THE COMMON BADGER OF EUROPE AND ASIA

The Eurasian Badger, *Meles,* was the subject of a bloody sport in England in the early part of the last century. This tough, wedge-shaped little animal was placed in a barrel or a man-made hole inside a pit, and dogs were loosed upon it. With its long, sharp claws and its strong teeth, it fought back as best it could as the dogs tried to draw it from its hole.

This cruel pastime, ended by law in 1850, has left its mark in our language, but nowadays we are more likely to badger people than to badger the badger.

The Badger's Badge. Upon its face the Eurasian badger wears the badge for which it is named. Each side of the white head is marked with a conspicuous black line that runs from the nose over and surrounding the eye and over the ear. Its body looks gray to us for each hair is partly black and partly white. (Badger hair is used in the manufacture of the best shaving brushes; in fact, the French word *blaireau* means both "shaving brush" and "badger.")

This animal measures up to three feet long, and, with its short black legs and stump of a tail, suggests a small bear. It weighs about twenty-seven pounds, on an average.

The Badger at Home. Lacking the ferocity of the weasel and the wolverine, the badger prefers to use its claws for digging. A shy, cautious creature, it spends the daylight hours underground, in the home it has excavated for itself. Its den, or "earth," is usually in a wooded hillside, at the end of "sets," or holes, which may penetrate for a hundred yards or more. These subterranean tunnels form a winding labyrinth three (badger) stories deep. The entrances are always marked by huge piles of dirt, indicating that the animal is constantly at work enlarging and improving the "earth."

The badger likes to sleep on a bed of dry leaves, moss, and straw. But first it must collect them and bring them underground, and it goes about the job in a most painstaking way. To begin with, the badger gathers the bedding up into a small heap. Next it cuddles the bundle between its forepaws and nose. Taking care that it does not lose any of its cargo, the badger shuffles backward to the entrance. Now it backs down into the hole, and so to the den.

Mating Time. It is not unusual for several families to occupy the same badger "earth" during August and September, but they separate before the winter sets in. Mating season for the badgers extends from July to mid-November. The sow normally has one litter a year, in February or March. Her usual number of babies is two but occasionally she bears triplets. The young grow rapidly, and are ready to leave the care of their parents in the fall.

Badgers never depart from their dens before dark. Then they hunt for all manner of animals, including beetles, worms, hedgehogs, small rodents, and rabbits. They readily detect their prey by scent and dig them out of the ground if necessary. Fruits, nuts, and vegetables are also food for the badger, which may store them in its den in the fall, for winter use. It does not hibernate, but may sleep when the temperature drops to or below zero.

A Remarkable Badger "Funeral." The badgers have few natural enemies, and many live out the normal life span of ten years. They probably die in an underground chamber, which is then sealed off by other tenants of the badger "earth." There is even on record one remarkable instance of a badger "funeral." The event—it took place in England—was witnessed by Brian Vesey-Fitzgerald in 1941.

A female badger was seen excavating a large hole in an abandoned rabbit warren. Her efforts were interrupted by several journeys which she made back and forth between the rabbit warren and her set. All the time she seemed agitated and uttered strange cries.

The excavation completed, the female was joined by another badger, a male, and both retreated to the set. A short time later he was seen dragging a dead badger by the leg (another male—it could have been her mate) with the female giving some assistance from the rear. The body was duly deposited in the open grave and covered with earth. The female returned home; the helpful male went elsewhere and was not seen again.

Where We Find Them. The range of the Old World badgers reaches from the British Isles and Spain across Europe and northern Asia to Japan; the southern limit in Asia is the Himalayas. The badgers of Eurasia are separable into four general groups: the typical or European Badger, the Siberian Badger, the Caucasian Badger, and the Japanese Badger.

THE AMERICAN BADGER

The American Badger, *Taxidea,* is a superb digger, like its Old World kinsman. Using all four feet, it can sink underground in a matter of a few seconds. It is perhaps the fastest excavator in America; according to report, it can outdig both the pocket gopher and the mole, famous masters of the trade.

The badger makes the most of its long, powerful claws. It feeds to a large extent on ground squirrels, which it digs out of their burrows. By some ingenious method of calculation, known only to itself, the badger sinks a shaft straight down to the spot where the rodent is concealed. It rarely, if ever, misses the exact location, and so saves itself the almost impossible job of trying to catch its prey by entering and widening the squirrels' long tunnel from the entrance. When the victims are more than the badger has an appetite for, it will bury their carcasses against a leaner day.

Lizards, insects, gophers, rabbits, mice, and birds—these, also, the badger pursues. When larger animals pursue it in turn, it will fight back—unless they are just too large, like the coyote. Then the badger seeks safety underground.

We find the American badger in central North America from the Great Lakes region north through Alberta and British Columbia, and southwest through Nebraska to California and northern Mexico. (Wisconsin is known as the Badger State, but not simply because of its badgers. The allusion is to the early lead miners, who dug their winter homes in its hillsides, we are told.)

The American badger is a creature of the open country, often making its home in plains, prairies, and deserts. Here it lives four or five feet below the surface in a cozy den which it lines with dry leaves or grass, like its Eurasian relatives. It reaches the den by means of a tunnel many feet in length. During the day, it remains indoors.

MORE ACTIVE THAN IT LOOKS

The American badger is a squat, heavy-bodied animal with large claws, at home on the plains and in the forests of North America. It encounters few animals big enough to be a menace to it; if it feels itself endangered, it can quickly dig its way to safety in the ground. The badger is not a swift runner, and it is not able to climb up a tree.

The Badger in Winter. In the northern limits of its range the badger puts on fat during the fall and then holes up for the winter, blocking the tunnel to its den with soil. It does not go into a true state of hibernation, but alternately drowses and wakens. Occasionally it will leave its den and go hunting across the snow, but it eats little during the food-scarce cold months. In the south it remains active the year round.

"Delayed" Babies. The American badger mates in the late fall of the year or in the early winter. Apparently the development of the babies in the mother's body is delayed for the first two months in regions where it is really cold (this does not happen with the Eurasian badger) and the total period may take thirteen weeks.

Two to seven blind and hairless young are born as late as May or June in northern areas. They open their eyes when they are about five weeks old; now they are half-grown and ready to be weaned. From this time until they are two-thirds grown, the mother brings food to them or (later) takes them on hunting trips.

By fall the young badgers are big fellows, and move off in different directions, each to claim a domain of its own, as their mother enters a new breeding season.

Coarse Fur, but Useful. Much like their relatives in Europe and Asia, the American badgers are flattened, stocky, short-legged animals, with very short tails. They stand about nine inches at the shoulder, are two feet long or more, and weigh from twelve to twenty-four pounds, being somewhat smaller than the Eurasian badger.

The animal's general color is silvery gray. The face is dark brown and marked with a narrow central white stripe; the cheeks are white, too. The "badge" is thus quite different from the Eurasian badger's.

American badger fur is rather coarse and is used for coat trimming; it is much too soft to be satisfactory for shaving brushes. There is only one species of American badger, with three varying regional types.

The American Badger on Trial. The badger is often considered a pest. People know the animal is a digger; when they ride along on horseback and are thrown because the horse has put its foot in a hole, they blame the badger. So the poor creature frequently gets shot on sight.

The evidence against the badger is, as it happens, of a highly circumstantial nature, and would not stand up in a court of wildlife experts. They would rather point out that there are plenty of other diggers on the prairies; why blame the badger alone? The animal kills venomous snakes and every year destroys a large number of rodents that are troublesome to crops. For the great good it does, the badger well deserves commutation of the all-too-frequent death sentence.

It should be said, too, in favor of the American badgers, that like their Old World counterparts they can be tamed if taken young.

People who have raised them declare they make friendly, intelligent pets.

BADGERS OF FAR-OFF LANDS

Badgers with Warning Signals. There are other badgers, but about them we hear little for they live in remote parts of the earth. The Sand or Hog Badger, *Arctonyx*, of southeastern Asia, has a white tail that is comparatively long for a badger; while on the islands of Java, Sumatra, and Borneo, dwells the Teledu, *Mydaus,* a small brown badger with a broad white band down its back. These white markings are the warning signals often carried by animals capable of discouraging possible enemies by discharging an offensive-smelling liquid musk.

The Ratel. Throughout Africa and in Asia Minor and southern Asia the Ratel, *Mellivora,* is as famous as the badger is in Europe and the New World. Enjoying the reputation of a fearless and desperate fighter, it is a powerful, thickset animal about the size of a badger, with tiny ears. In color the ratel is usually gray or white on the back and jet black below; as you might suppose from its skunklike color scheme, it is protected from many of its enemies by its fetid discharge.

The ratel is at home in the rocky hills, on the grassy plains, and in the forests (though it does not climb trees). Armed with powerful claws, it can tear down termite nests and anthills to get at the larvae; reptiles, rodents, rabbits, and birds, as well as fruit, are also included in its diet.

The ratel's thick hide, which covers its body like a loose coat of rubber, is impervious alike to the fangs of venomous snakes, the quills of porcupines, and the stings of bees. The animal is partial to honey in particular, and forms an interesting association with the little bird known as the Honey-Guide. On discovering a bees' nest, this bird emits a series of high-pitched notes that are recognized by the ratel. Following the cries of the bird, the animal soon discovers the bees' nest and proceeds to tear it apart, gorging itself on the young bees and honey. The bird, too, comes in for a share of the feast, which it could not have without the aid of the ratel.

Its hunger satisfied, the ratel lies up in a den among the rocks or in a hole in the ground. It is not a social creature and travels either singly or in pairs. The female gives birth to a litter of only two cubs six months after mating, which explains why the ratel is never very

IT KNOWS HOW TO DEFEND ITSELF
The ratel is to Africa and parts of Asia what the badger is to Europe and America. This lively animal is a prodigious digger, and can also climb trees when it has to. Its strong claws and teeth will make almost any enemy think twice before attacking it. When disturbed, the ratel produces a powerful stench like the skunk.

common anywhere. It does have a rather long life expectancy for a member of the weasel family: the ratel has been known to live over twenty-three years in captivity.

SKUNKS—DANGEROUS BUT NOT DEADLY

The Common or Striped Skunk, *Mephitis,* and its equally unpopular relatives, the Hog-nosed Skunk and the Little Spotted Skunk, are American animals famous for the degree to which they have perfected the art of defensive chemical warfare.

Some Old World members of the weasel family, we have seen, can make themselves objectionable by ejecting a foul-smelling fluid, but the discharge they fire is mild and ineffective compared with the barrage set off by the "big guns" of the skunks. (Most weasels and badgers cannot actually spray their odor, and we suspect that in many of these animals it is used primarily in the mating season.)

Not so with the skunk. Provoke it, and you will learn to your sorrow that it can project a fine spray for a distance of nine feet or more. The fluid has a most distasteful and nauseating stench and produces intense smarting and burning if it comes in contact with the membranes of the eyes, nose, or mouth. If it penetrates clothing, the odor may not depart for weeks.

THE SKUNK'S BIG GUNS IN ACTION

The skunk always carries two "guns" primed and ready to fire. They are really two large musk glands situated at the base of the tail. When the skunk becomes frightened or annoyed, it contracts the muscles surrounding the glands, forcing out the spray. With a good wind blowing, the smell may carry further than a half-mile.

The skunk can discharge one "gun" or fire both simultaneously. The first barrage is the most powerful, but there is enough ammunition for six successive "shots." After the "magazine" is empty, it is a little while before it is reloaded.

Not an animal that wastes its ammunition, the skunk uses it generally as a last resort only. Confronted with a formidable foe, the little stench-bearer first growls its displeasure and stamps its foot impatiently. If this is ineffective, its white striped tail, bristling with tension, is raised as a final warning, but fire is withheld so long as the very tip of the tail hangs limp. One step nearer by the intruder —up goes the tip of the tail—and the broadside is discharged with deadly accuracy at the head of the foe.

A direct hit at close range will cause tears to flow freely and produce temporary blindness. While the victim howls in pain, the skunk ambles off, as fragrant and pure as ever, for it is always careful not to defile itself with the evil-smelling liquid.

It is an odd and interesting fact that the malodorous oily yellow fluid produced by the skunk can be put to a pleasing use by man. He extracts it from the animal and refines it, removing the disagreeable smell. The liquid that remains has a great capacity to fix and retain aromas. Have you guessed yet the end that awaits the skunk's secretion? It is blended with subtle and alluring scents, and the result is —fine perfume!

ANOTHER ANIMAL WITH A STINK-SCREEN
The common or striped skunk bears white stripes of warning on its back. If an animal disregards this danger signal and attempts to molest the skunk, it can discharge a foul-smelling liquid, surrounding itself with an almost impenetrable stink-screen. Sometimes man extracts the fluid and uses it to produce fine perfume. "Deskunked," this creature makes a docile and pleasing pet.

EASY-GOING WAYS OF THE SKUNK

Perfectly aware of its power of defense, the skunk is slow and deliberate in its actions. If unmolested, it strolls along good-naturedly. Now and then it will stop to dig up a nest of yellowjackets (wasps) with its sharp claws, and eat the grubs, for insects are a staple in its diet. Or it may speed up to a trot and catch a fleeing mouse, snake, or frog. All kinds of creeping things are food for the skunk, as well as berries, fruits, and grain. People seldom see this hungry little carnivore on its foraging trips, however, for it is active mostly at night.

By day the skunk rests or sleeps. Its den is a hollow log or, more often, a burrow in the ground. During the very cold days in the winter the skunk stays at home; at this time it lives off the layers of fat it acquired in the fall, but it does not hibernate.

MATING AND MOTHERHOOD

Even before the winter snows start to melt, the male skunks travel far and wide to pay their respects to the females, which remain comfortably at home. Two suitors may fight bitterly for the possession of a female; they may even forget the "laws of decency" and defile each other with their obnoxious sprays. The mating season lasts through February and March.

Some fifty days after mating time the young are born—there are four to eight of them, without sight or furry coats. The mother can nurse six babies at once; if there are more, they must wait their turn. The babies open their eyes when three weeks old, and fourteen days later they are out following their mother in single file. At the age of two months they are weaned, and depend on their own resources in early fall.

A young skunk is easy to capture and soon learns to be tame. The scent glands can be removed and thereafter the animal generally is an ideal pet, docile and loving. It will, incidentally, keep a house free of rodents.

SKUNK OR "ALASKA SABLE"?

The striped skunk is at home in Canada, the United States, and as far south as Honduras. About the size of a house cat, it stands seven inches at the shoulder, and is roughly eighteen inches long, plus a seven-inch tail.

Full grown, the animal may weigh from four to ten pounds. On the glossy coat of long, limp hair, two broad white lines (united on the head) run backward down the sides of the body to the tip of the bushy tail. The face has a single stripe from the forehead to the middle of the nose. However, the amount of white varies with the animal, some skunks being almost completely black, and a fair number of subspecies have been named.

Skunks are not very wary when it comes to traps, and great numbers of these creatures are taken each year. Their pelts are in demand in the fur trade, which frequently sells them under the more pleasing names of "Alaska sable" or "black marten."

SPOTTED AND HOG-NOSED SKUNKS

Considerably smaller than the striped skunk is the Spotted Skunk, *Spilogale,* a slender, weasel-like animal that weighs only one or two pounds. Its body color is about equally divided between black and white, the white markings being a series of more or less broken narrow lines that give us the impression of spots. Only from ten to fourteen inches in head and body length, this little creature has a tail about five or six inches long, and quite bushy.

SMALLER THAN A HOUSE CAT

The little spotted skunk is an expert in chemical warfare, just like its big cousin the striped skunk. Few animals will venture to bother it as it roams about in search of the small insects it generally feeds on. A lynx or a great horned owl will, however, occasionally make a meal of this relative of the weasel.

The spotted skunk has a habit of standing on its front paws and holding the rear end of its body in the air like a schoolboy showing off. This is often done in play, but it is also a warning signal. The little spotted skunk is so small that it has to raise its body up to get a good "shot" at a dog or a fox.

"Phoby Cat." Sometimes called the "polecat" or "little striped skunk," in the southern states this small creature is also known as the "phoby cat," or "hydrophobia cat." During the mating season the actions of the little spotted skunk seem to border on insanity.

It is reported that in its mating madness the spotted skunk has entered a wolf's den, taken the cubs by the ears, and has shaken and knocked them about generally; also it is said to have sprayed a bull in the face. But there is no scientific reason for thinking this small stench-bearer is more subject to hydrophobia than any other animal, and in other respects its habits are much the same as those of other members of the skunk tribe.

The little spotted skunk makes its home from southern British Columbia in the west and northern Virginia in the east through Mexico to Costa Rica. It is a creature of the plains and the dry desert regions. Its long, soft fur is known as "civet cat" in the fur trade. Civet cats, as such, are entirely different animals, of course, and are discussed in a later chapter.

A Nose for Insects. In the southwestern United States we come upon a much larger species, the Hog-nosed Skunk, *Conepatus,* that also makes its home through Mexico and as far south as Chile and Patagonia. A robust animal about the size of a striped skunk, it possesses a striking adaptation for getting its livelihood: the head is long and the muzzle naked, somewhat like a hog's snout. With this remarkable natural tool, the hog-nosed skunk roots in the ground for insects, which make up a good part of its diet.

Rather coarse black or brownish-black fur clothes this skunk, and, along its back, from the top of the head to the tip of the tail, there runs a broad white band, but this is variable—there may be two white lines or very little white indeed, particularly in the South American skunks.

We have already observed that poisonous animals or bad-tasting ones seem to advertise their nature to creatures that might otherwise make the mistake of attacking them. In the case of the skunks, the striking white marking, standing out against the black, provides an effective warning and—by no means incidentally—protects the bearers.

OTTERS—PLAYFUL FISHERMEN

THE NORTH AMERICAN OTTER

The North American Otter, *Lutra canadensis,* is the fastest mammal in the fresh-water lakes and rivers of its homeland. There it cruises along at six miles per hour, but it can go much faster if need be. It can swim a quarter of a mile under water, remaining submerged four minutes and more without coming up for air.

Above all else, otters are fishermen. They have been known to kill a fish up to twenty pounds in weight; usually, however, the quarry is much smaller. At times they take the cunning trout, but they are more inclined to hunt easier prey such as sunfish and other sluggish varieties. The otters catch the fish with their forepaws, then rip it apart with their teeth.

Except during the breeding season, otters are continually on the move and will travel a twenty-mile circuit of connecting lakes and rivers in two or three weeks. Where there is good fishing, they remain awhile, but not for long. When the water freezes over, they often travel overland, looking for rivers or rapids that are still flowing. Unlucky are the ducks, muskrats, and young beavers the otters encounter, for these fishermen like to vary their diet now and then. They are active both day and night.

The otter is streamlined for darting through water. It has a lithe, muscular body, a broad, flat head, small ears, and a long, powerful, tapering tail which serves as a rudder. Its limbs are short, but the strong hind feet are large and broadly webbed. Its oily coat is rich dark brown in color, with very full and dense fur that keeps the animal warm in the water.

Few animals will attack this water-loving member of the weasel family. When a large beast goes after it, the otter escapes by diving into the water or, in winter, alternately racing and sliding across the snow. Sometimes it will stand and fight. It can give a good account of itself, even against dogs.

Favorite Otter Games. In character the otter is above even the suspicion of having bad habits. It is gentle and friendly with all its associates, and likes to sport and play.

This animal's favorite pastime is to coast down a steep "slide" as children love to do; in the summer the bank of a stream is used. Taking turns, a family of otters will plunge down one after the other in quick succession, the water from their bodies greasing the slide and heightening the fun. In winter the highest snowbank in the vicinity is used for a slide, and the sport becomes fast and hilarious.

The Otters at Home. The otter's den is usually a hole in the bank of a stream or lake. This swimmer likes quick and easy access to its home, and so the main entrance is under water. There is a back door, too, used for ventilation, and this, for safety's sake, is hidden in the bushes on the bank. For comfort, soft moss and dry leaves line the floor of the den.

We are not sure exactly when the otter's mating season occurs, and there is some question as to whether or not both parents take part in raising the family. The baby otters are born in April or May and as a rule they are twins; occasionally there are three, but rarely more. It is a month before their eyes open; then the young are taught to swim.

For the first few trips in the water, the young otters ride on the mother's back. One day she submerges and leaves the kittens to struggle as best they can in the shallow water. Now it is sink or swim— well, not exactly so, for Mother is always close by to help if serious difficulties should arise.

Otters raised in captivity are esteemed as pets, and some do eminent service as retrievers, particularly of waterfowl. With a normal life span of eight or nine years, otters may live up to the age of sixteen under favorable conditions.

There is little variation in the general appearance and habits of the otter throughout its entire range. This valuable fur-bearer and its related species cover most of the continent, though not so abundantly as in former times. They may be found within a fifty-mile radius of some of the largest cities of North America. On an average, they weigh about twenty pounds and are some thirty inches in length, plus the foot-long tail.

SEA OTTERS—BIGGEST OF THEIR TRIBE

The Sea Otter, *Enhydra*, is as much at home in the sea as a seal. The greatest of the otters, it was friendly and trusting when first discovered, but persistent, relentless hunting for its valuable fur has made it extremely shy of man, and whittled down its numbers. Today it rarely comes to land. Instead, it passes its life offshore in great beds of floating kelp, a type of brown seaweed. Its range is limited to the shores of the North Pacific.

"Saltiest" of the Otters. The otters of our inland waterways, adept as they are in lakes and rivers, rate as mere landlubbers beside the salty sea otter. It is born in the water, it eats in the water, sleeps in the water, grows old and dies in the water.

The sea otter loves to float, and swims as easily as a fish. Generally it lies on its back and propels itself with its tail. For greater speed it turns right side up, and, its body undulating, it strikes out with both webbed hind feet. Sometimes it uses them in unison, sometimes alternately. Often it races along at a rate of ten miles an hour.

Though the sea otter takes some fish, it is not a confirmed fisherman. It may go down a hundred feet or more in search of its daily fare, dredging from the ocean floor sea urchins, crustaceans, cuttlefish, mussels, clams, abalone, and other shellfish. Bringing its victim back to the surface, the sea otter spreads the lunch out on its belly and chest, and leisurely eats as it floats on its back.

Like most mammals that live in the water, this one does not drink, though it consumes some salt water with its food.

Scratching Itself in the Water. You might suppose the sea otter would find it a problem to scratch itself in the water. Nothing could be further from the truth. Not only does the sea otter find scratching with one, or two, or three paws easy—this water-dweller can scratch with all four at once. each paw working in a different spot and in a different direction.

Life of a Baby Sea Otter. Sea otters are scarce, and we lack complete knowledge of their life history. We believe, however, that they breed throughout the year and that the parents mate for life. Nine months after mating time a single pup is born—not in a nest or den but on a thick bed of floating kelp. The locale usually is a sheltered natural harbor. Sometimes, though, it is a rocky island, but one that is bare of human habitation and a safe distance offshore. Unlike so many of the weasel's cousins, the pup is born with its eyes wide open.

Nursing her baby, watching over it, and giving it good care take up a large part of the mother sea otter's time for six months or even a year. Doing all of these things in the water is an art. The mother suckles the pup as she floats on her back in the water. (Sea otters normally spend their resting and sleeping hours floating in this fashion among beds of kelp.) In a playful mood, often she tosses it in the air and catches it again.

Traveling with baby, Mrs. Sea Otter lies on her back in the water and paddles along with her webbed hind feet, clutching the pup to her breast with her tiny but strong front paws. When she must go off for food, she leaves her little one floating hidden in the kelp.

Mrs. Sea Otter does not approve of dirty children. She often gives her pup a very thorough cleaning, and none too gently at that. She rolls the baby first one way and then another, carefully cleaning its fur with her teeth and tongue from end to end. When this ordeal is over, the pup relaxes on her chest and goes to sleep with its little feet folded across its belly, its paws clasped over its chest.

A sea otter mother's love for her young one is such that she will expose herself to death rather than desert the baby. If it is taken from her, she will cry bitterly like a small child. (So, too, will the baby.) Even when a pup is a year old, and a new baby is born, the family will stay together—perhaps much longer, so strong are the bonds of affection. At four years of age, the pups are full grown.

We have said that the sea otter is the largest of the otters. What little it may lose in length when compared with one of its big relatives, the giant river otter of Brazil, it more than gains in bulk. A big sea otter may weigh up to eighty pounds; its head and body length varies from three to four feet, and the tail adds another foot. A heavy, thickset animal, it is much less sleek and graceful in appearance than the river otters. The pelt is very full, soft, and deep; it is brownish black in color and more or less finely grizzled.

The Sea Otter's Fight for Survival. With the exception of the lurking killer whale, the sea otter has few natural enemies. Even at its slow rate of reproduction it maintained a fair population before its fur became commercially valuable. But when a sea otter pelt brought one hundred to twenty-five hundred dollars, overhunting became the rule, and the species was well-nigh exterminated.

Fortunately, conservationists took an interest in the matter: today the sea otter enjoys full protection in accordance with an international code that provides refuge and outlaws the sale of pelts. Over a period of years strict enforcement of this code has saved the animal from being wiped out altogether. In time we may glimpse the fascinating sea otter more and more, playing and hunting in its favorite haunts off the shores of the Pacific, from southern California to the Kurile Islands.

OTHER INTERESTING OTTERS

Otters are much alike, wherever we find them. The South and Central American otters differ from the North American species only in size and certain minor features. Perhaps the most noteworthy is the Giant Otter, Saro, or Flat-tailed Otter of Brazil, *Pteronura*. A native of the waters of the Amazon River basin, it is one of the largest river otters, measuring five feet in length.

In Australia, Madagascar, and on the islands of the South Pacific we do not encounter the otters, but they are common throughout the Old World. Some have marked peculiarities. In the Clawless Otter, *Paraonyx*, an African animal, the forefeet are small, with five naked fingers without claws; only the third and fourth fingers on the hind feet bear minute claws. Its big cousin, the Giant African Otter, *Aonyx*, weighs sixty pounds and may be longer than five feet. Dark brown in color, it is often tinted with white and has a broad splash of white on its throat and chin. This otter's claws, too, are rudimentary or absent altogether, so that it lacks adequate defenses against its dreaded enemy, the crocodile.

In Asia and Sumatra we even find a Hairy-nosed Otter, *Lutra sumatrana;* the nose pad, naked in most species, is covered with fine hair, but whether this has any special use as an adaptation cannot be said.

The Eurasian Otter, *Lutra lutra,* dwells in the rivers throughout the Old World from England west to Burma and southern China, and from the Mediterranean region of Africa north to the Arctic coast. It is hunted with otter hounds in England and France, a sport that dates back to the Middle Ages, when it was the pastime of royalty.

Otters, we have observed, are sociable creatures on land. It is believed that, in the water, they often act in concert and surround or drive a shoal of fish. One reputable observer in India saw six otters swim out in a semicircle on Chilka Lake, each about fifty yards from the next. Every now and then one otter would dive and retrieve a fish, carry it to the bank, and hurry back to join the ranks of its fellow fishermen.

Genets, Civets, Mongooses, and Their Kin — Lithe "Weasel Cats"

COMBINE the long, slender body of the weasel—a rough representation of the head of the fox—the short limbs of the marten —and the tail and disposition of the cat—and there you have the "weasel cats," as we may call this group. In the warmer parts of the Old World they have taken the place occupied by the weasels in the north.

Many of the weasel cats have scent glands, like the weasel family. Some of these creatures—in this they resemble the members of the cat family—possess sharp claws, which they carry sheathed in their feet when there is no need to slash or climb. (Others have nail-like claws that cannot be moved in and out.) Again like their cousins the cats, the genets, civets, and mongooses walk softly and spring swiftly upon their prey.

There is a large army of weasel cats, and they control the many small animals that breed at high speed the year round in tropical regions. Beasts of prey, they are nevertheless ready to compromise with hard times. When rodents and small game abound, these resourceful little carnivores live by killing. However, a dearth of animal life is no major catastrophe for them, as it would be for the cats or the weasels proper; the weasel cats supplement their flesh diet with insects, fruit, and even vegetables.

The weasel cats are not considered high-class fur-bearers, though the pelts of some species are used. Often the coats they wear are quite handsome. The fur of many is ornately or even gaily marked with spots and stripes, while a good number of these creatures are brightly colored. All make up a family called the Viverridae, a name which comes from the Latin word for "ferret."

GENETS—SMALL, SAVAGE MARAUDERS

Today no one but the specialist seems to consider the genets either exciting or a promising subject for study—yet these beautiful, graceful creatures never fail to attract the attention of the person who sees them. The European genet's soft, grayish fur is dappled with black (it was popular in the past and was sold in European markets as far back as A.D. 600 but has long since fallen into disrepute).

The genet is not a large animal; the many species range between eighteen and twenty-three inches in head and body length; the tapering tail, about as long again, is ornately banded with dark brown or black rings. The pointed face, with prominent ears, sits gracefully on a long, slender body with short legs. The animal's sharp hooked claws may be drawn in or extended, like a cat's; they are not only well suited for climbing trees but also for striking down fast-moving prey. Running down the genet's back there is a line of stiff hairs which stand erect when the beast is excited.

The genet, in its various forms, has an enormous range: it is found all the way from Spain in southern Europe to western Asia, and south through East Africa to the Cape. (It is commonest in Africa.) For some strange reason the creature has bypassed the greater part of Asia in establishing itself in its present domain.

The question of why animals penetrate certain regions and not others near by, poses a fascinating problem for the naturalist. Barriers are chiefly climatic or physical. When they are impassable—like the edges of oceans—accidents or factors outside the "laws of nature" may eventually permit some species to pass across. (Thus, for example, the wild dogs known as dingoes appear to have reached Australia in the boats of ancient man.) The genet, on the other hand, has, or seems to have, a full visaed passport to Asia—yet somewhere there is a taboo around most of that continent, keeping the animal out. Pos-

THEY PATROL THE NORTH AMERICAN WATERWAYS

With its streamlined body, thick fur, webbed feet, and strong, muscular tail, the otter is superbly endowed for activities in the water. Generally it makes its den in the bank of a stream or pond. The entrance is under water, and the otter may sally forth at any hour of the day or night in quest of a fish dinner. A swift and agile swimmer, the animal experiences little difficulty in overtaking the slower varieties of fish, as well as frogs and young beavers. So wily and skillful at eluding capture is the otter itself that its only serious enemy is man. Otters raised in captivity have proved to be quite tame and docile. They enjoy performing tricks, and exhibit considerable talent as trackers. (Illustration by Fred Ludekens, courtesy of Weyerhaeuser Timber Company.)

sibly the competition of native species is the decisive element here, but it is not obviously so.

A HUNTER OF SMALL GAME

All the genets are night prowlers, lying up during daylight hours in hollow trees, a crevice in the rocks, or a burrow in the ground. After nightfall the long, lithe body weaves through tall grass and thickets like a snake. More often the animal is glimpsed in the trees. Once in a while it may be seen before the sun has actually set, traveling either singly or in pairs; it moves cautiously, preferring dark, shady places where rocks and bushes provide cover. A home-loving creature, the genet returns daily to the same hideaway.

THE GENET—WEASEL CAT OF AFRICA
Though nothing seems to bar its entry into Asia, the genet has mysteriously refrained from settling there, except in certain southern parts. Its main home is Africa, but it is also found in southern Europe. A fierce little rat and mouse killer, the genet has unsheathed claws with which it attacks its victims.

The genet is above all a small-game hunter. It seeks out rats and mice that prowl about the jungle floor. It will devour any reptiles or insects that cross its path, and climbs about in the trees and thickets in search of small birds roosting there. Remains of hares and guinea fowl have been found outside its den and it is well known as a raider of chicken pens. On occasion it goes for bigger game.

When cornered, a genet will put up a good fight, growling and spitting like a house cat. It can slash out with its claws faster than the eye can follow. Still, it is no match for a dog. It has a reasonably long life expectancy, and has been known to reach twelve years of age.

There is no fixed breeding season among the genets, nor do they bear large families. Two or three is about the average for a litter. Almost any kind of retreat will serve as a nursery, so long as it is safe, warm and dry.

As we find in most other kinds of animals, there are several species. Africa has a number of varieties such as the Leopard Genet, the Tiger Genet, and the Crested Genet. All are more or less conspicuously marked and colored as the popular names indicate. They are variations of the European Genet, *Genetta*. The genet of southern Europe was used as a domestic cat by the ancient Greeks and as late as the sixteenth century was common and tame in such cities as Constantinople.

LINSANGS—HANDSOME TREE "CATS" OF THE JUNGLE

The linsangs are the most catlike of all the weasel cats. These creatures of tropical Asia and the East Indies rather resemble the genets in general form, only they are somewhat smaller—about fifteen or sixteen inches is the average length, plus a tail almost as long again. They are handsome fellows, too—the Spotted Linsang's slender body and superb tail are golden brown with a bold pattern of large black spots; the Banded Linsang has five broad bands running across its body, and the tail is banded with alternating dark and light markings.

Linsangs live by hunting live game, and will disdain any food except meat. Though appearing to be better suited for travel on the ground, like the genets they are extremely active in the trees. They breed twice a year—once in February and again in August. The babies come two to the litter as a rule, and are born in a hollow tree, so far as we know.

The linsangs got their name from the Javanese. These animals make up the genus *Prionodon*, which means "saw-tooth"; the teeth really do look jagged and sawlike. The so-called African Linsang, *Poiana,* of the Congo, is in reality a small genet with a spotted coat like the rest of the genets.

IT TAKES TO TREES LIKE A CAT

The weasel-cat family has certain distinguishing features—a foxlike face, short legs, a long body like a weasel, and the tail and temperament of a cat. The banded linsang of Asia and the East Indies follows this description, but is more catlike in its habits than any other member of the family. Like the felines, it spends much of its time in trees and, appropriately enough, it feeds on birds.

CIVET CATS—THE SKUNKS' OLD WORLD RIVALS

A good many of the readers of this book will never have heard of the civet cats before encountering them here. That is not surprising, for these weasel cats, like the others, make their home in the warmer parts of the Old World. Small carnivores, they prowl the jungleland at night. Even naturalists do not know too much about their intimate home life.

In their native regions, the civet cats are important for two chief reasons. First of all, they unwittingly serve as foresters, being instrumental in the planting of trees. In addition to flesh, civets eat fruits and berries. They do not digest the seeds. These are distributed over a considerable distance, where they germinate and eventually grow into trees.

But this helpful work is not the main source of the civets' value to mankind. The animals' name comes from an Arabic word, *zabad,* which refers to a scent—civet—extracted from the musk glands. A good commercial price is set upon civet, this substance being used extensively in the Orient as a basis for perfume and as a drug.

THE SCENT OF THE CIVET CAT

There is nothing mysterious about the civet or secretion. It is made up of free ammonia, resin, fat, and volatile oil, and is located in a double-pocket pouch under the skin of the animal's abdomen, with an opening near the tail. The natives insert a spoon in this opening and extract the jelly-like dark yellow substance. This sounds easy to do, yet requires much skill; the civet cat not only possesses sharp teeth but it is strong and agile as well, and can inflict nasty scratches with its claws. (The animals, of course, are kept in cages.) The musk is extracted every fourteen or twenty days.

In nature, the civet cat uses its musk glands for scenting tree trunks, the ground, and similar objects, as a means of communication, so that members of a species will be able to find each other at night in a dark forest. Like most night-prowling animals, the civet cats—so far as we know—are generally silent and might have a difficult time keeping in touch with one another if they lacked the scent.

The larger carnivores occasionally attack civet cats. In such an emergency, some of them will suddenly and unexpectedly discharge their evil-smelling, burning secretion into the face of the foe. This frustrates the attacker long enough for the civet to escape.

The civet cats possess yet another protective device which reminds us further of the skunks, those other adepts in gas warfare. Civet cats are strikingly marked, so that they can be easily recognized, remembered, and avoided by would-be enemies.

SOME WELL-KNOWN CIVET CATS

One of the best known of these weasel cats—and an excellent producer of civet—is the civet cat of India and the Orient. This big creature (it has a head and body length of two feet, plus a tail one and one-half feet long) is easy to identify: it has a full, black-and-white-ringed tail, many ill-defined dark markings on its grizzled body, and across the throat there runs a broad black band, set off by areas of white. A prominent crest of long erectile hairs extends down the middle of the back. To complete this striking picture, the feet are black. The fur of this heavy-bodied animal (the oriental civet may weigh twenty-five pounds) is thick and soft, making it of considerable importance to the fur trade.

All the civet cats have well-developed musk glands, and the Rasse, *Viverricula,* a smaller species of eastern Asia, has been introduced into Madagascar, Socotra, and other islands for the sake of its scent. The African Civet, *Civettictis,* is much like the large oriental species both in size and markings but its fur is coarse and limp—it is used commercially only for trimming cloth coats. This animal is probably the "sentoivane" of African folklore—the mysterious creature whose hairs are said to be used by witch doctors to dye milk red.

There is a fisherman among the civets, a beautiful species with a dark chestnut-brown body, white lips and throat, and a bushy reddish tail. The Water Civet, *Osbornictis,* catches fish in the rivers and streams that thread through the jungles of the Congo. It has sharp teeth for holding its slippery finny prey and the soles of the feet are naked for easy travel on mud flats. (In other civets the soles are more or less hairy.)

THE PALM CIVETS

So far we have had the civets that live on the ground and feed largely by hunting small animal life. The palm civets (there are several kinds in Asia and Africa) live in the trees and subsist largely on fruit. One, the Asiatic Palm Civet, *Paradoxurus,* is known throughout India and Ceylon as the "toddy cat"—it is especially fond of toddy, the juice of the palm tree, which it drinks from the vessels attached to the trees by the natives to receive the liquid.

Like all the palm civets, this one is a creature of the night, and lies up during the day curled in a ball among the fronds of palm trees. Mango groves are also one of its favorite resorts; it not infrequently haunts human habitations and sleeps in thatched roofs.

The Otter Civet or Mampalon, *Cynogale,* of the Malay region, is the only civet that has really taken to the water while retaining its tree-climbing habits. It has the flat head, broad toes and feet, and thick, dense fur of an aquatic animal. It swims and fishes like an otter and is as much at home in the water as on dry land.

THE ONLY CIVET CAT WITH A GRASPING TAIL
All civet cats have bushy tails, but none can compare with the strong, useful one of the tree-dwelling binturong of Asia. Its tail—almost as long as the binturong's entire body— is used for grasping and hanging from trees. Equally unique is the animal's raucous howl, for civet cats are usually still creatures. To compensate for their lack of voice, they spread the secretions of their musk glands along forest byways to communicate with one another.

Most remarkable of the Asiatic civets is the Binturong, *Arctictis*. This lop-eared creature resembles a large palm civet—it is over two feet long, with a tail of almost the same length—and wears a black, shaggy coat. But its most outstanding peculiarity is the lengthy, powerful tail. Like the monkeys of South America, the binturong can hang by its tail or possibly use it as a fifth hand, a great convenience for an animal that lives in the trees.

The binturong is at home in the forests of Assam and west to the Philippines, including Sumatra and Borneo. It appears to be the only noisy member of the civet group. Its loud howls, we are told, will often shatter the relative quiet of the jungle night.

CURIOUS CIVET CATS OF MADAGASCAR

Madagascar is noted for its many strange, primitive forms of animal life (the lemurs and tenrecs are some others we have already looked at), and not the least curious among them are the local weasel cats. Several are exceedingly graceful animals, no larger than rats. One, the agile little Vontsira, *Galidia,* has a bright reddish-brown coat and a bushy tail and bounds about in the trees just like a squirrel during the daytime. The Striped Madagascar Civet, *Galidictis,* is ornately marked with six or eight black stripes down the back; there are several species, with narrow or broad stripes, and these animals are of some economic value as mouse-catchers.

AN ODDITY AMONG CIVET CATS
Civet cats are amazingly diversified in habit and structure. A case in point is the falanouc of Madagascar, which has switched from flesh-eating to a diet of insects and fruit. Notice that its muzzle is very narrow and slender and it has delicate jaws.

There are still other civet oddities in Madagascar. One of the most interesting is the Falanouc, *Eupleres*. This creature offers a remarkable instance of a carnivorous animal that has given up a flesh diet and taken to eating insects and soft fruit; its teeth and jaws are extremely small and weak. For the rest, it is a large, brown, fuzzy-haired animal about the size of a house cat, with a bottle-brush of a tail.

The Foussa, *Fossa,* is another strange Malagasy civet. A robust animal with four black lines down the back, it feeds on insects and lizards. It should not be confused with the fossa, which is described later.

MONGOOSES—EXPERT SNAKE-KILLERS

The mongoose, a long-bodied, weasel-like animal with a lengthy, bushy tail, is famed as a killer of snakes. Although no larger than a house cat, it will engage even a seven-foot foe. It does not generally seek combat with reptiles, but, when hungry, it needs no other incentive to attack them. In southern Asia and in Africa, where poisonous snakes abound, the mongoose is one of the commonest of carnivores.

An experienced old mongoose will quickly kill a cobra. Like a clever boxer, it provokes the deadly snake to strike—but the uncanny, expert judgment and sharp reflexes of the mongoose enable it to dance away unharmed. Time and again the snake lashes out and misses. (In the battle the mongoose carries the stiff hairs of its body and tail at right angles, which makes the animal appear larger; presumably this is a factor in causing the snake to strike short.)

Each time the reptile drops to the ground fully extended at the end of its strike, the mongoose springs in and attempts to sink its teeth into the back of its enemy's head. Finally it inflicts a fatal wound, and the mongoose eats the snake, head first, including the poison glands. When fully gorged, it lies down to sleep; it resumes the feast on awakening.

Sometimes, to be sure, the mongoose takes a beating. The natives of the tropical lands where the animal dwells say that it retires to the jungle after being bitten by a venomous snake and eats certain roots as an antidote for the poison. Such stories are without foundation. The mongoose is not immune to the snake's venom, and it takes the greatest care to avoid being bitten. When artificially injected, the poison is fatal.

However, there are mongooses and mongooses, and some of them give us reason to assume that they are better able to withstand the bite of a venomous snake than are many other animals. In a staged fight between a large cobra and a mongoose, the latter survived although apparently severely bitten on several occasions by the cobra. This mongoose did not seem particularly interested in avoiding the strike of the cobra or in seizing it by the head. It bit the snake whenever the opportunity offered and at one time seized it by the lower jaw. The possibility exists that the mongoose, through its constant eating of snakes, may occasionally acquire some degree of immunity against the poison.

ONE OF THE WORLD'S BEST SNAKE-KILLERS
The brave and cocky little mongoose may be only two feet long—yet it will attack and kill a seven-foot poisonous snake. It is also one of the most effective natural enemies of mice, rats, and scorpions, and by cutting down their numbers performs a vitally important service to man. Unfortunately, the animal can lose its popularity and usefulness by attacking poultry; imported into the West Indies, it has become a nuisance. The Indian mongoose is the "Rikki-tikki-tavi" of Kipling's famous tale in *The Jungle Book.*

The mongoose is capable of killing any creature up to its own size. Besides reptiles, it feeds on birds, insects, rats, and similar animals. More active by day than by night, it usually hunts in the early mornings and late evenings, though it may be about during the midday heat and at any hour of the night.

This animal is interesting to watch. It has a habit of stopping frequently to glance around with its sharp red eyes or to listen with its head cocked to one side and one foot raised; it seems always ready to dart at any lurking prey or to scurry off if alarmed. When cornered, it can climb, but it rarely does so. Its long claws are more suited for digging than for climbing trees.

Despite its naturally savage disposition, the mongoose may be tamed. Taken young and treated properly, it can be handled without fear and will keep buildings free of rats. Sometimes it enters people's houses without invitation, and becomes part of the family. It will live on friendly terms with dogs and cats but can seldom be taught not to kill poultry.

The mongoose was introduced in the West Indies and Hawaii, where it has unfortunately become a menace to chickens and many other harmless and desirable animals. It was brought in to destroy the rats which infest the islands, but the rats have found a way to meet this threat; they now live in the trees, where they are safe from the mongoose.

Mongooses in a general way resemble the civets and genets but their claws cannot be drawn in like a cat's. Possessing a comparatively lengthy and hairy tail, a pointed face, and low rounded ears, they do not, like the civets, have scent glands. The fur is usually a grizzled brown or black.

MANY KINDS OF MONGOOSES

Europe's Only Mongoose. The warmer regions of the earth are the home of many different types of mongoose, each with its own peculiarities. Only one kind of mongoose lives in Europe—southern Spain to be exact. This creature, which is also found in great numbers in southern Asia and most of Africa, is the Common Mongoose, *Herpestes*. A slender animal, it measures close to two feet in head and body; its tapered tail is several inches shorter. It has short legs, with large feet, and its head is rather small and pointed. The woolly coat is a uniform mixture of pale buff and black, except for the tip of the tail, which is all black.

The Crab-eating Mongoose. In Asia we find the Crab-eating Mongoose, *Herpestes urva*, a large creature with long, thick fur like that of a woodchuck or badger. Gray in color, it has a horizontal white stripe on each side of the neck and its feet are blackish brown. It weighs up to six pounds. The crab-eating mongoose frequents watercourses, where it feeds on crabs, frogs, and small rodents, and sometimes goes fishing in the water.

The Indian Mongoose. In India, Assam, and Afghanistan dwells a smaller species, the Indian Mongoose, *Herpestes edwardsii*. It weighs about three pounds, and its color is iron gray. The young, three or four in number, are born in holes dug in the ground by the adults. It is the Indian mongoose that was introduced into many of the West Indies Islands. These animals became so numerous at Botany Bay, St. Thomas, that two or three individuals would fight over table scraps thrown to them.

"The Tracker." One of the largest of the mongooses is the Gray Mongoose, or Ichneumon, *Herpestes ichneumon,* found pretty much

THE INQUISITIVE MONGOOSE
The mongoose is enormously curious about people, their activities and their belongings. Unless it is discouraged, it will approach human beings in order to watch them at close hand. Should a bright piece of jewelry catch its eye, this mischievous sneak thief may grab it and run off. Above is the Malagasy mongoose, one of Madagascar's striped varieties.

throughout Africa. Its over-all length is forty-four inches; about half of this is the black-tipped tail. The gray mongoose normally travels about singly or in pairs, but as many as fourteen have been seen hunting in a pack.

This large mongoose preys on small mammals, reptiles, frogs, fish, and fresh-water crustaceans. It got its name "ichneumon" ("the tracker") because it was believed to be especially fond of crocodile eggs, hunting them assiduously. Revered by the ancient Egyptians, it was frequently mummified.

Africa's Horde of Mongooses. Africa has many other species. The large White-tailed Mongoose, *Ichneumia,* of the central and southern regions, does not always have on its tail the white tip for which the animal is named, but may be quite blackish all over. It spends the day in its hole in the ground, coming out at night to prey upon birds and small mammals. The Marsh Mongoose, *Atilax,* a large, brownish creature, swims and dives well in the lakes and marshes it frequents, and feeds upon much the same kind of food as the ichneumon.

Striped mongooses exist in many forms, and the Banded or Zebra Mongoose, *Mungos mungo,* can readily be recognized by the numerous thin bands of alternating light buff and dark brown that cross its lower back and fade into finely mixed buff and black on its shoulders. This is a rather small creature that prefers to roam abroad during daylight. It goes about in troops of six or more and is most abundant near rivers and marshes. Its typical diet consists principally of insect life such as termites, beetles, and cockroaches.

When nature permits a creature to multiply greatly, as it has the mongoose, we often find it in many different sizes, some considerably smaller than others. The Dwarf Mongoose, *Helogale,* measures ten inches or less from nose to rump, and the tail is about eight inches long; this animal is colored dark brown finely mixed with yellow. The dwarf mongoose travels about during the day, hunting in packs of fifteen or more. Largely an eater of insects, it varies its diet with fruits and small mammals.

A pretty, little South African creature is the Suricate, or Slender-tailed Meerkat, *Suricata.* It is light gray or pale buff, with broken dark bands crossing its lower back. This inhabitant of the grassveld and arid plains dwells sociably in burrows, from which it emerges in the daytime to sit up on its haunches like a ground squirrel, and look curiously about. Insects make up the greater part of its diet. It is often tamed.

FOSSAS—THE BIG CATS OF MADAGASCAR

The Fossa, *Cryptoprocta*, once enjoyed a reputation for great ferocity—so much so that the single species in existence was named *Cryptoprocta ferox*. Occasionally there are reports that this sharp-clawed catlike animal attacks sheep and young cattle, and it is well known to the natives of Madagascar because of its raids on their chickens. But the old tales that ascribed to the fossa the bloodthirstiness of the lion and tiger are nowadays taken with a generous sprinkling of salt.

The fossa is a curiosity among the carnivores. This one species comprises a whole subfamily in the animal kingdom and appears to

A KILLER IN FABLE BUT NOT IN FACT

The fossa, a big flesh-eating cat of Madagascar, has been falsely likened to the tiger in savagery. However, any true account of its so-called ferocity reveals only run-of-the-mill attacks on poultry, sheep, and young cattle. The five-foot-long fossa seems to represent a halfway mark between the civet cat and the true cat.

represent a bridge between the weasel cat family and the true cats. Harsh short fur, reddish brown or brownish gray in hue, covers its slender body. The legs are short and the body appears very long because it is so slender. (Actually, the animal may reach a total length of five feet, with the well-haired tail almost half of this.) The claws are needle-sharp and hooked like those of a cat; the fossa can draw them in and out, too. On the ground it walks on the soles of its feet, whereas the cats, as we shall soon see, move about on their toes.

The trees are home to the agile fossa, which inhabits the rainforests of eastern Madagascar as well as the drier forests of the west. Here it preys upon birds and lemurs. It is most active at night, but is sometimes seen abroad in the early morning or late evening. Mostly it keeps to itself.

The fossa is the largest carnivore in Madagascar, where it takes the place of the big cats.

Hyenas and Aardwolves—Eaters of Carrion

HYENAS—THE BONE-CRUNCHERS

HYENAS scour the plains throughout Africa, Palestine, Arabia, and India in search of animal remains. These sturdy, unhandsome beasts are the bone-crunchers of the animal kingdom. Their teeth are massive and their jaws powerful enough to crack and crush the thigh bones of large animals like the zebra and even the buffalo.

Such eating equipment has its uses. Most people believe that hyenas are exclusively eaters of carrion. As a rule, however, few dead animals ever reach the actual putrefying carrion stage on the plains of Africa; often the best a hyena can expect is a feast of bones.

On one occasion, in Kenya Colony, the author checked the time it took nature to dispose of a dead animal. Five minutes after a zebra had been shot and killed, the first scout vulture came. In ten minutes there were thirty vultures feeding on the zebra, and twenty minutes later only the bones and the hide remained. About this time—it was late in the evening—two hyenas located the kill. By next morning nothing was left of the dead zebra.

Equipped with a keen sense of smell, the hyena can detect a carcass many miles away. It makes for any spot over which vultures are flying, being assured of the presence of a dead animal. To a large extent it depends on the kills left by lions and troops of wild dogs. Lack of speed prevents the hyena from becoming a habitual game destroyer but it will kill domestic stock.

Despite its powerful jaws and teeth, the hyena rarely attempts to defend itself. When cornered, it will try to escape rather than fight for its freedom. If escape is not possible, it will play dead until its attackers drop their guard. Then it springs to its feet and dashes off.

Most hunters consider the hyena one of the most degraded of animals. That the beast is reluctant to devour its own kind seems to indicate that it does have a moral standard. It is surprisingly free from body odors, and smells much sweeter than a lion or a jackal. In fact, the natives readily eat the meat of the hyena and are keen to get the heart, believing that it will bring them courage. This is rather strange, since, as we have seen, the hyena seldom puts up a fight when the odds are against it, and is generally referred to as a coward.

Prehistoric Europe knew the hyena well. Once it haunted caverns as far west as England, leaving behind it a curious trail, much as it does today. The dung of the hyena dries into hard white balls chiefly composed of bone fragments. They are almost indestructible, and have been found fossilized in the caves that were tenanted by these extinct forms of hyena thousands of years ago.

LAUGHING HYENAS—BEASTS OF MIGHT AND MAGIC

The Spotted Hyena, or Laughing Hyena, *Crocuta crocuta,* is the largest and strongest of the scavengers. A full-grown spotted hyena may stand from two and one-half to three feet at the shoulders and measure as much as five and one-half feet in head and body length. Some weigh up to 175 pounds.

This robust carnivore is as hideous as its reputation. It has a broad, ugly face, large, rounded ears, a short tail, and heavy limbs. The coarse, scanty fur is gray or buff in color, with a good many irregular blotches of brown or black. Even the posture of the hyena is ungraceful: the animal's front limbs are longer than its hind ones, and the body slopes downward from the high neck and shoulders to the foot-long coarse-haired tail.

The peculiarities of the hyena do not end here. Unlike most four-footed creatures, it does not trot, but paces—that is, the fore and hind limbs on each side of the body move forward together, producing a rolling gait much like that of the camel.

Under normal conditions the hyena does not hunt living healthy game but follows great herds of zebra and antelope and attacks the sick, the weak, the maimed, the aged, and the young. Where civilization has driven big game from large areas and the hyena is left without its natural prey, it will attack domestic sheep and cattle, but only when driven by extreme hunger. Possessed of extraordinary vitality, it can drag a two-hundred-pound carcass as much as one hundred yards.

The hyena's gluttony, like its strength, is proverbial. Theodore Roosevelt tells of finding a hyena trapped inside a dead elephant. It had crept inside the carcass and gorged itself with so much flesh from the walls of the elephant's stomach that it was too fat to get out the way it had entered.

Daytime is for slumber, so far as the hyena is concerned. Its home is a burrow in the ground or a dark cave in the rocks. It is a heavy sleeper, and can be approached quite closely without being disturbed. Usually it lives in hilly territory on the margins of desert country, and descends to the plains to look for food at sunset, but first it visits a nearby pool to drink. Then the hunt begins.

THE HYENA'S LAUGH

Scarcely a night passes on the African veld when a traveler will not hear the strange cry of the prowling bone-crusher. Its voice is extraordinary and the sounds it produces are legion.

The hyena's characteristic howl is a crescendo beginning on a low, mournful tone and ending with a shrill, high-pitched note. When the animal approaches a carcass it utters an entirely different cry, the weirdest of all. It is a chilling, diabolical caricature of the human laugh, a hysterical cackle, which has earned the name of "laughing hyena" for this beast. The hyena is a ventriloquist, and the sound offers little clue as to the exact whereabouts of the animal.

Although the hyena is solitary in its habits, when a kill is made or found, as many as nineteen or twenty of the animals may gather. Their loud quarreling over the food carries far through the night.

THE EVIL-LOOKING HYENA

Hyenas have the unflattering distinction of being among the most gruesome members of the animal kingdom, in appearance as well as habits. They prey upon feeble, injured, or old animals; when attacked themselves, they feign death in order to avoid fighting. Though a well-known eater of carrion, the hyena often finds a carcass only after the vultures have already picked it clean of flesh. With its powerful teeth, the hyena finishes the job by chewing up the bones. Pictured above is the spotted or laughing hyena.

HYENA FACT AND LEGEND

The spotted hyena is very bold at night and for this reason it is much feared. Accounts have greatly exaggerated its size and ferociousness and given rise to widespread belief in an uncanny creature known as the Nandi bear or chimiset. In different parts of the country this strange beast may go under other names as well, but most of the tales about it follow the same pattern. They tell of a bloodthirsty animal with long, grizzly hair—an animal that attacks natives at night, either mauling them badly or killing them. It is supposed to leave a very large footprint. Many white people are convinced that this weird creature really prowls about the African jungles, but it is totally unknown to science.

Still, in all these stories a certain amount of fact gleams through —enough to illuminate the hyena and its deeds. Although the spotted hyena will rarely attack people during the day, things are different after sundown. On hot nights the natives often sleep out in the open and there are many cases where they have actually been attacked by hyenas. The animals usually go for the face; it is not too uncommon to see natives that have been frightfully scarred by such an assault.

Also, it is a common practice in many parts of Asia and Africa for natives to move aged people, about to die, out of their huts and villages. Being superstitious about death, the natives never let it happen in their dwellings. The old people are left to meet their end out in the open, and we cannot be surprised if the hyena does not turn up its nose at such golden opportunities. Many times the beast has been reported as a grave-robber.

DEATH OF A HYENA

Hyenas are often reputed to commit gruesome acts upon their own bodies. One of the most horrible sights the author has ever witnessed met his eyes when he came out of the brush one day just as a hunter shot a hyena. The bullet struck the beast in the abdomen and ripped it open. The hyena, as we have remarked, is noted for its unusual vitality. This animal, though mortally wounded, continued to gallop away. Without stopping, it reached back and snapped off the protruding intestines, which only dragged out more.

The author saw this awful performance repeated time and again. The animal never paused in its headlong rush even though two more bullets entered its side; finally a fourth shot in the shoulder put the creature out of its misery.

Such behavior, unnatural as it may seem to us, is no oddity in nature. It is by no means restricted to the hyena. The author once saw a red squirrel almost disembowel itself before it could be killed outright. In this case it seemed that the animal considered the protruding intestines as a foreign object attached to its abdomen, and the cause of its pain.

There is nothing unusual in the fact, sometimes commented upon with astonishment, that a hyena will chew its foot off when caught in a trap; here again, most animals will do the same, and the action is easily explained. The pressure from the jaws of the trap cuts off circulation, and the paw soon becomes numb. Thus the animal is quite unaware that it is biting its own foot off in its effort to escape.

AN ODD FEMALE

One marked peculiarity of the spotted hyenas is that the female exceeds the male in size. To this the female has added another oddity: her sexual organs are quite exceptional in structure and closely resemble those of the male in outward appearance. This phenomenon, unique among the carnivores, is not found in other hyenas. It has given rise to a native superstition that the spotted hyena can assume the role of male or female at will; many white people also hold this belief.

Of course some animals do change their sex—certain snails and fishes are famous in this respect. But, up until the present, the scientific world has greeted with skepticism any claim that a mammal of one sex could alter in its characteristics enough to breed as a member of the other sex. There just has not been sufficiently convincing proof presented.

Of great interest, however, is certain evidence concerning the spotted hyena. C. E. Fronk, M.D., of the Fronk Clinic, Honolulu, while hunting in Tanganyika not long ago, shot a full-grown male spotted hyena which, on dissection of its sexual organs, revealed rudimentary female organs, he reports. A second specimen he shot was a well-developed female that revealed rudimentary male organs. A third full-grown animal showed equally rudimentary organs of both male and female, neither sex being dominant at the time. A Mr. Carr Hartley of Tanganyika further states that one living hyena in his possession has both fathered and mothered at least one litter of puppies. This report has strengthened the growing supposition.

It is possible that the doctor was mistaken in his assumption that the animals he examined were adult. A report, based on observations on mating spotted hyenas in zoological gardens, by Karl M. Schreeder, published in 1952, seems to prove conclusively that this animal is not bisexual.

In embryo, a mammal is potentially both male and female; as it develops, one sex becomes dominant. Nature has its imperfect products, and there may be signs of maleness and femaleness together in one animal. Such a creature is never capable of the functions of both sexes, and is usually incapable of the functions of either.

YOUNG HYENAS

The nursery for the young hyenas is a large hole in the ground. The pups, numbering two to four in a litter, are born in March or April, about three months after mating time. They are seal brown in color, without any spots or stripes. After a month or two the fur becomes lighter in patches, leaving the characteristic dark spots. It is questionable whether the male plays an active part in raising the family.

Under natural conditions the spotted hyena has practically no enemies and has a long life expectancy. One lived twenty-five years in a zoo. Taken young, hyenas make docile pets, and become quite attached to their owners.

The spotted hyena is found throughout Africa from Ethiopia and Senegal south to the Cape of Good Hope. There is only one species, but six varying forms occur in different regions.

HYENAS STRIPED AND BROWN

In India, Palestine, Arabia, and North Africa to Tanganyika we encounter another common type, the Striped Hyena, *Hyaena hyaena*. It is smaller than the spotted hyena, its head and body length being about three and one-half feet, and its tail one and one-half feet long; the average weight is about seventy-four pounds. This animal is soiled grayish in color with narrow tawny and blackish stripes running across the body and legs. Its life habits are much the same as those of the spotted hyena.

An interesting example of how an animal takes up a specialized kind of existence is shown by the Brown Hyena, *Hyaena brunnea*, also known as the Strand Wolf or Strandjut. This South African species (it does not range north of the Zambesi River) haunts the beaches and shore lines, where it feeds on marine refuse. It is more timid and retiring than the spotted hyena, and is not likely to attack human beings. Although best known as a haunter of seashores, it also occurs far inland.

The brown hyena is a little smaller and more lightly built than the spotted hyena. Nevertheless, it is a powerful brute, and one of its kind caught in a trap lugged away the sixty-pound log to which the mechanism was attached, dragging it four miles during one night —faster, for a short distance, than a man could run, hampered with this impediment.

For a hyena, this one has extremely long hair (about ten inches) on its back. It has a coarse blackish-gray coat, and stripes only on the legs.

AARDWOLVES—AFRICAN TERMITE-EATERS

The Aardwolf, *Proteles cristatus*, looks like a small hyena, but it is very mild and inoffensive in its character. Common through South

THE HYENA'S MEEK RELATIVE

Despite its name, the aardwolf is related to hyenas, not wolves. Its appearance is deceptive for though it looks like a small hyena, this timid creature prefers to feed on insects. When menaced, it bristles its mane and ejects an offensive-smelling fluid from its anal glands. The name "aardwolf" is Dutch for "earth wolf"—derived from the aardwolf's habit of making its home in burrows.

and East Africa, and north to Somaliland, it lives in open sandy plains, scrubby brush country, and rocky hills.

For the aardwolf, a hole in the ground is home. This "earth" is sometimes dug by the animal itself, but more often it moves into a deserted ant-bear's den. Now and then a number of aardwolves may dwell in the same burrow. It was because of the animal's habit of living in the ground that it acquired its Dutch name, aardwolf ("earth wolf"). It is not a wolf but, as its appearance and posture suggest, a close relative of the hyena.

Because the aardwolf spends the day underground, it is frequently overlooked in places where it is quite abundant in numbers. It has a pointed muzzle and large, erect ears. Its long fur is coarse in texture; it is light gray or buff in color, with bands of dark brown running across the back.

The word *cristatus,* in the aardwolf's scientific name, means "crested," and this creature has a sort of mane—a distinct crest of long hairs running down the back. When attacked, the aardwolf erects its mane. This gives the animal a formidable appearance that belies its essentially timid nature. Under provocation, the aardwolf also emits a malodorous fluid from its anal glands.

An animal's teeth will tell you much about how it gains its livelihood. The aardwolf's mouth is quite unlike the hyena's: the jaws are weak, the teeth small. This is hardly the equipment for a tearer of flesh much less a cruncher of bones, and in fact the aardwolf is rather specialized to an insect diet. When the aardwolf sets forth on its nightly hunts, much of the food it seeks is white ants, which it consumes in great masses. Other insects and scraps from kills left by the larges carnivores round out the aardwolf's diet.

Aardwolves bear their young in a burrow in November or December. There are two to four babies in one litter, and more than one female and her young may occupy the same den. The aardwolf is fairly sociable, and packs of half a dozen or more may travel about in search of food, though pairs of hunters or single hunters are equally common. The aardwolf's cry is much like the hyena's.

In South Africa, hunting the aardwolf with dogs has been a popular sport for many years. The animal is not fleet of foot and the dogs overtake it easily. The aardwolf must depend upon ruse to save itself; it often escapes its pursuers by dodging and doubling back over its tracks in the low bush.

In zoos the aardwolf, or maanhaar-jackall as it is sometimes called, has lived up to thirteen years. Only one species exists, with six geographical forms. The animal is a little more than two feet long and it has a bushy tail some six inches in length. At the shoulders it stands about twenty inches. The genus name, *Proteles,* means "forward perfect"—the aardwolf's fore feet, following the basic mammal pattern, have five toes, whereas the hyena only has four on each foot. With the hyenas, the aardwolves make up the family Hyaenidae.

The Cats—Stalkers and Springers

THE CATS, from the tabby to the tiger, are a bundle of high-tension muscles, ever ready to explode into action. At rest they offer a perfect picture of complacence and relaxation. They purr, they are soft and peaceful. But in a fraction of a second they may be transformed into snarling, slashing terrors—vibrant machines of destruction, energy on the loose.

Cats are springers. Just as dogs are runners, relying upon sustained speed to overtake and bring down their prey, cats are masters of the art of leaping. From a running, walking, standing, or sitting position, they can suddenly catapult themselves into the air and hit their quarry with a stunning impact. They land with claws extended and jaws wide open, teeth bared ready to sink into the victim's throat.

A CAT'S CLAWS

In the world of flesh-eaters, the cats (family Felidae) are the masters of their trade. They have the longest and sharpest canine teeth of all the carnivores. In cutting through flesh and sinew, the side teeth operate like shears: the knifelike edges in each jaw slice up and down, cut past each other, but do not meet. (There are, in the mouth of a cat, no bone-crushing teeth such as we find in a dog or a bear.) The tongue is wonderfully fitted to help out. Its upper surface is rasplike, and the largest cats will draw blood by merely licking the surface of the skin.

Cats have the sharpest claws of all the mammals. Perfect cutting tools, they are compressed on each side and hooked. With the exception of the cheetah's, the claws of the cats are retractile—that is, they can be withdrawn at will into sheaths in the paws, or they can be extended for action. Thus the animals can trot along silently on their foot pads, keeping the claws safely protected, then bring them out as sharp as ever when there is work for them to do. A dog's claws are always extended.

EXQUISITELY KEEN SENSES

All this marvelous equipment for getting their livelihood would be worth little to the cats, which hunt mostly at night, if they could not detect their prey at a distance. Here, too, nature has not left them in the lurch. They have moist noses, like dogs, and can smell and hear extremely well.

In a cat's ears there are hairs that catch minute vibrations in the air and tell the animal of movements it has not even seen. Its whiskers are also sensitive feelers that work in much the same way, registering the slightest contact at the tip, and transmitting the sensation to the nerves at the root.

SEEING IN THE DARK

Everyone knows that cats—tame or wild—can see in the dark. But just how do they do it? What, too, is the cause of the familiar green glare in the eyes of cats at night?

This glare is known as eyeshine. The lining at the back of a cat's eye is coated with masses of minute particles called guanin, which have a metallic luster of silver or gold. When light strikes the guanin, the particles amplify and brighten the dimly lighted picture focused on the mirror or retina inside the eye, for better visibility.

The slightest trace of light is caught by the guanin, and a glow is created by it.

The purpose of guanin is not to reflect light and illuminate the outside world. It is only when bright artificial light is suddenly directed into the eyes of a cat at night that the overabundance or surplus of light is reflected back. Given time, the luminative particles will retreat into their cells and the eyeshine will stop.

The dark pupils of the cat's eyes dilate at night, to allow all possible light to enter. It is interesting to note that these hunters of the gloom have the largest eyes of all the carnivores.

CATS OLD AND NEW

Cats vary from medium to large in size. Although they are not native to the Australian region and Madagascar, we find them in most other parts of the world, particularly in its hotter sections. (However, they originated in the colder regions—hence the warm, thick fur.)

In prehistoric times, one of the commonest of the cats in Europe, Asia, Africa, and North and South America was the famous saber-toothed tiger. About the size of a modern lion or tiger, it had enormous saber-like teeth projecting from its upper jaw. Apparently it preyed on animals with leathery hides, and could not have overcome them with a more modest armament.

It was a long step from this ancient warrior to today's domestic cat. The ancestors of our domestic cat were probably the African Wild Cat, *Felis chaus,* and the Kaffir Cat, *Felis lybica* (others no doubt are also in its family tree). These two were tamed by the Egyptians of olden times and ultimately brought to Europe. Here they were crossed with local species, and many of our modern cats sprang from the match.

Typical domestic cats usually have vertical black stripes on the flanks called "mackerel" by cat fanciers; but there are numerous curious and divergent breeds, among them the Manx cat, which lacks a tail; the Persian, which has long, silky hair; and the Siamese, whose hind legs are longer than the front ones.

Domestic cats have their cult, but their popularity today is only a pale shadow of the esteem they enjoyed among the ancient Egyptians, who were among the first to tame them. Cats were sacred to the goddess Bast, who was herself cat-headed. In tomb paintings we sometimes see rather long-eared, ginger-colored cats, with lengthy, dark-ringed tails, sitting on chairs; one cat is portrayed wearing a collar and chewing a bone. One interesting painting depicts a long-faced cat perched on a papyrus stem, and we are led to believe that the animal filled the role of a retriever on hunting expeditions.

Herodotus tells us that the death of a cat was an occasion of deepest mourning among the Egyptians. It was a common practice to embalm the felines and wrap them in mummy bandages. Great numbers were reverently laid to rest in sacred cat cemeteries at Bubastis, a city devoted to the worship of cats, and other places along the Nile. In some localities the quantities of cat bones dug up in recent times were so vast that they were spread on the land or shipped abroad as fertilizer.

Some Interesting Smaller Wild Cats

EUROPE'S WILD CAT

Once common in England, the European Wild Cat, *Felis silvestris*, has retreated as civilization has moved forward. Today this savage creature still may be seen in Scotland and across Central Europe into Asia Minor and northern Asia. It resembles a tabby cat in size and general color (perhaps it is one of its ancestors) but is more heavily built and more powerful. The Scotch wild cat is about two feet long, with the tail half as long again.

The European wild cat chooses for its home rocky and densely wooded regions. Its den is hidden in a thicket or crevice in the rocks or under an old tree stump. A fierce, ill-tempered beast, it haunts the shores of lakes and rivers at night, searching for rabbits, grouse, mountain hares, small birds, and, occasionally, fish. It stalks its game by sight until within a short distance. Then the wild cat puts on tremendous speed, making the final attack as unexpected as possible.

This animal is quite untameable, and makes a most unsatisfactory pet. It never turns docile, even to those who feed it. Most other cats become amenable to discipline but the wild cat always has its back to the wall—with ears down and eyes glittering, it holds its paws forever ready to strike at the least provocation. Captive animals have lived as long as sixteen years.

THE JUNGLE CAT

One of the most familiar cats of India and North Africa is the Jungle Cat or African Wild Cat, *Felis chaus.* It ranges through southern Asia as far east as Thailand and Yunnan China. This feline haunts the brush jungles, tall grass, and reed beds near rivers and lakes but mostly in areas that are comparatively dry. The author found it common in the arid regions near the Caspian Sea in Persia and saw several asleep on dry mud banks in broken country.

About the size of a large house cat, the jungle cat is colored gray to tawny and has a distinct crest of hairs along its back. It has long legs and is very swift and strong for its size. Its food is mainly small mammals and birds up to the size of the peacock. The discovery of the quills of the porcupine in its feet indicates that it occasionally attacks this animal. An African subspecies, the Egyptian Fettered Cat, or the Swamp Cat, was tamed by the ancient Egyptians, and mummified cats of this type are found in the Egyptian tombs.

THE KAFFIR CAT AND THE BLACK-FOOTED CAT

The Kaffir Cat, or Gray Wild Cat, *Felis lybica,* is the common wild cat of Africa, from Egypt to the Cape of Good Hope. It looks like a tabby cat, its fur being tawny or light buff in color as a rule.

The kaffir, like almost all the cats, keeps to itself, remaining under cover in dense brush or tall grass. It is, however, a husky creature and can defend itself against almost any dog. When at bay, it erects the ruff around its neck and presents a most formidable appearance to its foes.

The smallest of the wild cats is the Black-footed Cat, or Sebala Cat, *Felis (Microfelis) nigripes*—it is only fourteen inches long, plus a six-inch tail. Native to the arid plains of the Kalahari Desert region and South Africa, it lies up during the day in the hole of the springhaas or some other burrowing animal.

A shy creature, the black-footed cat usually remains savage in captivity, though it will live on amicable terms with other cats. It breeds readily with domestic cats and other small wild species of typical cats. The black-footed cat's litter, like that of many others in this group, contains two or three kittens.

LYNXES AND BOBCATS

The Canadian Lynx, *Felis (Lynx) canadensis,* dwells in the ever-green forests of the North Country of Canada, where fallen timber and dense windfalls present an almost impenetrable barrier to man.

A black-barred side-ruff and ears heavily tufted and edged with black frame this feline's solemn-eyed face and give it a handsome, almost regal appearance. But gaunt, lanky hindquarters, bobtail, and

"MR. SOBERSIDES"

Long side whiskers make the Canadian lynx look solemn and old-fashioned. Despite its name, it is also found in the United States, usually in northern evergreen forests. The animal's broad feet and strong legs enable it to tread the snowy terrain. Lynx fur—grayish brown with white spots—is in demand in the fur trade because of its long, soft, feather-light hair. Man takes a greater toll of the lynx than does any of its natural enemies.

exceptionally long hind legs and oversized feet are incongruous with the elegance of the animal's mien. Although the large, padded feet make the going across the snow easier, the lynx is an awkward animal when it speeds up to a gallop.

Despite its name, the Canadian lynx ranges as far south as Colo-

rado and Oregon in the west, northern New York in the east. It is
much sought by trappers and hunters for its long, soft fur, which is
grizzled or grayish brown in color and spotted with black. The pelt
is highly valued in the fur trade, and is warm as well as handsome.

Famous for the sharpness of its sight, the lynx usually hunts at
night. It feeds largely on the snowshoe rabbit, but when the supply
of these animals fails, as happens from time to time, many of the cats
die of starvation. Sometimes the lynx ekes out its diet with beaver,
and it is a deadly enemy of the fox. It will prey on deer, but these
swift, massive animals are no easy quarry for the three-foot-long lynx.
It prefers to creep up on them while they are lying down, and then
spring at the neck, holding on till the victim is dead. The lynx can
strike with unbelievable swiftness at the crucial moment.

Oddly enough for a cat, the lynx is not averse to getting itself wet.
Those who have watched it say that it takes to the water without being in any sense driven, and that it swims as well as a dog. One lynx
was seen crossing the arm of a lake two miles wide.

Family Life of the Lynx. During the mating season—in late winter
or early spring—there is considerable caterwauling as the tom lynxes
fight for a mate, but usually there is more sound than actual struggle. About two months after mating time a litter of kittens—generally four—is born in the shelter of a thick windfall or under an
overhanging ledge (typical lairs of the lynx). Blind at birth, they
open their eyes for the first time when ten days old. Their mother
suckles them for two or three months, when they are old enough to
travel with her on her hunting trips.

By midsummer the kittens are weaned, and begin the task of hunting for themselves. The family stays together until the autumn, and
may continue together until the end of the year, by which time the
kittens are fully grown. But when the mating season rolls around
again, all family ties are broken and the young are ready to seek their
own mates.

Life in the wild is hard for the lynx. Although it does not have
many enemies, food is often scarce and the animal may have to risk
its life to get it. Under favorable circumstances it might live fifteen
years, but that would be a record.

The Not-So-Fearful Bobcats. Much like the Canadian lynx, but
smaller, is the Bay Lynx, Bobcat, or Wild Cat, *Lynx rufus* ("red

lynx"), as it is variously known. This creature has brown fur, indistinctly marked with darker spots and lines, but its feet are more normal than the Canadian lynx's. Its range is not so northerly, extending from southern Canada into Mexico. Varying from this animal in size and color are many North American bobcats that all belong in the genus *Lynx* but dwell in restricted localities.

The bobcats have a reputation for ferocity that is more a matter of seeming than of reality. Their usual fare is rats, mice, rabbits, and snakes, and they are most unlikely to attack man. Sometimes they prey on small domestic stock and poultry.

Bobcat hunting is a popular sport in the southeastern United States. The animal is not easy to tree; it will give a pack of fast foxhounds a good run for their money, sometimes eluding them for hours. When the bobcat can no longer escape, it strikes out ferociously at the dogs. Though they generally put it out of action, they have wounds to nurse and lick.

Most of the bobcats appear to have no fixed breeding season. The mother bears two to four babies at a time in her den, which may be in a cave, dense shrubbery, or a hollow log.

Quick Thinking of a Bobcat Mother. To a gentleman named Blennerhassett, who lived in West Virginia, we owe a fascinating picture of how a mother bobcat protects her own. While on a fishing trip in the mountains of that state, he saw a mother bobcat with her two kittens emerge from a clump of underbrush. The cat seemed to be giving her young a lesson, when suddenly she grabbed one of them by the loose skin of its neck and deposited it in the crotch of a tree near by. Leaving the startled youngster there, she darted back for the remaining one.

Just as the mother bobcat got her second baby up the tree, an old razorback boar dashed out of the brush, followed by a wild sow with a litter of little pigs. The cat had barely gone ten feet up when the boar was stamping with rage at the foot of the tree.

Leaving her kittens at a safe distance from the ground, the cat took her position lower down; now it seemed that she was going to fight the boar.

But the wise old cat had no such intentions. She waited and waited until the boar was at a safe distance. Then she sprang at one of the little pigs and made off with it as fast as her long legs could carry her. Over logs and rocks she raced, with the boar foaming at the mouth in hot pursuit.

The trail ended at a cliff. Here the cat dropped the pig and sprang to safety. Presently she returned to the tree, retrieved her kittens, and trotted off into the forest.

It would seem that this bobcat showed considerable forethought in her method of decoying the boar away from her little ones. Being a parent herself, she knew full well that the infuriated wild razorback could not ignore the pitiful cries of his young and would give chase, and that her own babies would be left safely behind.

Old World Lynxes. The Old World has its lynxes, too, though man, the hunter, has made them much scarcer than they used to be. The European Lynx, *Lynx lynx,* closely resembling the Canadian lynx, is found throughout the wooded portions of Europe and Asia from the extreme north to the Alps, the Pyrenees, and Tibet, and from the Atlantic coast east to the Pacific coast in Siberia. There are a number of regional lynxes that vary in color from a Chinese variety that is reddish brown with dark spots, to yellowish brown or brownish gray in the typical European lynx.

CARACALS—OFTEN TRAINED FOR HUNTING

The Caracal, *Felis (Caracal) caracal,* is among the most active of the feline tribe. Except for the cheetah, it is the least catlike of all in its movements.

The natives of India often train this animal for hunting because of its remarkable speed and its skill in jumping. Trained caracals are let loose amongst pigeons feeding on the ground and one cat may strike down ten or twelve before they can escape by flight. The cat will spring five or six feet in the air to knock down a pigeon.

"Caracal" means "black ears" in Turkish, and this slender, lynxlike animal does indeed have large, blackish ears that are tufted at the tip. Its fur is rather short and tawny brown in color. The tail is not long (nine inches) compared to the body (about two and one-half feet). The animal may weigh up to forty pounds and stands high on its long limbs. This handsome cat has eyes that shine like bright emeralds, due to the luster of the enlarged pupils; the iris is an amber yellow

The caracal is essentially a creature of hot, dry country. In Asia it is found over the greater part of Arabia, as well as in Turkey, Syria, Iraq, and the Peninsula of India. In Africa it ranges from the Mediterranean Sea to the Cape of Good Hope, in all types of country but the thick tropical coastal forests. Its den may be a hollow tree, a crevice in the rocks, or a hole in the ground (a porcupine or aardvark burrow), and here it bears its two to five young. The caracal preys on peacocks, cranes, partridges, hares, and occasionally gazelles.

OCELOTS—FAMED FOR THEIR FUR

The Ocelot, *Felis (Leopardus) pardalis,* is an American jungle cat that loves darkness. At home in the gloom of dense forests, it never leaves its lair until the evening light is gone and the dusk has turned to darkness. The darker the night the farther the ocelot will prowl. Even moonlight nights impede its activities.

Usually the ocelot spends its time on the ground, in dense cover on brush-laden hillsides. But it is also fond of climbing in the trees: it often goes aloft to rifle bird nests and may even nap upstairs during daylight hours. That it can find its prey in the branches of the dark forest is a tribute to its keen senses. It can climb easily and quickly enough for its own purpose, though it is not in a class with the squirrels and monkeys.

This long, lithe animal will seek refuge up a tree when danger threatens. However, it does not leave the ground at the first yap of a pack of hounds. It can run like a fox and knows how to backtrack and double-cross its trail.

The ocelot feeds on almost any kind of animal life that it can master, including—besides birds—rodents, snakes, lizards, and opossums. On one occasion an ocelot killed a large boa, six or seven feet long, and, when discovered, had eaten the head and neck. An ocelot will consume from three to five pounds of meat a night.

For its den the ocelot nearly always selects a rocky cave or, failing this, a hollow tree. The home, wherever it is, is lined with great care. The animal chooses a bedding of dry grass, twigs, and the like, and chews it till it is soft and pliable, for this creature likes its comfort.

The mating season is probably about June. The kittens, nearly always twins, are born in September or October, with their eyes tightly closed. When taken young enough, an ocelot can be tamed, but the less tractable temper and large size of the full-grown adult make it somewhat undesirable for a house pet.

Perhaps the ocelot is most familiar to us through the use of its fur on women's coats and collars. It is one of the handsomest of the cats. Its basic color is light buff, with a pearly overtone. Longitudinal black stripes score its face, head, and neck; there are black spots splashed across the limb and tail, and dots and black rings cover the rest of the body in an attractive, rather chainlike pattern. From the tip of its nose to the end of its tail the animal is three or four feet long.

THE OCELOT WEARS AN ATTRACTIVE COAT
One of the brightest furs used to decorate women's coats is that of the ocelot, a wild cat of South America and Mexico. Against a light buff background, an interesting medley of black rings, spots, and stripes makes a striking contrast. The hair of the ocelot is soft and short. This animal is a fierce fighter, and has even been known to kill boas.

The range of the ocelot extends from the southwestern United States down to Paraguay. The animal is now scarce north of the Rio Grande, but farther south it is quite common.

MORE ABOUT THE LESSER CATS

The Cat With Long Legs. Every kind of cat lives in its own chosen field; each of these springers has characteristics best suited for a particular kind of life and surroundings. The Serval, *Felis (Leptailurus) serval,* a beautiful thirty-four-pound golden buff-colored cat, marked profusely with bold black spots, is found over most of Africa south of the Sahara. Its long legs are a superb adaptation for an animal that lives by running on the ground. This creature haunts the reed-fringed lakes and rivers where waterfowl and hares are to be had. There are two distinct species, the Large Spotted Serval and the Small Spotted Serval.

The Cat That Eats Fruit. All animals live to eat or to be eaten. We generally look upon cats as hunters and flesh-eaters, and correctly so, but there are exceptions; the Flat-headed Cat, *Felis (Ictailurus) planiceps,* smallest of the wild cats in tropical eastern Asia, actually prefers eating nice juicy fruit to catching rats and mice. (Lions often devour ripe watermelons on the Kalahari Desert, but this they seem to do more to obtain liquid than to satisfy their appetites.)

The Cat That Goes Fishing. A cat may wash its face with its paws and do a good job of it, but cats in general just do not like water; most resent getting even their feet wet. A bath is unheard of in the cat family. Yet we find that there is a cat that haunts the banks of rivers and streams in the tropical regions of India and east to Malaya.

This animal, the Fishing Cat, *Felis (Zibethailurus) viverrina,* has turned from the hereditary feline practice of hunting and has gone a-fishing. Having a cat's dislike of getting wet, it does not enter the water. Instead, it crouches on overhanging banks and with a sweep of its paw scoops up fish as they sail unsuspectingly by.

Fresh-water mollusks are also eaten by this short-limbed, sturdy, spotted cat (it is about two and a half feet long). It will resort to killing animals and birds where fishing does not fill its needs, and has been known to carry off dogs and even small children.

The Marbled Cat. The superb long tail of the Marbled Cat, *Felis (Pardofelis) marmorata,* tells us that this handsome creature lives in tall trees; the large irregularly spaced dark blotches that mark its coat are indiscernible against the living tracery of dark forests. The marbled cat travels the dense jungles from the Himalayas east to Borneo, where it becomes a mahogany red and is known as the Bay Cat.

The Golden Cat. Among the rock-bound wastes of southeastern Asia, from Tibet to Malaya, lives one of the largest and most attractive of the medium-sized cats, the Golden Cat, *Felis (Profelis) temminckii*. The bright reddish brown coat of this creature blends perfectly with the rocky background of its home. It is an important animal to the Chinese, who call it *huang pao*—"yellow leopard"—and pay a high price for its bones in medicine shops. A related species of golden cat ranges the forests of West Africa.

The Chinese Money Cat. There is an animal that goes by the intriguing popular name of the Chinese Money Cat. To scientists it is better known as the Asiatic Leopard Cat, *Felis (Prionailurus) bengalensis*. This feline's mercenary name comes from its many spots, which resemble Chinese cash—a kind of decoration that makes ideal camouflage for a forest-loving animal.

The Rusty Spotted Cat. In the broken bush country of southern India and western Ghats is the home of the Rusty Spotted Cat, *Felis rubiginosus*. Its rust-colored spots are arranged in rows or stripes that make this cat almost invisible as it steals silently through the fields of tall grass.

The Desert Cat. At night on the great deserts of western Indian that stretch westward to northern Africa, the gerbils and numerous other rodents are out to feast on the few blades of grass and seeds that are thinly scattered over the sandy wastes. Here the Desert Cat, *Felis constantina,* a house-cat-sized species with pale sandy-colored fur, marked with numerous small black spots, keeps their number in check.

The Rock-Dweller. The Manul or Pallas Cat, *Felis (Otocolobus) manul,* is a small spotted cat that dwells in the high mountains of Tibet and northward into Siberia. Its eyes, placed high in the face, and the low-set ears give it a most ferocious appearance. So far as we may gather, the position of the eyes is an adaptation for peering over edges of rocks in search of prey, thus exposing the smallest amount of the head possible.

SOME INTERESTING SOUTH AMERICAN CATS

The Cat like a Weasel. Perhaps the strangest of all the cat family is the Yaguarundi or Eyra, *Felis (Herpailurus) eyra.* This short-legged, long-bodied cat with a lengthy tail resembles a weasel more than it does a cat and fills much the same position in tropical America that the weasel cats do in the Old World. In Mexico it is known as the Otter Cat in tribute to its readiness to take to the water.

The yaguarundi is only two feet long but it is a ferocious, untamable creature. Its home is in the tangled thickets and dense brush of the plains as well as the forested country from Texas south to Argentina. It is one of the few species that come in two distinct color phases (that is, it may have a coat of one or the other of two colors): one a speckled gray or black and the other a bright rusty red.

Stripes and Spots Galore. The Andean Highland Cat, *Felis (Oreailurus) jacobita,* of South America, takes the place of the snow leopard in the New World; it is pale gray in color and more or less marked with the ocelot's stripes. It is a big cat, too, nearly three feet long without its lengthy tail.

On the upland grass plains that stretch from Patagonia to northern Argentina is the Pampas Cat, *Felis (Dendrailurus) pajeros,* a large yellowish cat with rather coarse fur. In the extreme southern part of South America there is Geoffroy's Spotted Cat, *Felis (Oncifelis) geoffroyi,* while the Margay, *Felis (Noctifelis) wiedii,* a much smaller cat liberally marked with black stripes and spots, lives in the forests of Paraguay and north to Texas. A cat with small spots —the Tiger Cat, *Felis pardinoides*—is the smallest of the American wild cats. It haunts the forests from Costa Rica to Chile.

The Big Cats

COUGARS—POWERFUL VOICES AND BODIES

THE COUGAR, *Felis (Puma) concolor,* is a fear-inspiring sight to the traveler who glimpses this great, powerful beast crouching in the branches of a tree in a deep forest. Its eyes seem to glow like fire in its small, round head. The lithe six-foot body, covered with short, tawny or grayish-brown fur, and the long, heavy tail are vibrant with deadly energy. Those who have heard this feline's weird drawn-out shriek declare it to be the wildest and most hair-raising sound that ever broke the stillness of the American wilderness.

The cougar is a big-game hunter. Usually it spends the day sleeping in some rocky cavern or sunning itself on a high, warm ledge. After dark the cougar leaves its lair and sets forth on a silent hunt. More than once it has been seen swimming across rivers at least a mile wide. It may range twenty miles through the night.

This big cat's natural prey are the deer and sometimes the elk, but it will track down other animals like the skunk, and its victims often include domestic stock—cattle, sheep, horses, and pigs. Stalking the doomed animal in the shadows, the cougar approaches soundlessly for the final rush. Now it gathers its feet under its body and humps its back. The taut muscles burst into action. In one, two, or three quick bounds, the cougar is upon its quarry, hurling it to the ground and piercing its throat or neck with long, murderous fangs.

The cougar is no mean jumper; it can spring twenty feet in one leap. It has no fear of dropping from a height, and has been known to jump from a perch sixty feet high without doing itself injury.

This animal, we see, has enormous power concealed in its graceful body. It can drag a victim that weighs five times its own 160 pounds for a good one hundred yards. If the kill is large, the cougar will eat its fill, then cover the remnants with brush. Later it will come back and make a second or a third meal of the carcass.

Except for the jaguar, the cougar is the largest of the New World cats. The two are almost irreconcilable foes and when they meet there is the devil to pay. The jaguar is bigger and more powerful, but it cannot match the cougar's remarkable agility. The odds are naturally in the jaguar's favor, yet frequently it loses the bout.

NOT A MAN-KILLER

Ferocious the cougar certainly is, but not when it comes up against man. Authentic accounts of attacks upon human beings by this big cat are scarce. It evinces considerable curiosity about people and their actions and will prowl about an abandoned camp or dwelling. But let somebody appear on the scene and the cougar moves off into the woods.

Because of the damage it does to domestic stock, this big cat is extensively hunted. The hunters use dogs to corner the cougar. When it sees no other way out, the animal takes to a tree. Such a move is

IT COMES TO SPY UPON MAN, NOT TO KILL HIM
Anyone who has ever heard the blood-curdling shriek of the cougar, or puma, or seen its powerful, menacing body poised on a tree branch, has surely turned in terror. Yet the otherwise savage cougar does not attack man; it is merely curious about him and likes to poke around his habitations. The cougar's victims are game and domestic animals; its appetite for sheep and cattle causes farmers severe losses.

likely to be fatal for the cougar; a well-placed shot will quickly finish the hunt.

A TAME COUGAR

Now and then you will hear of people rearing tame cougars. Some years ago, in Utah, the author made the acquaintance of a forester who kept as a house pet a cougar that he had raised from a kitten. The big cat was exceedingly playful, and whenever the ranger returned home in the evening, the cougar would make a pretense of hiding behind a chair. Naturally the man was well aware of what was going on, since the chair would hardly conceal the great bulk of the animal. But, entering into the spirit of the game, he would sit down and open his evening paper. With one bound the huge cat would leap over the paper, land on the forester's shoulder, and nuzzle his head and neck in a friendly, loving manner.

Eventually the animal had to go; it had ripped the rugs to pieces and scratched the paint off the walls in sharpening its claws. Transferred to a zoo, the cougar became more and more irritable and savage and would not let the keepers near it.

Two years later the forester visited the zoo. Despite the keepers' insistent warnings, the man walked to the cage, opened the door, and walked in. To the amazement of all the watchers, the cougar jumped on the forester's shoulder, nearly knocking him over, and nuzzled his neck and face. The cat had not forgotten its friend.

COUGAR KITTENS

The mating season of the cougar is very irregular; this cat breeds at almost any time of the year. About three kittens are born some ninety days after a brief courtship.

At birth, a kitten measures about twelve inches and weighs one pound; it is blind and covered with fine yellowish fur spotted with black. The kitten opens its eyes on the eighth or ninth day and cuts its first teeth about ten days later. The spots usually fade from the fur when the animal is six months of age. The kittens stay with their mother until they are a year or sometimes two years old. A long life among the cougars is twenty years.

COUGARS TODAY AND YESTERDAY

There are twenty-seven subspecies of the cougar known. It travels under various names—Puma, Panther, Painter, Catamount, and Mountain Lion—and was once very abundant in the Americas from southern Canada to Patagonia. Today its range in the United States has shrunk to the more remote wilderness of Florida, Louisiana, and the western states from British Columbia to Mexico.

The cougar is still fairly well represented in Central America and South America, where it was a popular game animal long before the coming of the white man. The Inca rulers and their Indian subjects had spectacular hunting excursions, in which the big cat figured prominently. As many as thirty thousand drivers took part in these roundups, destroying great numbers of cougars and other predatory animals.

In Baja California, on the other hand, the natives depended on the cougar for food in quite another way. The hungry Indians, we are told, watched for the gathering of the buzzards and carefully searched the ground where these scavengers were. Often they would find the remains of a cougar feast which the lordly cat had left, in true feline fashion, hidden away beneath soil and leaves.

LEOPARDS OR PANTHERS—FIERCE AND TREACHEROUS

The Leopard, Panther, or Golden Cash Leopard, *Panthera pardus*, outstrips both the lion and the tiger in pure malevolence and savagery. The smallest of the three, this cat is barely inferior to its two big cousins in fighting ability. The natives of Africa often say they would rather face a lion than a leopard any time.

This wary, treacherous beast is much more given to climbing and lurking in the trees than either the lion or tiger. It can leap more than ten feet in the air and run up the side of a tree with astonishing speed. Sometimes it drags its prey up into the branches with it, so that it can dine in peace, away from other marauders.

Although the leopard may be about in the daytime, it is most active in the darkness. A clever tracker, a patient waiter in ambush, it preys on domestic cattle and sheep, deer, antelope, monkeys, and small wildlife. It knows better than to attack a pack of baboons, for these can defend themselves; a single baboon, however, might not be so fortunate.

The panther will spring after its quarry, overtaking it in a few long leaps. It can subdue its smaller victims in a few instants by breaking their spines, strangling them, or tearing open their throats.

INTELLIGENCE OF THE LEOPARD

In intelligence the leopard ranks high; it is quick to learn, and retains anything that is to its advantage. One thing it learns early is ruse, and it occasionally resorts to the subtlest and wiliest subterfuge to make a kill.

THE LEOPARD—A DECEITFUL FIGHTER
Savage and wily, the leopard, or panther, is especially dangerous because its fondness for dog's flesh may bring it close to human dwellings. Leopards sometimes turn into notorious man-eaters, cleverly eluding capture for long, bloody years. Not generally known is the fact that the leopard isn't always clearly spotted—the black panther is also a leopard. Some leopards raised in captivity may grow up to be quite docile.

With a deer in the neighborhood, the leopard has been observed to roll on the ground and to indulge in various other playful antics. The deer, its curiosity aroused, moves closer, but remains suspicious. Still the cat carries on, and the deer, in wonderment, draws nearer in order to see better. Those last few steps are the ones the trickster has been waiting for—they bring the intended victim within easy striking distance.

A FEARLESS ANIMAL

The domestic dog is one of the leopard's favorite foods. At Lihn-shan, a small village in China, a very bold leopard entered the open window of a house, went right to the bed where the owner was sleeping, and made off with a dog that was tied there. The next night it returned and carried away another dog from the room.

It seems that a man is less likely to change his ways than is a leopard. The following night the man tethered another dog to his bed; this night the leopard did not show up, but on the next it did and, though a watch was kept, it escaped with its victim into the forest. A few days later it carried off a pig from a village only a few miles away.

Eventually the leopard was tracked down and killed, but not before it had wounded three natives.

Normally, a leopard will not attack a man. If provoked or wounded, however, the animal will turn on human beings and fight. Once in a great while a leopard will become a man-killer, and take many lives in a short span of time.

WHERE WE FIND THEM

In the warmer and some of the colder parts of the Old World, the leopard is far commoner than the lion or the tiger. It ranges from the Black Sea in Europe east to Burma and the Malay Peninsula, including all of India and Ceylon, and north into Amurland, Siberia. In Africa it is found almost everywhere except in the Sahara.

DIFFERENT KINDS OF LEOPARDS

Leopards vary greatly in size. Some are as long as nine feet, including the extensive tail; others are seven feet in total length or smaller. Their average weight is about one hundred pounds. Twenty years is as long as a leopard is likely to live. It bears two to five young in a litter.

Originally people believed that the leopard and the panther were two different animals. However, the difference proved to be only one of size or sex: the male, the larger of the species, was the so-called "panther" and the female the "leopard."

The entire body of a typical leopard is profusely covered with large and small black spots, evenly scattered over the pale yellowish-buff fur. The spots are arranged in groups of four or five in a circle, or rosette, about a center of somewhat darker shade than the main body color. But we find many variations among the leopards, the most striking being a jet-colored creature known as the Black Panther, which is fairly common in Ethiopia and the East Indies.

The kind of coat a leopard wears will depend very much upon the climate of its native land. Leopards in hot countries have short, close fur, while, in the colder regions, especially Siberia, the hair is long, thick, soft, and deep.

It is in Siberia that we meet the handsomest of all these cats, the Siberian Leopard, a magnificent creature with bluish-gray eyes and long-haired spotted fur almost pearl gray in color. Its agreeable appearance is matched by a pleasant disposition, and in captivity this cat is the most amiable and tractable of its species.

"FALSE LEOPARDS"

The Clouded Leopard. Two of the most attractive of all the cats are called leopards but are not leopards at all. One of these is the Clouded Leopard, *Panthera (Neofelis) nebulosa,* of southeastern Asia. It has thick, soft, and full fur, beautifully decorated with spots and stripes. A savage and extremely wary creature, it inhabits the densest of forests and is active only at night, so that it is rarely seen.

Although only about three feet long, this beast is powerfully built and has relatively longer canine teeth than other cats, so that it is capable of killing fair-sized game, including deer, though generally it preys on smaller mammals and birds.

The clouded leopard is not apt to attack man unprovoked, but there is an instance where a clouded leopard that had killed several head of cattle started to stalk a native boy; fortunately the boy was able to split the skull of the spotted grayish-brown cat with his knife.

In captivity, the clouded leopard often becomes quite tame and lets itself be handled.

The Snow Leopard. The other "leopard" that is not a leopard is known by various names: Snow Leopard, Ounce, or Irbis, *Panthera (Uncia) uncia.* It is often looked for by men who brave the cold, high altitudes from the Himalayas north to the Altai Mountains, where it dwells. Its superb coat of deep, soft fur, pale gray or creamy buff, ornamented with large rosettes, or broken black rings, is a grand reward for the efforts of any hunter.

NOT A TRUE LEOPARD, THOUGH IT HAS THE LEOPARD'S SPOTS
Erroneously named a "leopard," probably because it is spotted with the familiar black rings or rosettes, the snow leopard or ounce has a beautiful coat of pale gray or buff. This beast lives high above the timber line of the Himalayas and, like many animals that dwell in cold places, has a soft, long-haired pelt.

The snow leopard is about the size of an average leopard but less powerful. It preys on mountain sheep, goats, hares, and other small game.

LIONS—THE SOCIABLE BIG CATS

The Lion, or Simba, *Panthera (Leo) leo,* has for a long time been known as the King of Beasts. It certainly looks the part: it has size, a dignified and noble face, and what would seem great pride. Then, of course, it wears a long, stately mane around its neck, which adds to the beast's air of majesty.

But if the lion is a king, it is not one by virtue of savagery. On the contrary, this animal usually has a friendly nature. All other cats travel alone or in pairs; the lion is the only one that moves about in a group or "pride." Occasionally you may see a lion by itself, but these creatures love company, and more often there are five or six together.

The lions will not fight over prey. As many as six male lions have been observed feeding on one kill, and other than a resentful growl when two got hold of the same chunk of meat, there was no display of ill-feeling. At one time, on the Serengeti Plains of East Africa, the author had twenty-five lions, including lionesses and cubs, feeding around him, some not ten feet away. They all got up and left peacefully, without haste, when he stood up.

The lion favors open broken country and grassy plains rather than dense tropical forests. In southern Asia today it is a rarity, but it is still found throughout most of Africa south of the Sahara Desert, being more or less plentiful where there is an abundance of big game. During the day lions often lie up in clumps of tall elephant grass or tangled brush. On the open veldt they are seen resting without any cover in broad daylight, for the royal family of the carnivores has few natural enemies to fear.

HOW THE LIONS KILL

Although these great beasts may be active by day, their working hours are chiefly at night. The lion hunts the larger game such as waterbuck, wildebeest, and kudu, but it seems to prefer the zebra.

Frequently, the big cat lies in wait for its prey near water holes and grazing grounds. In attacking, the lion creeps stealthily on its quarry, coming up from the side or rear. Its head down and its tail erect, it utters low growls. It may be one hundred feet off when it breaks into the final rush, and it dashes toward its prey at a speed of about forty miles an hour or more.

In its attack on a zebra, an experienced lion will gallop alongside the animal and slap it on the neck with its mighty paw. Then the king of beasts slows down and waits for the zebra to fall. The lion's blow may not cut the skin, but it is delivered with such accuracy that it will dislocate the zebra's neck. More often, the lion sinks its teeth into the neck of its prey. With one paw hooked onto the victim's shoulder, it reaches with the other around the animal's head and twists it back, throwing the zebra to the ground and breaking its neck.

Not nearly so bloodthirsty as some of the other big cats, the lion never destroys other animals for the fun of it. A lion kills to live: it kills only when it must eat, and then only one animal at a time. A single carcass will satisfy a lion's hunger for several days.

Normally when a lion has brought down a victim, it feeds on the spot. Afterward it sits close by to guard the carcass from thieves. In a nearby tree, vultures will settle and wait patiently for the lion to leave. But the lion remains until it has made a number of meals off the kill. Then the vultures and the hyenas close in.

MAN-EATING LIONS

We have seen that lions respect man. As a rule, they are more apt to run than attack when met on the veldt, unless provoked or hunted. Still, now and then, you will hear of a man-eater. The percentage of lions that turn man-killer is low. Lions that prey on human beings are usually (but not always) older individuals that have become incapable of killing wild game for themselves. They make their attack only under cover of darkness, and then drag their victim away and hide in the bush.

Two man-eating lions have won a place in history: they actually held up the construction of the Uganda Railway in East Africa. Time and again they returned and carried off and devoured men working on the railroad. Apparently these beasts—they were both males—had a close bond of friendship, as lions occasionally will.

The engineer in charge, a Mr. Patterson, said that, in advancing to the attack on the railway camps, the lions would roar loudly to one another. But they were always absolutely silent during the hour preceding the actual seizure of their unfortunate victims, so it was hard to tell exactly where they would attack. Ultimately Mr. Patterson succeeded in shooting them (December, 1898) but not before they had killed and eaten twenty-eight Indian coolies as well as scores of African natives.

Another lion, after killing several men around a station on the railroad, even managed to carry off and eat the superintendent of the division. This gentleman had come down in his private car, which was run in on a siding. He sat up at a window that night, gun in hand, to watch for the lion, but after a while he fell asleep. The lion climbed on the platform, entered the car, and made off with its would-be slayer.

The man-eating lion, rare though it is, presents a serious menace. If it has killed one time, it is likely to kill again; the taste for human flesh, once acquired, is usually retained for life. Thus, in Africa, the killing of a human being by a lion is the signal for organizing an extensive hunt. With modern weapons, the animal is quickly exterminated, though not without considerable risk to the hunter.

TRAINED LIONS

In circuses, lions are closely watched. Because they are highly intelligent, quick to learn, and friendly, it is simple to teach them tricks and get them to obey commands. The trainer's axiom, however, is: "Easily trained but never tamed."

Lions do occasionally kill their trainers. Nearly always, though, such unfortunate incidents appear to be the trainer's fault—he displays nervousness or changes his routine slightly, and the big cat gets upset. A lion can break a man's back with one blow of its heavy paw.

THE LION'S HONEYMOON

The docile part of a lion's nature, we perceive, is not uppermost all the time. In the breeding season this carnivore will even turn on its own kind. A lion must fight for a mate and it will engage its competitors in a fierce battle. Sometimes the beast has to defeat three or four rivals before it can claim its favorite lioness.

Once victory is won, the pair go off together on their honeymoon. They may travel for miles until they find a place that offers them suitable privacy. During the honeymoon, which may last two weeks or more, they do little hunting or eating. At this time the lion is really dangerous, and any man or beast that trespasses on its privacy is quickly annihilated.

In East Africa the author once saw a lion and a lioness alone together at the edge of the bush. The guide took one look at the couple and hustled the author off in the opposite direction. There could be no mistaking the lion's objection to intruders. The animal's ears were pulled firmly down, the tip of the tail was lashing back and forth, and there was a ferocious snarl on the lips, which were drawn tightly back, exposing a formidable array of teeth.

The lion is often said to take a single mate. So far as we know, its state of wedded bliss may last a year or longer. The animals definitely do not mate for life, and some males are polygamous.

LION CUBS

The lions have a variable breeding season. About 108 days after the mating, four cubs (the average number in a litter—though six are not unusual) are born. They are striped and thickly spotted, but their markings fade as the animals mature. Some, it has been said, have their eyes open at birth, but usually they are closed until the sixth day. In size the newborn babies resemble adult house cats.

The cubs are nursed until they are three months of age. Teething is a painful experience, and they may die in the process if separated from the parents. The cubs are not able to kill for themselves until they are a year old (at this time they are big enough to be on their own), and the mane does not begin to show until the male is three. Often the lion will supply the lioness with food while she is nursing newborn cubs, and will bring game to feed the growing family.

When half-grown, the whelps are expert climbers. They lose this skill as they grow older and heavier. Occasionally one may see a full-grown lion climb into the lower branches of a tree, but this is unusual.

When five or six years of age, a lion is in its prime. The average lion has a life span of fifteen years, but a long-lived one may reach the age of twenty-five.

MALE AND FEMALE

Lions are big fellows. A large male may weigh five hundred pounds and stand about three feet or more at the shoulder; such a beast measures seven feet in length, exclusive of its three-foot tail. The lioness, smaller and less powerful than her mate, will weigh up to three hundred pounds.

The coat of a lion is short haired and coarse, and uniformly tawny or pale sandy-brown in color. The tip of the tail is tufted with dark-brown or black hairs, and completely hidden in it is the so-called "spur" or "claw," a naked, horny patch of skin. What purpose, if any, is served by the spur we do not know.

THE KING OF THE BEASTS IS A GOOD "FAMILY MAN"

The lion leads a surprisingly domestic existence. Generally traveling in family parties, it hunts for antelopes or zebras, and will amiably share the kill with its fellows. Exceptions to the lion's peacefulness occur during the breeding season, when the male will take his hard-won mate off for a secluded honeymoon, and deal swift, violent punishment to intruders. Normally lions will not attack man unless they have been provoked.

A lioness almost never has a mane. In the males, this growth of long hair is quite variable. Most wild lions possess only a scant, ragged, and straggly shock of hair. In menageries, particularly in northern climates, they are more likely to show the full, luxuriant ruff we commonly associate with them.

Although the lion is famous for its roar, the sound is almost never heard during daylight hours. But every evening after sunset, and throughout the night, the big cat periodically utters its ferocious-sounding grunts. "Uuummph-uuupf-mmmff" comes close to recording a typical, less forceful roar in words—if you want to give a realistic imitation, try producing these sounds from deep down in your throat.

HOME OF THE LIONS

Africa is the continent that has most of the world's lions, but even there they are not nearly so common as they used to be. They have disappeared from the extreme north and south. India also was once much more thickly populated with these great cats, which ranged from Sind in the northwest to Bengal in the northeast; but by 1880 the species was almost wholly exterminated except in the Gujarat region, where it still manages to hang on in the wilderness of the Gir forests.

You may well raise a skeptical eyebrow when you see lions and tigers grouped together in a motion-picture scene. There are no tigers in Africa, and lions are seldom seen in India. They are reported to have lingered on in Turkey, Iraq, and Iran until just before our day, but they long ago disappeared from Greece, Asia Minor, and Syria, where they were not uncommon in historic times. These big cats were well known to the Hebrew people, and there are few books of the Bible, either in the Old Testament or the New, that do not contain some mention of them. The strength of the lion is an often-repeated Scriptural reference.

An African lion was the first foreign wild animal to be exhibited in the United States. Its appearance in this country was officially announced in the *Boston Gazette* of September 26, 1720. It must have been a profoundly exciting sight for the people of that day, for zoos did not become common in the New World until much later. When the Emperor of Morocco presented a lion to President Andrew Jackson, he was somewhat embarrassed by the gift, and asked Congress what to do with it. Following their advice, it was sold at auction and the proceeds were given to local orphanages. More recent Presidents have been able to solve such problems by turning them over to zoo curators.

TIGERS—ASIA'S BIGGEST CATS

The Tiger, *Panthera (Tigris) tigris,* outdoes the lion in acts of brutal savagery and feats of power. Or that, in any event, is the conviction of men who have hunted or trained these two beasts. Still, both are almost of a size, and the tiger more nearly resembles the lion than any other member of the cat family.

The most striking differences between the two animals are the striped coat the tiger wears, and its lack of a mane. An old tiger will grow a rich ruff of long hair on its cheeks, but never a mane. Never, that is, unless it is half a lion. So closely related are the lion and the tiger that they may crossbreed in captivity.

You may have seen the interesting offspring of such a match in a zoo: the cross usually has stripes and will sometimes, when it reaches adulthood, sport a mane. A cross between a male lion and a female tiger is known as a liger; vice versa, it is a tigon (or tiglon). These hybrids are not common, however, for the tiger will rarely breed in captivity.

The tiger is the typical big cat of Asia. It lives as far north as Amurland, in Siberia, as far south as India and the Malay Peninsula. It is not native to Africa, and the closest it gets to Europe is the Caucasus, where people still report encountering it from time to time in the Elburz Mountains south of the Caspian Sea. Thus it is quite correct to picture the tiger as a giant cat slinking through the bush and the tangled growths of the steaming tropics—but remember that not all tigers will conform to this image. In its snow-covered winter homeland the Siberian Tiger must face temperatures that fall to seventy degrees below zero.

A CLIMBER AND A SWIMMER

A born climber, the tiger is a creature of the forests, preferring dense underbrush to big timber. Here its stripes seem to serve it as camouflage, blending in with the alternating dark and light of the woodland. The stripes also harmonize neatly with the dark and the dry grass on which the tiger rests. Crouching in the shade of the foliage, where it seeks to avoid the heat of the tropical day, the animal is not easy to detect. It favors places where there is good cover, and where it may find water without traveling far.

The more things an animal can do, the better is it equipped to survive. To its considerable advantage, the tiger is one of the cats that can swim. (So are the lion, the lynx, and a few others.) It shows no qualms about leaping into a stream. If it observes prey on the other bank or on an island in midstream, it will swim across at a good rate. With hunters at its heels, it often saves its life by taking to the water. The animal is an extraordinarily good jumper, too—it can cover fifteen feet in a single bound.

TIGER KITTENS

The tiger has no fixed mating season. The young—two to four make up the average birth—come into the world about one hundred days after the courtship. Newly born, the kittens weigh some two or three pounds, and their eyes are sightless; the little cats cannot see before they are two weeks old. A thoroughly devoted parent, their mother watches over them with great tenderness, nursing them on her milk until they are capable of devouring meat. Anyone who tries to take her kittens from her will have to fight for his life. What role the father plays is not clearly known.

When the kittens are about six weeks old, they may begin to travel with the mother as she goes about her duties as flesh-winner for the family. On hunts or at rest, they pass a sportive kittenhood, playing and chasing their tails like cats the world over.

But by the time they have reached the age of six months or so, the little cats must look to putting aside kittenish ways; now they are big enough and strong enough to apply the tiger techniques of hunting they have learned from their parent. The kittens start with smaller game, like young pigs, and become increasingly adept at springing upon their prey from ambush and slaying it with a quick bite in the neck. They are a year old before they are able to shift for themselves. Although tigers are not social at other times, the family may stay together until the young are nearly two years old.

Tigers slow down as they get on in years, and they do not kill so readily. Their teeth wear down and their power diminishes in time; they must learn to content themselves with less. But a young tiger is supercharged with vitality; it appears to take a special delight in killing and at times exhibits a nature that is extremely bloodthirsty. If the occasion presents itself, the animal will slay as many victims as it finds available, without regard for its needs. And those needs are not small, as witnessed by the fact that a zoo tiger requires ten pounds of meat merely to keep its great body pacing back and forth in confinement, each day.

TIGERS ON THE PROWL

For many generations tigers have bedeviled the poor farmer folk of India. In that traditionally hungry land, all it takes to undo a village is the presence of a tiger in the neighboring woods. Under cover of darkness, the animal will steal forth and kill and carry off a treasured sheep, cow, or calf. If the carcass is of good size, the tiger may not be heard of again for several days; it rests in some hidden place, and dines repeatedly on the kill.

THE KILLER CAT
Just as powerful as the lion, the tiger is, by contrast, cruel, bloodthirsty, and solitary. It climbs, jumps, and, unlike most cats, even swims excellently. In India, the Bengal tiger alone has killed sixty thousand sheep, cows, and goats in one year. But, on the little-known credit side, the tiger helps to maintain a balance in nature by preying upon deer and wild pigs, common despoilers of plant life.

But when nothing remains of the kill, hunger drives the great beast forth, and the village suffers another loss. This may go on for some time, since the peasants regard the tiger with superstitious dread, and are often slow to take action against it. In a single year the Bengal tiger is reported to have killed sixty thousand sheep, horses, and other livestock. Tigers also prey upon deer, antelope, and wild pigs, but in such instances the big cats actually do man a service, since these vegetable-eaters often cause serious damage to crops.

TIGERS WITH A TASTE FOR HUMAN FLESH

Although tigers are not man-killers by nature, now and then they, like lions, acquire a taste for human flesh. This is especially true of tigers that are old, infirm, or crippled. Lacking the strength to cope with their natural prey—some intended victims, like the buffalo, have powerful horns, and are quite capable of killing the big cats—these older animals may discover that man is a helpless creature, relatively speaking.

When once a tiger takes to killing man, it usually becomes a persistent menace to the local population. In India, in some districts, between two and three hundred natives have been slain in a single year, close to a thousand in the whole country. Many villages have been deserted entirely because of the large numbers of deaths caused by these fearful man-eaters.

There are many remarkable legends told about tigers in India. According to some tales, the tiger is in reality a human being who has been transformed into an animal. Many natives also believe that the tiger holds the ghosts of its victims in thrall. The spirits of those men that have been killed and eaten by a tiger, the natives say, sit on the great cat's head and go everywhere with it. Not only do they warn the tiger against danger but, entertaining malice toward their fellow men, they aid the beast in destroying them.

APPEASING THE TIGER'S SPIRIT IN SIBERIA

In Siberia, too, the tiger is greatly feared, the natives considering it to be favored by their gods. When the author went to Amurland, in eastern Siberia, to hunt for tigers, he engaged a native of the Golde tribe, a Mongoloid clan, as a guide but was told there were certain formalities that had to be complied with before the guide would leave his village.

The night before the hunting party left, a tiger feast was held in the village's largest hut and a shaman or witch doctor had to be hired to officiate. He came decked in all manner of trinkets and feathers to conduct the ceremony. A priestly fee, payable in liquor, was asked in advance, but kerosene proved acceptable as a substitute. A place was cleared on the floor, and the shaman went into as wild a dance as you could imagine. The air was thick with the smoke of evil-smelling tobacco and the babble of a strange tongue was everywhere as the party began in true oriental fashion.

Suddenly the shaman stopped in his mad dance and began to sway unsteadily; the great spirit of the forest was entering his body. Everyone fell silent. The flickering wicks of the few smoky homemade lamps burned dimly on as the shaman sank slowly to the floor and was still. Presently he got to his knees and started to hop around like a rabbit, the sweat pouring down his face. He stopped in front of the author and seized his arm. Now the shaman coughed violently until a small white stone fell from his mouth into the author's hand. That was a guarantee that we would get one great white rabbit.

After an interval of about an hour, the shaman went into an even more fantastic dance. Again he was seized by a trance, but this time he crawled around like a bear and coughed up a large brown stone. It was now assured that the author would get a big brown bear.

The finale came at midnight. Previously, the dances had been wild and fantastic, but this one was weird and violent—the spirit of the tiger had entered. The shaman time and again literally hit the ceiling, crashed down on the floor, then bounced up again like a ball. After the trance he sprang through the air in great leaps. He visited the author three times, on each occasion coughing up a stone in the author's hand.

Now there was great rejoicing. Three tigers had been added to our bag. Forgiveness was asked of the tigers with the explanation that the natives needed the money and the foreigners would get the animals anyhow even if one of the Golde people did not act as guide.

It seems only fair to add that the author did get one big white rabbit, a giant brown bear that for some unexplainable reason had left its den in midwinter, and three beautiful Siberian tigers, two of which can be seen on exhibition at the American Museum of Natural History.

HUNTING THE TIGER

For any big-game hunter, the tiger is a great prize. There are a fair number of ways to kill it. The natives of India often favor a pitfall, but Westerners prefer high-powered rifles.

Sometimes tigers are shot from a platform erected in a tree close to a tethered animal. The most popular method of hunting tigers, however, is from the backs of elephants. A well-trained shikaree (sportsman's) elephant will stand the charge of a tiger while the hunters shoot it down. Occasionally the elephant will even rush to meet the tiger, much to the discomfort of the hunters in the howdah. The tiger will often roar when hit, though some say that the female remains silent.

TIGERS BIG AND SMALL

Although tigers are not found over nearly so wide a range as lions, they show much more variation from place to place. The typical Indian or Bengal tiger weighs about four hundred pounds. It may measure nine feet or longer (one-third of this is the tail). Long, narrow black stripes mark its limbs and body, which are tawny yellow in color, fading to whitish on the under parts. The Caucasian tiger has brownish stripes, while the fur of the Siberian cat is lighter in color and, in keeping with the climate, the hair is longer, thicker, and more luxuriant. Occasionally, a completely black or white tiger is born in an average litter.

The tigers of India and the more northern parts of the range are the largest and strongest of all. The Siberian tiger, giant of the species, reaches a total length of over thirteen feet and, if good and fat, will weigh over 650 pounds; the average male stands three feet at the shoulder, and weighs some 500 pounds. The smallest is the Bali tiger. In captivity, tigers have lived as long as twenty-five years.

JAGUARS—BIGGEST CATS OF THE NEW WORLD

The Jaguar, *Panthera (Jaguarius) onca*, is the New World's biggest cat. A sturdy, powerful creature, it may be six or eight feet long, over-all, and weigh up to 250 pounds. No wonder the people of Mexico and Central America call the jaguar *el tigre*, and make a hasty retreat when they glimpse its tawny, black-spotted form in some dense jungle thicket. Among the cats, only the lion and tiger are larger than the jaguar.

Although this great, dangerous beast has disappeared from many of the places it once haunted, it is still found from Patagonia all the way through South and Central America, and as far north as Texas, New Mexico, and Arizona in the United States. Commonest in the tropical lowlands, where it often dwells in the marshes, it will make its home in arid and mountainous regions as well.

At night, the jaguar's deep, throaty roar wakes the jungle and fills its inhabitants with terror. No living creature is secure from the big cat's savage assault. Along the rivers it will tackle the alligator or the huge capybara, giant of the rodent race. It will pounce upon the turtle, turn it over, and rip it out of its shell. A strong swimmer, the jaguar often will not abandon the intended victim that seeks safety in the water. Even the monkeys in the trees sense imminent danger when they hear the lithe cat snarl, for they know it can climb and leap from branch to branch with impressive agility. The peccaries, wild pigs of the jungle, are a special favorite of the jaguar's, and domestic stock, too, frequently falls prey to it.

Every now and then the jaguar decides it would like a fish dinner. So it looks for a low branch that reaches out over a stream, or a rock that offers equally convenient access to the water. Fishermen might well envy the jaguar its easy angling technique. Resting on the comfortable perch it has selected, the cat extends its paw into the water and scoops up the fish. There are reports that the jaguar uses its tail as a lure, but there is some doubt about this.

There is, however, sufficient evidence to prove that the jaguar does on occasion attack man. It is the only American animal that becomes a man-eater by habit. Not every jaguar will kill people—only certain individuals are guilty. Instances of such attacks are becoming less common; the cats seem to be learning to avoid the man with the gun.

A DANGEROUS SPORT

Hunting the jaguar is a dangerous sport, but many consider it worth the risk because the animal's pelt is valuable. Dogs are used to track the big cat and bring it to bay.

Although the animal is a fast runner, it soon gets winded. Like the cougar, it will sometimes go up a tree, where it can be shot. But some jaguars prefer to stay on the ground and fight. Even when wounded they will tear apart any dog that comes too close. The hunter himself must be wary of a sudden, desperate charge by the enraged beast.

"TIGER" OF THE NEW WORLD

The jaguar is a fierce, predatory cat of North and South America. At first glance, it looks like a leopard, but one can see that its head is larger, its body heavier and broader, and the rosettes on its coat are wider. The jaguar is a good swimmer, and likes the water. With enviable ease, it sits by a stream, dips its great paw into the water, and brings up a fish dinner. Peccaries, sloths, and capybaras are among its favorite victims.

THE CHILDREN AND THE JAGUAR

We are indebted to Humboldt, a great German naturalist of the last century, for many realistic views of the intimate lives of South America's animals. Perhaps the most famous of his accounts is the picturesque story of an unferocious big cat—the "Ferdinand" of the jaguars.

Humboldt tells us of two Indian children who were playing in a small clearing in the deep forest. Suddenly, out of the dark shadows of the jungle, came a jaguar. The beast started to leap and gambol around the children, as though it wanted to join in their play. The children were fascinated as they watched the big, sleek, yellow-and-black animal gleaming in the bright sunlight. Closer and closer it bounded to the trusting children.

Accidentally perhaps, or possibly in play, the jaguar bumped into the younger of the two and gave the child a gentle pat. But the claws were unsheathed and they scratched the child's forehead. Blood began to flow. The other child immediately seized a stick and smacked the jaguar in the face. The much-surprised animal slunk off into the forest and was never heard of again.

Fact or fiction? Probably the latter, for the jaguar is a ferocious beast and the story has a pattern typical of folklore. Stili, strange things happen in the animal world; nor should we forget that Humboldt himself had reason to accept the tale as true.

A HANDSOME CAT

One of the handsomest of all cats, the jaguar has a coat that is rich yellow or tawny in color, marked with a chain of black spots down the back, bordered by five rows of black rosettes, running lengthwise on the sides. Its tail, limbs, and head are heavily spotted and lined with black. The larger head, stocky and more robust form, shorter tail, and larger rosettes serve to distinguish it from the leopard. At least a dozen subspecies are known. Black jaguars are not unusual, especially in the valley of the Amazon. There are spots present even on these, but only a good light will reveal them.

The jaguar may mate at any time of the year. About one hundred days later, two to four kittens are born. They are more heavily spotted than the adults, but lack rosettes. The male appears to be a permanent member of the family; a good husband and a providing father, he is ready to feed and protect his young at all times. But when the kittens are a year old, they are capable of shifting for themselves, and when they reach three years they are old enough to breed. Their life span is twenty years.

CHEETAHS—FASTEST ANIMALS ON LAND

The Cheetah, Guepard, or Hunting Leopard, *Acinonyx jubatus,* of Asia and Africa, is the fastest land animal on earth. Leaping from a position of rest, it can reach a speed of forty-five miles per hour in two seconds. But that is not even the top rate of this lightning-swift cat; timed by a stop watch, it has actually raced along at seventy miles per hour!

Although the cheetah is able to outrun a greyhound, it cannot keep up its extraordinary pace for long. Four or five hundred yards would be its limit, and then it is pretty well winded. But still it is evident that so speedy and big a cat—it is as large as the leopard—can, if trained, be a remarkable help to hunters.

Long, long ago the rajahs of India recognized the cheetah's remarkable abilities and put them to use. They found that the cat, if taken too young, was not aggressive enough. What was needed was a cheetah that had learned the savage ways of its kind, yet could be trained to respond to its masters' cues.

The Indian hunters learned there were certain trees to which the wild cheetahs came to whet their claws. Here the men would lie in wait for the unsuspecting animals. They ensnared the beasts by means of nooses, carried them off despite their savage resistance, and put them through a rigid course of training. The result? Cats that hunted like dogs.

HUNTING WITH A CHEETAH

A hunt with a cheetah was one of the most thrilling spectacles that yesterday's India had to offer. The hunters carried the tame cheetah afield in a cart; they had the animal hooded like a falcon. When they discovered the game—usually gazelles or black bucks, the common long-horned antelopes of India—they would whip off the cat's hood and direct its sharp eyes to the intended victim. Taking advantage of every available scrap of cover, the cheetah would creep to within a quarter of a mile of the unsuspecting quarry and then hurl itself toward it at top speed.

Gazelles and antelopes are no mean runners. When they know their lives are in the balance, they will put every ounce of energy, every dodge and device they possess, into a great, heart-breaking effort to save themselves. In endurance these creatures are superior to the cheetah. If they can stay ahead of it long enough, they will live to run again another day. But in the early part of the contest the cheetah has the advantage of greater speed.

In the crucial first few hundred yards of these life-and-death races, the buck would plunge forward with each muscle straining and an

agonized look in its large eyes, the huge spotted cat following relentlessly at its heels. If the cheetah had a good start, the end was not
long in coming. The feline's bared fangs, once they reached the antelope's throat, could tear it to shreds in a matter of seconds.

LIKE A FLASH OF LIGHTNING
Swiftest runner of all land animals, the cheetah, or hunting leopard, can, in an initial
burst of speed, run seventy miles per hour. After four or five hundred yards, however, it
slows down. In India, where the cheetah is trained for the hunt like a dog, it must catch
its prey in this first speed; otherwise, the sought-after antelope and gazelle, with their
greater endurance, will stay in the lead. The cheetah, though a true cat, has the long,
slender legs and unsheathed claws found in dogs.

MOST DOGLIKE OF THE CATS

The most like a dog of all the cats, the cheetah is superbly equipped
for running. It has long, slender legs, so that it stands two and one-
half feet high at the shoulder. Its feet are narrow but large. The
claws in particular remind us of the dog's—they are stout and always
unsheathed, for the cheetah cannot draw them back completely, unlike other cats.

Its body, admirably muscled but lithe, is streamlined, so that it
offers little resistance to the air as the animal makes its headlong
dashes. The long tail aids it in turning.

The cheetah is becoming a rarity in Asia, although it was once
found in many places, from the Caspian Sea to Sumatra. In Africa,
too, it is disappearing, along with the big game, as man encroaches on

its ancient domain, but you may still glimpse it in East Africa, Senegal, the Sudan, Transvaal, Bechuanaland, and Rhodesia.

This feline spends its resting hours in tall grass or lairs among the rocks. Departing from the habits of many of its kind, it is abroad during daylight hours, even in the hot season. It hunts by sight rather than smell, and bright moonlit nights will bring it out of its hideout. Usually two or three animals travel in company; occasionally parties of four or five have been seen together, but we believe these are family groups. Medium-sized and small antelopes like the duiker and the impala are the game the cheetah favors.

Compared to its deep-voiced cousin the tiger, the cheetah can hardly be called a noisy animal. In a pleased and restful mood, it will purr, reminding us of a house cat. Tame, the animal is esteemed by its keepers for its friendliness.

SOUGHT FOR ITS PELT

A handsome animal, the cheetah yields a valuable pelt to those who hunt it down. Its close fur is sandy brown in color and covered with a good many solid black spots. In the King Cheetah of Rhodesia, an exceptionally large, fine species, the spots tend to fuse together into stripes. (The true leopard has rosettes instead.) There is a black streak on each side of the beast's face. On the nape of its neck it has a short mane. An adult weighs about one hundred pounds and has a total length of about seven feet, of which two and one-half are the tail.

When pursued by dogs, the wild cheetah will take to a tree. One surprised its hunters by going two-thirds of the way up a tall, straight coconut palm before it was slain.

Cheetahs have lived in zoos for nearly sixteen years, but they could hardly survive that long in the wild.

Sea Lions, Walruses, and Seals —
Mammals with Finfeet

WHENEVER we watch seals, we cannot help marveling at the difference between the way they move in the water and the way they travel on land. In the water, they are all amazing speed and grace, scarcely raising a ripple on the surface as they streak forward. On land, they are clumsy, awkward waddlers.

This contrast is typical of all the creatures in the order Pinnipedia —the sea lions, walruses, and true seals. We call them pinnipeds, or— if you prefer a more recognizable term—finfeet. They are land-and-water animals with finned flippers; warm-blooded mammals specially adapted for life in the water. Unlike the whales and porpoises, the pinnipeds are not entirely independent of land; they spend part of their existence on the seashore or on floating ice. As for speedy travel in the water, these finfeet are hardly the equals of the whales. On the other hand, seals and walruses have greater agility in the water—they can maneuver with perfect safety in the pounding surf around ragged rocks.

Distant ages ago the ancestors of these animals were exclusively creatures of the land. No doubt they hunted along the shores and beaches for food left by the receding tides.

How long do you think it took the ancestral finfeets to change from land-bound animals to seafaring mariners? A great span of time indeed, it must have been—probably more than several million years. (It takes about a million years to develop a species.) Gradually, little by little, the ancient pinnipeds went further and further into the water. By degrees they became streamlined and fashioned for a life in the deep. Dire necessity may have driven them to this change, as whole continents were gradually swallowed up by the sea, and animal life either took to the water or perished.

Today, the finfeet as a group are at their most abundant in northern waters; however, we find them in all seas except the warmer parts of the Indian Ocean. As we have seen, these creatures have streamlined bodies to cut down water resistance as much as possible, and their fore and hind limbs have been modified into flippers. The animals are usually covered with hair or fur to keep them warm in their Arctic home, but we notice this difference among them—the walruses and true seals are more thoroughly insulated with a heavy layer of blubber than the sea lions. Consequently, the walruses and true seals are less dependent on a warm coat of hair.

Eared Seals or Sea Lions

Perhaps you have been wondering about such terms as "true seals," "eared seals," "sea lions," and the like. How are they similar, how do they differ? The true seals are the ones most highly specialized for life in the water. As part of this more advanced adaptation, they do not have outside ears.

But there are other creatures that look very much like these true seals, with one noticeable difference—they have external ears, and are called eared seals. Another name for eared seals is "sea lions" (they are not lions in any sense at all; they are lions of the sea). The hallmark, then, of the eared seals or sea lions is that they are less highly adapted for life in the sea. Not only do they have a small external ear; they are superior to the true seals when it comes to moving about on land. The eared seals are able to rotate their hind limbs forward to support the body as they progress on land; their front flippers are large, long, and for the most part naked.

The sea lions have short, sleek hair and tight-fitting fur which varies in color from species to species—generally some shade of gray or brown. These animals—they make up the family Otariidae—are particularly given to living in herds; they are even more sociable than other kinds of seals. The adults are of course thoroughly at home in the water, but the young, born on land, must learn how to swim. It is rather strange that though there are sea lions in the North and South Pacific, the South Atlantic and other southern waters, they have never reached the North Atlantic.

EATING TOOLS AND HABITS

Before we turn to some of the different kinds of sea lions, it will be interesting to get some notion of what seals in general eat and how they eat. They are all great fish-eaters—fish is their staple food. But, depending on the species, they add crustaceans, squids, and even shellfish to their daily rations. Each side of both jaws is lined with interlocking rows of sharp-pointed teeth—ideal weapons for seizing and holding their finny prey.

The seal has no broad-crowned molars for crushing and grinding food. Consequently the animal must swallow food whole—generally the prey is eaten while it is still alive, for that matter. Many seals also bolt quantities of stones and gravel, not, as some sailors more or less jocularly suggest, for ballast, but to help mill their food. This habit reminds us of certain grain-eating birds, which need gravel to grind the hard corn in the gizzard. Of course, the quantity of stone or gravel that most birds will take is trifling compared to what the seals require. On the average, sixteen pounds of stones—some as large as a hen's eggs—are taken from a sea lion's stomach.

Examination of the stomach contents of the seals that travel in great herds yields another interesting bit of information: Herring is the mainstay of their diet. The Leopard Seal of the Antarctic is the only species that feeds on warm-blooded animal life. It has large, vicious-looking teeth for cutting and tearing flesh; but even this seal lacks crushing molars, and it must bolt penguins and other sea birds more or less in big chunks. Still, it cannot digest the feathers and must get rid of them through the mouth after the meat has been dissolved.

NORTHERN FUR SEALS

The Northern Fur Seal, or Sea Bear, *Callorhinus alascanus,* also known as the Alaska Fur Seal, has the finest fur of all the seal tribe. (The term "sea bear" is merely a popular name. The northern fur seal is an eared seal—not a bear at all.) Of medium size, the northern fur seal is about six feet long, with a weight of five hundred to seven hundred pounds. These figures apply to grown bulls; females are much smaller.

The northern fur seal is famous for the thick, soft fur that underlies the longer, glistening guard hairs. Fur processors remove the coarse outer hairs, leaving the silky plush of the inner coat—the commercially valuable sealskin. The bull is black, with a cape of gray hair on the shoulders and a swollen neck. The female is mainly gray.

MATING HABITS OF THE NORTHERN FUR SEAL

Every spring since time immemorial the northern fur seals have left their Pacific haunts to converge on the small, bleak Pribilof Islands in the North Pacific to breed. Nothing keeps them from following this inexorable routine; though the animals were slaughtered in the many thousands for their fur, those that escaped always returned to the islands to mate.

Once the breeding season is over and the pups are raised, the fur seal puts out to sea again and does not go ashore until the following

PROVIDER OF THE CHOICEST SEALSKIN
The softest and most beautiful sealskins that we use commercially come from the northern fur seal or sea bear. This elegant fur is really the inner layer of the animal's fur; above it is an outer layer of coarse hair which must first be removed. The islands where vast hordes of the northern fur seals congregate each spring to breed were once scenes of mass slaughter by get-rich-quick sealers. Without the legal protection now enforced, this splendid fur-bearing animal might have been completely exterminated.

spring. The fur seal winters in southern waters at latitudes roughly parallel with California.

The northern fur seal is a herd animal. The bulls have large harems usually numbering forty or fifty cows—though this figure may be as large as a hundred cows. In April or May the bulls push ahead of the main herd, clamber on land, and take up their positions on the island shores. The first-comers get the best places—but they must fight to hold them. Each station covers an area of seventy-five to a hundred square feet. The choice locations are naturally those near the water's edge.

From the middle of June to mid-July, the mature females, now heavy with young, begin to arrive; they are met by the nearest bull and escorted to his station. The cows give birth to a single pup within a few hours of their arrival—or within a day or two at most. The biggest and strongest bulls get the most females; the weaker move into "idle-bull" position behind the main harems and take what opportunity offers them. The "bachelors," too young to mate, congregate in small, solitary groups.

Once a bull has established his position, he never leaves his harem until it is time to depart from the island. He trusts neither his "wives" nor his neighbors; so, from two to three months he goes without food, continually uttering threatening bellows as warnings to any bull that might challenge his proprietary rights or dally with any notions of conjugal poaching.

By August all the pups are born, and the females have mated again. The old bulls, gaunt from their prolonged and self-imposed fasting, brawling, and guarding, abandon their truculence and assume their more normal group mode of life for another year. However, the mating season is not quite over for all the members of the colony. About this time thousands of virgin females, which begin to breed at two years of age, come ashore to mate and are excitedly met by idle-bulls that have more or less patiently bided their time.

The pups, born with wide-open blue eyes, learn to swim by the time they are six to eight weeks old. They are weaned in three or four months, about the time when the main body of the colony puts out to sea. On their winter cruise, seals travel some six thousand miles and are subject to attack by the killer whale, which may swallow as many as twenty or more seals in quick succession. The mortality rate among seals is particularly high during their first three years; nearly fifty per cent of the pups never reach maturity. There are many deaths from accidents on the breeding grounds, and aside from the losses inflicted by sharks and killer whales, some animals perish during severe storms.

The life span of fur seals is about twenty years, but few of them ever die of old age. Still, twenty-one-year-old females have occasionally been seen with pups, and some bulls have lived to be twenty-two years old.

THE FUR TRADE AND ITS EXCESSES

The same urge that forces the fur seals to forge on to the Pribilof Islands to perpetuate their kind has often led them to their deaths at the hands of sealers. For the animals the story has been one of turmoil, tragedy, and death; for man, it has meant millions of dollars. Twice the fur seals have come near extermination, but today three million of them visit the islands of the North Pacific every spring to breed. The size and activity of these vast gatherings of wildlife are almost incredible.

The Russians took over the Pribilof Islands in 1786, and soon Russian fortune-hunters swarmed over the islands, slaughtering the seals without stint and persecuting and even murdering the natives as well. Thousands of seals were clubbed to death and left to rot on the beaches until the air was foul and contaminated with the stench of their bodies. At last the Russian government learned what was going on and put a stop to the ruthless waste of the world's most valuable source of fur. Thus the seals were given a breathing spell.

However, when the United States purchased the islands from Russia in 1867 the sealing rights were leased to unscrupulous sealers who readily copied the sordid pattern of the early Russian sealers. With more modern equipment and faster ships available, the massacre of the seals was even greater than under the Russians. Sealers from other nations carried the slaughter to the high seas, until the point was reached where four out of every five seals were being exterminated. On one occasion a thousand baby seals, whose mothers had been slain, were counted dead on the shore.

Conservationists brought pressure to bear on Washington, and in 1887 England, Russia, Japan, France, Germany, Sweden, and Norway got together with the United States to frame a convention to stop unrestricted sealing in the North Pacific, but the treaty was not ratified. The relentless slaughter continued until the herds were reduced to less than 124,000.

Then, suddenly and without friction, the North Pacific Sealing Convention was signed by the four most interested powers. Their nationals were forbidden to seal in the Pacific north of latitude 30° north. To increase the number of the animals, they were given five years of grace from sealing. At the end of this period, they were to be harvested by the United States and a division made of the proceeds of the skins sold at auction.

Auction sales now total about $2,500,000, and dressed, dyed skins sold at the auction fetch an average of about eighty-five dollars apiece. Nowadays twenty-five thousand to thirty thousand can safely be harvested each year. Oil and other products are rendered from the carcasses. Bachelor seals are mostly used for pelts; since these are the young males who have not reached the age when they have mating brawls, their fur is likely to be in top condition. Old males are never used, and females are kept for breeding.

The Southern Fur Seal, *Arctocephalus* ("bear-headed"), varies in size from about five and one-half feet in length and 450 pounds in weight for the Townsend Fur Seal, one of the rarest forms, to approximately seven feet in length and eight hundred pounds in weight for the South African Cape Seal.

Once widely and liberally distributed along the Pacific shores of Mexico and the coastal waters of South America, Africa, and Australia, the southern fur seal is similar in appearance to its northern cousin. The southern variety differs in skeletal structure and in its fur, which is of somewhat inferior grade. There are seven geographical species, all of them reduced to the border of extinction.

CALIFORNIA SEA LIONS—EASILY TRAINED

The California Sea Lion, *Zalophus californianus,* is the trained seal of the stage and the one frequently seen in zoological gardens and circuses. A moderately large, dark-brown seal with thick, close hair and a poor grade of short under fur, it is found along the Pacific coast of North America from southern Mexico to northern California. Males measure eight feet long and weigh up to six hundred pounds.

The life history of California sea lions is much like that of the northern fur seal. Less jealous of their harems, the bulls even take time out for feeding. Though fond of fish, the sea lion is even more partial to squids and is thus no serious menace to food fishes.

TRAINED SEALS AND THEIR ANTICS

Most of us have seen performing seals and been amazed at their ability to learn tricks. As it happens, they are not true seals but eared seals or sea lions—the California species. Their genuine aptitude for training comes from their love of sport and play, a well-developed sense of balance, and their desire for attention. They are extremely active, and anything in the nature of exercise or exhibitionism appeals to them—especially if there is a fish as a reward in sight. They have a fair share of intelligence and can size up a situation with very little instruction.

THE SEA LION—EVER-POPULAR ENTERTAINER
The California sea lion, found all along the Pacific coast of North America, is the playful performer of theaters and circuses. Easily trained, intelligent, and equipped with a good sense of balance, this animal will, for the sake of fish and applause, run through a delightful array of tricks. The California sea lion has small external ears, and hind limbs which can be rotated forward, a boon to the creature when it moves about on land.

Given the sea lion's sense of coordination, the long, flexible neck is just right for balancing a big rubber ball on the tip of the animal's nose. The sea lion can even be taught to play a tune on a row of trumpets, but this is a matter of routine practice; the creature has no notion that it is producing a tune.

There is no doubt that most mammals are affected by swing music. Sea lions respond readily, and with a little practice soon learn to sway and even dance to a tune. But it is the reward at the end of the act that the seal really has in mind. Its motto is: No reward, no show.

STELLER'S SEA LION—IT MAY WEIGH A TON

Steller's or the Northern Sea Lion, *Eumetopias jubata,* an enormous brownish creature, is the largest of all sea lions. Steller, the German scientist who first discovered this animal, named it *Leo marinus* ("lion of the sea"), as he noted the greatly swollen neck of the males and the leonine eyes with their golden pupil and white iris. Full-grown males may reach a length of thirteen feet and weigh as much as fifteen hundred to two thousand pounds. The female is less than half the size of the bull.

This great sea lion has much the same habits as the fur seal, though the colonies and harems are not so large. The bull is not jealous and does not fight so desperately over his harem as a fur seal bull; in fact, there is more fidelity among the females. When a battle does ensue, the fighters pay no attention to the pups underfoot and many are mercilessly crushed to death.

The baby sea lion comes into the world with its big blue eyes open —at least they are wide open almost immediately after birth. It soon gains control of its limbs and romps among the yellow hulks of adults. In a few days it can move swiftly—as indeed it must if it is to escape being crushed by the battling bulls. Weighing between thirty-five and fifty pounds at birth, the pups will weigh about one hundred pounds two months later. The front part of the animal develops more rapidly than the rest of the body; an adult male sea lion has a large, swollen neck and enormous shoulders.

TEACHING A BABY TO SWIM

Familiar as we are with the sea lions' gracefulness in the water, it seems incredible that they have to be taught to swim. The baby sea lion does have to learn to swim; we are told that the mother picks up the pup by the back of the neck and carries it to the water for its introductory swimming lesson. At first the baby struggles in the surf —but by the time it is two months old, it ploughs proudly through the breakers and rides the waves like a veteran.

With the end of summer and the close of the breeding season, the big brown animal leaves the cold, damp, icy coast of Alaska and travels south to the warmer waters of Mexico. Its summer range is the rocky coast of Alaska north to the Bering Strait.

This large sea lion was hunted extensively for its blubber; the hide and intestines were used for a number of purposes, including the manufacture of raincoats. Our present laws prohibit indiscriminate killing of sea lions, but fishermen may destroy them when they interfere with fishing activities. A census of sea lions on the California coast in 1947 showed a population of 5,666 Steller's sea lions and 3,050 California sea lions.

OTHER EARED SEALS OR SEA LIONS

The Japanese Sea Lion is now believed to be extinct, and has been relegated to museum status. The South American Sea Lion, also known as *lobo del mar* (Spanish for "wolf of the sea"), is found on both sides of the South American continent; it has maintained itself better than other seals in South American waters. The male Australian Sea Lion differs from other sea lions in having a patch of yellow on the crown of the head and back of the neck. The little-known Hooker's Sea Lion, of the Auckland Islands south of New Zealand, has a flattened head and a comparatively long muzzle.

Walruses — at Home on Arctic Ice Packs

The walrus lives in the loneliest and most desolate kingdom in the world. Its days, spent on floating ice, are beset with bitter cold, raging snowstorms, and fierce blizzards. Strangely enough—from our point of view—the walrus seems to enjoy this kind of existence. Few other creatures could maintain themselves amidst such drastic conditions.

Not many mammals are so grotesquely ungainly as the walrus, with its crude, wrinkled exterior, yet it has a majestic grandeur all the same. It was born on a cake of ice, covered with a blanket of late-spring snow, and rocked to sleep by stormy winds, with the sound of the grinding ice pack in its ears. Though fat and pudgy, its little pug face has an appealing beauty to the two-thousand-pound mother walrus; awkwardly but lovingly she tucks her baby's little body between her flippers with her long, gleaming tusks.

CLUMSY LORD OF THE ICE FLOES
The droll-looking walrus serenely spends its life amid raging blizzards and the most intensely cold climates found anywhere on earth. Generally peaceful, this creature uses its fierce tusks for fighting the polar bear and the killer whale, and for obtaining its main food, shellfish. By scraping its tusks along the bottom of the ocean, the walrus loosens the clams and other shellfish imbedded in the sand. Pictured above is the Pacific walrus.

The bitter-cold winter storms are of little consequence to the walrus mother—they are all part of her life. Her eyesight is not of the best, but she has a sharp sense of smell and is ever on the alert for the prowling polar bear.

As one of these marauders approaches, she rises to her full height, and her neck bulges as she utters a deep, guttural, challenging bellow of defiance. She swings around to follow the circling bear; one step too close, and with a flash down comes the full force of her tusks. Not so easily dismayed, the bear continues his attack. Occasionally, by dint of persistent harassing, the bear will manage to rob the mother of her child; but the chances are that he will crawl away to lick his wounds, a sadder and perhaps wiser animal.

But it is really the killer whale that is the deadly foe of the walrus. Caught in the sea away from the friendly shelter of the ice, a mother walrus will wage a desperate struggle with a school of these tigers of the sea to protect her young. But as fast as she sinks her harpoon-like tusks into a whale, another swings into action and it becomes doubtful whether she can save her own life.

The ice itself can become a hazard. The ice packs may jam into a vast, grinding mass fifty miles wide where not even a walrus could survive; however, few of the animals are ever trapped this way. Most creatures that travel in herds have their sentinels posted, but when a herd of walruses are enjoying a blissful sleep and snoring contentedly, no one is left to watch for approaching danger. However from time to time a member of the group will wake up with a start and look around before continuing its deep slumber. At the first unusual sound the whole herd springs into action.

The combined roar and bellowing produced by a herd of disturbed walruses can be heard for several miles. On occasion their hoarse roar has warned ships in time to escape being shattered on fog-misted icebergs.

LIFE OF A WALRUS

The Walrus, *Odobenus,* or "whale horse," as it was known to the Norsemen, is easily recognized by its long ivory tusks. They may reach a length of thirty inches—in fact, the extra-large ones measure up to thirty-eight inches and weigh a good eleven pounds. Both male and female have tusks, but they are heavier in the bulls. An enormous creature, the walrus has a practically hairless skin which is wrinkled and roughened like the bark of an old oak tree. Large males are ten to eleven feet long and weigh between two thousand and three thousand pounds.

The walruses, which make up the family Odobenidae, are like the sea lions in some ways, different in other ways. Walruses have the same kind of flippers, for example—they can rotate the rear flippers in order to get about more easily on land. However, the walruses, unlike the sea lions, have no outside ears.

Though this animal is a slow, clumsy swimmer, it is big enough to protect itself from most natural enemies with the exception of the killer whale. Feeding on the ocean bottom, it uses its tusks to dig up clams and other shellfish. It cracks the shells with its back teeth but then swallows the shells along with the meat. Crushed by action of the stomach and small stones, the meat is then digested and the empty shells are ejected through the mouth.

The walruses enjoy a family life that is more peaceful than the sea lions'. Bulls, calves, and cows mingle together, albeit in a somewhat quarrelsome manner. Discord arises chiefly from their dislike of being disturbed when sleeping. One walrus may accidentally nudge another, whereupon the offended sleeper wakes up with a mighty, trumpet-like roar and takes a prodigious slap at its nearest neighbor. The latter, in turn, utters an ear-splitting bellow and passes the blow on to the accompaniment of similar deafening sounds of protest— until the whole colony is in a turmoil.

The cow walrus has but one calf at a time, giving birth on the ice floes in May or June, nearly a year after mating. As we have seen, she has a strongly developed maternal instinct and will sell her life dear in the protection of her calf. Once aroused, a walrus will charge any suspicious stranger that comes near. Male and female separate in July but they are found together again in late August or September.

During its early life, the baby walrus rides on its mother's back in the water and holds fast with its flippers when she submerges for food. The young walrus is dependent on its mother for nourishment until it is two years old, when its tusks are long enough for digging clams. Until this time it must live on the mother's milk.

The walrus is generally restricted to the ice floes and rocky coast of the Arctic Ocean, although it has been recorded as far south as Newfoundland and northern Scotland. There are two named forms of walruses: the Atlantic Walrus and the Pacific Walrus. At one time walruses were hunted extensively for their blubber; but nowadays there are so few left that such ventures are no longer worth while commercially. The Eskimos use the hide, which is from half an inch to three inches thick, to make their shelters and cover their boats. The meat and fat serve for food, and the ivory tusks are made into tools and carved ornaments.

Earless Seals, or True Seals

The true seals are strongly adapted for a water-dwelling existence. To begin with, they lack an external ear. The hind limbs are modified into flippers for swimming, but they extend straight out behind; the seal cannot rotate them forward for greater support on land. As for the forelimbs, they have developed into short paddles used mainly for balancing and turning in the water. The entire animal, including the limbs, flippers, and the short tail, is covered with short, coarse hair, without any trace of underfur. The true seals (they make up the family Phocidae) are sometimes called "hair seals."

Seals must leave the water to breed, and to bear their young, which remain on land for several weeks before being taught to swim. The true seals have spread to all the oceans of the world; yet, despite the fact that they are primarily ocean-dwellers, they have ascended many large rivers and even entered inland lakes. Swimming on the surface and breathing normally, the animals have an average heartbeat rate of one hundred per minute; when they dive the heart action slows up to ten beats per minute.

Seal meat and blubber are the Eskimo's chief sources of food during the cold winter months, and he uses the seal skin to make clothing. It is in the northern regions that seals are found in the greatest abundance. Commercial sealers now plunder the great herds of seal in the North Atlantic and annually slaughter many thousands for leather and oil.

HARBOR SEALS—SWIFT AND SHY

The Harbor Seal, *Phoca vitulina,* is the common seal of the temperate and colder regions of the Northern Hemisphere. This small species is frequently seen along the reefs, coastal islands, and in sheltered harbors. Never straying far from land, it ascends large rivers, often beyond the influence of the tide, and occasionally makes its appearance in inland lakes. A harbor seal is capable of traveling twelve or fifteen miles an hour—but it cannot keep up this speed for more than half a mile.

The color pattern varies quite a bit. The normal shade is yellowish gray spotted with dark brown, but the fur may intergrade to black spotted with white. The full-grown male easily measures five feet long and weighs one hundred pounds or more. The first coat of the harbor seal is white and woolly, but this is shed immediately after—or even before—birth in the spring. The newborn pup, which is nursed for four or five weeks, has a cry that reminds us of a lamb bleating.

While the harbor seal does not congregate in large colonies, it is nevertheless fond of company. Family groups of two or three females with their young and a male or two are not uncommon. Apparently unable to sleep in the water, this seal comes ashore regularly to rest and sun itself on the rocks.

Having experienced man's assaults through many generations, the harbor seal is understandably shy and elusive. Yet it soon responds to kind treatment and protection, making a surprisingly affectionate pet for those living at the water's edge. However, not many of us would care to have a big, wet seal tracking mud into the house and taking possession of an upholstered couch or chair!

The harbor seal has a varied diet, feeding on tom cod, flounder, herring, pollack, and other fish as well as squids and octopus.

Experts now recognize six forms of harbor seal. The local subspecies dwell on the European and American sides of the Atlantic from Labrador to Maine and occasionally as far south as North Carolina, and in Asiatic and American coastal waters of the Pacific as far south as Baja California.

RINGED SEALS—MOST NORTHERLY OF MAMMALS

The Ringed Seal, *Phoca hispida,* ranges north probably farther than any other mammal; it is the common seal of the polar region, and we rarely find it south of the Arctic Ocean. Though similar in size and color to the harbor seal, it is quite a different animal. The ring seal's markings are a number of rings, or white spots with dark centers. In the Hudson Bay area it is most common along the east coast, where the Eskimos call it *netcheck.*

The ringed seal is able to submerge for about seven to nine minutes; in case of need, it can stay under water for twenty minutes without coming up for air. The seal needs about forty-five seconds to change the air in its lungs between normal submersions.

This seal is not a migrator; in northern waters, when the shore ice creeps out to sea, the animal keeps a breathing hole open, visiting it periodically to rest and breathe. This habit sometimes means death for the seal—it is here that the Eskimo lies in wait to harpoon it when it makes its routine visit.

Before the spring thaw in March or April, either single or twin pups are born. The nursery is a burrow in the hard snow and has a tunnel connecting it with the breathing-hole in the ice. The new-born ringed seal is covered with soft, white, woolly fur, although even yearlings may still be whitish along the back.

HARP SEALS—GREAT HERDS OF THE NORTH ATLANTIC

The Harp Seal, Saddle-backed or Greenland Seal, *Phoca groenlandica,* is bigger than the harbor seal. Large bulls measure up to six feet in length and weigh between six hundred and eight hundred pounds. Despite persistent commercial hunting, the harp seal still occurs in large herds in the North Atlantic. It migrates with the seasons and in winter follows the floes of the open ice as far south as Newfound-land.

Thousands of young, each weighing about nine pounds, are born in March off the Grand Banks of Newfoundland; there is usually one in a litter, and twins are rare. Coarse, pale-gray hair replaces the white, woolly birthday coat in about four weeks, when the pups are ready to enter the water. Sealers call the baby seals "white-coats."

If we stop to think about it, we realize that this color change has protective value. The newborn and those not yet able to swim are white, inconspicuous against the snow-covered ice packs on which they lie; the gray fur of the young that have taken to the water is far less noticeable than white would be in the sea. Incidentally, the harps or saddle stripes of the male (described later) are not com-pleted until the fourth year.

During the early stages of infancy the young are left on the drift-ing ice while the parents go forth daily to fish. Since there may be several thousand offspring in a group, it is remarkable indeed that each mother should find her own pup at the close of day. Soon after the end of April the young "harps" have learned to swim and are catching fish for themselves. The herd now moves north and even-tually reaches the coast of Greenland.

The harp seal feeds on whitefish, cod, and in part on crustaceans. Descending to a depth of two hundred feet, it may stay under water twenty minutes at a time. This fast seal can cruise along at a maximum of twenty miles an hour, but its average speed is much less. In the fall migrations the great herds at one time numbered as many as five hundred thousand head. More than one hundred thousand harp seals are still taken every year in the Arctic; the catch is valued at over $250,000,000. Oil and leather are the chief products.

THE HOODED SEAL BLOWS UP ITS "HOOD" WHEN EXCITED

Extending from the tip of the male hooded seal's nose to the top of its head is a bag or bladder of inflatable muscular tissue. Whenever the seal becomes excited, as during mating time, the bag swells up like a balloon. The hooded seal inhabits the waters of the North Atlantic and Arctic Oceans, where the harp seal is also found. But the hooded seal does not mingle with the harp, choosing to remain on floes well out in deep waters.

The male harp seal is light gray or yellowish white in color, with characteristic bands of brown extending from the neck over the shoulders and down each side in the form of a saddle, or harp. The female differs from the male in size and coloring; she is smaller, and the dull-white or straw-colored fur has indistinct back markings or lacks them completely.

GRAY SEALS—WITH FACES ALMOST HUMAN

The Gray Seal, *Halichoerus grypus,* is the subject of many myths. In Scandinavian folklore there is a belief that the gray seal is the reincarnation of either a human soul or a fallen angel, and that some fearful retribution will fall upon the man who molests it.

Shetland Islanders tell of sea monsters called "Finns" that have the power to take on the shape of human beings. On winter nights they come ashore as gray seals to dance on the sands. They cast off their skins and act like men and women, but they cannot return to the sea without their skins. Some of the "Finn" women, so the leg ends tell us, were captured and married by the Shetlanders. There are islanders today who pride themselves on being descended from "Finn" women.

The Welsh have similar traditions, and so do the Irish—the Irish clan of Coneely is said to be directly descended from a seal-woman. In Scotland, too, there is a legendary folklore connected with the gray seal. The clan of MacOdrum, for example, was known as the "seal-eaters." The clan was supposed to have certain affinities with the gray seal. Some old-timers will beg for the front flippers of a gray seal which has been killed, though they are not interested in parts of any other species of seal. Apparently these flippers were the parts used in an ancient ceremonial feast—a pagan festival in honor of the Scandinavian god Odin.

BATTLES AT MATING TIME

Late in August or September the gray seal bulls crawl out on the rocky beaches where their ancestors have appeared for centuries. Here they sprawl in the sunshine. A week or so later the females drift ashore, and are greeted by the males. There is, as we might expect, considerable bellowing and competition between the males for possession of the females. Often fierce battles take place. Rolling from side to side, the bulls show their white teeth to competitors, and frequently inflict deep gashes in the necks of their adversaries.

Within a few hours after landing, the females give birth to a single calf clothed in long white fur. At birth a calf will weigh about thirty pounds. Two weeks later, its weight has increased to eighty-four pounds. The cows mate ten or twelve days after the calves are born.

Each bull has its own domain, which covers about one-tenth of an acre. While the males fight furiously for their territorial rights, they do not dominate the females. In fact, females are granted equal rights with the males and are not herded together by a jealous bull, as in the case of the sea lions. If a cow lands on a bull's domain and stays there, she is his—but if she chooses to cross over into another's field, he raises no objection and shows no further interest in her.

By November, peace reigns once more. The fighting and bellowing have ceased. The males live together in perfect harmony. A passing female does not attract even an uninterested glance.

BABY GRAY SEALS

Gray seals, especially the pups, are almost human in appearance. Their big, round eyes seem to stare out of a comely round face with a most appealing expression. During its early days the pup gets full-time attention from the mother seal. She nurses it on milk, rich and yellow with butter fat, for two or three weeks. During this time the devoted mother stays home without food in order to guard and fondle her baby and even to scratch its back. With a little tummy full of rich milk, the pup may yawn, put the tip of a flipper in its mouth, murmuring contentedly like a child, and fall fast asleep.

It is curious that at first the calves can use their hind feet to propel themselves along and flip them alternately like regular land mammals. Two or three days later they have lost this trait and never use the hind limbs again for progress on land. Many scientists hold that baby seals must be taught to swim. This is not exactly true. Young gray seals are born with a thick, woolly, white coat. They can swim from the very first, but the heavy swaddling clothes of the newborn infants are too absorbent to permit them to remain afloat long in the water.

The baby seals change their warm white clothes for the regular adult gray coats between the second and fourth week. They are weaned during the third week, when the cows are ready to go to sea, and they must feed themselves. For the next two weeks they live on their accumulated fat, but soon hunger drives them to sea, where they quickly learn to find food and swim in the shallow water.

Within a few days the young seals are out in the deep, fishing like veterans. They soon learn to catch mollusks and crustaceans; when grown, they will also feed on rock fish and even six-foot conger eels. In this respect they are beneficial to commercial fisheries, as they destroy predatory fish.

CREATURES OF THE ROCKY COASTS

The gray seal is limited to a narrow belt across the North Atlantic. It does not range as far as the ice fields of the north, nor, on the other hand, does it continue south into the milder temperate regions. Instead, it haunts the rockbound coasts and outlying islands on both sides of the Atlantic at latitudes of southern Canada and Great Britain, where the sea is deep and the rough, troubled waters are rarely still.

Gray is of course the dominant color of this species, but individuals may vary from almost black to pale tints, often blotched with irregular splashes of darker tones. The gray seal is about the size of a harp seal; large males measure a good eight feet and weigh about six hundred pounds.

Though the gray seal may make extended cruises at sea, it generally remains in the neighborhood of the ancestral breeding grounds; in fact, a few members of the colony stay close by those rocky places the year round.

BEARDED SEALS—GIANTS OF THE ARCTIC

The Bearded Seal, *Erignathus barbatus,* gets its name from the festoons of coarse, flattened bristles that hang from each side of its mouth. (Sealers have another name for this species—they call it the "square flipper," after the characteristic shape of the limbs.) The animal is one of the largest of the northern varieties: the male bearded seal is ten or twelve feet long and weighs in the neighborhood of eight hundred pounds. Now and then we come across a giant that may reach fifteen hundred pounds. Females are about seven feet in length and weigh much less than the males.

Dwelling on the shore ice in the North Atlantic and Arctic regions, the bearded seal is more or less solitary, often living alone or in small family groups. The pelt is of little value in the fur trade but is esteemed by the Eskimos for the extra-thick hide, which they cut up for harpoon lines and other heavy-duty gear.

LEOPARD SEALS—THEY EAT THEIR OWN KIND

The Leopard Seal, *Hydrurga leptonyx,* is among the best known of the Antarctic seals. A ferocious creature, it preys on other seals as well as fish. Many seals have teeth that are mere pegs for catching and holding fish—not so the leopard seal, which is equipped with large molars well adapted for rending and tearing the flesh of the animals devoured by this carnivorous finfoot.

The leopard seal is large—males reach a length of ten to twelve feet, females are about seven feet long. The coarse coat of yellowish-gray hair is dappled with numerous black spots and sometimes with light blotches on the back.

ELEPHANT SEALS—BIGGEST OF THEIR TRIBE

The Elephant Seal, *Mirounga*, is not only the largest of the seals but also the ugliest and clumsiest. Its name is derived from its enormous size—also from the peculiar, apparently useless, elongated snout of cavernous tissue. In the relaxed state this appendage hangs eight or nine inches below the mouth. When a bull utters its deep, ventril-

A SEAL WITH A STRANGE-LOOKING NOSE

The name "elephant seal" accurately describes this largest of all seals, which can weigh more than five thousand pounds. Its long nose, faintly similar to the elephant's trunk, is made of tissue which hangs slackly down over the animal's mouth when it is quiet. When the seal roars, this queer projection blows up with air. An unusually thick layer of blubber under the elephant seal's hide causes it to quiver like a mass of gelatin when the animal shuffles along. This seal was formerly slain in great numbers for its fat and oil.

oqual roar, this snout swells up with air and the tip curls into the seal's mouth.

Large males reach a length of eighteen or twenty feet, weighing a fantastic five thousand pounds or more. The females are about ten feet long. When one of these ponderous and grotesque leviathans is on shore, its huge body settles into an almost formless heap, its coarse skin wrinkled, furrowed, and cracked. When the time comes to shed the bleached brown coat, the cuticle peels off in large blisters along with the hair, looking as if it had been severely burned by the sun.

The elephant seal has very simple tastes—it lives to sleep and eat. Let a rude jolt break its slumber and its mighty front flipper drives a stinging shower of sand and small stones—very accurately, by the way—at the cause of the disturbance. This done, the seal promptly goes back to sleep.

In the water the elephant seal moves gracefully and rhythmically, and is capable of cruising along at a fair speed. It descends to considerable depths to feed, consuming slow-moving fishes—ratfish, dogfish, and the like—as well as small sharks and squids. The sea elephant's stomach, like the birds' crop, contains a quantity of stones and pebbles that apparently mill the food for digestion.

The breeding pattern is much the same as among the other seals. The males come ashore about the middle of August, and some time later they select their harems from among the newly arriving females. There follows the characteristic brawling and commotion for the rest of the breeding season. Some time between February and June the female gives birth to one black pup on the beach, some distance away from the main herd.

The elephant seal has been killed for its fat and oil for many generations. Formerly the herds numbered in the thousands; today they have become so scarce that commercial hunting is no longer profitable.

The Northern Sea Elephant, reduced to a few individuals on Guadalupe Island off Baja California, was saved from extinction by the Mexican government in 1911. A garrison was posted on the island with orders to shoot poachers and other molesters of the herds. Formerly found on islands of the South Atlantic, South Pacific, Indian, and Antarctic Oceans, this seal has few if any survivors.

The Southern Elephant Seal is responding to protection on Campbell Island, three hundred miles south of New Zealand; but, like its northern cousin, this species has become all but extinct.

SOME OTHER INTERESTING SEALS

The Ribbon Seal, a rare variety that dwells along the coasts of Alaska, the Aleutian Islands, and the Kurile Islands, is the most ornately marked of the seal tribe. It is highly prized by the Eskimos. The Crab-eating Seal of the Antarctic ice packs is a much larger an-

ALMOST LIKE A FISH OUT OF WATER
Superlative swimmers, the true seals are but barely able to walk on land. Their hind limbs are flippers, which extend backward instead of rotating forward, as in the eared seals; their front limbs are like paddles. When the true seal walks, its hind flippers and tail are raised above the ground. It propels its body forward by contracting its muscles and using its front paddles. Pictured here is the ribbon seal of Alaska, an unusual and beautifully striped animal.

imal with an interesting peculiarity—it has lobes in its teeth. Water passes out of the lobes when the jaws are closed, but crustaceans cannot pass through these strainers; thus the victims are held back and swallowed. The Ross Seal, another Antarctic denizen, is small and seldom encountered. Much more common is Weddell's Seal, which lives in the same region.

The Monk Seal favors warm climates—we find it in the Mediterranean, the Caribbean, and in the Pacific, in the neighborhood of the Hawaiian Islands and Midway Island. The Hooded Seal, on the other hand, prefers pretty much the same surroundings as the harp seal—the ice floes of the North Atlantic and Arctic waters. The "hood" is an inflatable bag of muscular tissue extending from the muzzle over the top of the head. Only the males have this feature. When they are excited, especially during the mating season, the bladder swells up, giving them a most sinister appearance. The males fight savagely during the mating season, and the roars of the spring battles can be heard at a great distance.

Sea Cows, Manatees, and Dugongs— Sirens But Not Seductive

IF YOU HAVE ever seen these massive, grotesque creatures, you can relish how fantastically inappropriate it would be to call them "sirens." Yet sirens they used to be called—even the scientists gravely endorsed the use of this incongruous name by placing these unromantic animals in the order Sirenia.

How did this come about? Centuries ago, when the animal kingdom was by no means so thoroughly explored as it is today, sailors returning from the Red Sea and Indian Ocean brought back tales of flying fishes, of gold, pearls, precious stones—and strange creatures.

What kind of strange creatures? Well, they were supposed to be half fish and half human, and they were glimpsed frolicking about close to land. To the sailors, at first they suggested mermaids. It was a faintly plausible illusion to at least this extent, that a female dugong carries her baby in her arms and nurses it at her breast in much the same way that a human mother does.

The Japanese capitalized on the tradition. There was a "factory" in Japan which prepared so-called stuffed "mermaids" that were sold as the real thing. The famous Fejee Mermaid, which Barnum exhibited at his Museum in 1842, very likely originated in Japan. As thousands flocked to see this hoax, the great showman's gate receipts swelled mightily.

The sirenians, timid animals with a vegetarian diet, are adapted for life in the water. They never leave it—not even to breed. On land they would be completely helpless, unable to propel themselves or to secure food. Scientists conjecture that the sirenians—like the whales in similar straits—might even collapse their lungs by the sheer weight of their bodies.

Sirenians occupy the shallower waters between the deep sea and dry land, frequenting sheltered harbors, bays, lagoons, and estuaries; some even ascend large rivers. In the shallow water they are safe from attack by such raiders of the high seas as the killer whale and shark. We find sirenians in both the New World and the Old; they favor the warmer regions, though in past ages they were not unknown in the Bering Sea.

The sirenians are descended from a long line of water-dwelling ancestors that crawled up on land and then took to the water once more. Scientists tell us that these creatures derive from the ancestral stock whence the elephants and hyraxes originated; however, the relationship is remote.

The sirenians are massive. But they are also spindle shaped, tapering in front to a round head with small eyes and a blunt, sometimes jowly muzzle. The body is rounded in outline and narrows down toward the tail, which in turn flares out horizontally to form a broad, flat paddle. Sirenians have a grayish-colored skin; some are sparsely bristled all over, others only on the muzzle. We find no trace of hind limbs in present-day sirenians, but they do have paddle-like forelimbs. These animals need to be able to submerge quickly, and their exceptionally dense and heavy bones make this fairly easy.

Sirenians feed on seaweed and other plants which they find in salt and brackish water. As such fodder is none too plentiful, the animals are never very common anywhere. Grazing like cattle, they have no occasion for speed in getting a living. There are two kinds of sirenians in existence, the Dugong (family Dugongidae) and the Manatee (family Trichechidae). The Sea Cow (family Hydrodamalidae) has been extinct for almost two centuries.

DUGONGS—BIG GAME OF THE OCEANS

The Dugong, or Halicore, *Dugong dugon*. The Australian aborigines have an accomplished technique for hunting the dugong. They use a harpoon fitted with a detachable wooden handle, fastened to a line. When the harpoon strikes the dugong, it is anchored by the barbed tip and the shaft floats free except for the attached line. By following the floating shaft, the hunters can trail the dugong until it is tired out —this takes about half an hour. Then the hunters draw their canoe alongside the exhausted quarry and close its nostrils with wooden plugs. Apparently unable to breathe through the mouth, the dugong suffocates.

The dugong is by no means limited to Australian waters. We find it in the warm coastal waters of the East, in the shallow bays and estuaries from the Red Sea to the Indian Ocean, east to the Solomon and Marshall Islands and south to northern Australia.

A full-grown male may reach a length of nine feet; the female is smaller. The dugong's body is covered with blubber and a thick hide —together, they are about an inch in thickness; the hide is hairless except around the mouth. (It is believed, by the way, that the Israelites covered the ark of the Covenant with skins of the dugong.) The animal's looks are not improved by the downward bend of the jaw that accommodates a pair of incisor teeth developed over the ages into sharp-edged tusks. These continue to grow throughout the life of the dugong. The tail has two lobes, and is rather like a whale's.

While these creatures are not given to living in groups, several may graze in one place on their favored foods—green seaweed and other water plants. When feeding, the dugong comes up for air every five or ten minutes; the nostrils are opened to take in fresh air but are closed like valves when the animal submerges. Dugongs have poor eyesight, but their hearing is good, despite their lack of an outside ear. The female gives birth to one young at a time, twelve months after mating. She carries the baby about in her flippers.

NORTHERN SEA COWS—GIANTS OF YESTERDAY

The Northern or Steller's Sea Cow, *Hydrodamalis stelleri,* is extinct. It took man until 1741 to discover the sea cow, but from then he needed only twenty-seven years to destroy the entire race. It was Vitus

Bering and George Wilhelm Steller, the naturalist that sailed with him, who first found the sea cow on their arrival at Bering Island.

Where Steller's sea cow came from and how it reached its shallow offshore home are among the unfathomed mysteries of bygone ages. The animal was virtually a prisoner, for any attempt to leave the protection of the islands where it dwelled meant certain death; fierce killer whales patrolled the neighboring waters. The chances are that there were less than fifteen hundred animals in the isolated colony where they were discovered, and that they would have become extinct in the course of time even without man's efficient assistance.

The sea cow, one of the strangest-looking animals of modern times, reached a length of twenty-five or thirty feet and weighed over four tons. It was covered with a rough, coarse hide cracked and wrinkled like the bark of a gnarled old oak tree. It had no teeth; instead, two pairs of grooved, horny plates ground the seaweed on which it fed. Lacking any trace whatever of hind limbs, the sea cow had curiously clublike forelimbs doubled under in the form of a hook. These were used not for swimming but to haul the huge body along in shallow water.

Steller tells us that the sea cows lived cattle-wise in herds offshore. In resting or sleeping, sea cows would roll over on their back in quiet waters and allow themselves to drift like logs. Occupied with little else but the search for food, they tore seaweed from rocks and ate incessantly. Yet they apparently had room for the finer feelings: they showed an uncommon solicitude for one another—when one was harpooned, all the rest would try to release it.

MANATEES—TOO PEACEABLE FOR THEIR OWN GOOD

The Manatee, *Trichechus*, is a large, robust, water-dwelling mammal. It averages about seven feet in length and some 450 pounds in weight. Exceptional manatees may measure twelve feet, with an estimated weight of two thousand pounds.

According to native folklore in Mexico, the male manatee sometimes comes ashore on dark nights and carries off the women in the villages along river banks. However, as the manatee is helpless on land, even the natives can hardly take this superstitious notion very seriously.

The people of tropical America have been eating the flesh of the manatee for centuries. It is rich red meat, and is quite palatable. The oil or fat is sweet, and is used by the natives for cooking. At first taken for a fish, the manatee could be eaten on meatless fast days. Later on, religion caught up with science and the manatee disappeared from Friday and Lenten menus.

As for the eating habits of the manatee itself, it is a strict vegetarian, consuming anywhere from sixty to a hundred pounds of seaweed in a single day. Usually it has six teeth on each side of the upper and lower jaws. As worn-out teeth fall out in front, the whole line pushes forward and a new tooth comes in place at the rear.

The manatee has valvelike nostrils; the eyes are small and sunken. Its head is blunt, with thick, pendulous lips. An interesting feature of the upper lip is that it is split lengthwise in two lobes that move independently as the animal feeds. Stubby hairs are scattered over the body, while on the muzzle we find larger stiff bristles. The fore-limbs are modified into broad flippers with rudimentary nails, while the tail is broad, flat, and rounded like a huge paddle.

Fifteen minutes is usually the maximum that a manatee will stay submerged. However, in an emergency an adult can stay down for nearly half an hour. When resting, the manatee floats in the water with its back humped up, the head and tail dangling. In shallow water it curls its tail under, with the upper side resting on the bottom. Breathing normally, the animal has a heart rate of fifty beats a minute, but this is slowed down to thirty in a dive.

Despite its clumsy appearance and expressionless face, the manatee is not quite so stupid as is generally supposed. One manatee in the Miami aquarium frequently offered its right flipper to shake hands, and it would "rub noses" with its keeper. On more than one occasion, a pair of manatees have been seen kissing each other. The manatees are sociable and peaceful in their ways of life; we find very little quarreling among them. Life, however, is not always tranquil for the manatees in the wild state. There is a constant threat of death in the crocodile-infested waters, while lurking sharks prevent the manatees from escaping to deep waters. If they managed to reach greater depths, they would meet added peril from killer whales. The basic condition of the manatee's existence is that it is not equipped for defense.

We divide the manatees into four species: the African Manatee, found along the west coast from Senegal to the Cuanza River in Angola; the West Indies Manatee, of the Caribbean; the Florida Manatee, dwelling in the coastal waters of eastern North America from North Carolina to Florida and Central America; and Natrerer's Manatee, occurring in the rivers of northeastern South America. In the northern part of the manatee's range there is some seasonal migration.

ONCE THOUGHT TO BE HALF FISH AND HALF HUMAN
A long time ago the manatee, seen from afar by imaginative sailors, was taken for a human fish. This mistake probably arose from the fact that the mother manatee looks surprisingly human as she holds her nursing baby to her mammary glands, located on her chest. Although the manatee is a mammal, it lives in the water and cannot move on land. Seen here is the Florida manatee, found in the coastal waters of eastern North America.

MANATEES MAKE GOOD PARENTS

The young, generally one or two, come into the world in April or May and weigh about sixty pounds. Born under water, they are immediately raised to the surface by the mother. Like all mammals, the manatee is a warm-blooded, air-breathing creature that would suffocate if it could not get air. Every three or four minutes, night and day, mother and baby must come to the surface to breathe. The mammary glands are located on the chest, and the pup is clasped in the mother's flippers as it nurses with its head above water.

It is fascinating to watch the manatees taking care of the young. When an 850-pound female gave birth to a forty-pound baby at the Miami aquarium, she took the baby up to air on her shoulder. The male parent was so solicitous of its welfare that when the female did not take it up soon enough to satisfy him, he prodded her with his flukes.

Another birth occurred in a salt-water pool at Windley Key, Florida, after the mother had been kept alone in the pool for 152 days. In this instance, observers saw the cow in shallow water. Suddenly she rolled herself on her side, and when she righted herself the baby was on her back. She kept her offspring in this position out of water for forty-five minutes; then submerged but quickly rose to the surface again. She repeated this action several times, gradually increasing the tempo and the length of time she stayed under water.

Neither the cow nor the calf came to the surface while nursing. Not infrequently the calf linked its flippers through the mother's in a most human manner and they both swam about the pool with linked arms.

As has been suggested, the male manatee is a good husband and a devoted father. A baby manatee born in a zoological park was seen to receive fond care from both its parents; when one parent was ready to relinquish its charge, the other was there to take over. The little fellow's first days of life were spent being tossed back and forth without a chance to swim.

A youngster remains with the parents until it is half grown. Once the offspring are able to get about by themselves, the manatees gather in groups of fifteen or twenty. They are surprisingly active as they sport and play.

Elephants — the World's Largest and Most Powerful Land Animals

MORE THAN ANY OTHER living creature, the elephant challenges and fires our imaginations. A unique combination of huge size, strange appearance, tremendous power, unexpected gracefulness and smoothly rhythmical action, it is perpetually on the move.

Seeing a herd of these gigantic pachyderms in their native haunts at close range seems to take us back to some faraway geological time, into an eerie and mysterious age when such mighty mammals were the greatest power on the earth.

The Asiatic and two African species of today are all that remain of a once great elephant population that roamed over most of the Northern Hemisphere. Not more than fifteen thousand years ago—only yesterday in geological time!—woolly mammoths were plentiful on the grassy tundra of the polar region of the North. They had gigantic curling tusks and a winter coat of thick hair that almost reached the ground. Some of them, like the Columbia and Imperial mammoths of North America and the straight-tusked varieties of Italy, stood thirteen feet and over at the shoulder. On Cyprus and other Mediterranean islands, on the other hand, there were dwarf elephants no bigger than a pony. Mastodons were common in Europe, Asia, and North America; they even roamed Manhattan Island.

There is some evidence, by the way, that early man slew the elephant with his primitive weapons. Later—though still in prehistoric times—man captured the elephant alive and trained the huge creature to do his bidding.

A CLOSE LOOK AT THE ELEPHANT

Elephants are the largest and most powerful land animals alive in the world today. These monsters of the tropical jungles and grassy plains of Asia and Africa are mighty enough to command immunity from attack by any other living wild creature.

The elephant is covered with a thick gray hide, leathery and tough in texture. Though this hide is a good inch thick, an elephant is very sensitive to cold. Even a slight frost will give it a severe case of cramps. (Edmond Heller, the American zoologist, claimed that a sure cure for this ailment was a bucket of gin, water, and ginger with a kick to it that only an elephant could appreciate. After a couple of such treatments the crafty old patient will feign a return of the malady to get another dose of medicine. In fact, if indulged, the great creature will soon become a regular addict to liquor.)

Like the typical mammal, the elephant possesses hair, though this statement is rather academic—the short, stiff, sparsely distributed bristles can be better felt than seen. As for the elephant's superbly thick and bushy eyelashes, they are over five inches long, a detail most of us are apt to overlook. The long, ropelike tail has a wiry tuft at the tip. Indian craftsmen wrap the tail hairs with narrow bands of gold and fashion them into bracelets and rings.

The head is massive, the eyes small, the ears large and fanlike. The heavily muscled neck is short, which rather limits the elephant's ability to turn its head. The brain is small in proportion to the size of the body.

The elephant's teeth include the notable second pair of upper incisors that develop into picturesque ivory tusks and continue to grow throughout the life of the animal. We find these tusks foreshadowed in the ancestor of all the elephants—an animal that lived in North Africa during the late Eocene period, in the neighborhood of forty-five million years ago. In this prehistoric creature the rudimentary upper tusks were quite prominent and directed sharply downward, while the tusks in the lower jaw extended nearly straight ahead and were directed slightly upward.

In the elephant of today, the molar teeth (the only kind it has, aside from the tusks) are huge blocks, coming into place one at a time on each side of the upper and lower jaws. At no time does an elephant have more than twelve teeth in use. As a tooth wears out, it is gradually pushed forward and falls out, and another moves in from the back to take its place. In its lifetime the animal has twenty-four teeth in all; the first twelve are the milk teeth.

THE FANTASTIC TRUNK

Much of the sense of wonderment we feel when we see an elephant is due to its amazing trunk. This "proboscis," as the scientists call it, impresses not only little children but savants as well. (We can gather as much from the scientific name of the elephant order, which is Proboscidea.) The long, flexible, and muscular trunk is really the elephant's lengthened nose and upper lip. (The name "trunk," by the way, appears to be based on a misunderstanding, the word having been confused with the French *trompe*, which means "trumpet" or "proboscis." But, whether the term was originally right or wrong, we all know what is meant by the elephant's trunk.)

Obviously, the elephant did not develop this formidable appendage overnight. The fossil record shows us that as the prehistoric elephants became bulkier and bulkier and taller and taller, the neck shortened and the head and enormous tusks grew in size. Obtaining food would have become an arduous process if the massive creature had not developed a prehensile (grasping) upper lip which gradually evolved into a trunk for gathering things to eat.

And the elephant, a strict vegetarian, has quite a bit of food to gather! It must feed almost constantly to support its enormous body; its daily requirements are about a quarter of a ton of green fodder—or about 150 pounds of hay—and fifty gallons of water. The elephant's menu consists of foliage, grass canes, fruit, tubers, and bark; its favorite delicacy is the tender twigs and branches from the upper limbs of trees.

The giraffe, as you know, has a spectacular way of getting at high branches; the elephant's method of getting at the topmost branches is quite different. It simply pushes the tree over—not with its trunk, but with the front of its head and the great tusks. Getting behind the tree, the pachyderm rocks it with one, two, three steady surges; then a final mighty heave, and down it comes. Such a tree may have a trunk two to four feet around.

Thick and well protected on the outside, the elephant's trunk is delicate and sensitive inside; the animal is careful to guard it from heavy, smashing blows. The margin of the free end is formed into a lobe or lobes used as fingers to pick up small objects. In feeding, the trunk serves as an arm and hand for grasping the food, which is then brought to the mouth to be chewed and swallowed.

The elephant does not, as many suppose, drink through the trunk. Instead, it sucks up water and squirts it into the mouth. The proboscis also serves as a spray gun when the animal bathes itself in either water or dust—both of which it habitually enjoys.

The elephant has poor eyesight and its hearing is only fair; hence its sense of smell is very important. It is probably the most acute sense of smell in the animal kingdom, and it is located in the trunk. Watch the great creature, and you will observe that the trunk is constantly in motion, twisting and uncurling to catch the slightest taint of human or other contamination in the breeze.

Its wonderful trunk serves the elephant in many other ways. Not only is it used to test the wind—the animal examines suspicious objects and dangerous ground with it as well. The appendage is employed in lifting, and can hoist a weight of almost a ton; it has, on occasion, hurled a man a good forty yards.

The elephant even uses its trunk to express affection. During courtship, a cow elephant and a bull elephant caress each other with their trunks, and the cow is ever fondling her calf with her trunk.

In this multi-purpose organ, it has been said, there are 40,000-odd muscles. But whether there are more or fewer need concern us little —the trunk is a superb tool for elephant endeavors, and helps to make its possessor one of the wonders of the animal world.

AMENITIES OF ELEPHANT LIFE

The elephant is a herd animal. A big bull is the nominal leader, but in the field a wise old cow usually takes the lead. When on the march, the band travels in single file. Going down steep slopes, elephants slide on their bellies, with the back legs stretched out behind and the front legs extended forward.

As among all herd animals, the mature males are fierce rivals for supremacy. An old leader beaten in battle is not tolerated by his conqueror and is driven away. His wounded pride makes him irritable and bad-tempered. Such a solitary male usually turns "rogue"—a sulky, dangerous individual, looking for trouble and tearing trees out of the ground just to work off his tantrum.

There is no fixed mating season among elephants. From time to time the males carry on in an irresponsible and frenzied manner. This behavior, which apparently coincides with breeding intervals, is known as "must" or "musth." At such times the animals are cross-grained, moody, and generally unreliable.

Twenty-one months or so after mating time, a single calf is born covered with coarse black hair. It stands about three feet at the shoulder and weights approximately two hundred pounds. The calf sheds its milk tusks five or six months after birth, but it continues to suckle for another two years and remains under its mother's care for two years longer.

An elephant is ready to mate at eleven or twelve years; it reaches maturity at fourteen, or thereabouts, though it continues to increase in size and weight for some time after. What we might call the "wisdom tooth, the last tooth to make its appearance, is pushed into place

Koppers

EVEN THE FIERY-TEMPERED RHINOCEROS YIELDS GROUND BEFORE THIS GIANT

Before the advent of the high-powered rifle, the African bush elephant, largest land animal alive today, was the unchallenged master of the forests, veld, and swampland where it dwells. Its normal rate of travel is six miles or more and it can easily outdistance a man on foot; charging, it thunders along at twenty-five miles an hour. Tracking the elephant is no simple matter. Although the beast cannot see very well with its small eyes, its sense of smell is remarkably keen and its hearing acute, and it can be exceedingly quiet for all its great bulk. In settled areas, elephants sometimes prove to be serious nuisances: the animals will trample crops and raid granaries.

when the animal is some forty years old. The life expectancy of elephants is somewhat less than is popularly supposed; the usual range probably is not more than fifty to sixty years. The maximum recorded life span of eighty-four lacks definite confirmation.

ELEPHANTS ON SHOW

Today no zoo is complete without an elephant, but in former times seeing one of these giants was a rare and memorable occasion. The first captive Asiatic elephant to arrive in America was a two-year-old female brought from Calcutta to New York in 1796. The first African elephant to reach American shores arrived in New York in 1815 on a clipper ship from Liverpool.

The most famous of all elephants, or at least the one that received the most publicity, was Jumbo, purchased by P. T. Barnum from the London Zoological Society in 1882 for ten thousand dollars. The announcement of the sale filled all England with indignation; parents wrote agitated letters to the press, little children begged Barnum to spare their pet. John Ruskin, the Prince of Wales, and even Queen Victoria implored the Zoological Society to go back on its word. The House of Commons debated Jumbo's status, the London *Times* devoted a leading article and an editorial to Jumbo, and a suit was brought in the Court of Chancery to block the elephant's departure.

But Barnum was inexorable, and Jumbo arrived in New York on the *Assyrian Monarch*. The animal's transportation is said to have cost the famous showman an additional twenty thousand dollars. However, he recouped his costs handsomely, as Jumbo was a great favorite from the start. Jumbo, who is reported to have come originally from south of Lake Chad in the French Sudan, did not last long amid the perils of the New World: he was killed by a train in the freight yards at St. Thomas, Ontario, in 1885, at the age of twenty-four. The elephant's skeleton is on exhibition at the American Museum of Natural History in New York; the mounted skin is at Tufts College in Massachusetts. Jumbo stood ten feet nine inches at the shoulder and weighed six tons at the time of his death. His name, perhaps, will prove to be the most durable part of him; today it is applied to peanuts, sandwiches, photographs, and a host of other objects, having become a synonym for large size.

There is something about elephants that seems almost human. For the most part, they are friendly and kindly creatures. They have proved willing assistants to man and are credited with reasoning ability that ranks with that of the dog, the horse, and some of the great apes.

The elephant's first reaction to man is to hate him and distrust him more than any other creature on earth. Yet, once tamed, an elephant not only has complete confidence in its trainer—it is gentle, affectionate, and most considerate of children. Jumbo, when he traveled by rail, always had his keeper in a compartment of his car. A little door was cut in the partition so that during the night Jumbo could reach through with his trunk, touch his keeper, and thus be reassured that his friend and companion was there with him.

There is no doubt that Jumbo loved children. He never failed to make sympathetic response to the timid gestures of the youngsters when they presented their little offerings. His greatest joy seemed to be in giving a load of hilarious children a ride on his back; he would kneel on his forelegs, coaxing the fearful tots to climb onto his massive shoulders.

The belief that an elephant will bear a lasting grudge against any individual who has harmed it is far from true. In training, practically all elephants are punished by their trainers—often severely—for misbehavior. However, as long as the trainer is sure of himself and commands the respect of the animal, they will be on the best of terms afterwards.

History tells us that the Romans were great showmen and probably the first to exhibit elephants in a circus. According to Pliny, the Circus Maximus in Rome held 260,000 people; such ancient crowds must have thrilled to the spectacle of elephants in action just as we do today.

The American circus, or "rolling show," as it was called, started in 1796 with the arrival of the Asiatic elephant we have mentioned previously. The second elephant to reach America formed the nucleus of what was in time to become the famous Barnum and Bailey circus.

Circus elephants are always females, as bull elephants are apt to become uncontrollable and dangerous at certain seasons of the year. The great animals are one of the main drawing cards of the circus and zoo. They not only carry children on their backs—they can be taught many interesting tricks, such as playing ball, lying down, standing up on their hind legs, and even standing on their heads.

Aside from their value as entertainers, elephants have been useful to man in India for logging operations and hunting expeditions. In Africa the ivory trade has flourished for centuries. For about a thousand years the elephant played a role in ancient warfare.

THE ELEPHANT GOES TO WAR

Given the enormous size and strength of the elephant, we must rank it as one of man's great triumphs that he was able to tame and exploit this massive giant. The Carthaginians, those great traders and colonizers of old, domesticated elephants; the ancient people of India trained elephants from time immemorial and, as you will see later on, put them to excellent use in logging operations.

In the early days of Asiatic civilization the elephant played an important role in warfare. It was used chiefly in battering down fortified defenses—many of the gates of Indian cities were covered with long iron spikes as a protective measure against elephants' forcing open the city's barriers. When chess was invented in India, about A.D. 600 or thereabouts, one of the pieces was an elephant. Since chess is essentially a war game, at least as far as its origin is concerned, we can conclude that the military use of elephants must have been quite common in India.

The Indians used elephants in an effort to stem the advance of the army of Alexander the Great—this was about 320 B.C. The animals served much as tanks do today—the Indians mounted several archers in each howdah, with a view to supporting the infantry with added firepower. But the Macedonian foot and horse were well disciplined and apparently held their ground against this strange enemy.

The battle of Heraclea, fought in 280 B.C. by the forces of King Pyrrhus against the Romans, seems to have been the first time elephants were put into action against the Romans. Pyrrhus used his elephants as heavy cavalry, sending them in massed charges to trample down the Roman infantry. The effect was apparently quite terrifying, and the Romans were routed. However, Pyrrhus lost so many men that his victory was worthless—hence the phrase "Pyrrhic victory."

This was not the end of the elephants' career as fighters. The most famous instance of the military use of the beasts was in Hannibal's great victory over the Romans at Cannae, one of the decisive battles of world history, fought in 218 B.C. It must have required no little ingenuity on Hannibal's part to transport his thirty-seven elephants across the Alps (he invaded Italy not by sea, as we might have expected, but through Spain and southern France).

We do not know whether Hannibal used African or Asiatic elephants, nor do we have full details about just how he employed them against the Romans. But there seems little doubt that they must have had a very intimidating effect on the Romans, who were beholding the great, strange-looking creatures at their gates for the first time.

About six hundred years ago, when Tamerlane defeated Prince Mohammed at Delhi, he captured three thousand elephants, some of which he used in building the great mosque at Samarkand.

Though the Chinese domesticated horses and cattle at an early date, they made no mention of domesticated elephants until the Six Dynasties (A.D. 386-589).

AFRICAN ELEPHANTS

The Bush Elephant, *Loxodonta africana,* is the largest of present-day elephants. It reaches a maximum shoulder height of thirteen feet and weighs over six tons. However, bulls rarely exceed eleven feet, and cows are about seven feet at the shoulder. You can distinguish the bush elephant of Africa from the Asiatic species by the more blackish skin color, the larger ears, and more rounded, sloping forehead. Another difference is that in the African type the back is highest at the shoulder; the Asiatic elephant's back is slightly hollowed out at the shoulder. These two forms are all that is left of the family Elephantidae today.

The favorite fastness of the African elephant is the dense, shadeless bush, little taller than itself, but it also haunts the mountain forests, the giant grass veld, the bamboo forests and the reed swamps. Despite its enormous size and ponderous build, an African elephant can move through the bush as silently as almost any other animal.

On one occasion, when stalking an enormous bull, the author and his party suddenly saw its great form, covered with red dust, wavering above him, less than twenty-five yards away. Its trunk was extended straight out, waving gently to catch his scent. As he stood spellbound at the apparition, it vanished in the thick bush so silently and quickly that he almost doubted what he had actually seen.

Backtracking the animal's trail, the writer found tracks that showed the elephant had circled to see who the intruders were and had stood within ten feet of them, watching them go by. From its point of vantage it could have killed the whole party with little effort, if it had so desired.

The enormous ears of the African elephant serve as fans, and are kept constantly in motion during the heat of the day to circulate the air. Each ear is about three and one-half feet wide—over four feet wide and five feet long in large bulls. In these, the spread across the extended ears, including the head, is fully ten feet.

GIANT AMONG THE MAMMALS
The male bush elephant of Africa may stand a dozen feet in height, and weigh over six tons. His huge ears, each about three and a half feet wide, serve as fans, keeping the air around the animal moving. A full-grown African elephant seldom lies down to sleep. For the last thirty or forty years of his life, he slumbers in a standing position.

The trunk, which may measure up to ninety-eight inches for a large bull, has two finger-like extensions at the tip. There are three toes on the hind feet and five on the forefeet, but all we can see of the toes is the broad nails. The tail may be as much as fifty-seven inches long, with a fifteen-inch tuft of bristles at the tip.

Both bulls and cows have tusks. In the female they are usually smaller and more slender, but some cow-elephant tusks have reached almost six feet in length. The greatest tusk on record weighed 226 pounds and was over ten feet long.

ELEPHANTS WITH FOUR TUSKS

Years ago the natives in the remotest forests of the Belgian Congo used to tell stories about elephants with two sets of tusks. A few open-minded scholars believed that there might be such creatures—survivors, perhaps, of the now extinct mastodons. A search revealed no such animal, and these tales were forgotten, filed away as native folklore.

But four-tusked elephants are not a myth. Every twenty years or so, one is either shot or found dead. There is a splendid example of an elephant skull with four tusks in the Congo Museum in Belgium and another in the Explorers Club in New York. Most, if not all such skulls have come from the Congo. However, aside from the extra pair of perfectly formed tusks, the creatures are no different from other elephants that live in the same region; we can attribute their peculiarity to nothing more exciting than accidental variation.

ELEPHANTS AT REST AND IN MOTION

From about the time an African elephant reaches maturity until the moment it dies, it never lies down. Amazing as it may seem, the African elephant generally sleeps standing up for the last thirty or forty years of its life! It appears to be able to enjoy enough repose while in a standing position. The fact that its legs are built like supporting columns may explain why this stance is restful for the beast.

Young elephants, and occasionally some full-grown ones, sleep stretched out on their side. With a calf elephant it is an easy matter to lie down; but as it grows older and heavier, the task of lowering its huge bulk to the ground and raising it again when the elephant gets up, becomes increasingly difficult. In going down, the animal bends the front legs forward at the elbows and the hind legs backward at the knees. The elephant then rolls over on its side and stretches out. (The elephant's height, by the way, is approximately twice the circumference of the forefoot; often this measurement turns out to be remarkably accurate.)

Ordinarily an elephant walks at a fast shuffle; a rate of six to eight miles an hour is common. When enraged, this ponderous beast can charge for fifty yards at a speed of twenty-five miles an hour. Normally it cannot jump even a narrow ditch—its huge body must have support fore and aft at all times. However, a charging bull has been known to clear a wide ditch, though it was lame for some time afterwards.

Elephants know—and follow—the best routes through the forests and mountains. Many of the highways in Africa today proceed along the routes originally laid out by elephants. They can climb steep embankments and slide down them or walk along a narrow ledge three feet wide. In some instances, they grasp roots or branches to lever themselves up and over rocks.

When undisturbed, elephants make a peculiar rumbling sound which is apparently due to the workings of the digestive system—at least that is what it sounds like to the author. These rumblings can be heard a quarter of a mile away. When disturbed, the elephant stills the sound so as not to betray its presence.

African elephants are fond of bathing, but they are fastidious about the kind of water they drink. In Kenya the author found that they came a long way to dig holes in the sand of a dry river bed to get clean water after passing up a fast-flowing river with chocolate-colored water. The water pit is not dug with the tusks; about two feet deep, it is sunk by scraping with the forefeet and sending the sand and gravel flying.

The African elephant is generally conceded to be less tractable than its Indian cousin, though just as intelligent. Despite its more independent character, the African variety can be domesticated and trained for clearing land and other laborious farm work. The bush elephant was once common over most of the continent and frequented all types of country from plains and jungles to mountains of ten-thousand-feet elevation. It is still holding its own in some parts of equatorial Africa, where three subspecies are known to exist.

The Forest Elephant, *Loxodonta cyclotis,* makes its home in the rain forests of West Africa from Sierra Leone to Angola and east to the basin of the Congo River. On a comparative basis we can call it "little," as it rarely exceeds eight feet at the shoulder. Its ears, too, are relatively small and rounded for an African species. As for the hind feet, they usually have four toes instead of three. Immature forest elephants have been mistaken for pygmy elephants, but, given time, they always grow up unless artificially stunted.

AFRICAN ELEPHANT GRAVEYARDS—REAL OR IMAGINARY?

The legend of elephant graveyards—places where numbers of elephants go to die—is still believed by many African natives. They claim there is only one graveyard and that all elephants go there to meet their end. Nothing is ever said about rhino, giraffe, or antelope graveyards. What gives the legend a certain plausibility is the fact that the bones of a single elephant are rarely found.

In the early part of the eighteenth century, the Portuguese often came upon great piles of elephant tusks in Angola, but no skeletons. Sometimes the heaps, containing four tons of ivory, were surmounted by carved wooden idols and human skulls. At this distance in time, we can only guess at the meaning of such finds. Probably the natives had gathered the tusks. The skeletons may have been lost and scattered over a wide area.

After a bush fire in the late 1930's, an elephant-control officer discovered an area where there was a large collection of both elephant skeletons and ivory. It was supposed they were from wounded elephants that had gone there to die. At least the natives claimed they had seen many of the beasts go there—often they wounded them, but were afraid to follow and collect the ivory.

Vernon Brelsford, writing in the *African Wild Life Journal,* tells of the island of Minswa in the swamps of northern Rhodesia, a favorite retreat for elephants. One or two natives, he says, have gone to the island but never returned; no white man has ventured there. Brelsford himself canoed round its edges and heard the screams of elephants but refrained from landing. He believes there is a graveyard there—but says it is also a nursery and a home for very-much-alive elephants.

Time and again, large piles of elephant bones have been found in one place or another; but it is assumed that these represent herds massacred by natives or white men, for there are usually skeletons but no tusks. All in all, then, the great elephant cemetery, as such, appears to be a myth.

ELEPHANTS STICK TOGETHER

Most of us have heard rumors that elephants will not desert a comrade in distress and will even help it to escape if it has been wounded. One of the foremost authorities on African big game produced unquestionable proof that such rumors have a genuine basis in fact.

When Carl Akeley shot a big bull elephant, the great creature dropped, fatally wounded. Shortly afterwards, coming up over a rise, Akeley saw two other elephants, one on either side of the wounded animal, lifting it to its feet and trying their utmost to guide its faltering steps to safety. Ten or twelve other elephants gave assistance with their tusks and trunks in an effort to get their stricken relative back on his feet.

So impressed was he with this display of chivalry that Akeley executed the scene as he saw it, in bronze, for the American Museum of Natural History, as a lasting tribute to these great creatures of the African veld.

Akeley tells us some other curious things about these animals. Not the least interesting is the fact that baby elephants have playthings. He describes a sunbaked mud ball, two and a half feet in diameter, with which he saw a group of young elephants playing. They rolled it half a mile or more.

ASIATIC ELEPHANTS

The Asiatic or Indian Elephant, *Elephas maximus*, dwells in India, Ceylon, Burma, Indo-China, and the Malay Peninsula. After the cow the elephant is the second most venerated beast of the Hindus; the Hindu god Ganesh had the head of an elephant. The Buddhists class the elephant with the dove of peace. One of their legends tells of an elephant in "musth" that was sent to kill the Lord Buddha. They met, but when Buddha touched the beast on the forehead, it bowed low before him.

HOW ELEPHANTS ARE CAPTURED

There are several methods used in capturing elephants. Large, highly prized bulls are tracked down and taken in a simple but ingenious manner. Mahouts (professional elephant drivers), mounted on tame females, single out the desired bull. They then make their mounts available to him. In the course of becoming successively acquainted with the entire relay of females, the bull is kept awake day and night and finally succumbs to exhaustion and sleep. The bull wakes to find himself securely chained.

The method for capturing elephant herds is to drive them into an enclosure. While one group of men build the enclosure, or *kheddah,* another group surround the area about the herd by hastily constructing a bamboo fence. The *kheddah* itself is a corral formed of stout twelve-foot timbers set in a circle twenty to fifty feet in diameter, with a four-yard gap through which the herd is driven by native beaters.

In Nepal and Bengal, elephants are sometimes noosed or lassoed. Two tame elephants approach the wild one from either side, and the mahout throws the noose around its neck. In Ceylon, hand-roping is customary; but in Mysore, they capture elephants by driving them into pitfalls about ten feet long, seven and one-half feet wide, and fifteen feet deep. It is a tight fit, but the beast does not injure itself trying to escape.

HOW THE INDIAN ELEPHANT SLEEPS

The Asiatic elephant, unlike its African cousin, lies down to rest. When it is ready to go to sleep, it stands motionless in the forest like a statue. After about an hour, when the world is fast asleep, the elephant goes down so suddenly and quietly that in a flash of the eyelids its dark shadow seems to vanish in the air. It usually sleeps in two "shifts"—one from about ten in the morning to three in the afternoon, and the other from eleven at night to three in the morning.

COURTSHIP AND BRINGING UP THE YOUNG

Elephants do not readily breed in captivity, though captive animals will breed normally in natural surroundings. As elephants are shy about their love affairs, they have a hankering for privacy. One fantastic story tells how a female preparing for a honeymoon digs a pit, stocking around it several weeks' supply of fruits and fodder for herself and the prospective bridegroom. Here she waits, trumpeting love calls to her mate.

Normally a male and female elephant go through several days and even weeks of courtship. Then, for a month more the pair will graze and live together. Once the honeymoon is over, a female seeks the close friendship of another female and they remain inseparable until some time after the calf is born. It takes the watchful care of both to protect the calf from tigers. Most females first mate between the ages of eighteen and twenty-one.

In the natural state, most elephant calves are born in the spring, between March and April. The coming into the world of a baby elephant is quite an event in a herd of wild elephants. Calves are usually born during the night. There is a constant bellowing and trumpeting among the elders to herald the occasion. This terrifying din doubtless serves the purpose of scaring away marauders—especially tigers. For the first few weeks after the arrival of a calf, a herd will stay put in one locality and more or less keep a closed circle around the mother and her calf, particularly at night.

During the early days of the baby's life the mother, if disturbed, will pick up her calf with her trunk and carry it away to safety.

A baby elephant follows at its mother's heels for at least three or four years and is suckled at the breasts between her forelegs. On one occasion a sacred white elephant calf at the Mandalay palace whose mother died was reared by twenty-five Burmese women who suckled it.

Up to the age of five, the elephant's trunk is of little use to it; but at this time the youngster begins to gather fodder and gradually ceases to depend on its mother's milk. Females average four or five calves during a lifetime. Twins are occasionally born, and it is not uncommon for two calves of different ages to be following one mother. Occasionally a female will have as many as eight calves in a lifetime; one female reportedly gave birth to a calf on her sixty-first birthday.

At sixteen, young elephants have reached the adolescent stage and males begin flirting with females; but the bulls exhibit no sign of "musth" until they are over twenty-one. "Musth" is shown by a discharge of a strong-smelling waxy substance or fluid from glands near the eyes, just above the mouth. It normally occurs during hot weather and may last two weeks. From the age of thirty-five to forty-five the discharge is greatest and marks the period in which an elephant is in its prime; musth is usually connected with sexual excitement.

During "musth" the bull goes on a rampage and cannot be trusted.

Often the fluid drips down onto his mouth, which makes him even more ferocious. At the age of fifty, the discharge of fluid from the "musth" glands has subsided and finally disappears.

Animals in "musth" are not to be confused with rogue elephants that plunder and destroy. It is the social outcast that in some way has broken the laws of the herd and been expelled that becomes a savage, brooding rogue. Rogues that have been wounded and caused to suffer by man may also become a menace to all and everything they encounter. In ancient days a rogue elephant filled the office of public executioner in India. Occasionally there are female rogues.

ELEPHANTS AT WORK

It is curious that an elephant in the wild state, so suspicious and distrustful of man, should become one of the gentlest, most dependable, and most trustworthy of animals when domesticated.

Elephants have greater learning capacity than most animals; in fact, trained elephants never stop learning. They understand about twenty-five words of command.

When a trained elephant passes an implement, such as a spear, to a rider on its back, it soon learns to pass the handle and not the point. When going through a forest, an elephant is always careful to guard against the chance that its rider or riders may get struck by twigs or branches. It will pull away the small obstructing twigs with its trunk, push over small trees and go around the low, heavy branches of large trees.

Occasionally elephants try to play innocent tricks on their riders and squeal with delight when successful. Young elephants form a naughty habit of using clay to plug the bells worn around the neck so that they can steal bananas from cultivated plantations at night without being detected. Like children, they feel that stolen fruit is the sweetest.

A great deal has been written about the intelligence of the elephant. There seem to be grounds for believing that it has more reasoning power than either a dog or a horse. Here is a most interesting example of elephant reasoning:

In Burma, one of these beasts was ordered to lift a large log to an elevated position. When the animal realized that its burden might roll over its head and crush the rider, it suddenly dropped the log—

and then did the job in its own way. This time, without any instructions from the mahout, the animal seized a clublike piece of the wood and jammed it in between its trunk and tusks in a vertical position. Balancing the log on its tusks, the elephant raised it without any danger of its falling back on the rider; finally the beast placed its forefeet on a log to gain elevation and set the timber in place.

THE SACRED ELEPHANT

The Asiatic or Indian elephant, sacred to adherents of the Hindu religion, is smaller in size than its relatives in Africa. This animal is also easily recognized by its less conspicuous ears. Famed as a workman, the Indian elephant aids the Asiatic natives in moving lumber.

TAMING AND TRAINING THE ELEPHANT

It has been calculated that it costs about five thousand dollars to raise an elephant to the age when it begins to earn its own living. Used for farm purposes and for carrying great loads, the Asiatic elephant is easy to domesticate even if captured when adult. Its strength and intelligence are especially valuable in the teak forests, where the elephant shows remarkable ability, as we have just seen, to handle big timber. Bulls are most useful for this purpose, since their tusks are larger. An elephant can carry up to one ton (an average load is six hundred pounds), and can drag a two-ton log. It is claimed that during World War II the Japanese loaded their elephants to the extent of four tons per animal.

Wild elephants are usually taken at the age of eighteen or nineteen—the age at which they can start doing light work. However, these are rarely quite as serviceable as ranch-raised animals, for the cuts and burns from the ropes lashed around the feet of trapped elephants never heal completely.

Baby elephants go to school soon after they are weaned. A wise old female takes charge of perhaps half a dozen or more. An elephant is trained in about the same way as a horse, but the process is much slower. The calf is corraled in a small pen with a leather thong around one foot for control. A native boy or *oozie*, as he is called in Burma, is lowered onto its head by a pulley and raised when the calf bucks. This is kept up until the young elephant grows tired and gets used to the operation. By that time it will permit the *oozie* to sit quietly on its head.

Usually the mother elephant is permitted to stand by; her presence helps quiet her child, and she raises no objection to what is going on. The youngster learns its first lesson in less than twelve hours, and good behavior is rewarded with choice fruit. The next day the trainers repeat the lesson in the open, placing a light load on the pupil's back. Once this ordeal has been passed, the candidate is sent to school with other young elephants, where it is taught obedience and proper behavior.

This goes on for another ten years. By the time each growing individual has reached the age of fourteen years, it has been assigned a rider about its own age. Usually the two become inseparable and go through life together until death takes one of them. There is no one so proud as the copper-skinned Indian boy riding on his elephant. He knows every whim and fault of his companion. He scrubs the elephant from the tip of the trunk to the end of the tail with soap and water every morning, and then polishes the tusks with sand until they are gleaming white.

Though the elephant is ready for light work at the age of nineteen or so, it is not given really difficult tasks until it is twenty-five or older. By "light work" we mean going out with the experienced elephants to the mountains and helping move the heavy teak logs down impassable slopes to the rivers below.

Working elephants have a hard life—they must labor all day and then forage for their own food during the evening and night. The ones that are well cared for, work three days in a row and then rest the next two days. This goes on for nine months, after which the animals are given a complete rest for three months.

Elephants dislike nervous people and they refuse to be hurried. An elephant will be out of sorts all day if it is suddenly wakened in the morning. It likes to dawdle while it thinks about getting up. The elephant boy or mahout is well aware of this trait; after locating his elephant in the morning, he sits down close by and speaks gently to the great animal until such time as it condescends to arouse itself.

Elephants are still used as saddle animals, though much less so than formerly. They appear in religious rituals, processions, and other ceremonial events; occasionally they are still employed in hunting big game. A full-dress equipage, including the howdah, gold saddle-cloth, punkahs, ropes and other gear, adds up to about half a ton.

ASIATIC ELEPHANTS ARE "SMALLER"

Though Asiatic elephants are smaller than the African variety, they are anything but small.

The Asiatic elephant reaches a shoulder height of about nine feet —very large bulls may stand ten feet. The average weight of an Asiatic elephant is approximately three and one-half tons, with a maximum of six tons. The skin is gray, lighter in tone and somewhat smoother in texture than the hide of the African varieties.

Once in a while we come across a "white" Asiatic elephant—not really snow-white but rather clouded by a slate-gray cast. The experts distinguish three subspecies of Asiatic elephants, although for the most part the differences are not too clearly marked. There is one clear-cut distinction in the case of the Sumatra elephant—it has no tusks.

The Asiatic elephant has a bulging, protuberant forehead, but its ears are relatively small as compared with those of the African elephant. The tusks of the male reach a length of about eight feet—ten at most. The greatest recorded weight for one tusk is 126 pounds. In the female, tusks are either lacking or else so reduced in size that they rarely project beyond the lips. The trunk has only one finger-like lobe at the margin of the tip. There are five toes on the front feet and four toes on the hind feet.

ELEPHANT GRAVEYARDS IN ASIA

According to legend there are elephant graveyards in Asia as well as in Africa. Tradition has it that as its time draws near, the gaunt, aged Asiatic elephant makes its last long pilgrimage to these isolated spots to wait for death. Here, so we are told, the ground is strewn with huge bones bleached white in the tropical sun, and with ivory tusks that signify fabulous wealth for the finder.

While there are no elephant graveyards in the popular sense, the legend is not entirely groundless. Elephants do have a place where they go to die. Worn-out patriarchs that are reaching the end of their days seek the shade of the upper river valleys where food is plentiful and easy to get.

The end usually comes toward the close of the hot dry season. For a last drink, the weary old elephants, their cheeks now sunken, climb down into the almost dry river beds and here spray their hot, feverish body with water and cool sand. There they stay until, growing dizzy, they stagger and fall. At last the great old heart stops and all is still.

The vultures and hyenas take over; then come the monsoons— torrents of water carrying thousands of tons of mud and soil rush down the valley and bury all that is left of the once great creatures in tombs that are hidden for all time. Such is the end of an old elephant, but there is no long, weary trek to a common graveyard to die.

Hyraxes or Old World Conies —
Little Cousins of the Elephant

Picture, if you can, a rabbit without a tail, and with short legs and small ears. This will give you some idea of what a hyrax looks like. Hyraxes, also known as "dassies" or "conies," are rock-

THE WELL-ARMED BLACK RHINOCEROS OF AFRICA

The African black rhinoceros possesses two horns, in contrast to its one-horned relative the great Indian rhinoceros. Once spread over much of Africa, the black rhinoceros today is most often to be encountered in the eastern part of the continent, particularly on the plains and in the broken forests. Rhinoceroses are eaters of plants and in general are not very dangerous to human beings.

dwellers for the most part, though a few dwell in trees. Excellent climbers, they can scale the face of an almost perpendicular rock or tree trunk. They are very active, timid little creatures, always on the alert, ready to dive for safety in the rocks on the least provocation.

Limited to the Old World, the hyraxes are spread over most of Africa, and have a range that extends north through the Arab countries to Asia. They have found their way into the folklore of these regions. Thus, to the Zulu the alarm call of the hyrax is *Ma-'ng afa*, meaning "I am dying." In Natal, the natives claim that the hyrax is the only mammal that can stare directly at the sun.

These strange little animals have such marked peculiarities that scientists have placed them in an order all by themselves (Hyracoidea). Hyraxes are vegetarians, and their teeth are of the kind we see in certain hoofed mammals, particularly rhinoceroses. From their foot structure, we can tell that somewhere along the line in past history there was probably a connection between these little fellows and the lordly elephants. The four-toed feet of hyraxes end in blunt claws resembling miniature hoofs. As for the soles of the feet, they are naked but cushioned with well-developed footpads.

The family Procaviidae, which takes in all the hyraxes, is divided into three groups. The species making up these groups are all very similar in size, appearance, and general structure.

The Gray Hyrax, or Rock Hyrax, *Heterohyrax,* lives among rocks in colonies ranging from half a dozen to fifty animals. They feed on green vegetation during daylight hours but may continue feeding into the night. The young—there are two or three in a litter—are fully clothed and have their eyes open at birth.

These sociable creatures have a shrill communicating cry. When a hyrax looks outside its den and finds no imminent danger, it gives the all-clear signal. This is relayed by other members of the colony until the rocks resound with their cheerful voices.

——HYRAX OF THE BIBLE. There are several passages in the Bible where the word *shaphan* occurs. Translators have rendered this word as "cony," under the impression that a rabbit was meant. However, the reference is most likely to the Syrian Hyrax or Daman, *Heterohyrax syriacus,* which dwells in Syria and Palestine.

In the Old Testament we find such passages as, "and the cony, because he cheweth the cud and divideth not the hoof . . ." and "the

high hills are a refuge for the wild goats, and the rocks for the conies."
These descriptions enable us to recognize the hyrax—although the
animal does not actually chew the cud. However, the hyrax does live
in holes in the rocks and is extremely wary and timid, bearing out
Solomon's remarks about its habits.

The Tree Hyrax, *Dendrohyrax,* has longer and softer fur than the
rock hyrax and is a little larger in size. A native of the heavily forested
regions of Central and South Africa, especially of the Congo, the tree
hyrax is a solitary creature. Usually a single animal makes its home
in a hollow trunk or in the thick foliage of a tree. Frequenting only
the tallest of forest trees, it feeds on the leaves of the uppermost
branches. It restricts its wanderings to the night, never leaving its
roost until after sunset.

ITS FAMILY TREE CONTAINS AN ELEPHANT
The unprepossessing little hyrax, a creature that looks like a rabbit, is in an order of
mammals all by itself. This is so because it has certain features not found collectively in
any other animal. Interestingly enough, its feet reveal a relationship to the elephant.
The hyrax is fond of sitting among rocks and sunning itself, and is noted for the noise
it makes. It is much preyed upon by wild dogs. Shown here is the rock hyrax.

However, you must not conclude that the tree hyrax lives an exclusively "lone-wolf" existence, for it carries on a continual discourse
with its neighbors. Its cry is a long-drawn-out howl or roar, swelling
in volume. This goes on for half an hour, almost without interruption.
It is only the males that howl, usually one at a time. These performances may last from soon after sundown until two o'clock in the
morning.

Families are not large; occasionally there are twins, rarely more.
The young—as among the rock hyraxes—are born fully furred and
with eyes wide open.

The Big-toothed Hyrax, *Procavia,* the common African type that lives in colonies, is found almost anywhere on the continent where there are sizable outcrops of rock. Its head and body length is about twenty inches; the tail is a mere stub, less than an inch long. The rather coarse fur is brownish gray, though the shade varies quite a bit.

The Horse Family and the Tapirs

WHEN SCIENTISTS WANT to explain how the strange animals of the past—the weird-looking creatures whose bones we see in museums—developed into our familiar modern mammals, they often take the horse as an example. And with good reason—what could be more remarkable and clearer than the development of the "Dawn Horse" (Eohippus), a little, foxlike creature only eleven inches high, into the tall and stately horse that we know so well today?

The origin of the horse dates back some sixty million years to the Eocene period—the "Dawn Age" of mammals. The early horses appeared almost simultaneously in Europe and America. These small creatures had four toes on the front feet and three toes on the hind feet.

It was in America that the horses passed through the greater part of their evolution. Having neither horns nor claws to protect themselves with, they had to depend on speed. In the course of millions of years, the center toes, which bore most of the animals' weight, grew larger and larger, while the outside toes became smaller and smaller. What was left in the end was one vastly enlarged "toe"— the hoof. This was naturally much more suitable for swift running on hard, dry land than the original toes which it replaced. At the same time, horses grew in size; their weight increased from the hundred pounds or so of the Dawn Horse to the thousand pounds and more of later horses.

The horse seems to have had a checkered career—after all, a lot can happen in sixty million years. We possess good evidence that the horse died out in Europe at an early date; as for Asia, its supply of horses was restocked from America by way of a land bridge that once joined Siberia with Alaska.

However, America cannot claim the honor of having produced the immediate ancestor of our domestic horse. It seems that the entire tribe of American horses vanished during the Ice Age. The modern horse, then, originated in Europe or Asia. It was the Spaniards who reintroduced the animal into America.

THE HORSE IN HISTORY

It is hard for us to realize, in this age of high-powered automobiles and jet-propelled airplanes, what an important role the horse played in man's history for thousands of years. Horses were known to the Babylonians as far back as 2,300 B.C. and were used by them to draw their war chariots beginning about 1,700 B.C. It was the horse that made possible the far-flung conquests of Alexander the Great. Without the horse, the hordes of Alaric and Attila could hardly have managed to make their way west from central Asia to humble the Roman Empire. Again, the great conquests of Genghis Khan are unthinkable without his half-million horsemen. On foot, they would still have been superb soldiers, but they could never have covered as much territory as they did. The medieval knights and the Crusaders were equally dependent on their horses.

In American history we find the same pattern. The Indian warriors of the Plains, the gallant cavalry fighting of the Civil War, the Pony Express, the stagecoach era, the epic of the cowboy—all these distinctive aspects of the American past were made possible by the horse.

Up to the introduction of the railroad, all postal systems had to rely on the horse. Almost three thousand years ago, Herodotus, "the father of history," commented admiringly on the Persian postal system, which made use of swift horses. The Aztecs, on the other hand, had to use human runners, for they lacked horses before the coming of the white man.

When Cortez landed in Mexico, he had only sixteen horses. They were the first ever seen by the Aztecs, and these strange, seemingly towering animals struck the Indians with terror. Some twenty years later, when De Soto crossed the Mississippi in 1541, his men either abandoned or lost some of their horses. Most authorities believe that these animals formed the nucleus of the bands of wild horses later found west of the lower Mississippi.

The descendants of these horses came to be known as "mustangs"— an English pronunciation of the Spanish word *mesteño,* which means "strayed" or "wild." The cayuse (Indian pony), named after an Indian tribe, was part mustang; usually the animal was inferior, due to carelessness in selecting breeding stock.

Horses are long lived and some mares have been known to breed up to the age of twenty-five. One individual lived to be fifty years old —probably a record.

To horsemen, the word "horse" always means a male—the female is invariably called a mare. A young mare is a filly. A young male is a colt, but so, too, is a young female; a mature male is a stallion. Mares foal eleven months after mating time.

HORSE FEATS

Careful breeding and training of horses have resulted in some remarkable achievements. Man o' War was credited with a speed of 21 seconds for a quarter-mile—an hourly rate of 43 miles. (Of course, speed decreases as more distance is covered.) Trotting horses take a bit under two minutes for a mile. Workhorses are noted for their powers of endurance; a large dray horse dragged sixteen railroad trucks, weighing 55 tons, on steel tracks over a distance of 20 miles in six hours. The record jump for a hunter is somewhere between 33 and 37 feet.

"A HORSE OF A DIFFERENT COLOR"

The homely old phrase about "a horse of a different color" once had a significance which is probably lost on most of us nowadays. Certain breeds of horses invariably have a characteristic color. Hence the appearance of off-colors betrays to us the presence of crossbreeding or impurities in the breeding stock. There are several standardized horse colors—black, brown, bay, chestnut, dun, cream white, gray, roan, pinto, appaloosa, and, most beautiful of all, the palomino.

Domestic horses were probably derived from a now extinct large horse of central Europe, a smaller mountain pony, and the Mongolian wild horse which has lived on into our own time. We now have twenty-five or so distinct breeds.

HORSE BREEDING

Man has been breeding horses for centuries. He has many uses for these animals. Sometimes he needs a large, powerful creature; again, he may require speed. Temperament also matters, just as it does among humans: some kinds of horses must be placid, others mettlesome. The prizewinner at the horse show and the pit pony in the coal mine each have their clearly defined roles.

Horses are either purebred or crossbred. If both its parents are of the same breed, a horse is said to be purebred. A crossbred horse, then, is one with parents of different breeds. Purebreeding will intensify a given quality, possibly at the expense of others; crossbreeding, under favorable conditions, has brought about desirable combinations of good qualities.

People are prone to confuse purebred horses with Thoroughbred horses. The distinction is clear-cut and important. A purebred horse may be of any breed, as long as its parents also belonged to that breed. A Thoroughbred is a *specific* breed of horse. Every Thoroughbred is necessarily a purebred horse; but many purebred horses are not Thoroughbreds.

SOME NOTABLE WORKHORSES

The Shire horse, developed in England, is the largest of all horses. It stands some seventeen hands high (sixty-eight inches) and weights of 2,200-2,400 pounds are common. We owe this breed to Henry VIII, who had all horses of less than fifteen hands destroyed because they were eating too much in proportion to the amount of work they could perform. Thus the Shire horse evolved from the mating of large horses.

Another famous draft horse is the Clydesdale, weighing close to a ton. Both energetic and good looking, it is a favorite workhorse in the American Middle West. The Belgian horse, approximating the Shire horse in size and weight, is thought to be descended from the powerful animals that medieval knights used as chargers.

Percherons, originally bred in France, may weigh over a ton. They are exceptionally sturdy, hard-working animals. In the old days, they were the favored horses for stagecoach travel. In more recent times, Percherons were used a great deal for hauling delivery wagons and fire engines. The coming of the automobile has put an end to those activities, but to this day Percherons are probably used more than any other kind of horse in circuses.

Shetland ponies have a long and useful history of working in England's coal mines. Despite their small size, they are famous for their powers of endurance. (A pony, by the way, is a small horse—not necessarily a young one.)

GLAMOROUS BREEDS

When we come to the glamorous breeds, the most famous are perhaps the magnificent steeds of the Arabian deserts. These animals have been bred since about A.D. 800. Celebrated for stamina as well as swiftness, they have powerful lungs, slender legs, and broad hoofs. Hundreds of years of selective breeding have made them exceptionally able to resist heat, hunger, and thirst.

For the last four hundred years or so, Arabian horses have been mated with other breeds, producing handsome creatures with many outstanding qualities. The most notable animal of this type is the Thoroughbred, which started in England toward the end of the seventeenth century, when three Arabian stallions were bred to swift, light English mares. Later, Thoroughbreds were brought to America. The finest Thoroughbreds—Man o' War and Citation are perhaps the most famous—have made a great contribution to horse racing. They have also played a valuable role in breeding, by improving other strains and imparting their speed and stamina to them.

There has been much controversy—it goes back at least as far as the ancient Egyptians—as to whether a trotting horse ever has all its feet off the ground at one time. About 1875 or so, Leland Stanford bet twenty-five thousand dollars that a horse moving at full speed takes all four feet off the ground at the same time. He had an English photographer, Eadweard Muybridge, snap a series of photographs of a horse in motion to prove the point. (Muybridge's invention for photographing the horse in motion, it is interesting to note in passing, was the basic idea that brought about motion pictures. Later Muybridge worked with Edison on the possibility of talking pictures.)

A handsome horse developed from the Thoroughbred group is the Hackney breed. Originally, about 1750, these horses were used for private carriages, but later on they were used for hackney cabs as well—hence our word "hacks." Today the Hackney breed has no practical value but it is still exhibited at horse shows.

The Quarter horse, one of America's most famous breeds, is descended from English horses brought to the Virginia colony in the days of Pocahontas and John Smith. For years the Quarter horse was the most popular type of race horse in America. Later on, after the opening up of the West, the Quarter horse proved invaluable on cattle ranches. In recent years, the Quarter horse has been used a great deal as a saddle animal. Because of its outstanding intelligence and ready adaptability, this type often makes an admirable polo pony.

The Morgan horse, another popular, handsome American breed, which originated about 1800, is remarkably versatile. It began as a lowly farm horse, but soon came to be favored as a saddle horse and then as an Army and police mount. Some of the finest trotting and harness racing horses have come from the Morgan breed.

Another breed that deserves mention is the American Saddle Horse, developed over a century ago in Kentucky. This handsome animal, with its even disposition, graceful carriage, and equable gait, is the favored horse for pleasure-riding in the United States.

Fox hunting, traditionally an aristocratic sport, calls for horses of exceptional stamina and agility. Such horses are known as "Hunters," but they do not belong to any special breed. Long, patient training is required to develop the ability of these animals to jump over ditches and fences. Horses bred for steeplechase racing need even more rigorous training, for it is often literally true that their rider's life depends on them. Polo is the sport that makes the sharpest demands on a horse's skill, intelligence, and adaptability.

Handsomest of all horses, it has been said, are the Palominos, with their predominantly golden color. Though not a specific breed, they monopolize attention at shows and fairs because of their good looks. The flowing, flaxen mane and tail, setting off the rich, golden, bronze, or yellow coat diluted with various shades of chestnut or sorrel, is most pleasing to the eve.

WILD HORSES—DESTINED FOR EXTINCTION

Przewalski's Horse, or the Tarpan, *Equus przewalskii,* is the only wild horse left on earth today. True, there are many so-called "wild" horses in different parts of the world. However, with the exception of the tarpan, they are all descendants of domestic animals that have escaped from captivity.

SOLE SURVIVOR OF AN EXTINCT BREED

Scientifically speaking, a wild horse is not wild simply because it is found in an untamed state and resists capture and saddling. Such a horse is, more likely, the descendant of a domestic horse that escaped from captivity and went wild in its habits. In historic times a true wild horse has never been domesticated or bred by man, and the only one left in the world is Przewalski's horse, pictured above. Quite different from the modern horses we know, this hardy creature has a small body and a large head with a prominent muzzle. The animal appears to be intermediate between the true horses and asses.

Przewalski's horse first came to the notice of zoologists when the explorer for whom it is named brought back a skin and skull from his Asiatic journeys. The animal is a sturdy, comparatively small pony that stands about four feet at the shoulder. It has a rather large head, small ears, and heavy jaws and teeth. The mane is short and erect, but the tail is long-haired all the way. The summer coat is reddish brown with some white about the muzzle; in winter, the coat is longer and paler.

The range of Przewalski's horse is limited to the plains of the Altai Mountain region and extreme western Mongolia. In April or May, probably eleven months after mating time, the mares are ready to foal. At this time they retreat to quiet places where food and water are plentiful. Przewalski's horse interbreeds freely with "wild" ponies of the region, and hybrids are not uncommon.

THE HORSE FAMILY

The horse family is made up of asses and zebras as well as horses. Named after the horse—*equus* in Latin—this family (Equidae) is remarkable for the development of the foot. In all these animals, the foot has been reduced to a single digit, originally the third toe. This toe is enclosed in a compact, horny hoof.

The ankle and wrist have been raised high off the ground, becoming the so-called "knee" and hock of a horse. Such animals are adapted for high speed on hard, solid ground. Their teeth, with high crowns that gradually push upward with wear, are specialized for grazing and grinding close, coarse grass.

These animals have a long tail of whiplike hair. They use it to disperse the usual host of house flies and green horse flies—and also the more serious pests like the gadfly, which punctures the skin and deposits its eggs under the surface.

The equines are sociable creatures, running in herds that may contain hundreds of individuals. They breed about every other year. Mares usually have a single foal, born in an advanced stage of development. Its eyes are open and it is able to stand unsupported a few minutes after birth.

DONKEYS—USEFUL AND MUCH MALIGNED

The donkey, or domesticated ass, has an honorable history—the animal has served man well for many thousands of years. Derived from the Abyssinian or Somali Wild Ass, which is still in existence, the donkey was probably domesticated in the New Stone Age, some twelve thousand years ago. The name "ass" probably stems from the word *athôn*, which is Hebrew for she-ass. "Donkey" is a nickname derived from the animal's supposed dun color.

The ass has a shorter mane and shorter tail hair than the horse, and only the end half is provided with a brush. Of course its ears are much longer than those of a horse. Superior to the horse when it comes to carrying loads, the donkey is famous for its sure-footed negotiation of dangerously narrow mountain trails. Man has employed the donkey since time immemorial as a pack and draft animal. The Egyptians used it extensively in their monument-building as far back as 3,000 B.C.; they do not seem to have had horses until 1,900 B.C.

Despite its reputation for stubbornness and stupidity, the donkey has accomplished much of man's "dirty work" under singularly unrewarding conditions and often savage treatment. A patient and longsuffering creature, it outlives the horse; the donkey has a life expectancy of from twenty-five to forty-seven years. There is usually one foal at a time, about nine months after mating.

THE DONKEY IN BIBLICAL LORE AND LEGEND

The numerous Biblical references to the donkey indicate to us how extensively the animal was used in ancient times. Aside from heavy farm work, it had such thankless tasks as turning irrigation machines and large millstones. The donkey was a saddle animal as well as a beast of burden. Great men and rulers traveled on an ass colt, and such a mount was a token of a peaceful journey; the horse was reserved for war. Thus the Gospels depict Jesus entering Jerusalem on the colt of an ass.

We all know how mighty Samson slew a thousand Philistines with the jawbone of an ass. Then there is the famous story of Balaam and how his mount fell down on beholding the angel of the Lord standing with sword in hand. Quick to anger, Balaam struck the beast. Thereupon "the Lord opened the mouth of the ass, and she said unto Balaam, 'What have I done unto thee, that thou hast smitten me three times?' "

A charming legend relates that none was admitted to the Ark unless invited by Noah. With the coming of the floods, the Devil saw that he was going to be cut off from mankind. When the time arrived for the ass to go on board, it was taken with a fit of obstinacy. Losing patience, Noah struck the ass, crying out, "Enter, thou devil!" Needless to say, the Devil accepted the "invitation."

WILD COUSIN OF THE DOMESTIC DONKEY

With its small ears, slender head, and long legs, the Asiatic wild ass looks more like a horse than like man's willful servant the domestic donkey. (That creature, incidentally, is descended from African stock.) Swift of foot and sociable toward their own kind, the wild asses are sometimes seen in large numbers on the deserts of Asia, where the scarcity of water does not appear to inconvenience them. The animals show considerable curiosity about man, but will seldom allow him to come very near.

MULES—ANIMALS WITH NO FUTURE

The mule is a cross between a male donkey (jackass) and a female horse. Both sexes of the mule are almost always sterile. These hybrids rarely gallop and have a feeble bray unlike the voice of either an ass or horse. The cross between a male horse and a female donkey is known as a "hinny." It is smaller and inferior to the mule.

Man has bred mules since prehistoric times. They are now used largely for military transport, being particularly valuable in mountain warfare. Darwin tells us that troops of mules in South American mountain regions are led by steady old mares. These *madrinas* ("grandmothers") carry a bell. The mules show great affection for the *madrina* and it is almost impossible to separate them from her.

There is a quaint legend to account for the mule's inability to breed. It is said that when the Holy Family was about to travel into Egypt, St. Joseph chose a mule to carry them. However, the animal kicked Joseph and he became angry. He laid a curse upon the animal, to the effect that it should never have parents or descendants of its own kind.

WILD ASSES—METTLESOME CREATURES

There is a world of difference between the wild donkey or ass in its native desert and the domesticated breed. The wild ass moves with a spirited, high-actioned gait, trotting freely over the rocks and sand with the speed of a horse. It is frequently captured by Arabs. The donkeys are run down by fast dromedaries. Invariably, it is the foals that are caught; as for the adults, they gallop too far away over the boundless desert to be overtaken. Despite the arid nature of their surroundings, wild donkeys always seem to be in good condition, and their flesh is eaten by the natives.

Like all members of the horse family, wild asses are sociable creatures; in Mongolia, herds of a thousand head have been recorded. At foaling time the herds break up, and the mares, often accompanied by a stallion, retire to sheltered pastures where there is access to water. Pairing takes place in September and lasts about a month. May through June is the time for foaling. Usually the mare has one foal; occasionally there are twins.

A Mongolian wild ass can travel at the rate of forty miles an hour for the first mile; thereafter, its speed drops to thirty-five miles an hour. It can average as much as sixteen miles an hour for a distance of thirty miles. Though wild asses need water at regular intervals, they can go for a long time between drinks.

The African Wild Donkey, or Somali Wild Ass, *Equus asinus somalicus,* is probably the stock from which the domesticated donkey was derived. A handsome, strongly built animal, it stands about four feet six inches at the shoulder. Unlike the Asiatic wild asses, it has very large, long ears and narrow feet. The African wild ass gives voice to the loud bray of the familiar donkey—a very different sound from the squeals and guttural blowing of the Asiatic asses. The general body color is gray with white under parts, relieved by a white muzzle, a white patch around the eye, a black stripe down the back and another across the shoulders.

Both the Nubian wild ass and the related Algerian wild ass are now extinct in the wild state. However, several local variants—the Sudan, Somali, and Red Sea wild asses—still exist in limited numbers. These African wild asses frequent low, stony hill country and bleak wastes. They have a reputation for great speed and sure-footedness in rough country.

OTHER WILD ASSES

The Mongolian Wild Ass, *Equus hemionus,* also known as the Chigetal or Dziggetai, is a typical desert animal, slightly smaller than its North African cousins and has smaller ears. It dwells in the arid regions east of the Altai Mountains to Transbaikalia and the central Gobi Desert. The general color of the body is chestnut, varying from a grayish tone in the long winter coat to a more reddish shade as summer comes on.

The Onager, or Persian Wild Ass, known as the Ghorkhar in India, is somewhat smaller and more slender than the Mongolian wild ass. Its general color varies from cinnamon brown in the summer coat to yellow brown in the winter coat. This animal lives in the desert regions from Persia and Syria to northwestern India. It has a close relative in the wild ass of Baluchistan and western India, a comparatively light-colored creature.

The Kiang, or Tibetan Wild Ass, the largest and most handsome of the Asiatic wild asses, ranges over the high mountain plateaus of Tibet at altitudes up to sixteen thousand feet. Except for its larger size and slightly different color pattern it is much the same as the Mongolian wild ass.

ZEBRAS—AN OLD PUZZLE

The reader is doubtless familiar with the classic question about the zebra—is it a light-colored animal with dark stripes, or a dark-colored animal with light stripes? Here is the verdict of science: the color pattern of the zebra consists of dark or black stripes on a light background. The animal, therefore, is white—or nearly white—with black stripes.

The attractively striped horselike animals that come under the popular name of zebra are the representatives of the horse family in eastern and southern Africa. Zebras resemble asses in having a short, erect mane, large ears, and a large head. In most zebras, the hoof is narrower than a horse's hoof, but broader and more rounded than an ass's hoof. The Mountain Zebra has the large ears of the Somali wild ass and similar small narrow feet.

MEAT FOR THE LION

The zebra is choice food for the lion—wherever zebras are present in abundance, there you will find lions as well. Once struck down by a lion a zebra makes little show of resistance and succumbs quickly, resigned to the inevitable.

Ordinarily quick with its heels, the zebra also has important offensive weapons in its teeth. Wild dogs and other flesh-eaters seldom attack it—always with the important exception of the lion. Luckily the zebra possesses several defenses against the lion. It has a good sense of smell and excellent eyesight. The famous striped coat is helpful, for the stripes blend well with the shadows of branches against sunlight or moonlight.

Zebras drink regularly and are rarely more than five miles away from water. On their way to drink they are always on the alert for lions. They have no fixed time for drinking, but generally they approach a water hole late in the evening or early in the morning. However, the author has seen zebras at a water hole in the middle of the day.

A herd of zebras on their way to water are usually led by an old stallion; first galloping ahead, he pulls up short of the water hole to look for lurking lions. Satisfied that the approach is safe, he gives the "all clear"—a low neigh—and the herd moves in to drink. They are always nervous and alert when drinking, as if expecting lions—and seem relieved when they get away from the water onto the open plains.

OTHER ENEMIES—MAN AND DISEASE

In recent years, large numbers of zebras have been killed for their hides—these make tough leather, suitable for military shoes and equipment. Sportsmen often shoot zebras when other game is scarce. During epidemics of cattle disease, zebras die by the thousands. Fortunately

they are sufficiently numerous to quickly fill in their depleted ranks
—otherwise the lions would be obliged to turn their attention to domestic cattle and hunt man, too, more often than they do.

ZEBRA HERDS

During their migrations, zebras travel in large herds, sometimes over
a thousand in number. It is not easy to imagine a more awe-inspiring
sight than a herd of these ornately marked horses thundering through
the forest.

Like many other animals, zebras seem possessed with a desire to
overtake an automobile. On one occasion in East Africa a herd raced
up alongside the author's hunting car and crossed in front of him. It
took the herd nearly fifteen minutes to pass, traveling at full gallop,

ITS BRILLIANT STRIPES ARE ACTUALLY PROTECTIVE

In wooded areas, the celebrated black and white stripes of the zebra merge with sunlight
and shadow to create a natural camouflage. But protective coloration alone will not always
fool the zebra's mighty and persistent foe, the lion. To help it elude the stalking big cat,
the zebra relies upon its highly developed senses of hearing and of smell. Perhaps the
most beautiful stripes of all are found on the mountain zebra, above, which has intricate
horizontal markings on its hind parts.

four or five abreast. Most of the time there were no breaks in the fast-moving procession. Once on the other side of the trail, they vanished into the forest.

A CLOSER LOOK AT THE ZEBRAS

There are three kinds of zebras living today, and one extinct variety. Grevy's Zebra is the largest and one of the most elegant of the striped ponies. It stands four feet six inches at the shoulder and weighs between five hundred and seven hundred pounds. The entire head and body are finely lined. Grevy's zebra lives in the open brush-covered plains and in the lowlands of Abyssinia, Somaliland, and northern Kenya. The mare is just as big as the stallion.

Burchell's Zebra or Bontequagga, the common broad-striped zebra of Africa, dwells in most of the southern and eastern parts of the continent, where it frequents open plains, hills, and lightly forested country. This small-eared animal stands four feet two inches at the shoulder. The Mountain Zebra, the smallest of the striped ponies, is the most asslike of all, and perhaps the most attractively marked. It is confined to the mountains of South Africa.

The Quagga is now extinct; the last living individual died in 1872 in the London Zoo. Originally found in herds on the open plains of the Cape Colony, the quagga differed greatly in color and pattern of marking from Burchell's zebra. Nevertheless, the two animals are believed to have been closely related.

Essentially grass-eaters, zebras are fond of lightly forested country. They reach their maximum in brilliance and color pattern in the wooded portions of Central and East Africa. South and westward, as the forests thin out and the region becomes more arid, there is a gradual weakening of the striping. In the quagga of the south the stripes were dark brown and restricted to the neck and head. Zebras love to take dust baths and sand baths, and zebra country is full of well-worn rolling grounds.

The zebra's first burst of speed is remarkable; for more sustained running, it is credited with a speed of forty miles per hour, as timed by a car speedometer. The zebra has been domesticated and run in harness for exhibition purposes, but it is not to be trusted. It is stubborn and tires quickly when put to work.

Life expectancy for zebras in the natural state is about fifteen years, but they have lived as much as twenty-nine years in captivity. There appears to be no fixed breeding season, and the young are born between eleven and thirteen months after mating.

UNDERSTANDING THE ODD-TOED HOOFED MAMMALS

As we have seen, the horse family is made up of asses and zebras in addition to horses. But the horse family is only part of a larger group, the order of odd-toed hoofed mammals. This order, known as Perissodactyla ("odd-fingered"), also includes tapirs and rhinoceroses. The order has no representatives in Europe, in the Americas north of southern Mexico, or in Australia. The tapir, the only member of the order alive today in the New World, is not found in Africa.

Representatives of this order are not "ruminants"—they do not chew their cud. They have front teeth in both upper and lower jaws and, with the exception of the rhinoceros, do not have antlers or horns.

An interesting point about the odd-toed hoofed mammals is this: when scientists gave the animals this name, they used the term "odd-toed" to refer to the *structure* of the foot, not the *number* of toes. These mammals have an enlarged third toe, which extends up into the main leg-bone and bears all or a large portion of the weight of the body. This is especially true of the horse family, which has only one toe, and also applies to the other animals of the order, which have more than one toe. (Of course, whatever the number of toes, they are encased in a hoof.) As you will see in later chapters, there are other hoofed mammals that rest the weight of the body on *two* toes. We call them even-toed hoofed mammals.

TAPIRS—STRANGE, PRIMITIVE, TIMID, AND INOFFENSIVE

When you compare it with the highly specialized mammals of the modern age, you can see that the tapir is a strange, primitive creature. Its snout and upper lip are lengthened into a short, thick, flexible trunk that is used to draw twigs and branches into the mouth. It is a stockily built animal, with short legs and a plump, thick-skinned body covered with short, close hair. Its tail is a mere few inches long, the eyes are small, and the ears, of medium length, extend out and up from the sides of the head.

The tapir has four toes on the front feet, and three on the hind feet. The third toe, as we have seen in the case of the horse family, is the central axis of the foot. The tapir can spread its toes, which are encased at their ends in a small hoof. As already suggested, this animal is the only living odd-toed hoofed mammal that is native to the Americas.

Our tapirs of today are the last of a great race that all but vanished in geological time. Eventually they were left on opposite sides of the earth, without connecting links. The prehistoric tapirs were spread across the Northern Hemisphere, but today we find these animals only in the Malayan region of southern Asia and in two parts of the New World: Central America and northern South America. They have a distinct family all to themselves, the Tapiridae.

RELIC OF A PREHISTORIC AGE

The tapir, strange-looking and primitive, gives us a good living picture of a prehistoric animal. Its body reminds us of the pig, and its snout and upper lip are elongated into a trunk. A far better swimmer than runner, the animal takes refuge in water when pursued. Above is the Malay tapir. The coat of this curious creature is almost perfectly divided between two colors; the hind part is gray, the front part and legs are black.

Timid, inoffensive creatures, tapirs live in swamps or near watercourses. Taking readily to the water, they are said to be able to dive and walk along the river floor. Tapirs feed on water plants and browse on forest foliage. Active only at night for the most part, they are more or less solitary; no more than two or three individuals are ever seen together. Tapirs have no fixed breeding season. Usually one off-spring is produced; twins are rare.

Taken young, the tapir is quite docile and can even be expected to return if it is permitted to roam in the forest by itself. In South and Central America its only natural enemy is the jaguar; in Malaya the tiger and leopard assume this role. Putting up a creditable fight if cornered, the tapir can usually make good its escape if it has access to water.

SOUTH AMERICAN TAPIRS—FIGHTERS AND SWIMMERS

The South American Tapir, *Tapirus terrestris,* dwells in the warmer parts of South America, with a range extending from Panama to Argentina, Bolivia, and Paraguay. This blackish-brown animal is common in the forests of the Guianas, Venezuela, and Brazil, where the natives hunt it with the help of trained dogs. When hard pressed in such hunts, it is said to kick violently—sometimes it will seize a hound in its teeth and shake it furiously.

In the Wild. The tapir does not always follow a beaten trail, as most animals do; more often it doggedly pushes its way through the jungle with its head carried low. Not a fast runner, it can easily be overtaken on horseback when found some distance from water.

Leo E. Miller, writing of his experiences at Mt. Duida, Brazil, says, "I saw them moving singly through the forest and fording the shallow Rio Sina like shadows, so quietly did they move." Disturb them and they crash through the forest at a quick trot and even gallop. In their stomachs Miller found mostly palm nuts with seeds the size of hen's eggs. The pulp surrounding the seeds had been digested but the large hard seeds were intact.

In the Water. Theodore Roosevelt hunted tapirs on the Sepotuba River ("river of tapirs" in the local Indian dialect) of the Matto Grosso in Brazil. He noted that, when pursued, they always take to the water, wherever it is available. He saw a large male swimming with only its strange head above the surface; when diving, it curled its trunk under. Swimming rapidly downstream, it stayed under water for an astonishingly long time after diving. It passed completely under his dugout canoe, and came up on the opposite side halfway between him and the river bank.

A tapir shot in the water always goes to the bottom; but in about an hour the body will rise to the surface.

In Captivity. Captured young, the South American tapir quickly becomes tame. However, it does not respond to kindness and shows little interest in anyone. Give it a place to sleep and food to eat and it is satisfied with its lot; it seems to have no inclination to leave the shelter of a comfortable home. It is not apt to bite; when the animal is molested, a shrill hissing cry is the extent of its anger. The tapir has a gluttonous appetite and in captivity will devour almost anything—raw meat or even rags.

The tapir's flesh is considered excellent and is often used as food. Natives believe they can cure epilepsy by grinding down the creature's toenails and taking them in powdered form.

OTHER INTERESTING TAPIRS

The Mountain Tapir, or Pinchaque, *Tapirus roulini,* dwells in the mountain forest of Ecuador and Colombia up to elevations of eight thousand feet. It has a rounded head and is covered with coarse blackish hair about an inch long.

This animal gets its scientific name from Désiré Roulin, a doctor and zoologist, who accompanied Jean Baptiste Boussingault, the illustrious French scientist, from 1824 to 1827 on his Andean explorations. While crossing the bare mountain heights of the Andes in Colombia, Roulin came across this strange-looking animal, which resembles the typical South American tapir but has long, thick hair like a bear's. Roulin made a remarkable drawing of the creature, which has only recently been published.

The Central American Tapir ranges from southern Mexico to Panama, from sea level up to six thousand feet in the mountains. While the adult is uniformly blackish brown in color, its throat, chest, and face are more or less whitish. The head and body length comes to six feet five inches; the tail is only three inches long. A large male may weigh up to six hundred pounds.

The Malay Tapir lives in the Malay Peninsula and north as far as Tenasserim, Burma. It stands three and one-half feet at the shoulder and weighs about five hundred pounds. Its color is partly a soiled whitish, partly black or blackish.

Rhinoceroses — Temperamental Behemoths

THE RHINOCEROS, a huge, ungainly creature, is actually, or comes close to being, the second largest of all land mammals (the elephant is the biggest; the hippo vies with the rhino for second place).

Consequently, it is hard for our minds to accept the fact that the rhinoceros, sizable as it is, can rate only as a miniature, compared to one of its ancestors. Millions of years ago *Baluchitherium,* a hornless rhinoceros, had its heyday. This giant of central Asia stood seventeen feet nine inches at the shoulder and measured thirty-four feet from the tip of its big nose to the end of its tail!

Still and all, the rhinoceros is no midget. Its great bulk renders it practically immune to attack by lions, tigers, and other natural enemies. We might think, then, that the rhinoceros would be a contented, not to say complacent, creature. Not so!—though generally nonaggressive, to be sure, this hulking mammal is surly and unreliable in temper. When suddenly confronted with danger, it is apt to charge without provocation. Given time to digest the situation, it will usually seek safety in flight.

Why does the rhinoceros tend to charge on sudden impulse? We do not quite know. It has fairly acute senses of smell and hearing, but its eyesight is none too good and, if the truth must be told, it is not overly bright. Perhaps the headlong dash of the rhinoceros is instinctive, handed down from an age when the flesh-eaters were more powerful and less discriminating when scanning the bill of fare. (The rhinoceros itself is a strict vegetarian, limited to green foliage, grasses, and the like.)

At any rate, some present-day observers believe that the precipitate rush of the rhino may be due to curiosity, or perhaps its nearsightedness. Others claim that the animal is anxious to protect its young.

Today we find rhinoceroses only in the warmer parts of Africa and Asia and in Indonesia. But these behemoths, survivors of a bygone age (we place them with the horses and tapirs in the order of odd-toed hoofed mammals) when armed might was a determining factor in survival, once ranged over the entire Northern Hemisphere. The woolly rhinoceros, a prehistoric creature that lived millions of years ago in northern Europe and Asia along with the woolly mammoth, has been discovered in a remarkably good state of preservation, frozen in the Arctic ice. This find was unearthed in Siberia in 1731.

MEET MR. RHINO

The rhinoceros is a great, clumsy beast protected by a thick, scantily haired hide. Its legs are on the stubby side and its three-toed feet are shod with a broad, horny, compact sole. Its massive head is concave in front.

This head is armed with one or two horns that continue to grow throughout the rhino's life. We might plausibly suppose that the horn is connected to the skull by means of a bony core. The fact is, though, that the horn is merely an outgrowth of the skin, and is composed of a well-consolidated mass of hair. It is the horns that give these creatures their family name (Rhinocerotidae—"nose horns").

SEEING-EYE OF THE SHORT-SIGHTED RHINO

The rhinoceros is considered a good swimmer. It loves to wallow in mud and bathe in dust to rid itself of ticks and other skin parasites. Some birds make a practice of picking over the head or back of the animal, and are even enterprising enough to enter the rhino's ears in search of these insect pests. Tick birds also act as lookouts, giving warning of approaching intruders by their noisy, scolding chatter.

Incidentally, what was probably the first rhinoceros seen in Europe was advertised in the London *Gazette* in 1684. It was brought by East Indian merchants, and sold for two thousand pounds.

BLACK RHINOCEROSES—AFRICA'S COMMONEST

The African Black or Hook-lipped Rhinoceros, *Diceros bicornis* ("two-horned"), is the common species of Africa. Standing five feet at the shoulders, a full-grown male may weigh as much as three thousand pounds. Its upper lip, extended into a point, is prehensile for grasping twigs and leaves and drawing them into the mouth.

This rhino, as we can tell from its name, has two horns; it sometimes happens that females have longer horns than the males. As a rule, the front horn is the longer of the two, the record length being fifty-three and one-half inches. The average length, however, is about half that much.

There is no doubt that the black rhino has an excellent notion of local geography, and a sense of smell that is keen without being on a par with the elephant's or the buffalo's. Likewise its sense of hearing serves it well; but when it comes to vision, this animal, like all its cousins, scarcely sees any better than a nearsighted man without his glasses.

The African natives kill the black rhinoceros with their elephant spears. (Interestingly enough, they fear it nowhere near as much as they do the elephant.) The rhino's tough hide, one-half to three-quarters of an inch thick, makes splendid fighting shields; the natives bleach it almost white. As for the rhino's flesh, it is, as you might expect, coarse grained and rather tough. However, the Africans pound it with stones till it becomes fairly palatable. They consider the liver a great delicacy.

A DAY WITH THE RHINO

The black or hook-lipped rhinoceros usually has a home territory about ten miles in diameter. Inside this area there must be a water hole or other drinking place. If the water dries up, the beast will find a fresh supply somewhere else. It usually goes for a drink about midnight, but there is no fixed time. Although early morning and evening are the times of greatest activity, the black rhino may be abroad any hour of the day or night. It is an unsociable creature, and it is a rare occasion when we find more than two or three individuals (including a calf) together.

There was a time when the black rhinoceros was common over

most of Africa south of the Sahara; today it is plentiful only in East Africa. Though steep, rocky hill country is the ideal habitat for this animal, the author has often seen it on the plains. Like other members of its family, this rhino makes a ritual of rolling in the dry dust bowls. It is never so happy as when wallowing in soft, wet mud. Narrow, winding trails of the rhino lead in all directions from the wallow back into the bush.

THE RHINOCEROS HAS AN UNPREDICTABLE TEMPER
Though it often behaves peaceably enough, the rhinoceros is untrustworthy, and given to sudden temperamental flare-ups; for no apparent reason, it may rush forward in a fierce attack. The African black or hook-lipped rhinoceros, pictured above, will frequently become enraged by the scent of man and charge at him. The animal is capable of a speed of thirty miles or more an hour.

Primarily a browser, the rhino feeds on the shoots and leaves of low bushes; it is also partial to twigs, as well as herbage and some long grasses. It does most of its feeding during the early morning, late evening and night. Its droppings are usually deposited in saucer-like hollows which have been scooped out under a tree or bush. Not infrequently a great pile accumulates. One may observe trails extending from one dumping place to another; deep crescent-shaped furrows are plowed in the ground around these toilets.

The black rhino does most of its sleeping in some shady spot during the heat of the day. It slumbers in various positions—one animal was found fast asleep standing up, others have been seen sleeping on their sides, or with feet doubled up under the body. Some rhinos get up front feet first, like a horse; others rise hind legs first like a cow.

THE RHINO'S IMPETUOUS CHARGES

Suddenly startled, a rhino will snort like a horse. If it is really frightened, it lets out a shrill squeal. The black rhino is one of the few animals that will charge man without the slightest provocation. What causes this inherited animosity toward man is, as we have seen, a matter for debate. Whatever the cause, charge they will if you come upon them suddenly in the bush.

On one occasion, two full-grown rhinos charged at the author's hunting car from two directions. First they came on with heads carried high and then lowered them for a conclusive thrust, their murderous spiked horns directed straight ahead. At the critical moment, the author's "white hunter" fired his rifle. A perfect hit square on the horn swung one of the animals around so that it charged into its comrade and so saved the day.

Despite such occasional encounters, most of these animals turn and run at the approach of man. A rhino usually stampedes upwind—if you are in its line of travel, it will charge at you. But if you are downwind, the chances are it will not get your scent. The odor of the human body is a hateful stench in the nostrils of the rhino, as it is to most other wild game.

Despite its short legs and great body, the rhinoceros can keep abreast of a car going twenty-eight miles an hour. Charging, the animal can do thirty-five miles an hour. Just as we would expect, it is not quick in turning, and it is easy to dodge a charging rhino—if you do not get panic-stricken.

There is one creature to which the rhino always courteously concedes the right of way—the elephant. The chances are that it has learned from long experience to respect its formidable associate of the African veld.

CATCHING RHINOS AMERICAN STYLE

"Buffalo" Jones, the famous American cowboy, once lassoed a full-grown black rhino in Africa and finally succeeded in capturing it. Time and again, when the animal was roped, it dragged the horses from several directions until the lines snapped. Using his three horses in relays, Jones was gradually able to tire out the rhinoceros. Still, the horses were only slightly faster than the rhino, and they had many a narrow escape from the persistent charges of the infuriated beast. Eventually a lasso around a hind leg held the now exhausted animal and it was tethered to a tree.

In later days, museum expeditions have lassoed rhinos from a moving truck. Sometimes the lasso is attached to a heavy log which goes to the ground as the animal pulls. After the rhino has worn itself out pulling the log, it is more easily captured.

LOVE AMONG THE RHINOS

In his book, *Big Game Hunting and Adventure,* Marcus Daly tells an interesting story about the love life of the black rhinoceros. One moonlight night he was watching a bull and a cow standing motionless, a few yards apart. Suddenly the cow rushed around the bull at a fast pace. Then, as a climax to the dance, she jumped high in the air, came down flat on the ground, skidded along on her throat, rose, shook herself, and took up her original position facing the bull.

Now it was her mate's turn. Wheeling around and around his lady friend in a most amazing manner, often spinning like a top on sharp turns but never changing his course, he finally did the high jump and came to rest after skidding a considerable distance on his throat. When he got up, they alternated through the whole procedure for half an hour. At that point, thoroughly exhausted by their exertions, they went off for a drink, disappearing into the African night.

There is no fixed mating season for the black rhino. Reproduction is slow in this family, the young being born about eighteen months after mating time. There is usually one calf, weighing about seventy-five pounds. After a few hours, it is able to follow its mother around. But though the calf is quick to obtain the mother's care, it is slow to relinquish it. The youngster is suckled for about two years, and continues to stay with her until more than half grown. The mother will not mate again while she has a calf with her.

The life expectancy of the black rhino in the wild state is probably not over twenty-five years. A captive animal lived to the age of forty-seven.

WHITE RHINOCEROSES—BIGGEST OF THE TRIBE

The White Rhinoceros, or Burchell's Rhinoceros, *Ceratotherium simum,* is also known as the square-lipped rhinoceros. It is the biggest of all the rhinos. Standing six and one-half feet at the shoulder, the white rhino weighs up to four tons. Despite its bulk, this giant, like the elephant, has an uncanny knack of slipping silently away, even in dense thickets.

Among the white rhinos, both sexes have two horns, the front one being about twice the length of the rear one. It is not unusual for the front horn to measure three feet in length; the recorded maximum is five feet.

WHITE BUT NOT QUITE

Actually, the color of the white rhino's hide is smoky gray. View it by bright moonlight on the grassy plains, however, and the animal really appears white; so perhaps its name is not so inappropriate as many highly critical observers have claimed. In any event, the normal tone of the skin is somewhat obscured by the color of the mud in which the rhinoceros wallows ecstatically.

A FAIRLY GOOD-TEMPERED RHINO

The white rhinoceros seems mild tempered and slow compared to its more nervous and highly irascible black relative; and it is correspondingly less likely to charge blindly at a possible foe. It is more sociable, too. White rhinos frequently gather in parties that include a bull, a cow, and calves of assorted ages.

When feeding, the white rhinoceros moves slowly upwind as it grazes during the cool early morning and evening hours; during the heat of the day it slumbers peacefully under the ample shade of a tree. When disturbed, this ungainly beast makes off at a swift trot, its nose close to the ground. Pressed for speed, it will break into a gallop and keep up a fast pace for quite a distance.

YOUNG RHINOS

It is estimated that the female white rhino has her baby about seventeen or eighteen months after mating time. Slow as this rate of breeding is, it is faster than the black rhino's. Occasionally a cow will have twins, but such instances are rare. A calf is mature at about five or six years, and is then ready to breed.

Unlike the black rhino's calf, which tags along behind its mother, the white rhino's calf precedes the cow. The youngster is steered in the right direction by the pressure of the maternal horns on its rump. When a cow, accompanied by its young, is shot, the calf will charge the intruder—just as the baby elephant does in the same pitiful plight.

WHERE THEY LIVE

Today the white rhinoceros dwells in a comparatively limited region in Central Africa. Formerly common on the grassy prairies of South Africa, this rhinoceros had practically been eliminated there at the turn of the century, with a few survivors left to enjoy the protection of the game preserve in Zululand, Natal. Strangely enough, there are no white rhinos in the area lying between the northern and southern limits of its range.

THE GREAT INDIAN RHINOCEROS

The Great Indian Rhinoceros, or One-horned Rhinoceros, *Rhinoceros unicornis,* is the largest rhino found in Asia. A big male may stand slightly more than five and one-half feet at the shoulder and weigh about two tons or more. These creatures haunt the great plains of northern India, Assam, and Nepal, where the giant grass grows to a height of fifteen or twenty feet. Here the Indian rhino lives among the grassy runways like an enormous field mouse!

Both male and female are equipped with a single horn. It rarely exceeds a foot in length—though some rare specimens measure up to twenty-four inches.

AN "IRON-PLATED RHINOCEROS"

The Indian rhino's thick hide is folded into plates or shields, hinged at the joints and studded with small rounded lumps which—by a slight stretch of your imagination—can pass for rivet heads. This beast is often described as the "iron-plated rhinoceros," and, imaginatively speaking, it does look as if it had been put together in a machine shop. The skin, dark gray in color, is practically hairless—aside from a fringe on the ears and at the end of the tail.

VICIOUS TEMPERS

The Indian rhinoceros is likely to show extraordinary fits of temper without the least provocation. At such times it rushes about, uttering loud grunts, trampling down the bush, and cutting deep furrows in the ground with its horn. In the course of one of those seemingly meaningless displays of anger, it will furiously assault any moving object.

Even large bull elephants are not safe from the violence of this ill-tempered beast, and in the ferocious battle that ensues, a big tusker may acknowledge defeat and make a hurried retreat. In such duels the rhino is more likely to slash with its teeth than strike with its horn —the teeth are more effective weapons against the elephant's tough hide.

The female rhinoceros, despite these occasional ugly outbursts, is

THE RHINOCEROS HAS A "MAGICAL" HORN

The great Indian or one-horned rhinoceros is esteemed by the natives because of a superstitious belief that its horn will act as an aphrodisiac or an antidote to poison. The horn, though hard, is actually a clump of hairs held together by an adhesive substance; dissolved or made into a powder, it brings a high price throughout the Far East. Museums in the Orient must take precautions to protect their rhinoceros specimens from the natives.

all sweetness toward her calf and very solicitous for its welfare. In the midst of her protective fury against intruders, she may suddenly decide that discretion is the better part of maternal care, and prudently lead her calf to safety in flight.

The young rhino is born about eighteen or nineteen months after its parents have mated. A newborn calf is about two feet high at the shoulder and weighs between seventy-five and 120 pounds. Born in a very advanced stage of development, the youngster is able to follow its mother soon after birth. One Indian rhino lived to the age of fifty in a zoo.

A FAMOUS RHINO SUPERSTITION

In India, many superstitions center about the rhinoceros horn and its supposed exceptional medicinal qualities. (Europe once talked the same way about the unicorn's horn.) The most celebrated of its virtues, so it is held, is that the horn is an antidote against poison. The horn is used in treating a victim of poisoning—it is even used to detect the presence of poison!

For centuries, Indian rulers have drunk from cups made of rhinoceros horn, in the belief that this substance "sweats" on contact with poison. Such cups, mounted in silver or gold, are considered appropriate gifts for the highest dignitaries. Science can give no comfort to these beliefs; actual experiment with various poisons has elicited no reaction from the horn.

OTHER EASTERN RHINOS

The Javan or Lesser One-horned Rhinoceros, *Rhinoceros sondaicus,* reminds us in many ways of its great Indian cousin. However, the Javan variety is more slender and smaller, with a shoulder height of about four feet six inches, and a weight of over a ton. It has only one horn, which may be as much as ten inches long in the male. A few females are hornless; most have a very small horn.

The Javan rhino's skin is cracked into a mosaic pattern of scalelike disks, and the folds on the foreshoulder meet over the back of the lower neck. These folds in the Indian rhino curve backward toward the rear of the shoulder and do not meet.

Originally found in Burma, Assam, Indo-China, and through the

Malay Peninsula to Sumatra and Java, the Javan rhino has been exterminated over most of its former range. It favors thick jungle and marshland, but it has also been found in forested mountain country.

The Sumatran or Asiatic Two-horned Rhinoceros, *Dicerorhinus sumatrensis,* is the smallest of the living rhinos, rarely exceeding one ton in weight and four and one-half feet in shoulder height. This animal has two horns, one in line behind the other. The front one is the larger of the pair, reaching a length of fifteen or twenty inches in the male. The rear horn, placed between the eyes, is seldom more than seven inches long. The females' horns are smaller.

The Sumatran rhino often goes by the name of "the hairy rhinoceros"—the hair is hard to see but can easily be felt by hand. The newborn are covered with thick brown hair, which disappears in time.

Like the Javan rhinoceros, this beast frequents thick forest and bamboo country, where it leaves well-worn trails between wallows. Today the Sumatran rhino dwells in Sumatra, Borneo, and the Malay Peninsula.